When the mist nets are taken down late in the afternoon, there are shorebirds to be studied and identified along the coast.—ETHEL FLOYD

ALABAMA BIRDS

WALTER A. WEBER

ALABAMA BIRDS

by THOMAS A. IMHOF

Color Illustrations by Richard A. Parks and David C. Hulse

Published for the State of Alabama, Department of Conservation,

Game and Fish Division, 1962, by University of Alabama Press

PUBLISHED FOR THE STATE OF ALABAMA, DEPARTMENT OF CONSERVATION, GAME AND FISH DIVISION

JOHN PATTERSON, GOVERNOR OF ALABAMA

WILLIAM C. YOUNGER, DIRECTOR OF CONSERVATION

JOSEPH O. KILGORE, ASSISTANT DIRECTOR OF CONSERVATION

CHARLES D. KELLEY, CHIEF, GAME AND FISH DIVISION (ON MILITARY LEAVE 1961-)

REYNOLDS THRASHER, CHIEF, GAME AND FISH DIVISION (1961-)

BIRD BOOK COMMITTEE: RALPH H. ALLEN, JAMES E. KEELER (SCIENTIFIC EDITOR), WILLIAM L. HOLLAND, JR. (CHAIRMAN)

PUBLISHED BY UNIVERSITY OF ALABAMA PRESS, DRAWER 2877, UNIVERSITY, ALABAMA

LIBRARY OF CONGRESS CATALOG CARD NUMBER 61-18779

COPYRIGHT 1962 BY THE STATE OF ALABAMA, DEPARTMENT OF CONSERVATION

ENGRAVING BY ALABAMA ENGRAVING COMPANY; PRINTING AND BINDING BY PARAGON PRESS; DESIGNED BY EUGENIA PORTER

FRONTISPIECE (FACING TITLE PAGE): WILD TURKEY, PAINTED BY WALTER A. WEBER, OF THE NATIONAL GEOGRAPHIC SOCIETY, REPRODUCED BY COURTESY OF CLAUDE D. KELLEY.

FOREWORD

ALABAMA BIRDS was prepared in response to the many requests for a book on the identification and life histories of Alabama's birds. These requests have come from ornithologists, sportsmen's groups, garden clubs, schools, and individuals who love nature and desire to know more about bird life in Alabama. This is the first major publication concerning birds of this state since 1924, when BIRDS OF ALABAMA, by Arthur H. Howell, was published.

In 1955, Mr. Earl M. McGowin, who was at that time Director of Conservation, contracted with Mr. Thomas A. Imhof to compile data concerning birds in Alabama. Compilation continued until August 31, 1961. In 1960, Mr. William C. Younger, Director of Conservation, arranged for the publication of ALABAMA BIRDS by appointing a committee to carry out the project.

A search for artists was first made in Alabama and then continued nationwide, as it was felt that the best obtainable art work would add to the usefulness and beauty of the book. The resulting paintings have received praise from all who have attended the numerous showings of the original art works.

The author has clearly demonstrated that he has done extensive research, not only in published sources, but through interviews with other ornithologists and coöperators. The time spent by the author in the field seeking and collecting data for the book is shown by the large number of arrival and departure dates of the various species he has observed. Assembling and keeping up-to-date records of Alabama's 352 species of birds was a tremendous task and required nearly as much time and effort as the actual writing of the book.

Upon finding a need for a technical editor of the book, Mr. James E. Keeler was assigned these duties, including the repeated proofing required as the book progressed through the many steps of publication.

This, the first large publication produced by the Game and Fish Division of the Alabama Department of Conservation, is a book that anyone should be proud to own.

WILLIAM L. HOLLAND, JR.
Chairman, Bird Book Committee

ALABAMA DEPARTMENT OF CONSERVATION

PREFACE

BIRDS have fascinated me for as long as I can remember, and it is to my parents, Mr. and Mrs. Anthony M. Imhof, of Clearwater, Florida, who have always encouraged this interest, that I owe the foremost and deepest appreciation.

At first, most of the facts I learned about birds came from books, but then I began to learn much from companions in the field and especially from the birds themselves. The more I found out about birds, the more my fascination and admiration increased, and the more I wanted to know about them.

Many Alabamians, whether farm-folk, hunters, fishermen, or vacationers, enjoy the out-of-doors and know well the pleasure of being in the woods or getting acquainted with wild creatures. My personal experiences with birds are kin to this but possibly have a more scientific twist.

Recording birds on trips afield and becoming acquainted with more and more of them, I accumulated a fund of original data. I made exploratory trips to many parts of Alabama, for I wanted to know about all the birds of the state, not just those of the vicinity of Birmingham. To make my local lists more complete, I began assembling the records of my bird-student companions. Thus, almost without realizing it, I was well on my way to acquiring data for this book.

Several years after I began to assemble this information, Conservation Director Earl M. McGowin seriously considered a project to publish a bird book for the state. He was influenced by such people as M. Wilson Gaillard, a Mobile dentist, and Julian M. Rice, a Montgomery businessman. This project was launched in January, 1955, when I agreed to undertake the writing.

From then until now, almost seven years, I have spent most of my spare time gathering information from the field, museums, libraries, and other observers, or writing and rewriting the manuscript. Data from all 67 counties were accumulated, and I personally did field work in 64 of them. Frequently I visited local bird students and went afield with them in their favorite areas. As a result, I became well acquainted with nearly all the bird students in the state, encouraged them to record valuable local data, and experienced Southern hospitality at its best.

PREFACE

The Alabama Ornithological Society played a significant role in encouraging the recording of field data from all parts of the state. The names of over 300 observers appear with the records in this book and provide an acknowledgment proportional to the quantity and quality of each one's contribution. In general, the names of those who provided substantial amounts of field data appear most often in the occurrence paragraphs. It must be remembered, however, that for many species of birds, hundreds of unlisted records serve to verify their presence between the limiting dates in the text.

Data on time of breeding is seldom credited because of space limitations. In general, egg dates and similar records were submitted by the most active observers, those whose names appear most often in the occurrence paragraphs. However, a few people who submitted large amounts of breeding data deserve special mention: Harry E. Wheeler, C. William Summerour, Jr., Malcolm Harden, Jr., Alfred A. Walker, III, Henry M. Stevenson, Lewis S. Golsan, and M. Wilson Gaillard. Most of the information from Alabama feeding stations has been furnished by Edith L. Clark and Harriett H. Wright.

In the location and examination of Alabama specimens in collections outside the state, the writer confesses his inability to travel far and wide and make this examination personal and comprehensive. The following very kindly furnished lists of Alabama specimens in collections under their care: James C. Greenway, Museum of Comparative Zoölogy, Harvard University; Frank A. Iwen, University of Wisconsin; Josselyn Van Tyne, University of Michigan Museum of Zoölogy; and S. C. Dellinger, University of Arkansas.

I was able to visit and examine personally the following specimen collections: Auburn University Collection, Auburn Wildlife Collection, University of Alabama Collection, Avery Collection, Collection of the Department of Archives and History of the State of Alabama (mounted and unlabeled), Birmingham Public Museum Collection now in the Central Library in Birmingham, Alabama Department of Conservation Collection, Wheeler National Wildlife Refuge Collection, Museum of Zoölogy of Louisiana State University, Collection of Florida State University, private collection of John H. Steenis, and United States National Museum. Those who were especially helpful in this and other phases of the project are John W. Aldrich, Thomas Z. Atkeson, Jr., Thomas D. Burleigh, Ralph L. Chermock, Henry G. Good, George H. Lowery, Jr., Robert J. Newman, Robert W. Skinner, and Henry M. Stevenson. Dr. Aldrich in particular identified many Alabama specimens and provided valuable advice on technical matters.

Patuxent Wildlife Research Center was a particularly rewarding source of information. Chandler S. Robbins and his assistants very kindly made available the extensive file on the distribution of birds and the reference library which includes complete sets of bird journals and copies of nearly all regional bird books. Through the courtesy of Allen J. Duvall and his staff, the writer was able to extract a large fund of banding data on Alabama birds. To the banders themselves goes a special word of thanks from a fellow bander who knows full well the effort involved. Messrs. Duvall and Robbins were also generous in their help with many parts of the book, particularly the introductory material on banding and migration.

In organizing all this material into book form, the expert assistance of Oliver L. Austin and his wife, Elizabeth, was invaluable. The innumerable ways in which they helped me to write this book are greatly appreciated. George M. Kyle, James E. Keeler, and William L. Holland, Jr., with their sincere interest in the project, gave substantial assistance in numerous ways.

Among well over a hundred other people who provided courteous assistance, especially in connection with field investigations, the following are outstanding: Thomas Z. Atkeson, Jr., George W. Allen, W. Walter Beshears, Jr., Freddie Bosarge, Rebecca Brown, Allen D. Cruickshank, Wayne F. Colin, Lloyd C. Crawford, James R. Davis, Ernest G. Holt, Harold C. Loesch, Seth H. Low, Roxie Laybourne, Henry M. Stevenson, and last but not least, that grand old man of Gulf Coast ornithologists, Francis M. Weston.

Our artists, Richard A. Parks and David C. Hulse, have done a great deal to increase the beauty and completeness of this volume. I have had the pleasure of being in the field with both of these expert bird students, and gratefully acknowledge and deeply admire their rare combination of excellence in both an art and a science.

A project of this size represents the work of a great many people. I acknowledge gratefully the assistance of everyone who helped make this book a reality. Especially I would like to recognize the contribution of my wife, Janie, who, among many other things, did her best to see that I was free to work on the book. In the best tradition of the ideal marriage partner, she richly deserves a large share of the credit that may come to her husband.

FAIRFIELD, ALABAMA
DECEMBER, 1961

THOMAS A. IMHOF

CONTENTS

CONTENTS

[xiv]

CONTENTS

[xv]

PLATES

PHOTOGRAPHS

PHOTOGRAPHS

PHOTOGRAPHS

MAPS

MAPS

MAPS

GLOSSARY

Above In descriptions, refers to the back of head, back, and upper sides of tail and wings of a bird. Thus a bird may be said to be dark brown *above* and light brown below.

Abundant In great quantity; refers to a common bird which occurs in large numbers.

Accidental Taking place not according to the usual course of things. Thus a bird that is accidental in Alabama does not include this state in its normal range.

Adult A full-grown plant or animal.

Albino Any animal having, through deficiency in coloring matter, abnormally white skin and hair, accompanied by pink eyes. In birds, of course, the abnormal white color usually applies to the feathers. Partial albinos may have any part of the body abnormally white.

Amphipod A member of the order *Amphipoda*, which is characterized by having usually seven pairs of legs, with some of the feet directed forward and some backward. They belong to the crustaceans and are mostly marine, but, unlike lobsters and crabs, their eyes are not on stalks.

Anterior Situated in front.

Auricular Pertaining to the circle of feathers surrounding the opening of the ear in birds.

Axillaries, axillars A group of feathers on the under side of the wing near its juncture with the body.

Bar A band of color different from its background, but usually shorter and thicker than a stripe. In birds, most barring is found on the wing coverts and on the underparts.

Barbs A side branch of the shaft of a feather, one of the processes of the vane.

Basal Of or constituting the place from which a start is made. Thus, in referring to the bill of a bird, basal applies to that part nearest the body.

Below In descriptions, refers to the breast, belly, and under side of the tail of a bird.

Belt A line of color across the underparts of a bird which resembles a belt.

Bevy A flock of birds; especially a flock of quail or grouse.

Calcareous Partaking of the nature of lime; having the qualities of lime; or containing lime.

Cambium A thick, sticky secretion which, in spring, separates the sapwood of a woody plant from the fiber, or inner bark.

Carpal Pertaining to the wrist.

Carpal joint The wrist joint; in a bird this is at the bend of the wing which is usually referred to as the shoulder because its location is like that of a human shoulder.

Casual Coming without regularity, in distinction to regular. Thus a bird that is casual in Alabama does not occur here at regular intervals.

Caudal Pertaining to the tail.

Cere Naked skin that covers the base of the bill as in hawks and parrots.

Cervical Belonging to the neck.

Clutch The number of eggs upon which a bird sits.

Collar A ringed band of color around the neck of an animal.

Common Of frequent or usual occurrence.

Coniferous Pertaining to a cone-bearing tree or shrub, usually occurring in the colder parts of the world. The cypress is one of a very few conifers that are not evergreen. In Alabama, the most common conifers are the pines; thus a coniferous forest here would contain mostly pines.

Covert A feather on the wing or tail which lies over and covers the bases of the quills; generally used in the plural.

Covey A brood or hatch of birds; an old bird with her brood of young; hence, a small flock or number of birds together; applied to game, as, a covey of partridges.

Crest A tuft of feathers or other outgrowth upon the top of a bird's head.

GLOSSARY

Crested   Having a tuft like a crest.

Crown   The top of a bird's head.

Crustacea   One of the three primary classes into which ringed animals with jointed limbs are divided. The higher forms of this class include lobsters, shrimps, crawfish, and the like; the lower animals are of varied forms, as barnacles, wood lice, fish lice, and the like.

Crustacean   A member of the class *Crustacea.*

Cygnet   A young swan.

Deciduous   Falling; not perennial or permanent; specifically in botany applied both to trees whose leaves fall in autumn and to the leaves or other parts of plants which at this season fall.

Distribution   The act of dividing among a number; allotment in parts or portions. *Geographical distribution*: in botany or zoology, that branch of the respective sciences which treats of the distribution of plants and animals over the surface of the earth.

Disturbance habitat   An area modified substantially by man for purposes other than agriculture, animal husbandry, or management of wildlife resources; as cities, rights of way, most recreation areas.

Dorsal   Pertaining to or situated on or near the back of an animal or one of its organs.

Down   A fine soft covering of fowls under the feathers, particularly on the breasts of waterfowl, but also the first covering of the young of many birds.

Ear coverts   The feathers which cover the ear; the auriculars.

Eared   Having earlike parts or appendages; thus birds which have tufts of feathers near the ears.

Eartuft   A group of feathers near the ear of birds. Birds having these tufts are often called eared.

Eclipse plumage   A plumage worn by ducks in late summer, at which time the male closely resembles the female.

Facial disks   Areas on the faces of owls which often show somewhat contrasting colors.

Family   A group of individual animals, more extensive and higher in rank than a genus and less so than an order, based on fewer or less definite points of resemblance than a genus, and more or more definite ones than an order.

Fauna   The animals or animal life of any stated latitude, region, or age. *Avifauna*: the birds or birdlife of any stated latitude, region, or age.

Feral   A term applied to wild animals descended from tame stocks, or to animals having become wild after a state of domestication.

Filament   One of the soft threads or barbules of a down feather.

Flush   To cause to start, particularly to make a bird start from cover.

Frontal   Relating to the forehead.

Frontal shield   A bony covering of the forehead of certain birds, especially gallinules and coots.

Fulvous   Tawny; dull yellow, with a mixture of gray and brown.

Genus (plural *genera*)   A group of species agreeing with one another in the broad features of their organization but differing in detail, such differences being relatively constant and the species composing the group infertile with one another. In the classification of animals and plants the genus ranks next above the species, which constitutes the basic unit, and next below the family, which is a group of *genera.*

Greater wing covert   The larger feathers which cover the bases of the long wing quills. The lesser coverts cover the bases of the greater coverts as well as the wing quills. When the tips of the coverts are lighter in color the bird is said to have wing bars.

Gregarious   Having the habit of assembling or living in a flock; not habitually solitary or living alone.

Habitat   Habitation; the natural abode or locality of an animal or plant.

Hybrid   The offspring of an animal or plant produced by the crossing of different species. An intergrade is an intermediate form in a graded series; thus applying to an individual bird not assignable clearly to a particular subspecies.

Hymenopterous   Having the characteristics of the insect order *Hymenoptera*, which is characterized by having membranous wings and includes ants, bees, and wasps.

Immature   Not mature or ripe; unripe; that which has not arrived at a complete state.

Incubation   The act of sitting on eggs for the purpose of hatching young.

Indigenous   Native; produced naturally in a country or climate.

Interscapulars   Feathers that lie between the shoulder blades.

Iridescent. Having colors like the rainbow; prismatic.

Larva Any insect from the time it leaves the egg until it reaches the pupa state; the early form of any animal when unlike its mature form. Most insect larvae are wormlike and are characterized by rapid development, thus many insects are most destructive in this stage. Immature insects that closely resemble the adult are usually called nymphs.

Larval Belonging to a larva.

Lateral Pertaining to the side.

Lesser wing coverts The smaller feathers which cover the bases of the wing quills. These coverts also cover the bases of the greater wing coverts.

Local Limited or confined to a spot, place, or definite district.

Lore The space between the bill and the eye.

Lower tail coverts Those upper tail coverts which are closest to the tail.

Mandible A term more especially applied to birds, both the upper and under jaws of which, with their horny coverings, it serves to designate. The upper mandible is called the maxilla and the lower one is called the mandibula.

Marine Pertaining to the sea or living in the sea.

Maxilla The upper mandible of birds.

Melanism An abnormal deposit of pigment in the skin; especially, in the epidermis, hair, and feathers of mammals and birds; the reverse of albinism. This abnormal deposit of pigment usually results in the bird appearing black.

Melanistic Of or characterized by melanism.

Middle wing coverts Wing coverts which lie between the lesser and greater wing coverts and are intermediate in length.

Migrant A bird which passes or removes from one region or district to another for a temporary residence.

Migratory Passing from one climate to another.

Millipede A crustacean having many legs and many segments. Generally millipedes have two legs per segment whereas centipedes have one leg per segment.

Mist netting The act of catching birds for scientific purposes by the use of special nets so named because they are almost invisible.

Mollusk A member of the *Mollusca* which includes invertebrates with soft, unsegmented bodies usually covered with a single (univalve) or double (bivalve) shell. Clams, oysters, mussels, periwinkles, and snails belong to this group.

Molt The act or process of changing the feathers.

Mustache A stripe of color on the head or neck of a bird which resembles a mustache.

Nape The prominent or upper part of the back of the neck.

Nuptial plume Special feathers worn by certain birds during the breeding season, particularly those long feathers that grow from the back of the head of herons and egrets and extend down the back.

Occasional Incidental; casual; occurring at times, but not regular or systematic.

Opaque Impervious to the rays of light; not transparent.

Order A division of plants or animals intermediate between class or subclass and genus, consisting usually of a group of families related to one another by structural characteristics common to all.

Pectoral Having a brightly-colored breast.

Pellet A little ball; applied to birds, the ball of indigestible parts of the food of certain birds, especially owls, which is disgorged. These birds normally swallow the food whole or in large chunks and disgorge the pellets after the meat has been digested. These pellets are useful in locating nests and roosts and in studying the food habits.

Pensile Hanging; suspended. Applied most often to the nests of orioles and vireos.

Plumage The feathers that cover a bird.

Primary One of the large feathers on the outermost joint of a bird's wing.

Primary coverts Relatively short feathers near the forward edge of the wing which cover the base of the primaries.

Process Any protuberance, eminence, or projecting part of a bone.

Pupa The third stage in the development of an insect which passes through complete metamorphosis. On reaching its full growth the larva usually ceases to eat, and often becomes incased in a closed shell or case, after some time emerging as a perfect insect. Insects having complete metamorphosis pass through four stages markedly different from each other, egg, larva, pupa, and adult. Insects with incomplete metamorphosis have immature stages called nymphs which except

GLOSSARY

for size and their lack of wings resemble adults.

Raft   A group of birds, usually waterfowl or coots, swimming together in a compact group resembling a raft.

Rare   Uncommon; not frequent; thinly scattered.

Rectrix   (plural *rectrices*)   A long tail feather.

Resident   That which resides or dwells in a place for some time.   This term is usually applied only to breeding birds whether present for just a short time during the breeding season or throughout the year.   Although some winter birds may be present in a particular place for a longer period of time than some summering birds which breed, the term resident is seldom if ever applied to the wintering birds.

Rufous   Reddish; of a reddish or brownish-red color.

Scapular   Shoulder feather of a bird; used in the plural.

Secondary   One of the large feathers in the second row on the second bone of a bird's wing.   Apart from their being closer to the trunk of the bird, secondaries generally differ from primaries in being shorter and having squarer, less pointed tips.

Secondary covert   Relatively short feathers near the forward edge of the wing which cover the base of the secondaries.

Secretive   Having the tendency or disposition to conceal.   This term is generally applied to birds which because of their habits are difficult to locate or to observe well enough to identify.

Semipalmated   Half - webbed; denoting that the toes are connected together by a web extending only halfway to the tips.

Serrate, serrated   Notched on the edge like a saw; toothed.   In birds usually applied to the bill.

Sexes alike   Except by examination of the gonads, male and female cannot be distinguished in the hand.

Sexes similar   Male and female cannot normally be distinguished in the field.

Shaft   The stem or stock of a feather or quill.

Soporific   Causing sleep; tending to cause sleep.

Speculum   A bright spot, often iridescent, as on the wing of a duck or the tail or a peacock.

Subspecies   A geographical variety or race.

Summer bird   A bird which occurs normally in a given locality in summer.

Tail coverts   The feathers which cover the bases of the tail feathers.

Tarsus   That part of the leg of birds which extends from the toes to the first joint above; the shank.

Tertiary   A quill growing on the last or innermost joint of a bird's wing.

Uncommon   Not common; not usual; infrequent; rare.

Under tail coverts   Those tail coverts which lie on the underside of the bird's body; collectively, the crissum.   They are situated immediately behind the vent.

Under wing coverts   Those wing coverts which lie on the underside of the bird's wing; sometimes called wing linings.

Upper tail coverts   Those tail coverts which lie on the top side of the bird's body.

Web   a. The membrane which unites the toes of many water birds.   b. The series of barbs on either side of the shaft of a feather; so called because of the interlocking of the barbs and barbicels.

Winter bird   A bird which occurs normally in a given locality in winter.

Wattle   The fleshy lobe that grows under the throat of the domestic fowl, or any appendage of the like kind.

ALABAMA BIRDS

BIRD STUDY

INTRODUCTION

BIRD-WATCHING has been a popular pastime in northwestern Europe for nearly a century, but in the United States widespread participation is much more recent. A bare thirty years ago, only a relatively few deeply-interested people studied birds as a hobby, and even fewer were professionally involved. But today, perhaps because of increased leisure time, better educational and travel facilities, and more well-organized societies for the study of birds, bird-watching has been adopted by a very great many, and they are finding it a most fascinating avocation.

Birds have a tremendous appeal. They can be seen or heard almost everywhere at almost any time—in the city or in the wilderness, on the ocean or in the desert, in the arctic or the tropic, at night or by day. To some their principal attraction may be their trustful ways, pleasing songs, or handsome plumage. Others admire their remarkable feats: the long migrations, the ability to survive under adverse conditions, to outwit the hunter, and the like. Perhaps the most amazing accomplishment of nearly all birds is the ability to fly long distances. Thus the local bird student, who observes closely only a limited area, is constantly surprised at the number and variety of birds that pass through. As his experience and ability increase, he adds more species to his list, many of them rarities in a particular place or at a particular season, and he never seems to exhaust the possibilities: there is always the chance of recording an early or late nesting or migration date.

Because of the many facets of this science, ornithology attracts people of various interests. The talents of the artist, the photographer, the mathematician, physician, teacher, carpenter, writer, and many others are all usable in the pursuit of this natural science. But before any such specific knowledge can be applied, there is a first step in bird study: the student must learn where to find the different species and how to recognize them. And many amateur ornithologists remain satisfied with this phase alone, for it can be of great value to the science and can lead the devotee on trips as far afield as his time and money can take him.

[1]

ALABAMA BIRDS

The only two pieces of equipment required for ordinary bird study are a pair of binoculars and a suitable guide to local birds. For identification only, *A Field Guide to the Birds* by Roger Tory Peterson is a classic, and several other useful guides are listed in the Bibliography. For other life history information, particularly of a local nature, the state bird books are usually a more suitable guide to local birds, especially if they cover thoroughly identification and time and place of occurrence.

The best glass for bird study is a medium-powered prism binocular. Magnification below six power does not show sufficient detail, whereas higher magnification, which is accomplished by the sacrifice of light and size of field, requires a bigger glass and therefore needs a better aim and more support. For bird study, perhaps the best all-around binocular is a 7x50, but 6x30, 7x35, 8x40, and 10x50 glasses are also excellent for observing birds. It is best to have binoculars with lenses coated on both surfaces to reduce glare and a central focusing knob for the rapid changes needed to keep up with active birds.

In addition, bird students who live near the coast or in any other place where birds are often seen at a distance will find a telescope very useful, preferably one about 20 power and with a tripod or other means of support. Some high-powered telescopes can be bought cheaply, but they usually have a small objective lens and thus a very narrow field and poor light. For a 19.5 or 20 power telescope, the objective lens should be at least 60 millimeters in diameter if it is to be satisfactory for bird study. Beyond these things, the amount of equipment a bird student uses depends on his particular interests and his ability to buy. Among the most popular items are other bird books, recordings of bird songs, and photographic equipment. A notebook for keeping systematic records of observations is also useful.

Many other aids and incentives to the study of birds are available to the amateur through the bird societies. These furnish opportunities for him to meet other bird students and to learn and enjoy the birds through programs and field trips. He can also make a real contribution to science by taking part in a co-operative project or publishing his observations in a local or national bird journal.

The foremost society of ornithologists in the country is the American Ornithologists' Union, which publishes the quarterly *Auk*. The professional and most of the serious amateur ornithologists of the United States and Canada are members. Standards of this organization are high and its journal is worthy of the best professional group.

[2]

Supplementing the work of the A.O.U. is the Wilson Ornithological Society, which places more emphasis on field work and attracts a higher proportion of expert amateurs. It publishes the *Wilson Bulletin* quarterly.

The National Audubon Society stresses conservation and concerns itself largely with educational and legal aspects of ornithology. *Audubon Magazine,* published bimonthly, contains many articles on birds and helps its readers to understand all natural history, especially the manner in which many phases of its elements are interrelated and interdependent. One of the major research activities of the society investigates the life history of species threatened with extinction. Birds like the flamingos, Roseate Spoonbill, Wood Ibis, other wading birds, and the Bald Eagle are typical subjects for these studies, which are often supplemented by reports from amateur bird-watchers in local areas.

In collaboration with the United States Fish and Wildlife Service, the National Audubon Society publishes *Audubon Field Notes,* a bimonthly journal devoted especially to the field student of birds. Four times a year its seasonal reports from about twenty regions in the United States and Canada document the abundance and movements of birds. Its breeding and wintering censuses, conducted mostly by amateurs, report on the abundance of many species and on the ability of many types of habitats to support them. By far its most popular activity is the Christmas Bird Count, started in 1900. The concerted effort of observers uncovers a surprising variety of winter bird life, and participants in this work now number over 6,000 who turn in over 600 reports from all the states and provinces. Each year about 500 species are counted and about 100 of the reports list 100 or more species. The excitement, the careful planning, frequent reconnaissance, the hope for good weather, and the spirit of competition add up to an experience that few bird students want to miss.

Besides collaborating in the publication of *Audubon Field Notes,* the U. S. Fish and Wildlife Service, through its Bureau of Sport Fisheries and Wildlife, sponsors many co-operative studies of birds. It conducts migration studies and maintains enormous card files on the distribution and migration of birds throughout the country. It sponsors a banding program, supplying split-ring aluminum bands to qualified ornithologists throughout the United States and Canada. These banders since about 1924 have banded nearly eleven million birds. The records of recapture of these banded birds, filed on about one million IBM cards in the office at Patuxent Wildlife Research Center in Maryland, furnished data for the banding information in the species accounts of this book. The banders themselves publish the results of their studies in *Bird-banding,* an excellent quarterly magazine. Its high quality review section, together with those of *Auk* and

ALABAMA BIRDS

Wilson Bulletin keep the bird student abreast of current studies on birds throughout the world.

The Alabama Ornithological Society publishes quarterly *Alabama Birdlife*, which contains studies of Alabama birds and reports of local interest about them. The Society meets twice a year, usually once inland and once on the coast, the major activity of each meeting being field study. Several cities in Alabama have smaller bird or conservation groups. The Birmingham Audubon Society, for example, holds monthly meetings and field trips and each year sponsors five Audubon Screen Tours, which are excellent colored movies on wildlife with commentary by an expert naturalist.

Unless birds are being observed at a distance, the most efficient group for observing is a small one. Parties of two, one, and three, in that order, are closest to the ideal. An automobile is a nearly perfect blind, especially for waterfowl. If birds are near, it is well to look around first before you get out of the car, and, in fact, observations are often better made from the car where you may be sheltered and where you have a steady support for your binoculars.

Wherever possible, the sun should be behind the observer with the birds front lighted, not in shadow, and so, for example, an early morning bird walk should be planned going west. When finding birds in the field, stop frequently to listen and look, and keep to paths as much as possible. Crashing through the brush makes much noise, decreases visibility and increases the chance of encountering a snake or of picking up such pests as ticks and redbugs. Furthermore, it demands much attention in picking the route. It is rarely worthwhile.

The best time for observing birds is almost always early morning. About nine or ten o'clock, when the sun has heated the earth, birds may become less active In winter, when the temperature seldom goes above 70° F., birds are often active throughout the shorter days, and it is not as important for the observer to get up early. Another rewarding time of day is at dusk when many kinds of birds, particularly water birds, increase their activity. Some species are more active and easier to observe under certain weather conditions and at certain times of day; thus the bird student who takes note of the variety of bird habits can be in the right place at the right time in order to observe birds under the best conditions.

Perhaps the greatest weather hindrance to the observation of birds is wind, especially if it is over fifteen miles per hour. In high winds, birds tend to remain in denser cover, show themselves only briefly, and often fly so differently that they are difficult to identify. At the same time, a search of the lee side of dense cover, buildings, dunes, or other spots protected from the wind is often rewarding. In a drizzle or light rain, birds are generally active, but a heavy downpour nor-

[4]

mally stops their activity. Immediately after a heavy rain, they are usually as active as in the early morning.

In learning to identify birds, start with the common local species. Usually you will find in this group a representative of most of the land bird families. When you know the family characteristics of the local representatives, it often becomes a simple matter to place the migrating strangers in their proper group, and then identifying them as to species becomes easier. Quick and correct identifications are made by people who know how to use binoculars properly and who are well acquainted with the field marks of all species likely to be encountered. You can learn these field marks by frequent reference to the color plates and the first paragraph in each of the species accounts in this book. One of the secrets of recognizing birds lies in knowing which part of the bird to look at first, and the experienced bird student who can name almost every bird he encounters has mastered this technique. But even the expert must leave unidentified a small percentage of birds for lack of satisfactory observation.

Diversity of habitat and nearness to water are the biggest aids to locating a great variety of birds. Thus, more birds occur where the woods contain both pines and hardwoods, a well-developed shrub layer, or water. The edges of habitats, such as the borders of woods and fields, allow birds access to two kinds of terrain at the same time and are consequently highly appealing. Birds are attracted to water not only for bathing and drinking, but also because here they find thicker cover and more insects and other forms of life. An area in the general vicinity of salt water probably offers the greatest number of diverse habitats. When the bird student adds his list of birds of woods, fields, and other upland habitats to those of marshes, shores, and fresh, brackish, and salt water, he usually reaches the ultimate in variety.

Taking note of the kinds of trees and shrubs that attract birds is a further means of locating species. For instance, some birds frequent evergreens in winter; others, trees that leaf out first in spring, or those in fruit. Some look for isolated hardwoods in a pine forest, and others for isolated pines or cedars in a hardwood forest. They go where their food is abundant.

Hidden birds will often show themselves when they hear a squeaking sound like that made when calling a dog. To make this sound, press closed lips on a finger or the back of your hand and slowly draw in your breath. The squeak is most effective when the bird has to move to see the squeaker, who should therefore be at least partially hidden. This squeak sounds like a bird in distress, and it attracts nesting birds if they are close by, some birds in thick cover, and occasionally predators.

ALABAMA BIRDS

One of the best ways to see birds at close range is to attract them to the home. Their need for safety, food, water, cover, and nest-site should be considered for it is a decisive factor in this attraction. In any situation, some of these needs must be provided for.

A garden, to be attractive to birds, should have open areas like lawns for feeding and sufficient shrubbery, some of it evergreen, to provide cover. A reasonable amount of seclusion from human traffic and a fence to exclude certain animals provide protection from disturbance. A few mature trees furnish some shade and sunlight so that the birds have a choice of feeding as the weather permits. Either shade-loving or sun-loving plants may be grown.

The trees, shrubs, and vines most attractive to birds are those that provide the most food and cover. Thus, almost all of those that bear large quantities of fruits or nuts or that are evergreen qualify for this purpose. The most suitable for planting in Alabama in approximate decreasing order of attractiveness are as follows: wild cherry, holly (nearly all kinds), red cedar, red mulberry, dogwood, hackberry, all of the oaks and hickories, black gum, crab apple, hawthorn, grape, elderberry, French mulberry, bayberry, persimmon, Virginia creeper, sumac, raspberry, blackberry, and blueberry. Flowers most appealing to hummingbirds are usually red but may also be orange or purple. Those most frequently visited by the Ruby-throated Hummingbird are listed under that species.

Putting out food will attract birds throughout the year but especially in times of short supply such as during cold weather. Many types of feeders have been successful, and the desirable features of each are presented in order to help the reader choose the correct one. They are best placed in the open near a window, preferably the breakfast nook, where the birds can see and be seen. Protection from crawling animals is obtained by suspending a feeder from a thin overhead support, such as a tree limb, or by placing it on a pole preferably made of sheet metal or with suitable sheet-metal guards (inverted funnel shape) to discourage climbing. In winter the feeder should be sheltered from northerly winds by placing on the southern or southeastern side of a house or evergreen thicket. It should be several feet from this shelter so that the birds are sufficiently in the open to watch for danger while they are feeding.

There are many types of feeders, the most usual being a tray, a hopper arrangement, a small wire-mesh container, or a cavity into which food is stuffed. All of them should be provided with perches. The food tray or shelf should have a rim to prevent the food from being scattered by the wind or by the birds. Hoppers for grains and wire-mesh containers for suet, bread, or other larger food items prevent the food from being wasted or fouled with droppings, and should be chosen with this in mind. Food may be placed in a coconut, in holes drilled in a stick or limb, or in almost any container. If grain is spread on the ground, it should be on a rock or cement to prevent sprouting.

The main types of food that attract birds are grains, fats, nuts, and fruits. Almost any item in this group may be successful, but the most successful in Alabama seem to be such things as suet, sunflower seed, starter scratch feed, peanuts and peanut butter, pecans, walnuts, other nuts, grain products such as corn bread, white bread, cornmeal, doughnuts, cookies, other pastries except the salty ones, grits, and breakfast cereals. Squash seeds, watermelon seeds, other melon seeds, raisins, cut-up apple, cut-up hard-boiled egg, and seed mixes for cage birds or domestic birds, especially those that contain hemp, millet, corn, rice, wheat, rape, oats, buckwheat, and rye are also good. The nuts should be cracked but the meat need not be extracted. Peanut butter is often more acceptable when mixed with cornmeal. Only a few of these foods need be put out at any one time and place, and if a representative is available of the four main types of foods—fats, grains, nuts, and fruits—a variety of birds will patronize the feeders.

J. E. Keeler

BIRD FEEDER. An excellent means of attracting birds.

One way of combining these types of foods is to make a pudding. One proven recipe in Alabama is as follows:

Mix 1 cup bacon grease or any grease that solidifies, 1 cup sugar, and 5 cups water. Boil this mixture, then add 2 cups cornmeal, ½ cup flour, and 2 cups cold water. Make smooth by stirring until thick, then add 1 cup raisins, seeds, or nut meats as desired. Pour into pan, keep in refrigerator, and slice off as needed.

The food paragraphs of the species accounts list the foods favored by a particular bird. In many cases its food at Alabama feeding stations is mentioned, but with the finches and sparrows, which eat most grains and seeds, there is little need to be specific.

Spoiled food, which is an indication that too much food is being put out,

[7]

PURPLE MARTIN HOUSE. This box should be at least fifteen feet high on a pole in the open.

should be discarded as should wet food more than a day old, or it will sour or get mouldy. Food should be put out at regular intervals, for it must be remembered that a feeding station increases the local bird population to some extent, and any long break in the feeding routine would cause hardship for the birds, especially in winter.

Birds require water for drinking and bathing the year round. The best bird bath is a shallow, rough-bottomed receptacle of cement or clay whose depth is barely an inch at the outside. Easy to clean and with the water easily removable, it should be placed in the shade and reasonably close to an evergreen. Especially attractive is some fountain or dripping arrangement.

Encouraging birds to nest near the house gives us the opportunity to study, observe, and enjoy them even more closely. Baby animals have a charm all their own, and birds are no exception. For most species, nesting can be encouraged by the presence of sufficient mature trees and dense shrubs. Hole-nesting birds, however, usually need a nest box to encourage them to nest near the house.

Nest boxes are best made of wood, preferably a durable kind, but they may be built of a considerable variety of other materials. Metal boxes become cold in cold weather or are apt to roast the nestlings if exposed to the hot summer sun, but if this disadvantage can be eliminated by placing them in the shade or providing ventilation, some birds will accept them. The metal should, of course, have no rough edges or the birds may be injured. Bird tastes are many and varied, and wrens are probably the least particular. All nest boxes, though, are best provided with a perch and a hinged lid or other means of cleaning the box. This cleaning should be done at least once a year and preferably after each brood. For some species, the box should be made rustic by tacking sections of bark on the outside or by making the box from a section of a limb. Others merely require a neutral color—brown, black, orange—but many birds find the color of the box of little importance.

[8]

Species	Floor Space (inches)	Depth of Box (inches)	Entrance Height (inches)	Entrance Diameter (inches)	Feet Above Ground	Remarks
Wood Duck	10x18	10-24	12-16	4	10-20	in or near swamp
Barn Owl	10x18	15-18	4	6	12-18	high on barn
Screech Owl	8x8	12-15	9-12	3	10-30	orchard, grove
Flickers	7x7	16-18	14-16	2½	6-20	cover floor with 1"-2" wood chips
Red-headed Woodpecker	6x6	12-15	9-12	2	12-20	
Hairy Woodpecker	6x6	12-15	9-12	1½	12-20	
Downy Woodpecker	4x4	8-10	6-8	1¼	6-20	
Great Crested Flycatcher	6x6	8-10	6-8	2	8-20	rustic, in open woods or orchard
Eastern Phoebe	6x6	6	open sides		8-12	near water
Starling	6x6	16-18	14-16	2	10-25	near house
Barn Swallow	6x6	6	open sides		8-12	on barn, near water or large pasture
Carolina Chickadee	4x4	8-10	6-8	1⅛	6-15	rustic, near woods
White-breasted Nuthatch	4x4	8-10	6-8	1¼	12-20	
Tufted Titmouse	4x4	8-10	6-8	1¼	6-15	
House Wren	4x4	6-8	1-6	1-1¼	6-10	partially sunny, oblong entrance
Bewick's Wren	4x4	6-8	1-6	1-1¼	6-10	
Carolina Wren	4x4	6-8	1-6	1½	6-10	
Robin	6x8	8	open sides		6-15	partly shaded or under leaves
Eastern Bluebird	5x5	8	6	1½	5-10	open place in orchard
Prothonotary Warbler	4x4	8	5	1½	4-7	near water

BIRD BATH. Almost any shallow container of water will attract birds. It should be shaded and easy to drain and clean.

A nest box is more acceptable if it is weathered a bit, which will eliminate odors, and is in place before the birds arrive on their nesting grounds. (See the occurrence in Alabama paragraph of the pertinent species account.) The box is best placed on a tree or pole with the same precautions against climbing predators as for a feeder, but titmice and wrens may accept a swinging nest box. While nesting birds normally require a degree of privacy, usually those species that regularly occur near houses are most likely to accept a nest box close to a house. The account of the species desired as a nest-box occupant often contains some information useful in placing the nest box, such as its tolerance of man or the type of trees and other cover it prefers.

The accompanying table gives the nest-box requirements for individual species. Many of them will accept a larger cavity and simply fill it up to make it small enough to meet their needs. The size of the entrance hole is determined by the need to eliminate larger competitors and predators.

Information in the table on page 9 is adapted from *Your Book of Nature Activities*, published by Nelson-Doubleday in 1953.

ORNITHOLOGY IN ALABAMA

IN HIS BIRD BOOK of Alabama, Arthur H. Howell (1924:8-13) gives a necessarily brief summary of the bird work done in the state up to 1921. He notes (page 8) that before he undertook the biological survey of Alabama, less than 200 forms of birds were recorded here. Prominent naturalists had traveled through the state, but only a few lists and collections of specimens resulted. Among some of the early visitors who mentioned birds they saw in Alabama were Bernard, Duke of Saxe-Weimar (1825-26), Thomas Nuttall (1830), John James Audubon (1837), Charles Lanman (1853-54), and Philip Henry Gosse (1858).

Probably the first published local list of birds for Alabama was for Coosada, Elmore County. Nathan Clifford Brown of Portland, Maine, lived in Coosada from January 21 to April 13, 1878, and his list of 119 species was published in the forerunner of *Auk (Bull. Nuttall Orn. Club* 3:168-174, 1878 and 4:7-13, 1879). The first local collection of Alabama birds is that of Dr. William Cushman Avery of Greensboro whose approximately 900 specimens of 216 Alabama species and subspecies is well preserved in the Alabama Museum of Natural History on the University campus at Tuscaloosa. While Dr. Avery published but little, Ernest G. Holt has written an excellent annotated list of the Avery Collection (Museum Paper No. 4, 1921).

From February, 1891, to January, 1892, F. W. McCormack published a local list of 156 Colbert County birds in the Leighton *News.* He and F. R. King continued observations for a number of years and collected some birds, but the location of this list and collection is at present uncertain.

Aretas A. Saunders, whose pioneer work on bird song is well known, was in Coosa, Clay, and Talladega counties from March 7 to June 9, 1908, and published a list of 129 species (*Auk* 25:413-424, 1908).

About 1910, Lewis S. Golsan began a fruitful 35 years of bird work around Autaugaville. His egg collection and notebooks are now, since his death, deposited in the Alabama Museum of Natural History with the Avery Collection. His nephew, Ernest G. Holt of Montgomery, worked with him and contributed much to Alabama ornithology while a resident of this state.

At Anniston, R. H. Dean made bird observations from at least 1915 to 1925 and took several Christmas bird counts there. Other early observers include Edward W. Graves, who lived near Long Island, Jackson County, Bessie R. Samuel of Guntersville, W. F. Ponder of Talladega County, and Carrie E. Parkhurst of Talladega.

U. S. Fish & Wildlife Service

DR. A. H. HOWELL

In 1908 and from 1911 to 1916, a biological survey under federal auspices was conducted by Howell with the assistance of Holt, James S. Gutsell, James L. Peters, and Luther J. Goldman. This survey resulted in the publication of Alabama's first state bird book. It is possible that World War I delayed publication, for it was not published until 1924. A second edition came out in 1928.

Howell says (page 8) that 314 bird forms are listed in his book. Of this number, 40 are either subspecies, or species listed as likely to occur but without definite Alabama record. Thus the state list in 1924 was 274 species.

The Christmas Bird Counts were begun in New York in 1900, and the first report from Alabama, taken by Edward W. Graves at Long Island in 1909, listed 21 species. Prior to the publication of Howell's book, eleven of these counts had been published, and from 1928 to 1961 at least one count from Alabama was reported each year. The total published Christmas counts from Alabama as of May, 1961, is 93, and for the last 25 years, at least three per year have appeared. The number of these counts seems to be a rather reliable indication of the activity of bird students in the state.

For at least a decade beginning in 1923 Mrs. Helen McElhone Edwards led a group at Fairhope in making local observations. Many of their records were published in the Pensacola Region column of Francis M. Weston in *Bird-Lore*.

About this time, Dr. Henry G. Good began teaching at Auburn and eventually taught a course in ornithology. In 1936, Harold S. Peters established at Auburn the Alabama Co-operative Wildlife Research Unit, which is jointly sponsored by the Alabama Department of Conservation, the U. S. Fish and Wildlife Service, Auburn University, and the Wildlife Management Institute. These two activities spurred student interest in birds and resulted in a considerable amount of field data and a number of specimens stored both at the Research Unit and the Department of Zoölogy-Entomology of Auburn University.

Meanwhile, the big TVA dams were being completed, and in 1937 Alabama found itself the possessor of several big lakes in the Tennessee Valley. Wheeler National Wildlife Refuge was established on both sides of the river just east of Decatur. This refuge increased tremendously the waterfowl population of Alabama and became a model of wildlife management and conservation in action. Under the leadership of Thomas Z. Atkeson, Jr., Refuge Biologist, local bird listing and study was greatly stimulated, and a wealth of ornithological field data was assembled.

Howell's book mentions only one bird record from Birmingham. Soon after its publication, however, an increased interest in birds led to the establishment there of a small public museum and an Audubon society. In 1934, Henry M. Stevenson organized the Christmas Bird Counts in Birmingham and made field observations at many localities in north Alabama. Stevenson is now a professor of zoölogy at Florida State University, Tallahassee, but his interest in Alabama ornithology continues and he makes outstanding contributions though no longer a resident of this state.

In 1946, when the author settled in the Birmingham area, he and the group which carried on these Christmas Bird Counts, including Morton H. Perry, M. F. Prather, and Dr. Samuel R. Tipton, formed the Birmingham Audubon Society. The Audubon Screen Tours, illustrated lectures of this society, contribute to the cultural life of the city and to its knowledge of natural history. The Montgomery Audubon Society, which flourished in the late forties under the leadership of the late Julian M. Rice, also sponsored the Audubon Screen Tours.

The Alabama Ornithological Society was formed in April, 1952, under the energetic leadership of Mrs. Blanche E. Dean of Birmingham. Through this society bird students throughout Alabama can meet together, publicize their activities, and publish in a journal their observations and studies of birds.

Both Auburn University and the University of Alabama now offer courses in ornithology. Collections of bird skins in the state are few, and often they are not available to the general public. At both universities, small collections are used for instruction. At Tuscaloosa, the University of Alabama has also available the Avery Collection, primarily Greensboro specimens, in the Alabama Museum of Natural History, and at Auburn, the Co-operative Wildlife Research Unit has a small collection, distinct from the Auburn University Collection. At Montgomery, the Division of Game and Fish of the Department of Conservation is building a collection for educational purposes, and the Department of Archives and History has a small collection. Other small collections, though not on exhibit, are in the Birmingham Public Library, Wheeler Refuge, Florence State Teachers'

College, and Howard College. The collection at Alabama College, Montevallo, and the Regar Collection, Anniston, are, as far as is known, not of native birds.

Outside of the state, the following collections are known to have Alabama specimens: the United States National Museum, a rather large representation from the state as a result of the biological survey which served as a basis for Howell's book; Museum of Comparative Zoölogy, Harvard University; University of Michigan Museum of Zoölogy; University of Wisconsin, only one specimen, a Yellow Rail; University of Chicago; University of Cincinnati; Louisiana State University Museum of Zoölogy; Department of Biological Sciences, Florida State University; and the Fuertes Memorial Collection, Cornell University.

The beginning of work on a new state bird book in January, 1955, encouraged a considerable increase in field work in the state. This was further aided by the opening of the Dauphin Island Bridge in July, 1955, and the large increase in the number of active observers in Alabama. To increase the amount of coverage on the Alabama Gulf Coast, spring and fall migration counts in the Mobile Bay area and regular coastal Christmas Bird Counts were organized.

In the past ten years, probably more field work on birds has been conducted in Alabama than in all the time prior to 1951. This is verified by the preponderance of dates in the 1950's in the occurrence paragraphs of the species accounts. A more detailed account of this bird book project, together with acknowledgments, will be found in the preface. It is hoped that publication of this book will provide a continuing stimulus to bird study in Alabama.

PHYSIOGRAPHY OF ALABAMA

ALABAMA'S SOUTHERN POSITION, its high proportion of forested land, big water impoundments, natural prairie, and short but highly productive coastline, all tend to promote a richness, variety, and abundance of bird life. Other states that boast larger bird lists usually have a much larger area, a much longer coastline, or many more bird students.

The state contains 51,609 square miles of land and inland water and ranks twenty-ninth among the fifty states in size. Its 3,225,000 population makes it the seventeenth most populous state. It lies between 30° 13' and 35° 00' North latitude and between 84° 51' and 88° 31' West longitude, 200 miles west of the Atlantic Ocean and 100 miles east of the Mississippi River.

Topography. The northern half of Alabama marks the southern end of the Appalachian chain. Except for the Tennessee Valley, it is heavily forested and very hilly. These ridges and plateaus, which run generally northeast-southwest, terminate in the general area between Birmingham and Montgomery. Most of them are 1,000 to 1,800 feet above sea level, but a few points reach over 2,000, and the highest point in the state, Mount Cheaha, is 2,407 feet in elevation. The fertile valleys between these ridges are usually 500 to 700 feet above sea level. The Coosa Valley, a continuation of the Great Appalachian Valley, separates the Blue Ridge from the main Appalachian ridges. The Tennessee River forms a broad, rich valley across the top of the state, and the lakes formed by the TVA dams add much inland water area.

The Piedmont, which with the Talladega Mountains contains the only metamorphic rock in the state, is a steeply rolling, roughly triangular region of foothills on the eastern side. The area of Alabama north of the Coastal Plain totals about 20,800 square miles or about forty per cent of the state.

The dividing line between the hilly north and the southern Coastal Plain is the Fall Line, where rivers have their most noticeable drop and where water power, available at the head of river navigation, encourages the growth of such cities as Tuscaloosa, Wetumpka, Tallassee, and Phenix City. In northwestern Alabama, the Coastal Plain is separated from the Tennessee Valley by a divide of just over a thousand feet elevation near the Franklin-Marion county line.

The Coastal Plain of Alabama, about sixty per cent of the area of the state, is often hilly with high, rounded ridges and steep river bluffs, but it has a relatively more level terrain, fewer exposed rocks, a milder climate, more frequent swamps and marshes, and more sluggish rivers and branches. It contains a portion of the only extensive natural dry prairie east of the Mississippi River and south of the Ohio River. This prairie region, which in Alabama comprises about 4,000 square miles, is called the Black Belt after the color of its original topsoil, which is very fertile. In the southeastern corner of the state is an area of about 900 square miles, known as the Wiregrass Area for its dominant natural plant cover. In amount of land cleared for agriculture it is rivaled in Alabama only by parts of the Tennessee Valley.

Near the coast, swamps increase in size and number, especially along rivers. An area which extends for about fifty miles north from Mobile to at least the junction of the Alabama and Tombigbee rivers comprises the largest swamp in the state, about 450 square miles. This swamp is really a delta, somewhat misshapen by the high ground which nearly surrounds it. On the coast itself, extensive marshes are present at the head of Mobile Bay and on the shores and islands of Mississippi Sound. The southernmost parts of Alabama consist of a series of sandy, narrow peninsulas which separate the shallow bays from the Gulf.

[15]

RUSH MARSH IN UPPER MOBILE BAY. An abundance of submerged wild celery and various other foods here attract waterfowl during the winter months.

The coastline habitat of Alabama available to marine birds extends for 53 airline miles but provides 607 miles of tidal shoreline for wading birds and other salt-water and brackish-water birds.

Water. Inland waters in Alabama total 1,291 square miles, of which 737 are fresh and 554 are brackish, the latter all in the vicinity of Mobile Bay. Fresh waters include 453 square miles in big impoundments, 175 in rivers, creeks, and branches, and 109 in ponds. Present construction will bring the impoundment total to 611 square miles, the fresh-water total to 884, and the total inland waters to 1,438 square miles.

This inland water is subject to much pollution by human and industrial wastes. Pollution is undoubtedly the major problem today in the management of inland waters, for although floods are still a threat, much progress has been made in controlling them. The control of both pollution and floods increases the capacity of inland waters to support birds.

On the Alabama coast, the normal tide is weak and has little effect on water levels in brackish and salt waters, but these waters fluctuate considerably in level and salt content due mainly to wind direction and speed, rain, evaporation, and the outflow of fresh water from the rivers. Thus in the estuarine area in the

LAGOON AND SPARTINA MARSH ON WEST DAUPHIN ISLAND. Wading birds feed and rest in this habitat, and the Mottled Duck and Willet choose it for nesting.

vicinity of Mobile Bay, a broad zone of transition provides conditions that meet the requirements of many water birds.

Climate. Like other southeastern states, Alabama has long, warm summers and short, relatively mild winters. No great barriers impede the flow of polar air from the Hudson Bay region or tropical air from across the Gulf of Mexico.

During the months from November to March inclusive, when all but the ever-green trees and shrubs are bare and the tropical and polar air masses fight for dominance, cold, clear days alternate with cool or warm, cloudy rainy days. During this period, freezing temperatures are frequent but usually last for only a few hours. Occasional freezes that last for 24 hours or longer often do wide-spread damage to plant and animal life, especially in late spring when buds are out. Snow, when it comes, rarely lasts until noontime of the day it falls. If we consider winter as a period when little or no plant growth occurs and most cold-blooded animals are dormant, the winter in Alabama would then be really confined to those short periods of freezing weather.

April, as well as much of March, is a period of transition when the trees leaf out, insects become active, and the bulk of the summer-resident birds return from the south. Cold weather becomes less severe and less frequent until about

[17]

the first of May when tropical air becomes dominant. Summer here normally means clear, warm weather. During the course of an average summer day, the sun heats the earth, many cumulus clouds develop, and late afternoon, rather local thunderstorms may often occur. The Gulf Coast then receives enough heavy showers to make it the rainiest part of the state.

Cool weather sometimes occurs in late September, but it is generally late October before much of it arrives. Early fall cold fronts are usually rainless, and October is normally the driest month, with September almost as dry. In early November, the trees lose their leaves, and polar air again begins to assert its dominance.

The mean annual temperature of Alabama is about 64° F. In January, the coldest month, the temperature varies from 42° in the north to 54° in the south, but in July, the warmest month, it is about 80° nearly throughout the state. On the average, 32° temperature may be experienced in DeKalb County from October 28 to April 11, and the resulting growing season of 200 days is the shortest in the state. Near Mobile, 32° temperature may occur on the average from December 12 to February 17, so that this area has the longest growing season in the state, 300 days. These growing seasons coincide with the period when deciduous trees and shrubs have leaves, cold-blooded animals (especially insects) are active, and the majority of summer-resident birds are present. The average annual maximum temperature, usually recorded somewhere in the central part of the state, is 100°, and the minimum varies from about 6° in the Tennessee Valley to about 25° at Fort Morgan.

The mean annual precipitation of most of Alabama varies from 52 to 56 inches. Within about fifty miles of the Gulf, however, it is generally over 60 and in some parts of the Black Belt as low as 48. On a monthly basis, most parts of the state show a similar trend in rainfall with below average in May, September, October, and November, and above average from December to March. The only exception to this is the heavy summer rainfall of the Gulf Coast. The average annual number of days with one inch or more of snow cover is one to nine, with an annual fall of zero to five inches. This is generally confined to the northern third of the state. The central third usually experiences annual snow flurries but may go for years without any snow on the ground. The southern third may go for years without experiencing any snow at all.

The general climate of Alabama is therefore fairly uniform throughout. The main exceptions are the heavy summer rainfall on the coast and the approximately twelve-degree difference in winter temperature between the extreme north and the extreme south.

STAND OF YOUNG PINES WITH DECIDUOUS UNDERGROWTH. Common in Alabama, this habitat affords good foraging for many species and presents the bird student with excellent viewing.

BRUSHY THICKET ON EDGE OF BEAVER POND. Various species of warblers including the rare Bachman's Warbler find this good habitat for nesting.

ALABAMA BIRDS

Plantlife. Alabama has at least 31,250 square miles (twenty million acres) of forest, which is about 66 per cent of the total land area. Wise management maintains a rather constant amount of timberland and still permits Alabama to be one of the largest producers of lumber and lumber products in the nation. Impoundments, highway and other rights-of-way, and residential and industrial development eat into this total forested area, but the seedings and other reforestation practices of lumbering and agricultural interests help to keep the size of our forested area rather constant.

The number of species of wild plants in Alabama is about 4,500. In variety this is about the same as for other southeastern states if we discount the subtropical element in Florida. The proportion of evergreens increases from about sixteen per cent (mostly red cedar) in the Tennessee Valley to about ninety per cent (mostly longleaf and slash pine) near the coast. This change is due not only to an increase in the number and variety of pines and other evergreens but also to the fact that some species of plants become evergreen as one moves south. Some families of plants, such as oaks, hollies, and magnolias, have more deciduous representatives in north Alabama and more evergreen in the south.

This proportion of evergreens influences the distribution of many woodland birds in Alabama. For instance, the increasing number of evergreens near the coast limits the southward breeding distribution of many species such as the Wood Thrush, Red-eyed Vireo, and American Redstart that require or prefer deciduous trees. Conversely, the lessening proportion of evergreens as one goes inland seems to limit the northward winter distribution of other woodland birds such as the Blue-gray Gnatcatcher, Solitary Vireo, and Orange-crowned Warbler. Within about fifty miles of the Tennessee line, typical piney-woods birds—the Red-cockaded Woodpecker, Brown-headed Nuthatch, and Pine Warbler, for instance—become scarce or absent because natural pines are scarce or absent.

Hardwoods, especially the larger, well-developed trees such as oak, hickory, tulip-poplar, basswood, beech, and gums, are most abundant in rich moist soils in such places as mountain coves and river bottoms. It is here that one finds the greatest variety of woodland birds at all seasons.

The natural prairie or Black Belt was the site of the extensive cotton plantations, which still constitute the average non-southerner's concept of what Alabama looks like. At present, Alabama grows barely five per cent of the nation's cotton, and the Black Belt is largely pasture land, with the raising of livestock its major agricultural endeavor. The general aspect, rather western, is one of grassland, tall where not grazed or mowed, interspersed primarily with large oaks and clumps of red cedar.

[20]

BRUSH AREA ON THE GULF COAST, FORT MORGAN PENINSULA.   Spring and fall trans-Gulf migrants stop here for rest and food.

The coastal marshes contain considerable variety of plantlife for such a short coastline. This is very likely due to the great range of salt content and depth of water. Two grasses are predominant in the salt marshes—black rush (*Juncus roemoerians*), which is generally poor bird habitat, and salt marsh grass (several members of the genus *Spartina*), which is good bird habitat.

No wild purely subtropical plants such as mangrove and palm are known near the coast, probably because the freezes are sufficient to keep them from gaining a foothold. Many cultivated subtropicals, such as palms, citrus trees, tung, and banana grow successfully, but they attract few birds.

Human disturbance areas form a considerable portion of the state, and the plantlife of roadsides, gardens, parks, cemeteries, pastures, orchards, cropfields, hayfields, campuses, airports, athletic fields, and other recreational areas has a profound effect on local bird distribution. The birds we see most commonly in these areas owe their present-day abundance to the activities of man and their ability to adapt to the changes he makes. The birds that live successfully in these places are practically the only ones making long-range gains in abundance.

Thus, in Alabama, birds have access to a great variety of habitats. All stages of transition occur from no pine to pure pine, no evergreens to dense evergreen

[21]

SHELL MOUNDS ON DAUPHIN ISLAND. Migratory birds find a haven here before and after their long overwater flights. It is one of the most popular bird study areas in Alabama.

thickets, maximum human disturbance to almost none at all, open water to well-developed marsh, bare ground through the various types of grasslands, brushy, weedy, shrubby areas, or those with scattered trees to dense woodlands.

Birdlife. In the Tennessee Valley, the big TVA lakes attract many water birds, particularly in winter and on migration. Waterfowl are especially abundant at Wheeler National Wildlife Refuge and the state refuges and management areas at North Sauty Creek, Mud Creek, Raccoon Creek, Swan Creek, and Seven-mile Island. Shorebirds are more common in fall, when water levels are low enough to expose flats, and open-country birds are common at all seasons on the extensive farmlands. Piney-woods birds are scarce at all times, and many woodland birds occur only in limited areas such as bottomlands.

Productive areas for finding birds include the waterfowl refuges and management areas, bottomlands, exposed flats, the vicinity of dams and bridges, and along dirt roads in farming areas. Wheeler National Wildlife Refuge is probably the best inland area in Alabama for observing birds. Virtually the whole shoreline of the Tennessee River is excellent habitat with some places more attractive to woodland birds and others more attractive to water birds.

CHEAHA MOUNTAIN. Alabama's highest point is often nesting grounds for the Black-throated Green Warbler, Ovenbird, and Scarlet Tanager.

The Mountain Region features a high proportion of forested land and has a considerable variety of woodland birds as breeders, migrants, and winter visitors. On plateaus such as Sand Mountain and Lookout Mountain, extensive areas are cleared for farming, but there are large areas of woodland at high elevation in Monte Sano, DeSoto, Cheaha, and Oak Mountain state parks, and in the Talladega and William B. Bankhead national forests. These are excellent places for observing woodland birds. Habitat for open-country birds in this region is generally limited to airports and pastures. Swamps and marshes are few, and, except for a few diving ducks wintering on lakes, most water birds occur in the region only as migrants.

The Piedmont, an area of transition between the mountains and the Coastal Plain, is about as heavily forested as the Mountain Region. Its birdlife is similar to that of the Mountain Region except that a few Coastal Plain birds such as the Fish Crow and Ground Dove occur near Auburn, an especially productive area. Also, the bigger impoundments on the Coosa and Tallapoosa rivers attract more water birds. By virtue of its easterly position, Atlantic Coastal migrants are frequently recorded in the Piedmont.

[23]

TYPICAL VIEW OF ALABAMA'S PRAIRIE REGION. This short-grass area is especially attractive to meadowlarks, Grasshopper Sparrows and Dickcissels in summer and longspurs, Horned Larks, and pipits in winter.

In the Upper and Lower Coastal Plain, woodland birds are usually most numerous in the bottoms, where they are about as abundant as in the Mountain Region. Water birds are more numerous at all seasons here because the more level terrain contains more wet lands. Herons and egrets are particularly common as breeders, and the shorebirds and shallow-water birds, especially ducks, are frequent in winter and on migration. The natural prairie of the Black Belt attracts at all seasons more open-country birds (even some western species) than anywhere else in Alabama.

The best places to see birds in the Upper and Lower Coastal Plain are usually in river bottoms rich in hardwoods and in low-lying or fallow areas on the prairie. Especially attractive are the big swamps, the oxbow lakes, and other quiet backwaters along the river valleys, and the natural lakes of the Lower Coastal Plain. The numerous farm ponds provide resting places for water birds and shorebirds but are rarely large enough or contain sufficient food and marginal cover for much breeding or large-scale wintering.

In the two Gulf Coastal counties, the area north of U. S. Highway 90 is similar to the Lower Coastal Plain except for more extensive swampland. Almost all the areas near salt or brackish water are good places to see birds. Shallow-water

[24]

and brackish-water birds are best observed at the head of Mobile Bay from Cochrane Causeway on U. S. Highway 90 and in Mississippi Sound near Bayou La Batre, Coden, Cedar Point, or Dauphin Island. The vicinity of Mississippi Sound, with its low-lying islands, reefs, and shorelines, is by far the best locality in the state for shorebirds.

Bird-watching is especially rewarding in the entire area of the state south of U. S. Highway 90, and the culmination is in Dauphin Island, which is without question the best place in the state to observe birds. Besides all kinds of water birds and shorebirds, the island teems with woodland birds during migration seasons, and in fall many western birds occur there. The Pleasure Island Peninsula, which includes Fort Morgan, Gulf Shores, and Alabama Point, has many of the same attractions as Dauphin Island but to a lesser degree. Throughout Mobile and Baldwin counties, migrating and wintering woodland birds are especially attracted to the numerous live oaks.

Of the Alabama bird list of 352 species, 154 are definitely known to breed at present, and four others bred in the past but no longer do so. One very interesting fact about the birdlife of Alabama is that more birds occur here in winter than in summer. Even in considering water or land birds, those regular or accidental, or any other similar groupings on the state list, about five per cent more species are recorded here in winter than in summer. The number of individuals is also far higher in winter when huge flocks, especially of waterfowl and blackbirds, concentrate near good sources of food and cover. In summer, although a few heavily-populated breeding colonies exist, most of the birds are evenly distributed on breeding territories.

Alabama has a wonderful variety of terrain and excellent scenery, from mountain to marine, and it has an equally varied and equally photogenic birdlife to go with it.

BIRDS AND THE LAW

GREATLY TO THE BENEFIT OF EVERYONE, both federal and state governments have enacted certain laws designed to aid proper conservation of birds as a natural resource. Thus, some birds may never be killed, some may be killed only in rare circumstances, others only in certain quantities at certain times of the year, and still others may be killed at any time.

Some basic considerations determine these laws. First, all birds are owned by the state for the purpose of regulating their use and disposition. Second, migratory birds are regulated by federal statute and resident birds by state statute. Third, three categories of birds exist: protected birds, game birds, and non-protected birds.

Protected birds, usually referred to as songbirds because songbirds constitute the majority, may be killed or captured only for scientific purposes, and only by individuals authorized by permit. Those who hold permits are professional or seriously-interested amateur ornithologists, or government game personnel, who are usually professional biologists. Some birds whose numbers are very low may not even be killed for scientific purposes, and in Alabama, the Bald Eagle, Whooping Crane, Sandhill Crane, and Long-billed Curlew may not even be taken for scientific specimens. For migratory birds, both federal and state permits are required, but for resident birds only a state permit is necessary. A bird collected as a scientific specimen must be given to a public institution—for example, a museum or school. A bird captured for banding purposes must be released as soon as possible, and in no way may its life be jeopardized.

Birds are protected by law because they are a natural resource more valuable alive than dead. Usually they perform some economically beneficial function such as feeding on insects or weed seeds, or they are esthetically valuable because of their songs or plumages.

Resident and migratory game birds are those which may be hunted, in accordance with law or regulation. No game birds can be hunted, killed, sold, purchased, or possessed except as permitted by law or regulation. Migratory game birds are those so defined by the Bureau of Sport Fisheries and Wildlife of the U. S. Department of the Interior. This federal bureau also makes recommendations as to the number and kind of migratory game birds that may be hunted, always bearing in mind the preservation of a continuing harvest for the future.

Low population levels or poor nesting success often requires curtailment of the hunting season or bag limit, so that current state and federal game laws should always be consulted.

Migratory game birds which occur in Alabama are:

1. Waterfowl except swans. This, the family *Anatidae,* includes all the birds on our state list from Canada Goose to Red-breasted Merganser.

2. Rails, gallinules, and coots. This includes the family *Rallidae.*

3. Shorebirds. At present this includes only the American Woodcock and the Common Snipe. Formerly, many birds in the suborder *Charadrii* could be hunted, but these birds could not stand the hunting pressure, and their population levels dropped alarmingly.

4. Doves and wild pigeons. This includes the family *Columbidae,* but the small and trustful Ground Dove is by tradition not hunted in Alabama, and the feral Rock Dove (Common Pigeon) is not listed as a game bird.

Resident game birds are regulated by state law and include all the members of the order *Galliformes* which occur in the state. These are the Bobwhite and the Turkey. The Ruffed Grouse, a former resident now being reintroduced, and several foreign chicken-like game birds also being introduced may be declared legal game by the state. This would be done at such time as the officials of the Department of Conservation recommend that their numbers are sufficient for proper harvest.

A complete list of Alabama game birds follows:

Canada Goose	Oldsquaw
White-fronted Goose	White-winged Scoter
Snow Goose	Surf Scoter
Blue Goose	Common Scoter
Fulvous Tree Duck	Ruddy Duck
Mallard	Hooded Merganser
Black Duck	Common Merganser
Mottled Duck	Red-breasted Merganser
Gadwall	Bobwhite
Pintail	Turkey
Green-winged Teal	King Rail
Blue-winged Teal	Clapper Rail
European Widgeon	Virginia Rail
American Widgeon	Sora
Shoveler	Yellow Rail
Wood Duck	Purple Gallinule
Redhead	Common Gallinule
Ring-necked Duck	American Coot
Canvasback	American Woodcock
Greater Scaup	Common Snipe
Lesser Scaup	White-winged Dove
Common Goldeneye	Mourning Dove
Bufflehead	Ground Dove

The third category, non-protected birds, includes those judged to be locally harmful to the interests of man. These are enumerated by Alabama law as:

Turkey Vulture (listed as buzzard)

Black Vulture (listed as buzzard)

Sharp-shinned Hawk (also listed as blue darter and chicken hawk)
Cooper's Hawk (also listed as blue darter and chicken hawk)
Great Horned Owl
Common Crow (listed as crow)
Fish Crow (listed as crow)
Starling
House Sparrow (listed as English sparrow)

Various other federal and state laws are designed to ensure that hunting is carried out in a safe and sportsmanlike manner. Thus, regulations forbid the use of certain types of guns, live decoys, baiting, and so forth, or they prohibit hunting within range of houses, on or near routes of travel, or on refuges and sanctuaries.

Respect for these laws will in large measure ensure the future of the natural resources of Alabama.

MIGRATION

ONE OF THE DISTINCTIVE FEATURES of nearly all birds is their ability to fly, especially for long distances. Not all birds migrate, but those that do can occupy areas like the far north which are favorable only part of the year. Without the ability to migrate, the large host of insect-eating birds would have to change their diets in order to survive in winter, and ground-feeding birds would starve when snow and ice cut off their food supply. Furthermore, if birds remained to breed in their tropical or southern winter quarters, these areas would have to support them on a year-round basis. But by moving to northern regions, they can take advantage of the short-lived but abundant food there and return to wintering areas that have not been overtaxed by supporting vast numbers of nesting birds. One theory about the cause of migration holds that it is not so much the cold itself that causes birds to migrate from their northern breeding grounds, as the effects of the cold on their cover and food supply.

Any discussion of bird migration is based on working hypotheses. We do not often see birds actually migrating. We see them appear in a given locality at certain times of the year, and later they disappear from the same locality. We see them on the move but cannot always tell whether they are migrating or merely on a local flight. Thus many statements in this section may prove to be less general than now supposed, may be found to stem from different causes, or may even eventually be disproved.

All possible combinations of migratory performance occur. All, some, or none of the individuals of a particular species may migrate. When only part of the species migrates, the immatures of some—Blue Jay, Cardinal, and others—are most likely to migrate; the adult males of species such as the Grasshopper Sparrow, Robin, Osprey, and many others are most likely to remain on the breeding grounds. Some species, like the Red-breasted Nuthatch, Evening Grosbeak, Purple Finch, and Pine Siskin, may migrate only in certain years or migrate far in some years and hardly at all in others. Birds migrate between the arctic and the antarctic (Arctic Tern, Wilson's Petrel, and Sooty Shearwater), from the far north to the tropics (Blackpoll Warbler, Gray-cheeked Thrush), or from a rigorous temperate area to a less rigorous temperate area. Others, including most species of waterfowl, maintain themselves as far north as there is open water. Unfrozen ground without snow cover seems to control the migration of many birds, such as larks, most ground-feeding finches, and longspurs. Several species of waterfowl move only from a point inland to the coast, while other birds like juncos and woodpeckers move to a lower elevation in the mountains.

Some birds—most small land birds, for instance—migrate almost solely at night; some, such as hawks, nighthawks, swifts, and swallows, mostly by day; and some start at night and continue when daylight appears (waterfowl and cranes). Some birds make a leisurely flight, usually by day, and feed as they go, and others cover an ocean or continent in one flight. The average bird, however, apparently makes a series of overnight flights of a hundred miles or more and alternates these with several days of rest.

A rather thorough examination of the distribution and banding paragraphs of the species accounts gives the reader an idea of the magnitude and variety of migratory journeys. Particularly noteworthy are those of Wilson's Petrel, Greater and Sooty Shearwaters, and most of the plovers and sandpipers. The Arctic Tern, another famous migrant, is not on the Alabama list and with good reason, for the species is practically unknown in the United States south of Massachusetts. This species, which breeds mostly in the arctic, apparently on normal migration crosses the Atlantic Ocean to about the coast of France, moves down the coast of Africa to its western bulge near Dakar, thence again crosses the Atlantic to the eastern bulge of Brazil and flies on into the high southern latitudes.

Shorebirds and terns look well adapted to long flights, for they have long, pointed wings, but many species that do not appear to be built for speed or endurance nevertheless make remarkably long journeys. For instance, 18 of the 41 species of warblers which occur in Alabama, none of which weighs as much as an ounce, include South America in their winter ranges. Anyone who flushes a

Sora from the marsh and watches its apparently weak and hesitant flight finds it difficult to believe that some Soras migrate annually to South America. The longest waterfowl banding recovery for Alabama comes from our smallest duck, a Green-winged Teal, which flew from near the Arctic Circle in Alaska to Chewacla Creek near Auburn. A glance at the Cedar Waxwing banding map shows that in winter Alabama may be host to birds of this species from both the Atlantic and Pacific coasts.

While Chimney Swifts are very fast flyers, migrate primarily by day, and winter in South America, the birds by no means fly directly to their winter quarters. For example, one bird was banded in Rome, Georgia on July 26, 1953, was re-trapped a hundred miles away in Birmingham on September 12, 1953, and was trapped again in Rome on September 27, 1953. It is a matter of considerable amazement that these birds mill around so extensively in spite of facing a 2,000 mile journey to the Amazon Valley of Peru.

Some idea of the journeys that other Alabama birds undertake may be obtained from the distribution and banding paragraphs and the banding maps in the species accounts. The examples in the preceding paragraphs are a few of those for which we have evidence through banding. Even many of the tiniest birds—the warblers, the kinglets, the hummingbirds—make long migration journeys twice a year as a matter of course; in fact, many migratory birds spend more time on migration than they do on the breeding grounds.

The manner in which migration is performed is a marvel of the first order, and much of it is still not understood today. Birds have nearly all the problems of an airplane pilot, including the maintenance of a schedule, for some species are quite punctual in their arrivals and departures. Many of the dates in the occurrence paragraphs of the species accounts show this uniformity from one region to another, and when uniformity is lacking, it is usually due either to unevenness in local coverage or rarity of the species.

The birds, of course, must somehow know when to migrate. It is thought that in spring the reactivating of the sex glands gives most migratory birds the stimulus, and the depositing of fat as a reserve fuel provides the stamina to perform long migrations. It would seem at first that the increasing length of day, which is known to activate sex hormones, would be the external stimulus, but this does not explain how migration is initiated in the tropics under uniform length of day, nor in South America where the days are getting shorter.

The fat that migratory birds deposit as a reserve fuel has, per unit of weight, a very high caloric content and is therefore a very efficient fuel. Calculations show that the amount deposited is capable of furnishing the energy for a flight of from just under 400 to over 2,600 miles. Considering the water and desert barriers birds must cross on their journeys, many migratory species, including those that fly the Gulf of Mexico, must have the ability to negotiate from 500 to 2,000 miles in a single flight.

In fall, migration apparently takes place when the size and activity of the sex glands are reduced, and the moult, which uses considerable energy, does not interfere with the depositing of fat. Because of the varying lengths of time it takes to moult, deposit fat, and become physically capable of migration, adults and immatures in some species often migrate at different times.

In order to begin migration, a bird must also have proper external conditions. By far the most important external determinant is weather. Greatly simplified, the air above a north temperate area, which includes Alabama, is characterized by high and low pressure areas. The air spirals outward in a clockwise manner from a ridge of high pressure which contains colder, denser, drier air. Then it spirals inward in a counterclockwise manner to a trough of low pressure which contains warmer, lighter, wetter air.

The centers of these highs and lows are normally hundreds of miles apart, and they move generally easterly at one to eight hundred miles a day. A high cell is usually cloudless with fair weather, while a low is cloudy and stormy. The wind speed at a given place is usually determined by the rate of change in barometric pressure.

This circulation of air brings into contact air masses of opposing character, usually in Alabama continental polar and maritime tropical. Thus, on the eastern side of a low, with warm, moist air advancing usually on a strong southwesterly wind, we have a warm front. As the low moves eastward, we experience the weather of the western side of the low with cold, dry air advancing on a strong northwesterly wind as a cold front moves by. Colder, heavier air wedges underneath the warmer, lighter air, which is thus forced upward and cooled. Cooling reduces its ability to hold moisture and results in cloudiness and often in rain.

As we all know, weather often strongly affects airplane flights and schedules, but birds face far greater difficulties. Normally, they begin a migratory flight in good weather, but if drifting is not properly counteracted, the air circulation may bring them closer to the center of a low, and they may eventually encounter bad weather. The bird entering a stormy area near a low meets turbulence, greatly reduced visibility, rain, or worse, and a drastic change in wind direction. Generally it makes a forced landing, but if it is over water it must fly on through the weather and into the northerly wind beyond the cold front before it can land. A migrating bird that cannot correct for drift may be carried by the prevailing southeasterly course of the air circulation out over the Gulf of Mexico or the Atlantic Ocean.

In addition to bad weather, birds may also encounter man-made obstacles. These fall into two general categories. The first is a strong, fixed light which blinds a bird in the same manner as headlights blind a deer in the road, or a driver who meets another car with lights on high beam. Lights to aid navigation of ships and planes, such as those of lighthouses and ceilometers, or any other strong outdoor light, are most dangerous to migrating birds when they remain unblinking and facing in the same direction. In the second category are tall structures such as the Empire State Building in New York and the many television transmission towers. It requires very little reduction in visibility for a guy wire on one of these towers to be invisible to a bird whose eyes may be adjusting to the lights of a nearby city. At some of these obstacles casualties have been so numerous that bird students have found them a rich source of specimens and have used the casualties as a more or less random sample of night migration.

The means by which birds find their way, even over featureless areas such as oceans and deserts, and even at night, are still pretty much enshrouded in mystery. Many theories, some of them quite plausible, have been advanced. Birds have been said to find their way by the stars, by the position of the sun, by a sense of the magnetic lines of force in the earth, by a sense of the Coriolis force of the rotation of the earth, by memory, by following landmarks (especially river valleys and coastlines), and by other means. But whatever they use there is little doubt that many birds can navigate with amazing pinpoint accuracy. Thousands of bird-banding records prove beyond a doubt that many birds return to an exact spot. While the attachment to the breeding area is apparently greater and we have more evidence of return to the same nest or nest-site, evidence is mounting that at least some species also return to winter in the same spot.

Some individuals, especially immatures, drift off-course during their migratory journeys, and some that drift out over water perish, but many of them thus appear out of the normal range of the species and provide the local bird-watcher with rarities. These latter birds, if in sufficient numbers, may be the pioneers of range extensions.

For instance, western species that reach the northern Gulf Coast, possibly after many years of drifting individuals, often winter locally or in Florida instead of in Mexico. More than a dozen species of land birds on the Alabama list—prominently Brewer's Blackbird and Western Meadowlark—whose breeding ranges are wholly or almost wholly west of the Mississippi River, are among these. Apparently many western birds which drifted eastward as immatures making their first migration are able to repeat this migration as adults and thus winter far east of the normal—or original—range of the species.

The marvel of the navigational ability of a bird has intrigued bird students for a long time. It is possible that a better understanding of bird navigation may aid man in his navigation problems. Many more data are being accumulated annually. Bird students, both professional and amateur, are watching through telescopes birds migrating high overhead in the daytime sky or past the face of the moon at night, are mist-netting and banding birds by thousands, are training radar beams on them, and are studyng the internal mechanisms that set them in readiness to migrate. A vast number of arrival and departure dates of migrants are made available each year by hundreds of amateurs, and much of this information has been correlated with weather conditions.

Although it appears that birds migrate independently of the nature of the terrain, certain terrain features do concentrate them. Coastlines and river valleys seem to afford the best concentrations—probably because water birds and others find more food there—and on the coast birds react in various ways to the open water. For instance, on the Alabama Gulf Coast, some birds fly back inland to minimize the danger of drifting out to sea, some migrate around this water obstacle, and some wait until they build up their energy reserves of fat for an overwater flight.

The U. S. Fish and Wildlife Service and the various state and provincial agencies have shown that a study of bird migration routes makes for more effective management of waterfowl. Through an analysis of nesting success on a continent-wide basis, they can quite accurately forecast hunting-season abundance for a given species in a given area. This accuracy is such that length of season and bag limits can be adjusted to ensure adequate harvest and adequate hunting opportunities without endangering the breeding stock for the next season.

The height at which birds migrate often varies with weather conditions. In this and the next paragraph, some examples of observations are given. Further observations, however, may prove the range of altitude much greater, or that these figures are not normal. In clear weather with its high barometric pressure, birds fly high in the denser air. This height above the terrain may be as much as 5,000 feet for such birds as hawks and waterfowl, but 1,000 to 2,000 feet is usual for small land birds. On the other hand, observations of land birds arriving on the Louisiana Coast in spring in daytime during fair weather show them to be flying so high as to be barely visible with binoculars.

In bad weather, birds fly lower not only because the air is less dense and more effort is required to maintain altitude, but also because low clouds leave them only a narrow layer with good visibility. This explains why birds strike obstacles, often about 500 to 1,000 feet above the ground, in bad weather. In unsettled weather, such as in fog, rain, or low clouds, they often fly barely 100 feet up. Against a head wind, they fly just over the waves where the wind speed is a little less because of drag on the water surface, while if they were over land against a strong head wind, they would in almost all cases terminate their flight.

In Alabama as elsewhere, certain migrating birds appear to follow definite broad routes. Perhaps the most interesting one in this state is that of the birds which cross the Gulf of Mexico in spring. The distance to the Alabama Coast from Yucatan, the nearest jumping-off place, is at least 560 miles, a nineteen-hour flight in still air at thirty miles per hour, the assumed rate of land bird migration. One would expect the smaller land birds to reach the Alabama Coast at Fort Morgan or Dauphin Island almost exhausted, but instead in fair weather they not only cross the coast still going strong, but apparently often go farther inland than Birmingham, a total flight of over 800 miles!

Such a flight of 800 miles, flown at thirty miles per hour would take 27 hours, and with following winds of ten or twenty miles per hour, this time would be reduced to sixteen to twenty hours. This is well within the endurance limits of a healthy bird with a full reserve of fat. Examination of over 200 such birds temporarily halted by weather on Dauphin Island and caught for banding shows that almost half of them still have a great deal of their subcutaneous fat.

This crossing of the coast in fair weather applies to the whole northern Gulf Coast. When the wind is southerly and little or no rain has fallen, the whole area 200 to 250 miles inland from the Gulf is almost completely empty of birds that have crossed the water. Many bird-watchers have gone afield in this area on a beautiful spring day, and although they can find local breeders newly-arrived from across the Gulf, they only very rarely observe those birds whose destinations are farther north. In most of Alabama in spring, bird students have learned that it is worthwhile to be afield in bad weather or immediately following it. If it has rained recently or a northerly wind is blowing, migrants are often common.

If migrants meet foul weather over the Gulf, the situation is reversed, and many birds reach land exhausted while some do not reach it at all. When they encounter the stormy area of a low cell, they indeed have a difficult time. The rain, by soaking their feathers, increases their weight and chills them, and the less dense air makes it more difficult to maintain altitude. All of these factors draw heavily on their reserves of energy. After this comes the buffeting from turbulence, difficulty of navigation from strong winds and reduced visibility, and finally a northerly head wind beyond the cold front. Still, granting a thirty-mile-per-hour migration speed and nineteen-hour still-air flight to cross the Gulf, an average head wind of ten miles per hour can increase this journey to 28 hours, and one of twenty miles per hour can increase it to 56 hours.

The average cold front and its attendant weather forces birds to stop their migratory flight and the area that was empty of migrants in fair weather becomes full of them in bad weather. Those birds caught over the Gulf by the bad weather must continue until they reach land. Thus on the immediate coast, the concentrations are bigger, and the birds are often exhausted. On such occasions, a tree full of orioles, the ground covered with hungry birds of many kinds, birds literally "all over the place," hopping and fluttering around in strange places are common sights. While the birds themselves have actually had a difficult time of it, the bird-watcher is having a never-to-be-forgotten experience feasting his eyes at very close range on dozens or even hundreds of handsomely-plumaged birds that he normally sees only in ones or twos at a respectable distance.

Dauphin Island in Mobile County is probably the best place for such a sight, though Fort Morgan and Gulf Shores in Baldwin County sometimes have comparable concentrations. At such times, birds have been so tired that they could be picked off the bushes, and examination of those caught for banding reveals that some have entirely used up their fat reserves and even some muscle tissue.

The more than 200 migratory birds caught by the author for banding in spring on Dauphin Island fall into two categories with regard to physical condition. Those that have been grounded—precipitated is the term bird students use—by bad weather without having to battle it too long are in good condition and still retain most of their subcutaneous fat. These birds very likely continue their migration just as soon as the weather again becomes favorable, for there is then a marked local decrease in the number of migrants. Those that have been precipitated after having battled the elements for a long time out over the Gulf have stopped from exhaustion and are in poor condition with little or no fat. These birds are in no condition to continue migration and are those which remain in fair weather in order to replenish their fat reserves.

If the low pressure cell or the winds beyond the cold front are stronger than usual or penetrate deeper into the Gulf, many of these birds are unable to reach land and perish at sea. How often this happens is not certain, but it appears that these migratory birds are able to make up their losses rather quickly, and no single species or group of species is known to have suffered permanently from it. The hazards of migration are undoubtedly balanced by better reproductive capability and winter survival because as a result of these journeys the birds breed and winter in favorable surroundings.

ALABAMA BIRDS

Many other migrants, such as hawks, nighthawks, and swallows, make a more leisurely journey by traveling around the Gulf of Mexico. Usually they migrate by day and feed as they go, and although the route is much longer, it is less hazardous and it ensures them a constant supply of food along the way. Some of these birds travel through Florida and others through Texas; thus in spring migrants arrive in Alabama from the east and west as well as from the south.

Spring migration is characterized by an urgency to reach the breeding grounds as quickly as possible in order to claim a good nesting territory. After winter losses and before reproduction, the population of the species is at its lowest point of the year. The birds press forward at every opportunity, almost all being adults in full or nearly full breeding plumage, and the males usually in song. Thus in spring we have fewer, more conspicuous, more easily-identified birds present for a short period of time.

In late summer or early fall, usually immediately following the breeding season, many birds, especially immatures, perform a dispersal migration. Herons, ibises, and others leave their dense breeding colonies, where food supplies have been considerably depleted by the breeding birds, and take advantage of the late summer abundance of food in areas far from big breeding colonies. This late summer migration, performed also by non-colonial birds, is often northward and it probably played a significant role in northward range extensions of many species, for example, Common Egret, Cattle Egret, Glossy Ibis, Carolina Wren, Mockingbird, and Cardinal.

Swelled by young birds, fall migration is characterized by the large numbers of birds present, but they are usually in duller plumage, often silent, and often difficult to identify. Individuals wander more and remain longer in a particular locality. So we have in fall many more individuals, often difficult to find and identify, but present for a much longer period of time.

Apparently most small woodland birds in fall arrive in Alabama right after a cold front, for they take advantage of the northerly winds to move southward. Because the air circulation is counterclockwise into a low cell, birds thus migrating may encounter stormy weather. Many of them terminate their flight before this happens, but others find themselves flying in ever-lowering clouds and often rain. In this weather they are highly susceptible to striking tall objects or running afoul of bright lights such as those of ceilometers.

Occasionally in winter when the weather becomes especially severe some birds make an emergency migration. This usually happens when snow covers the ground and nearly all water is frozen. Ground-feeding birds, especially those of open country, such as larks, sparrows, and longspurs, often invade in numbers in mid-winter some of the open fields of the state such as in the Tennessee Valley and the Black Belt. Locally-wintering birds like the Fox Sparrow and Slate-colored Junco sometimes move farther south.

Some migrants appear to follow mountain ridges and many of these are hawks which, because they are better adapted for soaring, migrate by day in places where they can gain altitude by soaring on updrafts of air. Such places, easily located by the development of cumulus clouds directly overhead, are most common where the sun heats the ground or where the wind strikes the flanks of a mountain. Whenever and wherever proper conditions for soaring occur in fall, migrating hawks often occur. Under ideal conditions, especially after several idle days due to cloudiness or other adverse circumstances, such flocks number in the hundreds, and in one day over a thousand may be recorded. The birds spiral upward, often to several thousand feet, peel off, and glide, sometimes into the wind, to another updraft perhaps several miles away, and repeat the process. Away from the ridges, soaring hawks seldom concentrate in spiralling flocks, but oddly enough at Fort Morgan and on Dauphin Island they do. Almost all hawks take part in this type of migration, and the Broad-winged Hawk, which is most prominent, forms the largest flocks.

The spectacle of fall migration on the coast of Alabama is indeed varied. Of those birds that travel across the Gulf, some are physiologically ready to take advantage of the weather and move out in darkness, while others, lacking fat or possibly some other internal factor, linger and feed until they are ready. Others apparently start their overwater flight from quite far inland, for on or near the coast these birds can be heard overhead late at night moving southward and on out over the Gulf, and many birds found dead under a television tower in northwest Florida show that they have sufficient fat to complete this over-water flight. In rainy or foul weather, little if any migration takes place. Of those that migrate around the Gulf, some, such as swallows and hawks, move westward via Texas, others, such as the Gray Kingbird and some western species, eastward via Florida.

Some others which have drifted against the coast, apparently having migrated too far, fly back inland to the north. Many species, particularly hawks and swallows, have been observed flying northward away from the coast in fall. In the banding paragraph of the Mourning Dove there is an account of a bird that flew from Dauphin Island to near Flomaton in fall.

One of the most interesting features of fall migration on the Alabama Coast is the presence of western birds. It appears that many western birds have developed, or are developing, regular, comparatively new, more eastern migration routes and winter grounds. Certainly the annual occurrence of many of these species and the numbers in which they occur are more than could be accounted for by drifting or other chance happenings. Over a dozen species are involved, and they vary from the Sage Thrasher with one Alabama record to Brewer's Blackbird, which is abundant on the coast.

Waterfowl normally migrate at night but often continue their flight during the day. Each flight is probably a long-distance one, for the birds frequently remain north until a freeze, and favored places capable of supporting large flocks are far apart. The time element in Blue Goose banding recoveries indicates that some of them make a single flight from Hudson Bay to the Gulf of Mexico. In fall, many of these birds drift a bit eastward to Alabama and once they reach the Gulf they fly due westward to their traditional Louisiana wintering grounds. Those that land in Alabama are often weak and thin, further evidence of a very long single flight.

The bulk of the ducks and geese remain in Alabama for barely three months from mid-November to mid-February, for they move northward almost as soon as waters to the north thaw. Because of this short period, Alabama waterfowl areas can support fairly large numbers of birds.

More detailed information on migration is available in the species accounts, particularly the distribution, occurrence in Alabama and banding paragraphs and accompanying maps. The author, in compiling this information from the literature, from files, personal communications, and personal observation in the field, has become more than ever convinced that birds are truly remarkable creatures.

BANDING

BIRD BANDING is the process of marking a bird to distinguish it from others. Of the many ways of doing this, the most widespread, simplest, and most durable method is the placing of a numbered split-ring aluminum band on the leg. In Europe these are known as rings, and the process is called ringing.

Bands come in various sizes to fit any wild bird from eagles and pelicans to the smallest, the hummingbirds. The larger bands are stronger, and some are treated to resist the corrosion of sea water. Besides the number, a federal band carries the legend, "Write Fish and Wildlife Service, Wash. D.C., U.S.A." Smaller bands have an abbreviation of this, and some of the smallest have the legend on the inside of the band. The Spanish word *avise*, "notify," is on some bands. These lightweight bands give birds no more inconvenience than a ring or a wristwatch causes a human being.

In Europe, museums, universities, or bird research stations usually sponsor banding programs, but in America, bird banding, which started under the private American Bird-Banding Association, has been a responsibility of the United States government since about 1920. The original federal agency was the Bureau of Biological Survey, which is now the Bureau of Sport Fisheries and Wildlife of the U. S. Fish and Wildlife Service. With the co-operation of the Canadian Wildlife Service, this program covers both the United States and Canada.

The International Bird Banding Records Center is located at the Patuxent Wildlife Research Center, Laurel, Maryland. Here are filed the records of the banding of about eleven million birds and the return or recovery of nearly a million of these.

Ethel Floyd

MALE BLUE GROSBEAK IN MIST NET. The mist net is used to catch insectivorous birds for banding.

This federal agency supplies the bands, the forms to be filled out, the permit, and technical information. Banders include not only the employees of interested federal and state agencies but also private individuals, usually expert amateur bird students. Authorized banders must demonstrate their ability to identify the birds they catch for banding, use the banding technique to investigate a particular problem, and assume responsibility for making the proper reports. Many states, including Alabama, have their own bands and an agency to operate their program for the banding of resident, non-migratory, game birds by conservation personnel.

Government agencies generally concentrate on banding game birds or those of more than average economic importance. The private bander bands most of the small land birds. He provides the energy and equipment to catch them, his reward being the pleasure of catching and handling wild birds and of

[39]

hearing from them again. A bander's catch depends, of course, on a knowledge of the habits of birds and the ability to outsmart them, and his pleasure is much like that of the successful fisherman or hunter.

A banded bird caught within five miles of the place of banding is considered a *repeat* if this recapture is within ninety days and a *return* if over ninety days. If a banded bird is recaptured more than five miles from the place of banding, it is termed a *recovery*. A dead banded bird found anywhere, even at the place of banding, and at any time after banding, is termed a recovery for administrative purposes.

Because of the small proportion of banded to unbanded wild birds of any given species, the size of the country, and the number of banders, the recovery of a banded bird by another bander seldom occurs. Therefore, banders depend on the general public to find and report banded birds. A bird wearing a band does not belong to anyone, but the band does mean that some bander has expended considerable effort in capturing the bird and recording the details of its banding.

When a banded bird is found, the number should be reported to the U. S. Fish and Wildlife Service, Washington, D. C., together with as exact information as possible on where, when, how, and by whom the bird was found. All letters and numbers on the band should be copied exactly as they appear. If the bird is alive, it should be released with the band still on it. If dead or badly injured, the band should be removed, flattened, and attached with tape to the letter for examination by the federal office. If the bird wears a state band, the same procedure should be followed except that the information should go to the proper state office as indicated by the legend on the band.

After the International Bird Banding Records Center gets the information on banding from its files, both the bander and the finder are notified of the bird's history, and if the finder so requests, the band is returned to him.

It is by this method that we have learned much about the movements of birds. The reader need only look at the banding paragraphs in the species accounts to get an idea of the extent of this information.

Banding provides the bird student with the opportunity to study birds as individuals. Besides telling us where birds travel, recaptures of banded birds also tell us whether or not migrants make the same stop-overs each year, and often how long these stop-overs are. They provide information as to how long birds live, whether or not they return to the same place to breed or winter, or keep the same mates, how long a family remains together, whether any inbreeding occurs, and the like.

So far, banding has shown that few songbirds make the same stop-overs during migration. Waterfowl often do so, however, and other birds with limited habitats probably also stop in the same places each year on migration. Possibly small land birds gather in the same general area each year before making long flights, but returns to the same place of birds banded on migration are practically unknown in spite of large-scale banding of migrants. Repeats on such birds, however, show that on migration they sometimes linger for several weeks in the same locality.

Mortality in small land birds is very high (fifty to ninety per cent) in their first year, but once past this year, they may live for five to ten years or so. Generally the larger the bird, the longer it lives, for its tempo of life is slower and it has fewer natural enemies than small birds. Also, sea birds apparently live longer than land birds. Banding records show that these larger birds and the sea birds live, in some instances, as long as twenty years and occasionally longer, whereas in captivity they can sometimes live for fifty years. Other birds are intermediate between these two extremes.

The return of a bird to a particular breeding site is much better documented and has been recorded as much more frequent than return to the wintering site. This may be partly due to the fact that in winter many birds wander over a large area depending on local food supplies and water levels.

In some species, birds mate for life, swans and geese especially being noted for this. Small land birds, however, have such a high rate of mortality that circumstances require a new mate almost every year. Some Canada Geese are known to remain together as a family group throughout the winter. Much more remains to be learned about the individual lives of birds, but the fact that birds are hard to follow makes discoveries difficult but all the more intriguing.

Banding affords the serious bird student the opportunity of examining wild birds alive, which allows a more accurate identification as to age and sex and sometimes as to species and subspecies, than the use of binoculars at a distance. For instance, *Empidonax* flycatchers on migration, especially in fall, are usually impossible to identify as to species except in the hand, and little was known about their migration until banders began to capture, measure, and identify them in the hand in numbers. A great deal is being learned about determining the age and sex of birds by means of minor differences in plumage and by measurements that cannot be detected in the field.

Some bird students, especially banders, relate their profession or other interests to their bird study. A physician, therefore, may study bird diseases or an entomologist may collect lice, ticks, and fleas from birds. Other banders

BANDING AN OSPREY. An aluminum identification band is clamped around the bird's leg to provide information on life history and movements.

may study plumages and moults, fat deposits, and other phases of bird biology. The photographer has opportunity to photograph birds at very close range. The banding permit requires release of each bird immediately upon completion of identification, banding, note-taking, and such collateral functions as weighing, measuring, and photographing, which add value to the study. Banding opens up to the more serious bird student all sorts of opportunities for further study.

Most banders obtain birds for banding by operating traps or nets on their property. The area is made more attractive to birds by the use of a feeding station, by planting trees and shrubs which provide food and roosting cover, or by putting out food. Many terns, herons, and other colonial birds are banded before they are old enough to fly. Banding of other than colonial nestlings, however, is discouraged except in special cases.

The silk or nylon mist net has probably done more to increase our knowledge of birds than any other innovation since the widespread use of pocket field guides of the Peterson type. Since about 1950, the mist net has been available to the most experienced banders, and its use is rigidly restricted to scientific purposes only.

Mist netting allows the bander to go afield in many habitats and to catch birds, especially insect-eaters, that seldom visited his grain-baited traps. Species formerly banded only in small numbers are now being banded in numbers sufficient for us to learn as much about them as was once known only about the common dooryard grain-eating species. Banders are also now netting birds in places where migrants concentrate, such as on the coast.

Bird banding is thus a special tool of the ornithologist for studying individual birds as well as populations. The federal and state governments and the general public co-operate in this endeavor. The banding paragraphs of the species accounts contain records of the places Alabama migrants visit, and of the return of Alabama-banded birds to the place of banding. Without the co-operative effort of many banders, hunters, conservation agents, other government employees, and ordinary citizens from many states and countries, this information could never be presented.

YOUNG RED-TAILED HAWKS. This is one of the largest and most beneficial hawks.

C. W. Summerour

SPECIES ACCOUNTS

ALABAMA BIRDS are grouped and classified in this book according to the scientific categories of order, suborder, family, subfamily, and genus. Although other groupings are possible (such as by size, or by color, or by habits), the system followed in the *Check-list of North American Birds*, prepared by a committee of the American Ornithologists' Union, is the standard accepted by bird students everywhere.

The standardized names of the orders (ending in *-iformes*), families (ending in *-idae*), subfamilies (ending in *-inae*), and other groups and the names of species are taken from the fifth edition of the A.O.U. *Check-list* (1957).

The relationships of birds are systematically indicated by their grouping. Thus all the birds in a single category have similar structural features and presumably share a common ancestry. Two birds in the same genus, for example the Canvasback and the Redhead, are closely related. Two birds in different genera of the same subfamily are less closely related, for example the Canvasback and the Bufflehead. Two birds in different subfamilies of the same family are more distantly related, for example the Canvasback and the Whistling Swan. Two birds in different families of the same order are still more distantly related, for example the Killdeer and the American Woodcock. Even more remotely related are the Pied-billed Grebe and the Common Loon, which are in different orders. (For the exact classification of these eight birds, see page 59 for the Common Loon, page 65 for the Pied-billed Grebe, page 115 for the Whistling Swan, page 143 for the Redhead, page 147 for the Canvasback, page 154 for the Bufflehead, page 225 for the Killdeer, and page 231 for the American Woodcock.

When more than one representative of a group occurs in Alabama, a brief description of the group is provided to show the characteristics common to closely related birds. Only one genus, however, is described, *Empidonax;* the main characteristic of the other genera may be inferred from the species descriptions.

Through these descriptions of higher groups and the species which belong to them, many interesting facts about birds are revealed. For instance, although the Pied-billed Grebe (Family *Podicipedidae*) and the American Coot (Family

[44]

Rallidae) sit on the water like a duck (Family *Anatidae*), the resemblance ends there, for they are not ducks at all. (The family descriptions of these birds note their distinctive features.) Hawks and owls belong to widely separated orders (*Falconiformes* and *Strigiformes*) and are not as closely related as one might suppose from their food habits. The Starling (Family *Sturnidae*) is not a blackbird (Family *Icteridae*), but the Western Meadowlark is a blackbird. The Robin and Eastern Bluebird are thrushes (Family *Turdidae*), and, although the Mockingbird and the Brown Thrasher do not belong to the thrush family, they are in the immediately preceding group (Family *Mimidae*), which is a little more closely related to the wrens (Family *Troglodytidae*).

The accounts of the birds of Alabama follow a pattern so that the reader can easily find the same kind of information in the same place under each species. In most cases the paragraph titles are sufficient; however, some explanation of the method of treatment, the use of available data, the standards employed, and hints as to best use of the material are given below.

In this book are accounts of the 352 species of birds known to occur in Alabama. Of this number, 46 have their names enclosed in brackets to show that their status on the list is not completely acceptable. These 46 are listed near the end of this section.

Directly beneath the species name appears its scientific name, a standardized name in New Latin, by which the species is known in any part of the world. The first name, always capitalized, is that of the genus; the second, never capitalized, is that of the species; and the third name, also never capitalized and used rarely in this book, is that of the subspecies. Thus species with the same scientific first name always belong to the same genus and are closely related.

The name which follows the scientific name is that of the scientist who first satisfactorily described the species. Many readers will recognize the names of Linnaeus (Carolus Linnaeus, the Latinized version of Carl Linné, Swedish scientist who developed the binomial system of nomenclature), Wilson (Alexander Wilson, the father of American ornithology), and Audubon (John James Audubon, the famous painter and naturalist). If the name of the scientist appears in parentheses, the name of the genus has been changed from his original form in order to conform to more modern concepts of the relationships of birds.

The number in brackets which follows is the A.O.U. number of the species, which is used for coding purposes, such as in assembling large amounts of data on IBM cards in banding and other studies.

[45]

ALABAMA BIRDS

Of the species described, 329 are illustrated, and the plate and page number of the illustration follows the A.O.U. number. The remainder either occur far out at sea, or they are difficult to identify by sight alone, such as the *Empidonax* flycatchers, the Lesser Yellowlegs, and the Roseate Tern, and thus illustrations are not included.

Names on the next line are other names, most of them either common names formerly used for the species but no longer official, or local names in use in Alabama. The average Alabamian, not familiar with the A.O.U. *Check-list*, recognizes many birds by unofficial names. This listing of variant names, therefore, serves to help him and bird people of other states understand each other. Some of these names, which are often quite colorful, show the French influence around Mobile. Other names are equally vivid and often display a keen insight into the habits of birds.

The first paragraph of each account is a brief *description of the species* with field identification as its primary objective. The reader should refer to the appropriate color plate when reading it. Particularly distinctive features, useful in identification and usually referred to as field marks, are in italics. Many of these field marks have been determined through the field and museum experience of Alabama bird students, especially the author. Voice is described only where it is important in identification. The majority of Alabama birds have distinctive calls and songs which advertise that they belong to a particular species. The reader will find that if he knows the characteristics of the higher groups (orders, families, and others) and can thus place a bird in its proper family or sub-family, many problems of field identification will have been solved.

Where and when to find the bird in Alabama is the subject of the second paragraph. It tells the reader the time of year, part of state, and type of habitat in which the species usually occurs. For 62 species, a map indicates more precisely the part of the state in which they occur in a particular season. Generally the more a species is restricted to a particular type of terrain, the more detailed is the description of its habitat, and conversely, the more wide-spread a species is, the more general is this description. Often some information is given on the birds with which it associates, and mention is also made of its status as a breeder in Alabama.

In defining the terms used to describe the abundance and frequency of occurrence of birds in Alabama, account was taken of the use of these terms in other parts of the country and the amount of local field data available.

Accidental. One record. This usually means that Alabama is outside the normal range of the species.

Casual. Two to ten records, but not more than once in flocks nor remaining more than once for a period of over a week at the same place. This usually means that the species does not occur in Alabama at regular intervals.

Rare. Generally more than ten records, but if less, the bird occurs sometimes in flocks and sometimes remains for over a week at the same place. The indication is one of regular occurrence, usually annually, but in very small numbers.

Uncommon, Fairly Common, and *Common.* The word common here means that the species can be found in its habitat, at the right time of year, after proper search. Therefore, uncommon denotes a species that can thus be found less than half the time; fairly common, half or more than half the time; and common, all or nearly all the time.

Abundant. A common bird that occurs in large numbers.

The nesting and food paragraphs are combined for those species that are not known to nest nor suspected of nesting in Alabama, and the nesting information is as brief as possible. Although many state bird books do not include nesting information on species that do not breed in the state, it is furnished here for the sake of completeness. Naturally, no Alabama data are possible; so standard references, particularly the Life History Series by A. C. Bent, published by the United States National Museum, are the source. In a few cases the descriptions are drawn from the personal experience of the author in other parts of the country.

Nesting paragraphs on the 159 species which breed or bred in the state are based as far as possible on Alabama data. The extent to which this is so may be determined from the number of nestings included in the time-of-breeding data. Birds vary their habits, including their nesting habits, in different parts of their range, and descriptions of these southern variations all too seldom reach print. Some of these variations, seemingly quite general in Alabama, are: fewer ground nests; higher nest sites; the use of pines as a site or pine straw as material by species that normally nest in hardwoods; a more leisurely nesting season characterized by more but smaller clutches; and in the Coastal Plain the widespread use of Spanish moss as a nesting material.

The *food paragraph*, like the nesting paragraph, is drawn as far as possible from Alabama information. Every possible source was used, for besides material available in print, data were obtained from the stomachs of specimens collected in Alabama and field observations both in general and at feeding stations, even for some of the rarer species. Within each group, food items are listed in decreasing order of frequency. Thus, the items the bird eats most often are listed first, with that eaten least often, last.

ALABAMA BIRDS

The *distribution paragraph* is a summary of the American range of the species as given in the A.O.U. *Check-list.* In some cases this information has been modified to include Alabama data supplementing the *Check-list.* These additions are supported by occurrence data in the same species account.

The ranges of all species are stated in a uniform manner described in the A.O.U. *Check-list* page vi: "In general, the range outlines first the northern boundary, beginning at the northwest and continuing to the northeastern limit; then the southern boundary, beginning at the southwest and continuing to the southeast. The winter range is stated with migratory species, and migration routes, when of special significance, are noted."

As an example, the distribution paragraph of the Bobwhite states that it "is resident from Wyoming, southern Minnesota, southern Ontario, and southwestern Maine south to Sonora, Oaxaca, Guatemala, and Cuba." This means that if we draw a line on a map from Wyoming to southwestern Maine, making it pass through southern Minnesota and southern Ontario, we would then form the northern boundary of the range. In a similar manner, we would form the southern boundary by connecting with a line the Mexican states of Sonora and Oaxaca, then Guatemala and Cuba. The western boundary would be formed roughly by a line from Wyoming to Sonora and the eastern boundary roughly by a line along the Atlantic Coast from southwestern Maine to Cuba. All naturally-occurring Bobwhites are normally found within these boundaries.

In the more detailed A.O.U. *Check-list,* the description of the northern boundary of the range of the Bobwhite also mentions North Dakota, Wisconsin, Michigan, New York, Vermont, and New Hampshire. The distribution paragraph in this book is thus a less-detailed description of the same range.

The remainder of each of the species accounts contains more detailed, technical, numerical data of less general interest.

The first of these paragraphs concerns *occurrence in Alabama* as to time of the year and part of the state. For those species that occur throughout the year in all parts of the state, either a simple statement to that effect is made, or abundance data are substituted. Immediately following the paragraph title, the first statement, which is in parentheses, gives the extreme dates of occurrence for the whole state. This means that the species occurs somewhere in the state, but not necessarily throughout the state, during the period covered by the dates mentioned. The statement is often separated into normal and out-of-season occurrences. A record is usually deemed out-of-season when there is half a month or more between it and the normal season of occurrence of the species, but a shorter period of time is sometimes used in spring. For instance,

[48]

the Gray-cheeked Thrush is known as a transient in the southeastern United States, and the nearest places where it normally winters, as seen from the distribution paragraph, are Hispaniola and Nicaragua. We have four winter records between December 27 and January 1, which are of course within half a month of each other, but much more than half a month from November 10, our latest date when we disregard the four records above. Thus, these four records are judged out-of-season.

A very large portion of the records in this book of the occurrence of birds are sight records made by amateur bird-watchers. An even greater number of the same kind of records are not mentioned in the text but verify the presence of a species between the extreme dates mentioned. The author has evaluated as many of these records as possible to determine whether or not the observer or observers could validly make an identification beyond a reasonable doubt. Items considered include the reputation and experience of the observer both with the species in question and those with which it could be confused; the likelihood of the occurrence of the bird at the particular time, place, and habitat; the amount of light, glare, wind, and other weather conditions; proper binoculars or telescope used for the distance involved; field guides and other books consulted as an aid in identification; and the length of time the bird remained under observation. Over 300 observers are mentioned and for almost all records since about 1935, the author is personally acquainted with the observer and his ability to identify birds in the field.

In order to present a more detailed account of the occurrence of each species so that information can be better applied locally, the state has been divided into *six regions.* (See Map 1.) For instance, in determining when a bird would be expected to occur around Huntsville, Mobile dates would be almost useless, or at best misleading, but Decatur or Gadsden data would be quite useful.

Except for the Piedmont, a triangular section on the eastern side of the state, these regions consist of roughly parallel east-west bands. Thus they form rather even indicators of the advance and retreat of spring and fall migrants. These regions are designated so as to be readily-recognized areas within which the majority of bird species have the same status and as closely as possible the same season of occurrence. They are relatively uniform in size except for the Gulf Coast, and are partially determined by the larger soil areas of the state (see Map 2) brought to the nearest county line, a boundary which is usually easily recognized by the average person. Two notable exceptions to this are places in the northern part of the state where abrupt changes in elevation occur, and the Fall Line, which forms the readily-recognized northern boundary of the Coastal

Map 1

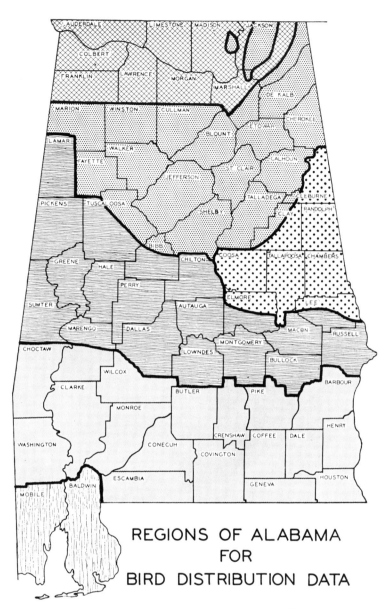

REGIONS OF ALABAMA
FOR
BIRD DISTRIBUTION DATA

 GULF COAST

 PIEDMONT

 LOWER COASTAL PLAIN

 MOUNTAIN REGION

 UPPER COASTAL PLAIN

 TENNESSEE VALLEY

[50]

Map 2

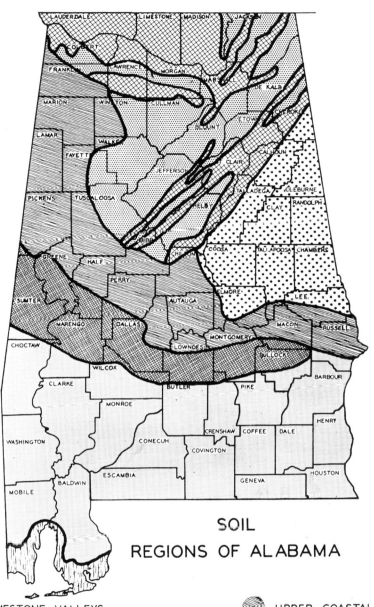

SOIL
REGIONS OF ALABAMA

 LIMESTONE VALLEYS

 BLACK BELT

 APPALACHIAN MOUNTAINS

 PIEDMONT PLATEAU

 UPPER COASTAL PLAIN

 LOWER COASTAL PLAIN

 GULF COAST STRIP

[51]

Plain. These regions are used as far as possible in describing the local distribution in the second paragraph of each species account.

The Tennessee Valley (eight counties), with its large area of inland water and with Wheeler National Wildlife Refuge, has excellent data on water birds and shorebirds. Because it is largely an agricultural area and is not as wooded as other parts of the state, data on warblers and other small woodland birds, especially those of piney woods, are not complete.

The Mountain Region (sixteen counties), the most heavily-wooded area and with the largest human population, has excellent data on small woodland birds and probably the most complete data on dates of occurrence of any area in the state. It lacks more complete information on water and open-country birds, perhaps because it lacks the habitat for them.

The Piedmont (seven counties), largely because of information from Auburn, has excellent spring data but rather poor fall data. Its birdlife reflects the transition between the mountains and the Coastal Plain as exemplified by the summer presence at Auburn of both the Fish Crow and Eastern Phoebe.

The Upper Coastal Plain (seventeen counties) is the site of a high proportion of the ornithological field work done in the state up to the time of Howell (1924). This area includes the Black Belt, a natural prairie which in Alabama covers slightly over 4,000 square miles. The southern edge of the Black Belt forms a natural bird boundary, as is apparent from the description of the local occurrence in the second paragraph of many species accounts. This southern edge coincides with the southern edge of the Upper Coastal Plain and divides the Coastal Plain, except for Mobile and Baldwin counties, into two nearly equal parts. For these reasons and because much bird data is available from towns like Greensboro, Marion, Prattville, and Montgomery, on or just north of the Black Belt, it appears best to include the Black Belt in the Upper Coastal Plain.

The Lower Coastal Plain (seventeen counties) is the largest area and also the one with the smallest amount of bird data. This is undoubtedly because it has the sparsest human population and therefore fewer bird students. With its extensive swamps, broad floodplains, and rich agricultural areas, its birdlife is undoubtedly as rich and varied as any in the state. This should be considered in evaluating records from this area and in determining what may be expected to occur locally.

The Gulf Coast (two counties) because of the salt water and the great variety of habitat is by far the best area in the state for birds. This variety is compounded by the large number of species which occur only near salt water, water birds which occur inland but in much larger numbers on the coast, woodland birds which as migrants concentrate in large numbers on the coast both spring and fall, western birds which migrate southeastwardly and concentrate against their first large water barrier, and the large number of wintering birds which remain there because of the mild coastal winters. In spite of the fact that Mobile, the second largest city in the state, is in this area, most of the bird data here have been furnished by weekend visitors.

All dates listed in this occurrence paragraph are extreme dates of occurrence, except out-of-season records which are listed separately. All available records up to August 31, 1961, are used. Records made since this date are used only where they, in the opinion of the author, make a substantial contribution to the local status of the species.

Abundance data, generally marked as "most seen," refer, except where noted otherwise in a very few cases, to the largest number of birds recorded by a single observer or single party in one calendar day (usually eight to ten party-hours). In co-operative counts, such as Christmas counts or the Mobile Bay area spring and fall counts, these high figures are the result of one calendar-day's activities of a group of observers or parties (usually fifty to seventy party-hours). These numbers have been listed not only to give as accurate a picture of Alabama birdlife as possible, but to allow accurate comparison with other times and places with similar data.

The *time of breeding* of the species in Alabama is indicated as fully as possible in the next paragraph. Based almost solely on dated records by reliable observers, these data deal with a specific part of the breeding cycle. Information is presented for all species that are known to breed in Alabama, although for some, such as the Painted Bunting, it is very meager. The amount of data does not necessarily represent the abundance of the bird as a breeding species, but rather how easily its nest can be discovered and examined. Because of these difficulties much information is still needed on many common breeding species.

For the sake of brevity, these data are only rarely separated as to locality. The raw data, however, almost invariably show that within a given species, the nesting season is at least a week earlier in the Tennessee Valley than it is on the Gulf Coast. One would think that the more southern birds would begin to breed earlier; but birds in the northern part of the state seem to nest first because they have a shorter summer in which to produce replacements for their annual mortality.

In many species, generally multiple-brooded, the breeding season extends over the greater part of the summer. Single-brooded species, provided sufficient data are available, show a much shorter breeding season, with egg dates extending for about a month. The wood warblers are notably single-brooded, yet of the twenty species that are known to breed in Alabama, eleven show signs of a possible second brood. These show egg dates extending over a period of almost two months and often longer, or the period from earliest egg date to latest dependent young is almost three months or more. Considering how extensive this nesting period is for the few data on which it is based (only two species with more than 22 nestings) this is probably significant, but positive proof will very likely take a long time to develop.

The very few accounts which have a *subspecies paragraph* describe races that can be separated in the field. Various populations of a given species can be distinguished from other populations of the species usually by differences of degree, such as in being larger or smaller, darker or lighter. These distinctions can generally be made only by accurate measuring or by direct comparison with other specimens. Furthermore, except where barriers exist, a wide zone of blending with other populations often makes it difficult to assign a particular bird to one race. Thus, except in rare cases, only specialists with long experience and with access to a very large collection of specimens are qualified to identify most subspecies. By not assigning any official common names to these subspecies, the A.O.U. indicates that it considers the naming of subspecies beyond the average bird student. It is deemed best, therefore, to leave data on all subspecies except those identifiable in the field, to reports of a much more technical nature.

The *banding paragraph* cites records of birds banded or recovered in Alabama, while background information on banding is contained in the introduction. The banding records are those available at Patuxent Wildlife Research Center, Laurel, Maryland, banding headquarters up to October 1, 1957, and any other interesting and unusual records which have come to our attention in the meantime (for example, the large number of Canada Geese that came to Alabama from Akimiski Island in James Bay, and the Sooty Tern which was very probably blown to Prattville by Hurricane Ethel). These banding records show where some Alabama birds travel. Some of them have gone as far as northern Alaska, Labrador, California, Nova Scotia, Peru, and Venezuela. For those species with sufficient recoveries, maps are furnished to show these travels.

The return of many species to their breeding locality each year is well documented, but little is known about this same affinity for the wintering area. Alabama banding records indicate that some birds, such as waterfowl, change their wintering grounds or move about much during the winter, for we have quite a few records of birds that have been banded or recovered in another part of the South in another winter. From the returns on at least nine wintering species, however, it appears that many small land birds return each winter to the same Alabama locality. It is difficult to procure any proof of identical wintering locality on species which are hard to band in large numbers or for those with many individuals also summering here.

The 46 species whose status on the Alabama list is not completely acceptable are divided into three groups: 1) No preserved specimen or other concrete evidence, but recent acceptable sight records. Those marked with a letter have been examined in the hand as a specimen not preserved (S), in the process of banding (B), or captured and released by a person competent to identify the species (C).

Red-throated Loon	Franklin's Gull
Eared Grebe	Roseate Tern
Wilson's Petrel	Rufous Hummingbird
White-tailed Tropic-bird	Bell's Vireo
Brown Booby	Kirtland's Warbler
White-fronted Goose (S)	Connecticut Warbler
European Widgeon	Mourning Warbler (B, S)
Common Scoter (S)	Bullock's Oriole
Harlan's Hawk	Western Tanager
Swainson's Hawk (B, S)	Black-headed Grosbeak
Rough-legged Hawk	Red Crossbill
Sandhill Crane (C)	Oregon Junco
Long-billed Curlew	Tree Sparrow
Northern Phalarope	Clay-colored Sparrow
Pomarine Jaeger	Harris' Sparrow
Parasitic Jaeger	Golden-crowned Sparrow
Great Black-backed Gull	Snow Bunting

2) No record since 1924, the time of publication of Howell's *Birds of Alabama.* These species are either extinct—no longer exist anywhere (X), extirpated—no longer exist in Alabama but do so elsewhere (E), or are recorded here so long ago that their occurrence is of historical interest (H).

Sooty Shearwater (H)	European Woodcock (H)
Scarlet Ibis (H)	Passenger Pigeon (X)
American Flamingo (H)	Carolina Parakeet (X)
Ruffed Grouse * (E)	Ivory-billed Woodpecker (X or E)
Whooping Crane (E)	Common Raven (E)
Common Redpoll (H)	

*Being re-introduced

3) Introduced but not well established. The one species is the Mute Swan. Many additional species, particularly chicken-like birds, have been introduced in the state, but thus far only three have been really successful, the Starling, the House Sparrow, and the Rock Dove (Common Pigeon).

These 46 species, whose presence on the Alabama list is not wholly acceptable, have species accounts because the purpose of this book is to give the reader as complete information as possible on the birds of the state. This is done with the understanding that some of these birds no longer occur and that others lack completely acceptable scientific proof of occurrence. The occurrence of every one of the 34 species without preserved specimen is based on the best possible data short of concrete evidence: sight records under excellent conditions, often in the hand, by ornithologists of unquestionable reputation. Sight records of other species are not even mentioned.

The information in these accounts might be entitled "What we know about Alabama birds as of 1961," for this book is really a progress report. Compare this with the information in Howell's *Birds of Alabama* (1924 and 1928) and you will see great progress in our knowledge of local birds. Compare this information with the A.O.U. *Check-list* and the bird books of nearby states, and you will note that Alabama should record much additional data, for example, species that should occur or should nest but are not at present known to do so. Furthermore, bird students from other states will in all probability look at our data and find species they should record. This comparison, of course, fosters healthy competition.

Thus these species accounts not only tell us what is known about Alabama birds, but what needs to be known. For instance, anyone who discovers the nest and eggs of the Painted Bunting in this state and who has read the account will know that his information is important and his discovery significant. Anyone who collects or has collected a specimen of one of the 34 species listed as without preserved specimen (and many of them are game birds), will know that it is worth recording and preserving.

It is expected that some of the information in these accounts will become out-of-date. Some species will be recorded a little outside the listed season of occurrence, and the like. But now that these species accounts are in print, they will stimulate the recording of additional information. This is progress, an important feature of all science.

Map 3

LAUDERDALE · Florence

LIMESTONE MADISON JACKSON

COLBERT · Huntsville Brownsboro
Leighton Wheeler · Monte Sano · Scottsboro
Refuge
FRANKLIN LAWRENCE Decatur · N. Sauty Hammondville
· Russellville MORGAN Refuge DeSoto Park
MARSHALL · Fort Payne
DE KALB
· Guntersville

MARION WINSTON CULLMAN CHEROKEE

BLOUNT ETOWAH
· Gadsden
LAMAR WALKER CALHOUN
FAYETTE ST. CLAIR · Anniston
JEFFERSON CLEBURNE
· Birmingham TALLADEGA · Mt. Cheaha
PICKENS TUSCALOOSA SHELBY CLAY RANDOLPH

· Tuscaloosa BIBB
COOSA TALLAPOOSA CHAMBERS
GREENE CHILTON · Weogufka
HALE PERRY ELMORE LEE
· Greensboro AUTAUGA · Auburn
SUMTER · Marion Prattville Coosada MACON RUSSELL
· Livingston DALLAS · Autaugaville Montgomery · Tuskegee
MARENGO Montgomery Barachias BULLOCK
LOWNDES BARBOUR
CHOCTAW WILCOX
CLARKE · Camden BUTLER PIKE · Clayton
MONROE HENRY
· Jackson CRENSHAW COFFEE DALE
WASHINGTON CONECUH · Lake Tholloco
· Choctaw COVINGTON Columbia
Bluff · Andalusia HOUSTON
ESCAMBIA GENEVA
MOBILE BALDWIN · Florala

· Mobile
· Cochrane
Causeway
· Fairhope
Bayou · Foley
LaBatre
· Coden
Alabama
Point
Dauphin Fort Gulf
Island Morgan Shores

LOCALITIES FREQUENTLY
MENTIONED IN THE TEXT

[57]

Plate 2

TOPOGRAPHY OF A BIRD

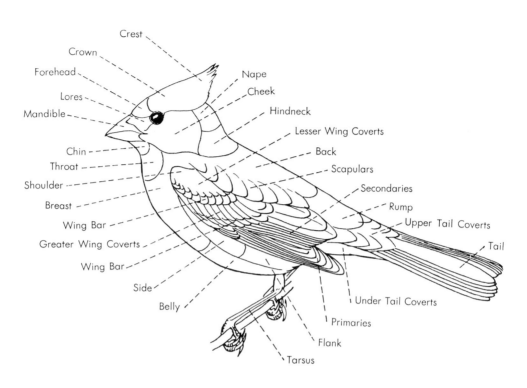

Crest

Crown

Forehead

Lores

Mandible

Nape

Cheek

Hindneck

Lesser Wing Coverts

Chin

Throat

Shoulder

Breast

Wing Bar

Greater Wing Coverts

Wing Bar

Side

Belly

Back

Scapulars

Secondaries

Rump

Upper Tail Coverts

Tail

Under Tail Coverts

Primaries

Flank

Tarsus

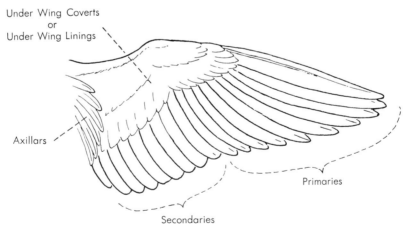

Under Wing Coverts
or
Under Wing Linings

Axillars

Primaries

Secondaries

Under-surface of a Bird's Wing

ORDER GAVIIFORMES: LOONS

FAMILY GAVIIDAE: LOONS

Loons are water birds about the size of a goose, with webbed feet, large heads, and short, thick necks. They resemble ducks, but they have pointed bills, shorter tails, and sit lower in the water. In flight they have a hunch-backed appearance which is caused by the droop of their tails and heads. Expert swimmers and divers, they usually prefer to escape danger by diving rather than by taking flight, and this characteristic plus their ability to stay under water for a long period of time has earned them the name "helldiver." Loons have to run along the surface of the water for some distance in order to gain sufficient speed for flight. On land they are very clumsy, their legs being set far back on their bodies to make for better swimming. Sometimes during storms a loon mistakes wet pavement for water and lands on it. It is then unable to regain flight unless it can reach a sizable body of water.

Common Loon
Gavia immer (Brünnich) [7] (Plate 3, facing page 64)
OTHER NAMES: Diver, Helldiver, Loon, Wah-loon

The Common Loon is a goose-sized bird that sits low in the water. In winter its back and the back of its neck are dark, and it is *dark* on the *top* of the *head*, while its under parts, including the neck and much of the face, are white. In breeding plumage, March to August, its head and neck are black and the upper parts and sides are marked with fine white spots and checks. The Common Loon's call, among the most distinctive and unusual of all bird calls, is a high-pitched, hollow laugh, which is usually given at dusk, during the night, or before storms.

This loon is common to abundant on the Alabama Coast in winter, and an occasional bird is observed there in summer. It usually frequents the deeper salt water. Inland, it is fairly common during migration, uncommon to rare in winter, and has been noted during only one summer in the Tennessee Valley. It breeds on northern lakes, has never been known to nest anywhere in this state, but may be found on any body of water here during migration. Although commonly solitary, this species occasionally occurs on migration in flocks as large as thirty or more.

NESTING AND FOOD. The nest of the Common Loon is usually found on a lake shore. Ordinarily it is a mere depression lined with grasses, sticks, and turf, normally containing two dark olive-gray, brown-stained, black-spotted eggs. Fish, often four to six inches in length and obtained by underwater pursuit, form the bird's main source of food. They are supplemented by smaller amounts of other aquatic animals, including insects.

DISTRIBUTION. The Common Loon breeds from Alaska, Baffin Island, Greenland, and Iceland south to northern California and the northern states including much of New England. It winters from southern Alaska, Maine, and Newfoundland south to northern Mexico and the Gulf of Mexico.

OCCURRENCE IN ALABAMA. (October 8 to May 26; occurs occasionally in summer.) *Tennessee Valley*: November 3 (Wheeler Refuge, *fide* T. Z. Atkeson, Jr.) to May 9 (Wheeler Refuge, *fide* T. Z. Atkeson, Jr.); also 1 cripple on June 15 and July 16, 1959 (Decatur, D. C. Hulse). *Mountain Region*: November 9 (1957, Warrior River near Birmingham, *fide* Adele West) to May 26 (1946, Birmingham, T. A. Imhof); most seen: migration, 8, April 14, 1948 (Birmingham, T. A. Imhof), winter, 4, December 20, 1958 (Lake Purdy, T. A. Imhof). *Piedmont*: November 22 (1959, Mitchell Lake, Harriett and D. O. Wright) to April 23 (1960, Mitchell Lake, Harriett and D. O. Wright). *Upper* *Coastal Plain*: November 20 (1956, Marion, R. T. Gaisser) to May 11 (1957, Marion, Lois McCollough); most seen, "a dozen," March 1878 (Coosada, N. C. Brown). *Lower Coastal Plain*: October 19 (1956, Florala, T. A. Imhof and L. C. Crawford) to April 28 (1961, Clio, Barbour Co., Edwin Ezell); most seen, 50, early December 1954 (Barbour County Lake, J. E. Keeler). *Gulf Coast*: October 8 (1933, Gulf Shores, F. M. Weston) to May 25 (1957, Fowl River, T. A. Imhof, M. W. Gaillard, and H. C. Loesch); also August 27, 1946 (Bon Secour Bay, T. A. Imhof) and September 24, 1955 (Gulf Shores, Ala. Orn. Soc.); most seen, 86, December 27, 1947 (Christmas Count, Foley).

[Red-throated Loon]
Gavia stellata (Pontoppidan)   [11]   (Plate 3, facing page 64)

Smaller than the Common Loon, the Red-throated Loon has a back spotted with white and a *lighter-colored head*. The *slight upturn* of its *small bill* is noticeable at a good distance, and is perhaps the best field mark. The triangular, red throat patch is worn only in the breeding season and is therefore seldom seen in the United States.

This bird is casual during winter in Alabama, both in the Tennessee Valley and on the coast. It frequents the same places as the Common Loon but ranges farther north. The Red-throated Loon has never been known to breed here.

[60]

NESTING AND FOOD. This loon lays two sparsely-spotted, reddish-brown to grayish-green eggs in a slight depression on the shore of small ponds usually on the tundra. It eats small fish and other marine life, obtained by diving, more often than not in deep water.

DISTRIBUTION. The Red-throated Loon breeds in the far north, mainly on the tundra, south to the Aleutian Islands, British Columbia, James Bay, and Newfoundland. It winters from the Aleutian Islands to Sonora and from the Great Lakes and Maine south to the northern Gulf Coast and southern Florida.

OCCURRENCE IN ALABAMA. (January 23 to May 1) *Tennessee Valley*: February 11, 1951 (North Sauty Refuge, Adele and E. M. West). *Mountain Region*: No record. *Piedmont*: No record. *Upper Coastal Plain*: No record. *Lower Coastal Plain*: No record. *Gulf Coast*: January 23, 1959 (Gulf Shores, Lovett Williams and R. W. Skinner), January 23, 1959 (Gulf State Park, Lovett Williams and R. W. Skinner); February 8, 1957 (Bon Secour Bay, T. A. Imhof, H. C. Loesch, M. W. Gaillard, and Barney Davis); May 1, 1954 (Fort Morgan, O. L. Austin, Jr. and T. A. Imhof).

ORDER PODICIPEDIFORMES: GREBES

FAMILY PODICIPEDIDAE: GREBES

Grebes are duck-sized water birds resembling miniature swans in the erect carriage of their small heads and thin necks. Their bills are thin and pointed, and they have lobed feet, short bodies, and small tails. In flight grebes look a little like a merganser, but they droop their head and neck like a loon. They rival the loon as divers, and are just as clumsy as the loon on land. Most grebe nests are soggy, decaying masses of vegetation, usually free floating. Grebes obtain most of their food by underwater pursuit.

Horned Grebe

Podiceps auritus (Linnaeus)   [3]   (Plate 3, facing page 64)
OTHER NAME: Sea Didapper

The Horned Grebe is slightly larger than the Pied-billed Grebe and appears *much paler,* especially on the *head* and *neck.* This bird has a dark gray back, head, and nape, and usually it has *pure white under parts,* including the *throat* and *front* of the *neck.* Occasionally a Horned Grebe will have a grayish smudge on its upper throat. The wings are light gray with a small white patch. In spring and summer, its plumage changes to black on its head, with large buffy eartufts, and its neck and flanks are reddish-brown.

In winter the Horned Grebe is abundant on the large bays of the Gulf Coast, uncommon in the Tennessee Valley, and rare elsewhere throughout the state. On migration it is uncommon on many lakes and ponds in the state and it is not known to breed in Alabama.

NESTING AND FOOD. This bird lays three to seven eggs in the usual floating grebe nest on prairie ponds, marshes, and sloughs. Its food consists of small fish, aquatic insects, crustaceans, and a few mollusks.

DISTRIBUTION. In North America the Horned Grebe breeds from central Alaska and northern Manitoba south to British Columbia and Wisconsin, and occasionally farther east. It winters from the Aleutian Islands to southern California, from Nova Scotia to southern Texas, and less commonly, inland to the Great Lakes.

OCCURRENCE IN ALABAMA. (October 8 to May 10.) *Tennessee Valley*: November 2 (1942, Wheeler Refuge, H. H. Grammer) to March 28 (1953, Wheeler Refuge, D. C. Hulse); also May 10, 1961 (Wheeler Refuge, H. H. Grammer and T. P. Sandlin). *Mountain Region*: October 27 (1956, Hammondville, DeKalb Co., Ala. Orn. Soc.) to May 10 (1952, Birmingham, T. A. Imhof); most seen, 5, December 27, 1942 (Christmas Count, Birmingham). *Piedmont*: November 22 (1959, Mitchell Lake, Harriett and D. O. Wright) to April 15 (1955, Auburn, H. G. Good). *Upper Coastal Plain*: October 8 (1960, Elmore Co., A. D. Hooper) to February 22 (1957, Marion, Lois McCollough). *Lower Coastal Plain*: February 26, 1955 (12 birds, Florala, T. A. Imhof). *Gulf Coast*: October 31 (1958, 4 birds, Dauphin Island, T. A. Imhof and Lois McCollough) to May 3 (1960, Dauphin Island, J. L. Dorn); most seen, 1350, February 8, 1957 (Perdido and Bon Secour bays, T. A. Imhof and others).

[Eared Grebe]

Podiceps caspicus (Hablizl)   [4]   (Plate 3, facing page 64)

There is a close resemblance between the Eared Grebe and its near relative, the Horned Grebe. The Eared Grebe is slightly smaller and has a *thinner, slightly upturned bill.* In winter, it is darker, with a *grayer neck,* it has a *whitish spot* behind the *eye,* and it has more white on its wings. During the breeding season it can be easily distinguished from other grebes by its *black neck.* Its nearly triangular head is held very erect on a thin neck, and the rear of its body rides high in the water.

The Eared Grebe is casual on the Alabama coast in winter and is not known to breed in the state. It breeds in fresh water and winters in salt water.

NESTING AND FOOD. The nest of this species differs little from that of the Horned Grebe. On salt water the Eared Grebe eats small crustaceans and on fresh water, aquatic and flying insects are its main food.

DISTRIBUTION. In the Western Hemisphere the Eared Grebe breeds from British Columbia and Minnesota south to Lower California and southern Texas. It winters from southern British Columbia to Colombia and, rarely, eastward to the Great Lakes and the Gulf of Mexico.

OCCURRENCE IN ALABAMA. *Gulf Coast only*: January 1 and March 26, 1960 (1 bird, possibly the same, Little Dauphin Island, Ava Tabor, Electa Levi, and Michael Caldwell).

[64]

Pied-billed Grebe

Podilymbus podiceps (Linnaeus) [6] (Plate 3, facing page 64)
OTHER NAMES: Didapper, Helldiver, Dabchick, Didipper

The Pied-billed Grebe is a *small, brown* grebe with a short, thick bill and white under tail coverts. In summer it has a *black throat patch* and a *black band* on its *bill*. The young bird resembles the winter adult except that it has a few brown lines on its cheeks. During the breeding season it gives a long series of low, cuckoo-like calls.

Although it is not a game bird, nor particularly edible, this grebe often finds itself the target of gunshot, whereupon it immediately dives, leaving no trace. It will surface far from danger, frequently choosing reeds and bringing only its head and bill above water. Swimming and diving better than a duck, this bird can dive head first, sink slowly backward, or swim with various parts of its body submerged.

In winter, the Pied-billed Grebe is common to abundant on ponds and lakes throughout Alabama. It summers here often, and occasionally breeds here. (See Map 4.) Generally it frequents the smaller bodies of water, and it is one of the few water birds more common inland than on the coast. Scattered individuals occur on almost all suitable ponds, and sometimes there are large flocks on migration.

NESTING. The nest is a soggy mass of decaying vegetation, often free floating but occasionally attached to reeds. There are four to six whitish eggs, which this grebe covers when it leaves the nest. The pond it prefers for nesting is small and has reedy borders. Alabama ponds seldom attract it because malaria control measures have largely done away with the reedy borders, and because there are so many predatory turtles.

FOOD. The Pied-billed Grebe feeds on crustaceans, small fish, water insects, frogs and other aquatic animals, and the seeds and soft parts of water plants.

DISTRIBUTION. This grebe breeds locally from British Columbia, Great Slave Lake, and New Brunswick south to Chile and Argentina. It winters north to southern British Columbia, Utah, Texas, Tennessee, the Potomac Valley, and occasionally farther north.

OCCURRENCE IN ALABAMA. (Throughout the year.) *Tennessee Valley:* August 19 (1893, Leighton, F. W. McCormack) to second week in May (Leighton, F. W. McCormack); frequent in summer, especially at Wheeler Refuge; most seen, 150,

April 17, 1936 (Wheeler Reservoir, A. R. Cahn). *Mountain Region*: August 3 (1936, Birmingham, H. M. Stevenson) to May 30 (1952 and 1955, Birmingham, T. A. Imhof); summers frequently; most seen: migration, 108, March 13, 1950 and September 5, 1952 (Birmingham, T. A. Imhof), winter, 134, December 20, 1958 (Christmas Count, Birmingham). *Piedmont*: October 1 (1957, Auburn, Lovett Williams) to April 19 (1924, Auburn, J. M. Robertson). *Upper Coastal Plain*: August 16 (1939, Tuscaloosa, H. M. Stevenson) to May 14 (1955, Marion, Lois McCollough); summers frequently; most seen, 56, October 27, 1956 (Marion, Lois McCollough). *Lower Coastal Plain*: September 20 (1957, Andalusia, T. A. Imhof and Lovett Williams) to April 5 (1957, Jackson, T. A. Imhof and W. U. Harris). *Gulf Coast*: August 20 (1953, Gulf Shores, F. M. Weston) to May 11 (1956, Spring Hill, M. W. Gaillard); summers frequently; most seen, 27, October 19, 1957 (Fall Count, Mobile Bay Area).

TIME OF BREEDING. Data on 6 nestings: Eggs, late April to May 15; dependent young, May 15 to July 10.

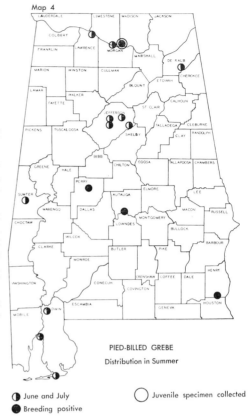

PIED-BILLED GREBE

Distribution in Summer

◗ June and July

● Breeding positive

○ Juvenile specimen collected

ORDER PROCELLARIIFORMES: ALBATROSSES, SHEARWATERS, PETRELS, AND ALLIES

These birds spend their lives at sea and usually come ashore only on islands to nest. Most of them have very long wings and all have remarkable powers of flight.

FAMILY PROCELLARIIDAE: SHEARWATERS AND FULMARS

SUBFAMILY PUFFININAE: SHEARWATERS

Shearwaters are birds of the open ocean. They can glide for great distances on stiffly posed, long, narrow wings. Frequently they fly so low that when they dip their wings they seem to "shear the water." Their nasal passages open through a distinctive tube which gives them better breathing control under water. The opening of this tube is double in shearwaters and fulmars (*Procellariidae*) and single in storm petrels (*Hydrobatidae*).

Most shearwaters nest in a burrow on an oceanic island. Here they lay one usually white egg. The period of incubation and development of the young is three to five months. In many cases these birds come ashore only for breeding purposes and then only at night. They can remain at sea indefinitely even in storms, and although they occasionally come within sight of land, they normally remain farther out to sea.

Greater Shearwater
Puffinus gravis (O'Reilly) [89]
OTHER NAMES: Albatross, Hag

The Greater Shearwater is about the size of a Ring-billed Gull. It is dark brown above and white below and has a well-defined *dark cap*, light gray hindneck, and a *white V-shaped patch* on the *base* of its *tail*.

It is accidental in summer on the Alabama coast, but it does not nest here. It frequents the open sea and rarely comes within sight of land.

[67]

FOOD. This species feeds on small sea animals, such as squids, sand eels, and small fish. Sometimes it picks up scraps from fishing vessels or from the surface of the sea.

DISTRIBUTION. So far as is known, the Greater Shearwater breeds only in the Tristan da Cunha Islands in the South Atlantic Ocean. Apart from the breeding season—our summer—it occurs almost throughout the Atlantic Ocean on both coasts, from Cape Horn and the Cape of Good Hope to Greenland and Scotland. Occasionally it enters more sheltered waters such as the Mediterranean Sea and the Gulf of Mexico.

OCCURRENCE IN ALABAMA. *Gulf Coast only*: One bird frequented the Mobile Pilot Ship (7 miles south of Dauphin Island) for most of July 1958. About July 30 it fell through the ship's ventilator into the galley and hit the cook on the head. John C. Gray brought the bird to Dr. M. W. Gaillard, but it died after 2 or 3 days and is now a specimen in the collection of the Univ. of Ala.

[Sooty Shearwater]

Puffinus griseus (Gmelin) [95]

OTHER NAMES: Albatross, Black Hag, Dark Petrel

The Sooty Shearwater, about the size of a Laughing Gull, is uniformly *dark brown* except for the *whitish under wing linings,* so that its color pattern in flight strikingly resembles that of the Black Duck.

FOOD. This shearwater feeds on various kinds of vegetable and animal life found floating on the sea, especially squids, small fish, and crustaceans.

DISTRIBUTION. The Sooty Shearwater breeds in New Zealand, on other nearby islands, and on islands near Cape Horn. It winters during our summer just off most—if not all—of the outer coasts of the Pacific and Atlantic oceans, north to Siberia, Alaska, Greenland, and Iceland.

OCCURRENCE IN ALABAMA. *Mountain Region only*: At Attalla, Edgar Magness found 1 bird after a heavy storm on May 4, 1898 (*Osprey* 3:45).

FAMILY HYDROBATIDAE: STORM PETRELS

Storm petrels are small, swallow-like oceanic birds, able to flutter so close to the waves that they appear to be walking on the water. In the hand, storm petrels can be distinguished from shearwaters and fulmars by the single opening to their nasal tubes. Their plumage is mostly black, and their nesting habits are similar to those of the shearwaters and fulmars. These little birds are virtually tireless, and they are found at rest only in a calm.

[Wilson's Petrel]

Oceanites oceanicus (Kuhl) [109]

OTHER NAME: Mother Carey's Chickens

Wilson's Petrel is about the size of a Purple Martin. It is *all black* except for a *white rump* and *yellow-webbed feet*. The tail is *squared off*, so that the *feet extend beyond it*.

FOOD. This petrel feeds on small marine life and refuse found on the surface of the ocean.

DISTRIBUTION. Wilson's Petrel is one of a very few birds which breed on the Antarctic Continent. It also breeds on nearby South Atlantic islands and winters during our summer in the Atlantic Ocean north to Labrador and the British Isles, in the Indian Ocean to the Red Sea and the Persian Gulf, and in the Pacific Ocean to Australia and California. It is rather common off our Atlantic Coast states from June to September, and frequently enters harbors.

OCCURRENCE IN ALABAMA. *Gulf Coast only*: At Fort Morgan, August 27, 1946, T. A. Imhof saw 10 birds close to shore flying into the entrance of Mobile Bay.

ORDER PELECANIFORMES: TROPIC-BIRDS, PELICANS, FRIGATE-BIRDS, AND ALLIES

This order includes all birds having all four toes webbed. In other web-footed birds, the web does not include the hind toe. All members have a throat pouch, but the pouch is well developed only in the pelicans. Some live far at sea, some along the coast, and others in swamps and lakes, but all are expert swimmers and divers.

FAMILY PHAETHONTIDAE: TROPIC-BIRDS

[White-tailed Tropic-bird]
Phaethon lepturus Daudin   [112]   (Plate 4, facing page 72)

At first glance, this *white* seabird looks much like a heavy-bodied Royal Tern, but the *central tail feathers* are extremely *long* and *thin,* much longer than those of any tern. The *adult* tropic-bird has an *orange bill,* and there is black through its eye, on the three or four outermost primaries, in a stripe across its back and wings, and on its flanks. The *immature* bird has a *yellow bill,* a much shorter tail, the upper parts thinly barred with black, and only faint signs of the black pattern of the adult. The *flight* of a tropic-bird is rather *high, rapid,* and *direct.*

This species is accidental in fall on the Alabama coast. Usually it remains far out at sea, but tropical storms drive it shoreward or even far inland. It does not breed here.

NESTING AND FOOD. The White-tailed Tropic-bird breeds in colonies on islands and lays a single brown-spotted, chalky-pink egg on the bare rock of a cliff or cave or on steeply-sloping ground. It feeds near dawn and dusk by diving into the sea much after the manner of a Brown Pelican or Gannet. Squids and flying fish are the principal items in its diet, but it also eats crabs and other fish.

DISTRIBUTION. This tropic-bird breeds widely in tropical parts of the Pacific, Indian, and Atlantic oceans. Outside the breeding season, it ranges even more widely, to Japan, Hawaii, Australia, and Florida, and casually to Nova Scotia.

Bay, Peter Petersen and Dennis Sheets
watched 1 of these birds fly directly overhead.

FAMILY PELECANIDAE: PELICANS

These birds have well-developed throat pouches and are bigger than other members of their order.

White Pelican
Pelecanus erythrorhynchos Gmelin   [125]   (Plate 4, facing page 72)

The White Pelican, even larger than the Brown Pelican, is *white* except for *large, black wing tips,* a yellow bill, and a big yellow throat pouch.

On the Gulf Coast of Alabama this species is common to abundant in winter and on migration. It is rare to uncommon here in summer but is not known to breed here. It is usually found in the Mississippi Sound and at the head of Mobile Bay. Inland it is uncommon on migration, occurring mostly in October. It is noted most often in the Tennessee Valley, where a few birds may winter, and less often in the Coosa-Alabama and Tombigbee valleys. It breeds in large colonies among tules and other reeds on the shores of some western lakes. In winter it frequents shallow salt water.

FOOD. The White Pelican eats small fish, salamanders, crawfish, and tadpoles, scooping them up with its large bill. Unlike the Brown Pelican it does not dive from a height. Usually several birds form a circle, and they thrust their long necks into the water for the surrounded fish. Studies show that about one per cent of the White Pelican's food is edible fish, and that on the Gulf Coast ninety per cent of the fish it eats are menhaden.

DISTRIBUTION. White Pelicans breed from British Columbia and southwestern Ontario south to southern California and South Dakota and also in southern Texas. Some birds winter from California to Guatemala, but many migrate diagonally across the plains to winter on the Gulf coasts of the United States, Mexico, and Cuba, and a few reach the Atlantic Coast.

OCCURRENCE IN ALABAMA.
(September 18 to June 7; rare in summer.)
Tennessee Valley: October 9 (1895, specimen in King collection, Leighton, F. R. King) to January 9 (1944, Wheeler Refuge, L. S. Givens) and May 9 (1944, Wheeler Refuge, H. H. Grammer and others) to June 7 (1945, Pickwick Reservoir, S. A. Weakley); most seen, 21, date unknown (Wheeler Refuge, T. Z. Atkeson, Jr.). *Mountain Region:* No record. *Piedmont:* No record. *Upper Coastal Plain:* Mountain Creek, Chilton Co., mounted specimen in the State Dept. of Archives and History, October 1921 (*fide* P. A. Brannon, *Auk,*

[72]

Richard Parks

39:411); Selma, February 1922 (*fide* P. A. Brannon, *op. cit.*); Livingston, undated specimen about 1890 (*fide* W. C. Avery); April and October 1955 (Epes, Sumter Co., Mrs. Steinhilber). *Lower Coastal Plain*: No record. *Gulf Coast*: September 18 (1959, 200 birds, Cochrane Causeway, J. L. Dusi) to May 17 (1958, Cochrane Causeway, T. A. Imhof and M. W. Gaillard); also July 1959 and July through September 1960 (maximum 50, Cochrane Causeway, J. L. Dorn, F. M. Weston, and H. M. Stevenson); most seen, 1000+, late October 1955 (Heron Bay, H. C. Loesch).

Brown Pelican
Pelecanus occidentalis Linnaeus   [126]   (Plate 4, facing page 72)

The Brown Pelican is a very *large dark brown* bird which carries its *big bill* and *pouch* resting on its breast. The adult has some white on the head, but the immature bird has a dark head. It frequents all salt-water areas, especially seaward, and occasionally occurs inland in the Coastal Plain after winter storms. It often loiters around docks and fishing piers seeking food and when it does so is frequently quite tame. Since about 1957 the local population has been decimated by an unknown cause, possibly disease, possibly nesting depredations. According to present information on breeding it probably bred in this state only prior to 1900.

This species is abundant throughout the year on the Gulf Coast of Alabama.

NESTING. The Brown Pelican breeds in colonies on lonely shores and isolated islands. There it builds a nest of sticks, coarse grass, and weeds on the ground or in low bushes. It lays two or three chalky-white eggs. Apparently the Alabama birds make a daily round trip in summer to the nearest known breeding colony, which is on the offshore Louisiana islands.

FOOD. Fish are the exclusive fare of the Brown Pelican. Usually the fish are from four and one-half to eleven and one-half inches long, and on the Gulf Coast are chiefly menhaden. This pelican also eats mullet, sheepshead, catfish, and toadfish.

DISTRIBUTION The Brown Pelican breeds along the Pacific Coast from California to Chile, wintering north to British Columbia, and along the Atlantic, Gulf, and Caribbean coasts from North Carolina to British Guiana, wintering north to North Carolina.

OCCURRENCE IN ALABAMA. (Throughout the year.) *Tennessee Valley*: No record. *Mountain Region*: No record. *Piedmont*: No record. *Upper Coastal Plain*: late January or early February 1922, specimen in State Dept. of Archives and History (Montgomery, P. A. Brannon, *Auk* 39:411). *Lower Coastal Plain*: February 1909, specimen not preserved (Omusee Creek, Henry Co., Sidney Morgan); February 1922, bird shot (Georgiana, Butler Co., *fide* P. A. Brannon, *op. cit.*); February 1922, specimen in State Dept. of Archives and History (Escambia Co., *fide* P. A. Brannon, *op. cit.*). *Gulf Coast*: Permanent resident; most seen, 1800, November 25, 1956 (Dauphin Island, Lois McCollough).

Note. Since 1956 this species has been virtually decimated on the northern Gulf Coast. The cause is not known.

BANDING. Of 4 banded Brown Pelicans recaptured in Alabama, 1 was at least 6 years old. Data follows: *banded,* Louisiana, nestling, June 30, 1939; *recovered,* Fairhope, November 27, 1939; *banded,* Louisiana, nestling, June 30, 1939; *recovered,* Mobile, March 6, 1940; *banded,* South Carolina, nestling, July 26, 1950; *recovered,* Bayou La Batre, December 1951; *banded,* Florida, St. Petersburg, November 2, 1932; *recovered,* Mobile Bay, July 3, 1938.

FAMILY SULIDAE: BOOBIES AND GANNETS

These goose-sized birds have long, powerful wings with dark, pointed tips, a pointed tail, and a thick, pointed bill slightly longer than the head. This pointed-at-both-ends shape is distinctive. These birds live at sea and often forage near shore but rarely if ever enter bays and sounds. They obtain fish, their almost exclusive food, by making a spectacular headlong dive into the sea, usually sending up a column of spray.

[Brown Booby]
Sula leucogaster (Boddaert)   [115]
OTHER NAMES: White-bellied Booby, Gooney Bird

Slightly smaller than the Gannet, the Brown Booby in adult plumage is dark brown with white underwing linings and *white under parts* which *contrast sharply* with the *dark chest.* Immature birds are brown like the immature Gannet and the other boobies, but the Brown Booby is *darker* on the *upper parts* and on the *head* and *chest,* which *contrast sharply* with the *whitish under parts.* The immature Gannet is larger and is coarsely spotted with white; the immature Blue-faced Booby has a dark belly; and the immature Red-footed Booby has a light-colored area on the back in front of the wings and a whitish belly but usually does not show the sharp, junco-like line of contrast on the chest.

In Alabama, the Brown Booby is accidental in the Gulf and does not breed in the state. The species occurs in tropical seas, often far from land, but sometimes close to shore.

NESTING AND FOOD. This booby nests on islands, usually in a situation where take-off is easy, such as on sloping ground. The nest, generally either a hollow in the ground or a low mound, normally contains two chalky to pale blue eggs. The Brown Booby subsists on various fish, especially flying fish and mullet.

DISTRIBUTION. The Brown Booby breeds in tropical parts of the Indian, Pacific, and Atlantic oceans, north in the Western Hemisphere to islands in the

Gulf of California, islands of eastern Mexico, Cuba, and the Bahamas. Outside the breeding season it ranges north casually throughout the Gulf of Mexico and the Atlantic coast of Florida and accidentally to South Carolina, New York, and Massachusetts.

OCCURRENCE IN ALABAMA. *Gulf Coast only*: Dauphin Island, August 26, 1961 (an adult, fishing just off the Gulf beach, observed at close range through a telescope for 15 minutes, H. D. Haberyan).

Gannet

Morus bassanus (Linnaeus)   [117]   (Plate 4, facing page 72)
OTHER NAMES: Booby, Gooney Bird

The Gannet's bill and its tail are so pointed that at a distance the bird has a distinctive pointed-at-both-ends shape very useful in identification. It is twice the size of a Ring-billed Gull and has a long neck, long wings, and a rather long tail. The *adult* is *white* with *large black wing tips,* and the *immature* bird is *brown* with a *pale belly.* Changing immatures, seen often in Alabama, show much white on the head and neck. Those who know the adult can recognize young Gannets easily by their size, shape, and actions.

On the Gulf, especially off Baldwin County, these North Atlantic seabirds are common in most winters. They usually range offshore from 100 yards to five miles. Almost invariably they fly westward, and apparently they follow a current which is deflected southward by the outflow of water from Mobile Bay. For this reason, Gannets are scarce a few miles west of Fort Morgan. These birds are not known to breed in Alabama.

NESTING AND FOOD. Gannets breed in large, world-famous colonies on North Atlantic sea cliffs. The colony on Bonaventure Island in the Gaspé Peninsula of Quebec attracts many tourists from this country each summer. On narrow ledges in these colonies the birds lay a single, chalky, greenish-blue egg on a small seaweed nest. They obtain their food, exclusively fish, by a spectacular headlong dive into the sea.

DISTRIBUTION. This species breeds on islands in the Gulf of St. Lawrence, in Iceland, and in the British Isles. It winters on the Atlantic and Gulf coasts from Virginia, and sometimes farther north, to Alabama, rarely Texas, and off the coasts and nearby islands of North Africa.

OCCURRENCE IN ALABAMA. *Gulf Coast only*: November 29 (1957, Gulf Shores, B. L. Monroe, Jr., and H. M. Stevenson) to May 10 (1958, Sand Island Light, John Gray); most seen, 103, April 21, 1956 (Gulf Shores, Fort Morgan, and Dauphin

Island, B. L. Monroe, Jr., and others); also
September 2, 1960, exhausted bird, now a

specimen in the Dept. of Conservation collection (Fort Morgan, J. L. Dorn).

FAMILY PHALACROCORACIDAE: CORMORANTS

Double-crested Cormorant

Phalacrocorax auritus (Lesson) [120] (Plate 4, facing page 72)
OTHER NAMES: Nigger Goose, Water Turkey

This cormorant is a *goose-sized black* bird with a yellow-orange throat patch
and a *long tail* and *neck*. The immature bird lacks the throat patch and is
pale on the belly. On the water, it sits low with head erect and *bill slanted
upward*. In flight it resembles a goose except that it beats its wings more rapidly
and does not call. It is apt to sit on piles or buoys in the water and hold its wings
partially spread as if sunning them.

The Double-crested Cormorant is abundant in winter and on migration on
the Gulf Coast. Occasionally it summers there in small numbers. Elsewhere
in the state it is fairly common as a transient, especially in the larger river valleys,
where it sometimes winters or summers. It is not known to breed anywhere in
Alabama. Inland the species has decreased markedly in the last twenty years,
especially in the Tennessee Valley, where it used to winter abundantly. It
prefers salt water, but on migration may be found anywhere in the state,
especially along rivers.

NESTING AND FOOD. The Double-crested Cormorant nests in colonies,
where it builds either a seaweed nest on the ground or a twig nest in a tall
tree near the water. It lays two to four pale bluish-green, chalky eggs. For
food it depends solely on fish, especially eels.

DISTRIBUTION. This species breeds from Alaska, central Alberta, James
Bay, and Newfoundland south to Lower California, central Mexico, Cuba, Florida,
and the Bahamas. It is probably resident on the Pacific Coast; farther east it
winters from Tennessee and New York south to British Honduras.

OCCURRENCE IN ALABAMA.
(Throughout the year.) *Tennessee Valley*:
October to May; summers occasionally; most
seen, 545, December 23, 1942 (Christmas
Count, Wheeler Refuge). *Mountain Region*:
November 3 (1949, Birmingham, T. A.
Imhof) to April 12 (1912, Lock 15, Warrior
River, A. H. Howell); occasional in summer;
most seen, 21, June 16, 1951 (Lock 17,
Warrior River, M. H. Perry). *Piedmont*:
November 14 (1952, Opelika, F. W. Fitch
and W. W. Beshears) to April 21 (1952,
Auburn, F. W. Fitch); also about June 11,
1949 (Lake Martin, banding recovery) and
about September 20, 1931 (Weogufka Creek,
banding recovery). *Upper Coastal Plain*:
October 8 (1938, Tuscaloosa, H. M. Steven-
son) to April 18 (1956, Marion, Lois McCollough); also June 17, 1955 (Demopolis, J. E.
Keeler) and July 31, 1909 (7 birds, Autauga-

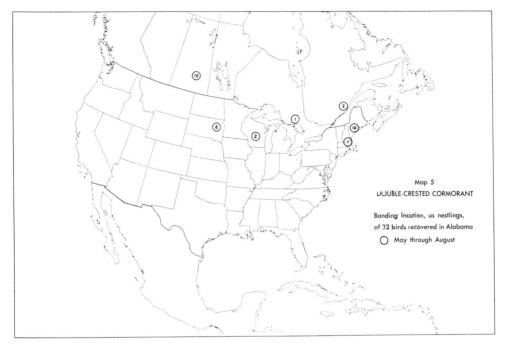

Map 5
DOUBLE-CRESTED CORMORANT

Banding location, as nestlings,
of 32 birds recovered in Alabama
○ May through August

ville, L. S. Golsan). *Lower Coastal Plain*: October 20 (1956, Coffee County Lake, T. A. Imhof and L. C. Crawford) to April 13 (1961, Jackson, T. A. Imhof and others). *Gulf Coast*: Common, August 24 (1956, Dauphin Island, T. A. Imhof and others) to May 14 (1950, 18 birds, Gulf Shores, H. M. Stevenson); most seen: winter, 1200+, February 28, 1959 (Dauphin Island, S. A. Gau-threaux and others) and 1100, December 27, 1958 (Mississippi Sound, T. A. Imhof and R. W. Skinner), spring, 815, April 13, 1957 (Spring Count, Mobile Bay Area).

BANDING. Of 32 banded cormorants recovered in Alabama, 19 were found on the Gulf Coast, 5 each in the Tennessee Valley and Lower Coastal Plain, and 3 in the Piedmont. For place of banding, see Map 5.

FAMILY ANHINGIDAE: DARTERS

Anhinga

Anhinga anhinga (Linnaeus)   [118]   (Plate 4, facing page 72)
OTHER NAMES: Water Turkey, Snake Bird, Darter

The Anhinga looks like a small, long-drawn-out cormorant. The adult male is black except for silvery patches on the wings. The female is brown-breasted, and young birds are almost entirely dark brown. The white-tipped tail when spread fanwise resembles that of a turkey. The Anhinga has such an extremely long, thin neck, and long tail, that it looks when soaring in the air like a flying cross. In the water, it often swims with just its head and snake-like neck visible.

ANHINGA NEST. This bird chose to build eight feet high in a cypress tree on the Tombigbee River north of Demopolis in June 1955.

This bird is an uncommon to fairly common, breeding summer resident in swamps, lakes, and ponds of the Coastal Plain, and rarely in the Tennessee Valley. In small numbers it winters in the big delta swamp above Mobile.

NESTING. The Anhinga breeds in small, often loose colonies, by itself, or in heronries. The nest is a bulky one built of sticks and sometimes decorated with Spanish moss and fresh leaves. It rests from 10 to 45 feet up in a bush or tree, perhaps a cypress, tupelo gum, or buttonbush, hanging over water in swamps or sloughs. The two to five elongated eggs are bluish to dark greenish-white with a chalky deposit.

FOOD. This bird varies its diet of mullet, sunfish, catfish, suckers, and pickerel with crawfish, crabs, shrimp, aquatic insects, tadpoles, water snakes, and small terrapins. It captures all these by underwater pursuit.

DISTRIBUTION. The Anhinga breeds from Sinaloa to Ecuador and from Texas, Arkansas, Tennessee, and North Carolina south to northern Argentina. In winter it withdraws slightly to the southward from northern portions of this area.

[78]

OCCURRENCE IN ALABAMA. (March 9 to October 19, winters locally.) *Tennessee Valley*: April 27 (1950, Wheeler Refuge, Gordon Cole, W. E. Jernigan, and others) to September 6 (1957, Wheeler Refuge, D. C. Hulse). *Mountain Region*: No record. *Piedmont*: No record. *Upper Coastal Plain*: March 9 (1956, Demopolis Lake, W. W. Beshears and T. A. Imhof) to mid-August 1936 (Bellamy, T. Z. Atkeson, Jr.); also February 16, 1957 (Marion, Lois McCollough); most seen, 55+, June 16, 1955 (Demopolis Lake, J. E. Keeler and W. W. Besh-

ears). *Lower Coastal Plain*: March 23 (1957), Choctaw Bluff, M. W. Gaillard) to October 23 (1957, Jackson, W. U. Harris); also January 11, 1958 (Hal's Lake, Clarke Co., T. A. Imhof, W. U. Harris, and J. R. Davis); most seen, 12, May 25, 1956 (McIntosh, W. F. Colin and T. A. Imhof). *Gulf Coast*: Permanent resident in the delta swamp above Mobile, but rarely seen south of that city except in summer in heronries near Fairhope.

TIME OF BREEDING. Data on 45+ nestings: Eggs, April 27 to June 16; dependent young, June 16 to July 27.

FAMILY FREGATIDAE: FRIGATE-BIRDS

Magnificent Frigate-bird

Fregata magnificens Mathews [128]   (Plate 4, facing page 72)

OTHER NAMES: Man-o'-war-bird, Frigate Pelican, Pirate Bird

This frigate-bird resembles an overgrown swallow. Although it is almost as long as a pelican, the long wings, long forked tail, and light body give it a buoyancy that permits it to float high over the sea on motionless wings for long periods of time. The male is black with a concealed red throat pouch, the female has a white breast, and the immature bird, a white head and belly.

The Magnificent Frigate-bird is a common to abundant non-breeding summer visitor on the outer islands and peninsulas of the Alabama Gulf Coast. Usually it can be spotted soaring high in the sky over the Gulf or over the outer beaches. An onshore breeze may bring large numbers shoreward and if strong enough may even carry a rare individual inland.

NESTING AND FOOD. This species nests in colonies on tropical islands, usually in February, and lays one to three plain white eggs in a small, crude, stick nest wedged in a bush or low tree. It eats various kinds of marine life snatched from the surface of the sea or from other seabirds. It can swoop down on another bird which is carrying food and after several attempts, force it to drop or disgorge its burden, whereupon the frigate-bird scoops up the food before it hits the water. Scraps of fish thrown from fishing vessels are also a part of its diet.

DISTRIBUTION. The Magnificent Frigate-bird breeds along the coast from Lower California to Ecuador, from the Bahamas to Brazil, and from the Cape Verde Islands to Gambia. After an early breeding season, it occurs coastally in the United States north to Oregon on the Pacific and to North Carolina on the Atlantic.

OCCURRENCE IN ALABAMA. (April 19 to December 5.) *Tennessee Valley*: No record. *Mountain Region*: No record. *Piedmont*: No record. *Upper Coastal Plain*: 1905 or 1906 (1 found dead after a severe storm, Prattville, L. S. Golsan and E. G. Holt). *Lower Coastal Plain*: No record. *Gulf Coast*: April 15 (1961, Dauphin Island, Ava Tabor and others) to December 5 (1951, Fort Morgan, J. E. Keeler); most seen, 300, July 26, 1930 (near Petit Bois Island, Helen Edwards).

ORDER CICONIIFORMES: HERONS, STORKS, IBISES, FLAMINGOS, AND ALLIES

Birds of this order have long bills, long legs, long, broad, rounded wings, and usually bare lores. They feed in marshes and other wet areas on all manner of aquatic animals. They often nest together in large colonies, choosing trees or bushes over water or the sand or mud of an inaccessible island, and they fly long distances to and from roosts or nesting colonies and their favorite feeding grounds.

FAMILY ARDEIDAE: HERONS, BITTERNS, AND ALLIES

Herons have long, powerful, sword-like bills, and in flight they tuck their necks in, thus bringing their heavy bills and their center of gravity closer to their wings. In Alabama, these birds are commonly called cranes, but cranes, ibises, and storks fly with their necks extended. Herons and bitterns are also distinguished from others of their order by the presence of a pecten or comb-like process on the middle toe. These birds fish for their prey with expert, lightning-quick thrusts of their bills. Their eggs are pale blue or pale green.

SUBFAMILY ARDEINAE: HERONS

Herons are largely bluish or white birds which fly with a slow beat of their arched, rounded wings.

Great Blue Heron
Ardea herodias Linnaeus   [194]   (Plate 5, facing page 88)
OTHER NAMES: Blue Crane, Big Blue Crane, Long Tom

An overall *blue-gray* color, with some *white* on the *head,* together with its *four-foot length,* should make the Great Blue Heron easy to identify. Its call is unpleasantly raucous.

This species occurs over a more widespread area in Alabama than any other heron, but in summer it is often outnumbered in a particular locality by the

Little Blue Heron. The Great Blue Heron is usually found throughout the year near its breeding colonies, and these, so far as is known, are in the Tennessee Valley and the Coastal Plain. Outside the breeding season it may be found in a great number of salt and fresh water habitats throughout the state, but it is uncommon in the eastern half of the Lower Coastal Plain. It is common on migration and in winter in the Mountain Region and the Piedmont, where it frequents lakes and ponds and roosts in tall pines that are common along their banks.

NESTING. Frequently this heron nests in colonies of from four to several hundred pairs, often with other herons, on the shore of a pond or river, or in a swamp. Its nest is bulky, and built of twigs high in a tall tree—a pine or tupelo gum, for instance. It lays three to six greenish-blue eggs.

FOOD. The Great Blue Heron varies its fish diet with frogs, crawfish, small snakes, salamanders, other water animals, and even grasshoppers and mice.

DISTRIBUTION. This heron breeds from Alaska and southern Quebec south to Mexico, the West Indies, and also in the Galapagos Islands. It winters from British Columbia, the Ohio Valley, and Massachusetts south to Colombia and Venezuela.

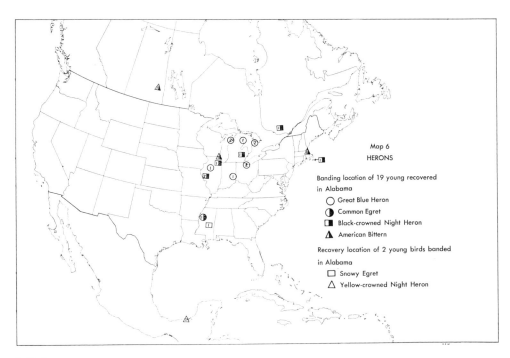

Map 6
HERONS

Banding location of 19 young recovered in Alabama

○ Great Blue Heron
◑ Common Egret
◧ Black-crowned Night Heron
▲ American Bittern

Recovery location of 2 young birds banded in Alabama

□ Snowy Egret
△ Yellow-crowned Night Heron

OCCURRENCE IN ALABAMA. (Throughout the year.) *Tennessee Valley*: Permanent resident; most seen, 250 pairs breeding, May 1948 (Wheeler Refuge, *fide* T. Z. Atkeson, Jr.), winter, 90, November 22, 1952 (Wheeler Refuge, T. A. Imhof). *Mountain Region*: July 29 (1950, Birmingham, T. A. Imhof) to May 12 (1937, Birmingham, H. M. Stevenson); also June 24, 1949(Birmingham, T. A. Imhof); most seen, 9, November 3, 1954 (Birmingham, T. A. Imhof). *Piedmont*: August 20 (1953, Auburn, W. F. Helms) to April 30 (1955, Auburn, H. G. Good and T. A. Imhof). *Upper Coastal Plain*: Permanent resident. *Lower Coastal Plain*:

Permanent resident. *Gulf Coast*: Permanent resident; most seen, 100 pairs breeding, May 1943 (Navy Cove, M. W. Gaillard).

TIME OF BREEDING. Data on over 300 nestings in 8 colonies; Building, late January to April; eggs, mid-March to May 20; dependent young, mid-April to June 16.

BANDING. Of 9 birds recovered in Alabama, 1 was 9 years old. (See Map 6 for place of banding.) Five of these birds were recovered in the Mountain Region, 2 in the Tennessee Valley, and 1 each in the Piedmont and on the Gulf Coast.

Green Heron

Butorides virescens (Linnaeus) [201] (Plate 5, facing page 88)

OTHER NAMES: Indian Hen, Shy Poke, Fly-up-the-creek

The Green Heron is a dark greenish-blue, crow-sized bird with chestnut neck and yellowish-green to orange legs. In flight it resembles a crow because it looks dark at a distance, but the heron has a longer neck and bill, and slower, more arched wing beats. When alarmed it raises a ragged crest and utters a loud cry.

This bird is a common, breeding, summer resident throughout Alabama, not as numerous as many other herons but more widely distributed. It finds suitable almost all the wetter areas frequented by other herons and also many smaller ponds, streams, and marshes. In general it is a solitary bird and is most active in early morning and late evening.

NESTING. Usually the Green Heron nests alone, but occasionally several pairs may breed near each other. The nest is a small, loosely-made, twig platform resting in the uppermost branches of a small tree which either hangs over water or is not far from it. It holds three to five pale greenish eggs.

FOOD. The Green Heron eats fish, frogs, crawfish, salamanders, spiders, water insects, and other small water animals.

DISTRIBUTION. This species breeds from Washington, Minnesota, and Nova Scotia south to Colombia and the West Indies. It winters north to Washington, the northern Gulf Coast, and South Carolina.

OCCURRENCE IN ALABAMA. (March 14 to November 20.) *Tennessee Valley*: March 30 (1890, Leighton, F. W. McCormack) to September 20 (Leighton, F. W. McCormack); also November 14, 1953 (Wheeler Refuge, T. A. Imhof) and No-

YOUNG GREEN HERONS. A typical pose when startled.

vember 20, 1947 (Wheeler Refuge, H. H. Grammer); most seen, 34, June 19, 1953 (Wheeler Refuge, T. A. Imhof). *Mountain Region*: April 1 (1949, Birmingham, T. A. Imhof) to October 10 (1935, Birmingham, H. M. Stevenson); most seen, 10, August 9, 1947 (Lake Purdy, T. A. Imhof). *Piedmont*: March 31 (1936, Auburn, H. S. Peters and others) to at least August 10 (1952, Stroud, H. M. Stevenson). *Upper Coastal Plain*: March 14 (1958, Livingston, Jenkins Jackson) to October 9 (1954, Marion, Lois McCollough); most seen, 26+, night of September 16-17, 1957 (Marion, Lois McCollough).

Lower Coastal Plain: March 24 (1958, Camden, Lovett Williams) to October 15 (1956, Point A Lake, Covington Co., L. C. Crawford). *Gulf Coast*: March 22 (1958, Dauphin Island, S. A. Gauthreaux and others) to November 9 (1957, Dauphin Island, Ava Tabor and others); most seen, 50, April 15, 1961 (Dauphin Island, T. A. Imhof and others).

TIME OF BREEDING Data on 32 nestings: Building, May 12; eggs, April 25 to June 3; dependent young, May 7 to July 29.

Little Blue Heron

Florida caerulea (Linnaeus)   [200]   (Plate 5, facing page 88)

OTHER NAMES: Blue Crane, White Crane

The adult of this medium-sized wader is dark blue with a dark maroon neck, dark greenish legs, and a dark blue bill which is lighter at the base. The immature bird is white except for a little blue in the wing tips and the dark bill and legs. As it matures, more and more blue appears in its plumage, and an occasional bird looks mottled.

NEST OF GREEN HERON. Less gregarious than other herons, this species usually chooses an individual nesting site.

E. E. and L. E. Foote

CICONIIFORMES: ARDEIDAE: LITTLE BLUE HERON

In Alabama the Little Blue Heron is a common to abundant, breeding, summer resident in the Coastal Plain and Tennessee Valley. (See Map 7.) In late summer and fall it occurs commonly throughout the state and is then the most abundant and widespread heron. It winters in small numbers on the coast and occasionally farther north in the Coastal Plain.

NESTING. This heron nests, usually with other herons, in large colonies on lake shores, in swamps, or on islands. The typical heron twig nest may be high in a tree or in a low bush over water, with two to four bluish-green eggs.

FOOD. According to information based on four birds collected in Alabama, the Little Blue Heron eats crawfish, small frogs, small fish, dragonflies, and spiders. This conforms to field observations both in Alabama and elsewhere.

DISTRIBUTION. This bird breeds from northern Mexico, Tennessee, and Massachusetts south to Peru and the West Indies. In late summer and fall, many birds, most of them young, wander north as far as southern Canada. It winters from coastal North Carolina and Texas southward.

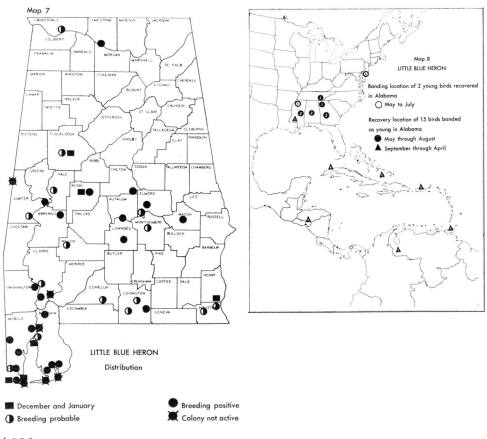

Map 7

LITTLE BLUE HERON
Distribution

■ December and January
◑ Breeding probable
● Breeding positive
✦ Colony not active

Map 8
LITTLE BLUE HERON

Banding location of 2 young birds recovered in Alabama
○ May to July

Recovery location of 15 birds banded as young in Alabama
● May through August
▲ September through April

[86]

LITTLE BLUE HERON COLONY.   Like most members of the Heron family, the Little Blue Heron is a colony nester.

NEST OF LITTLE BLUE HERON.   Unlike the bluish adults, the young birds are white.

PLATE 5

CATTLE EGRET
Adult, Sexes Similar
Page 89

CATTLE EGRET
Immature
Page 89

BLACK-CROWNED NIGHT HERON
Adult, Sexes Alike
Page 95

BLACK-CROWNED NIGHT HERON
Immature
Page 95

LITTLE BLUE HERON
Adult, Sexes Alike
Page 84

YELLOW-CROWNED NIGHT HERON
Adult, Sexes Alike
Page 98

LITTLE BLUE HERON
Immature
Page 84

YELLOW-CROWNED NIGHT HERON
Immature
Page 98

GREAT BLUE HERON
Adult, Sexes Alike
Page 81

COMMON EGRET
Adult, Sexes Alike
Page 92

GREEN HERON
Adult, Sexes Alike
Page 83

SNOWY EGRET
Adult, Sexes Alike
Page 93

REDDISH EGRET
Adult, Sexes Alike
Page 91

LOUISIANA HERON
Adult, Sexes Alike
Page 94

Richard A. Parks

OCCURRENCE IN ALABAMA. (Throughout the year.) *Tennessee Valley*: March 27 (1952, Wheeler Refuge, D. C. Hulse) to October 10 (1949, Wheeler Refuge, D. C. Hulse); most seen, 800, July 1951 (Southern Limestone Co., D. C. Hulse). *Mountain Region*: June 25 (1953 Birmingham, T. A. Imhof) to October 24 (1936, Easonville, St. Clair Co., H. M. Stevenson); also April 13, 1955 (Birmingham, *fide* Emmy Brownlie) and April 25, 1947 (Birmingham, T. A. Imhof); most seen, 35, August 9, 1947 (Lake Purdy, T. A. Imhof). *Piedmont*: April 1 (1953, Auburn, H. G. Good) to September 12 (1950, Hatchet Creek, Coosa Co., T. A. Imhof and L. C. Fievet). *Upper Coastal Plain*: March 9 (1956, Demopolis, T. A. Imhof and W. W. Beshears) to first week in December (Hayneville, J. M. Rice); also January 26, 1958 (3 birds, Marion, Ellen Heine);

wintered at Tuscaloosa, 1954-55 (R. L. Chermock); most seen, 600 pair, June 1955 (Hayneville, J. M. Rice and T. A. Imhof). *Lower Coastal Plain*: February 25 (1955, Open Pond, Covington Co., T. A. Imhof) to late November (Columbia, T. Z. Atkeson, Jr.); occasionally winters. *Gulf Coast*: Common, March 6 (1932, Fairhope, Homer Flagg) to November 2 (1958, Dauphin Island, R. W. Skinner and Lovett Williams); most seen, winter, 20, December 31, 1960 (Christmas Count, Mobile).

TIME OF BREEDING. Data on about 1850 nests in 18 colonies: Building, March to April 13; eggs, April 9 to July 2; dependent young, May 22 to July 30.

BANDING. See Map 8 for place of banding of 2 birds recovered in Alabama and place of recovery of 15 birds banded at Tuskegee by J. L. Dusi.

Cattle Egret
Bubulcus ibis Linnaeus   [200.1]   (Plate 5, facing page 88)

A newcomer to the Americas, the Cattle Egret is smaller and stockier than the Snowy Egret, and has heavy jowls unique in its family. It has little of the lankiness that is characteristic of most of our herons. The breeding *adult* wears *buffy tufts* on its *crown, back,* and *throat,* and these become quite pale in winter. Except for these tufts, and for the *yellowish bill* and *dark greenish-brown legs* (almost black at a distance) this species is white. Thus, the bill and leg pattern is much like that of the Common Egret. The Cattle Egret likes to feed among grazing cattle, a preference it shares with the immature Little Blue Heron and the Snowy Egret. The Cattle Egret's small size and its stockiness make it distinct from its companions, and once picked out, it can be identified by the field marks.

The Cattle Egret is at present (1961) a transient in Alabama, uncommon on the Gulf Coast and casual to rare inland in the Coastal Plain and Tennessee Valley. Evidence points to its probable breeding in Baldwin County and in Houston County near Dothan. (See Map 9.) Though it most often feeds in pastures among grazing cattle, it may also feed among other animals, usually hoofed ones, or on salt marshes, along roadsides, or in any grassy area—commonly drier ones than those frequented by other herons.

NESTING. The nest and eggs of the Cattle Egret are similar to those of other small herons. It usually breeds in colonies of other egrets and herons.

[89]

CICONIIFORMES: ARDEIDAE: CATTLE EGRET

FOOD. This bird feeds extensively on insects stirred up by large grazing animals, and on their ticks. Items from Alabama specimens include grasshoppers, crickets, beetles, earwigs, and slugs. This diet is supplemented by aquatic animals, such as fish and frogs, obtained from marshes and ponds in the usual heron manner.

DISTRIBUTION. The Cattle Egret is an Old World species, first noted in the Western Hemisphere in Surinam, South America, between 1877 and 1882. About 1950 it invaded the eastern United States via Florida, and since 1957, at least, has been noted north along the Atlantic Coast to Nova Scotia (breeding to New Jersey) and along the Gulf Coast to Texas (breeding). It winters from the northern Gulf Coast southward.

OCCURRENCE IN ALABAMA. (April 6 to November 8.) *Tennessee Valley*: April 12 and 13, 1961 (3 adults, Decatur, C. M. Parker, L. E. Nebrig, and others). *Mountain Region*: No record. *Piedmont*: No record. *Upper Coastal Plain*: May 12 to June 2, 1961 (1 bird, Prattville, *fide* J. E. Keeler). *Lower Coastal Plain*: July 6, 1960 (16 adults) and May 30, 1961 (18 adults near a heronry, Pansey, Houston Co., J. E. Keeler). *Gulf Coast*: Over 25 records as of 1961; April 6 (1960, Delchamps, Mobile Co., J. L. Dorn) to November 8 (1957, specimen in Univ. of Ala. collection, J. E. Keeler); probably breeds in Baldwin Co. at Josephine (May 29, 1958, 2 adults, J. E. Keeler) and near Tensaw (15 to 20 birds throughout the first half of June 1960, D. W. Walters).

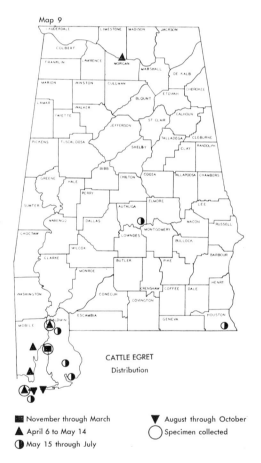

CATTLE EGRET

Distribution

■ November through March
▲ April 6 to May 14
◗ May 15 through July
▼ August through October
◯ Specimen collected

Reddish Egret

Dichromanassa rufescens (Gmelin)   [198]   (Plate 5, facing page 88)

This bird has two color phases as do the Screech Owl and a few other native birds. One phase is all white, and the other, more common, is dark blue-gray with a reddish-brown head and neck. In either phase it may be recognized by the *pale pinkish base* of the *dark bill*. It is slightly larger than the Little Blue Heron and closely resembles it in color pattern, even to the dark greenish-blue legs and dark-tipped bill. But the Reddish Egret has a very *shaggy head* and *neck,* a *pale cast* to the *primaries,* and *most unusual feeding antics,* which serve to identify it. When chasing fish in shallows, it dances, acts drunk, staggers, stops short, partly opens its wings, and goes through many another odd motion. Because the immature bird has an almost black bill and feet, and rarely shows the white at the base of the bill, it must be identified by the other field marks.

On the Gulf Coast, the Reddish Egret is fairly common on migration, and it occasionally lingers into winter. Inland, it has been noted only once in late summer in the Coastal Plain. It is not known to breed anywhere in the state. This heron is most common on the bay side of the outer islands and peninsulas and is less common as one goes east. It prefers to stay near salt water, and it feeds in shallow bays or on mudflats with shorebirds.

NESTING AND FOOD. This species builds a substantial nest of twigs lined with smaller twigs on the ground or close to it. It chooses colonies on coastal islands and lays three or four pale blue-green eggs. Small salt-water animals such as fish, crustaceans, and the like probably constitute the bill of fare. But beyond the fact that the main item in its diet is fish, little is definitely known of its food.

DISTRIBUTION. The Reddish Egret breeds from Lower California, coastal Texas, Louisiana, and southern Florida south to Sinaloa, Yucatan, Jamaica, and Hispaniola. After the breeding season it wanders to the northern Gulf Coast and northern Florida, and in winter, south to Venezuela.

OCCURRENCE IN ALABAMA. (Normal: March 17 to April 21 and July 16 to December 28; Out-of-season: June 2.) *Tennessee Valley*: No record. *Mountain Region*: No record. *Piedmont*: No record. *Upper Coastal Plain*: August 13, 1955 (farm pond 25 miles south of Montgomery, L. E. Goodnight). *Lower Coastal Plain*: No record. *Gulf Coast*: March 17 (1956, Dauphin Island, R. L. Chermock) to April 21 (1956, Dauphin Island, T. A. Imhof) and July 16 (1960, Dauphin Island, D. C. Holliman) to December 28 (1958, Dauphin Island, R. W. Skinner and others, and 1959, Cochrane Causeway, J. L. Dorn); also June 2, 1961 (a white-phased bird, Dauphin Island, J. E. Keeler); most seen, 5, several dates in July, August, and September, Dauphin Island.

Common Egret

Casmerodius albus (Linnaeus)   [196]   (Plate 5, facing page 88)
OTHER NAMES: American Egret, Egret, White Crane

The plumage of this beautiful bird is entirely white, but it has a bright *yellow bill* and *jet black legs* and looks like a slightly smaller, white version of the Great Blue Heron.

The Common Egret is a common to abundant, breeding, summer resident in the Coastal Plain and Tennessee Valley. It winters regularly on the Gulf Coast and locally inland near its breeding places. In the Mountain Region and Piedmont it is a common summer visitor and transient. The species inhabits the same marshes and swamps as does the Great Blue Heron and in late summer and fall visits ponds and lakes in Alabama.

Thanks to rigorous protective measures, this handsome heron is once more a part of the scene in southern swamps. When the fad for wild bird plumes in women's hats was rampant, this species was reduced drastically. The plumes most in demand were the aigrettes worn by herons only in the breeding season. Many adults were killed on the nest and the young left to die. About 1913 legislation was passed which forbade this traffic. The species has made a remarkable recovery and now is even extending its range northward. There is a new threat to its increase today, however, in the destruction of swamps.

NESTING. The Common Egret nests in colonies, often with the Great Blue Heron or the Little Blue Heron. It places its rather bulky nest of twigs high in tall trees standing in swamps, or in low bushes on inaccessible islands. It lays three to five bluish-green eggs. In 1924, when Arthur Howell wrote *Birds of Alabama,* no species of egret was known to nest in the state.

FOOD. Besides small fish, this heron eats frogs, lizards, mice, moles, insects, small water snakes, and even pond-lily seeds. Like other large herons, it feeds by standing still in or near the water and waiting for its prey to swim by.

DISTRIBUTION. The Common Egret breeds from Oregon, southern Minnesota, northern Ohio, and southern New Jersey south to Patagonia. In summer it wanders north to southern Canada and Newfoundland and in winter retires to the Gulf states, the Carolinas, and southward. The northern limit for all seasons is steadily advancing.

OCCURRENCE IN ALABAMA. (Throughout the year.) *Tennessee Valley*: March 8 (1958, Wheeler Refuge, J. H. Heflin) to November 29 (1949, Wheeler Refuge, E. A. Byford); 1 or more winter about every other year; most seen: breeding, 200+ pair, 1950 (Wheeler Refuge, T. Z. Atkeson, Jr.); winter, 30, January 1957 (Wheeler Refuge, *fide* T. Z. Atkeson, Jr.). *Mountain Region*: March 20 (1955, Birmingham, Adele West) to April 28 (1956, Leesburg, Cherokee Co., Edith Clark) and June 22 (1950, Birmingham, T. A. Imhof) to September 27 (1949, Birmingham, T. A. Imhof); also June 4, 1954 (Fort Payne, Ala. Orn. Soc.) and June 5, 1954 (White Plains, Calhoun Co., H. M. Stevenson and T. A. Imhof); most seen, 10, August 15, 1948 (Birmingham, T. A. Imhof). *Piedmont*: July 24 (1936, Auburn, F. S. Barkalow) to August 10 (1952, Stroud, H. M. Stevenson). *Upper Coastal Plain*: March 9 (1957, Marion, Lois McCollough) to November 27 (1956, Montgomery, J. E.

Keeler); frequent in winter; most seen, 500, September 18, 1956 (Demopolis Lake, W. W. Beshears). *Lower Coastal Plain*: Permanent resident; common, March 22 (1957, Clarke Co., T. A. Imhof) to November 5 (1959, Jackson, T. A. Imhof and F. B. Daniel). *Gulf Coast*: Permanent resident; most seen, fall, 114, October 6, 1956 (Fall Count, Mobile Bay Area); winter, 100, December 31, 1960 (Christmas Count, Mobile).

TIME OF BREEDING. Data on 500+ nestings in 6 colonies: Building, late March; eggs, April 9; young in nest, late April to early August.

BANDING. See Map 6.

Snowy Egret

Leucophoyx thula (Molina) [197] (Plate 5, facing page 88)
OTHER NAMES: White Crane, Little White Crane, Crazy Crane

The Snowy Egret is a rather small heron, *pure white* with a *black bill, black legs, and yellow feet* ("golden slippers"). It has yellow lores and a much shaggier crest than other white herons. The young Snowy Egret shows a yellow line running up the back of its dusky legs. This bird moves about considerably when feeding and constantly shuffles its feet and stirs up the mud to scare out its prey. This movement indicates the species, for the Common Egret is a "still" fisherman which waits for its prey to come within reach.

This bird is a common, breeding, summer resident in some parts of the Coastal Plain and the Tennessee Valley. In the rest of the state it is rare to common as a summer visitor or migrant. On the coast it is widespread and numerous and generally concentrates in winter at the head of Mobile Bay. It frequents the same places as does the Common Egret, but the smaller bird is more southerly and coastal in distribution.

NESTING. The Snowy Egret often joins colonies of other herons for breeding, especially near the coast. It builds a small nest of twigs, usually in low bushes in swamps or on islands, and lays two to five pale bluish-green eggs.

FOOD. It feeds actively in shallow waters on small fish and other small water animals, and on grass insects in pastures, where it associates as closely with cattle as does the Cattle Egret.

DISTRIBUTION. The Snowy Egret breeds from California, Idaho, Oklahoma, the Gulf states, and southern New Jersey south to Chile and Argentina. In late summer it wanders north to southern Canada and in winter occurs north to southern California, the northern Gulf Coast, and coastal North Carolina.

[93]

OCCURRENCE IN ALABAMA. (Throughout the year.) *Tennessee Valley*: April 9 (1951, Wheeler Refuge, J. H. Sutherlin and E. A. Byford) to September 12 (1949, Wheeler Refuge, J. H. Heflin); also November 1943 (Wheeler Refuge, Ernest Holland); most seen: Breeding, 15 adults, May 22, 1959 (southern Limestone Co., T. A. Imhof, D. C. Hulse, and R. W. Skinner); fall, 13, August 29, 1949 (Wheeler Refuge, T. A. Imhof). *Mountain Region*: April 19 (1957, Birmingham, Idalene Snead and Emmy Brownlie) and July 31 (1948, Birmingham, T. A. Imhof) to September 20 (1960, Birmingham, Harriett Wright). *Piedmont*: June 16, 1953 (Beauregard, Lee Co., W. F. Helms). *Upper Coastal Plain*: May (Tuscaloosa, R. L. Chermock) to late November (Hayneville, J. M. Rice); most seen, 25, September 18, 1956 (Demopolis Lake, W. W. Beshears). *Lower Coastal Plain*: March 1 (Columbia, T. Z. Atkeson, Jr.) to at least September 21 (1957, Geneva Co., T. A. Imhof and Lovett Williams). *Gulf Coast*: Permanent resident; most seen: fall, 36, September 23, 1955 (Dauphin Island, T. A. Imhof and W. W. Beshears); winter, 95, December 28, 1956 (Cochrane Causeway, T. A. Imhof, Rosemary Gaymer, and Clustie McTyeire) and 93, January 15, 1956 (Cochrane Causeway, C. S. Robbins).

TIME OF BREEDING. Data on about 115 nestings in 6 colonies: Eggs, May 3 to 22; dependent young, May 22 to June 27.

BANDING. See Map 6.

Louisiana Heron

Hydranassa tricolor (Muller)   [199]   (Plate 5, facing page 88)

OTHER NAME: Tri-colored Heron

The lanky Louisiana Heron is about the size of the Little Blue Heron. It is *dark purplish above* with reddish neck and clear *white, sharply-defined belly* and rump. The immature bird shows much reddish-brown on the head, neck, and wings.

On the Gulf Coast, particularly in Mobile County, this species is a fairly common summer resident. It also winters in small numbers, especially near its breeding colonies. Inland, in the Coastal Plain, it is a rare breeder and a rare summer visitor, and it has been recorded only once in the Tennessee Valley. It prefers coastal waters, particularly the marshes and shallows.

NESTING. On the coast it nests in colonies by itself or with the Snowy Egret, but scattered pairs are apt to breed in colonies of other herons, especially inland. Most colonies are on coastal islands where the nest of sticks, usually holding two to four bluish-green eggs, is built in high-tide bushes, in other shrubs and low trees, or on the ground in tall reeds.

FOOD. The Louisiana Heron eats many small water animals—small fish, insects, worms, slugs, snails, leeches, tadpoles, lizards, small shrimp, and even dragonflies.

DISTRIBUTION. This species breeds from Lower California, the Gulf states, and southern New Jersey south to Ecuador and Brazil. Young birds wander in late summer north to California, Indiana, and southern New York, and casually even farther. A few remain to winter as far north as they breed, but most retire south of the United States.

OCCURRENCE IN ALABAMA. (Throughout the year.) *Tennessee Valley*: May 21, 1948 (Russellville, E. O. Willis). *Mountain Region*: No record. *Piedmont*: No record. *Upper Coastal Plain*: Mid-April to fall, breeds rarely (Autaugaville, L. S. Golsan); mid-May 1956 (Marion, R. Jones); July 13, 1957 (Demopolis, T. A. Imhof and others). *Lower Coastal Plain*: May 22 (1943, Choctaw Bluff, M. W. Gaillard) to late summer (Jackson, W. U. Harris and G. A. Carleton, and Columbia, T. Z. Atkeson, Jr.). *Gulf Coast*: Permanent resident; common, April 7 (1959, Dauphin Island, Owen Davies) to November 16 (1915, Grand Bay, Mobile Co., A. H. Howell); most seen: Breeding, 80+, June 27, 1958 (Cat Island, T. A. Imhof, H. C. Loesch, and J. C. Gray), winter, 19, December 27, 1958 (Christmas Count, Dauphin Island).

TIME OF BREEDING. Data on 55+ nestings in 5 colonies: Eggs, May 22 to June 27; dependent young, June 17 to July 30.

Black-crowned Night Heron

Nycticorax nycticorax (Linnaeus) [202] (Plate 5, facing page 88)
OTHER NAME: Quok

Night herons are stockier than most other herons. The Black-crowned Night Heron is *black* on the *top* of the *head* and *back, gray-blue* on the *wings,* and clear *white* below, with a black bill and yellow legs. The *young* bird is *brown,* heavily *streaked below* and *spotted above.* It can be distinguished from the American Bittern by its slower, more flapping flight and lack of dark wing tips, and from the Yellow-crowned Night Heron by the larger, *coarser spotting, more brownish color,* and *shorter legs* which show only the toes beyond the tail in flight. Once the adult is well known, identifying the immature night heron is simpler than it sounds, for this bird utters a flat call, the "quok" which gives it its common name. The sound is heard frequently at night near coastal marshes.

On the Gulf Coast, the Black-crowned Night Heron is a locally common permanent resident which formerly bred on Dauphin Island, and probably still breeds at the head of Mobile Bay and near Mississippi Sound. Inland, it is uncommon, but well distributed on migration, and it breeds and winters rarely. It feeds actively in salt marshes and on the borders of large bodies of water. For roosting and nesting it chooses a variety of trees but especially likes cedars and other evergreens. This night heron can feed at any hour, but it usually prefers to eat at night and then spend the day in its roost.

NESTING. Elsewhere the species usually nests in large, almost pure colonies, but in Alabama it breeds in small numbers by itself or with other herons. The nest, loosely made of twigs, contains three to six pale sea-green

[95]

[96]

D. Hulse

eggs, and is placed in trees, in bushes, or upon rare occasions on the ground, generally many miles from the feeding grounds.

FOOD. The main food of this night heron is fish, but it also eats crawfish, shrimp, crabs, frogs, tadpoles, lizards, mice, and grasshoppers and other insects.

DISTRIBUTION. In the Western Hemisphere the Black-crowned Night Heron breeds from Washington and Quebec south locally to Patagonia, and it winters from Oregon, Texas, Alabama, and Massachusetts southward.

Map 10

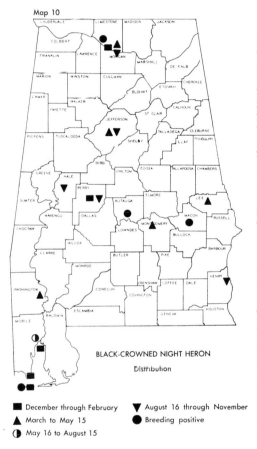

BLACK-CROWNED NIGHT HERON

Distribution

■ December through February
▲ March to May 15
◑ May 16 to August 15
▼ August 16 through November
● Breeding positive

OCCURRENCE IN ALABAMA. (Throughout the year.) *Tennessee Valley*: Permanent resident; most seen, breeding, 10, May 22, 1959 (Southern Limestone Co., T. A. Imhof, D. C. Hulse, and R. W. Skinner). *Mountain Region*: March 12 (1957, Birmingham, T. A. Imhof) to May 2 (1949, Birmingham, T. A. Imhof) and July 31 (1948, Birmingham, T. A. Imhof) to October 26 (1949, 7 birds, Birmingham, T. A. Imhof). *Piedmont*: April 18 and June 21, 1952 (Auburn, J. L. Dusi) and April 28, 1936 (H. S. Peters). *Upper Coastal Plain*: March 25 (1958, Autauga Co., R. W. Skinner) to April 1 (1959, Montgomery, R. W. Skinner); bred in Autauga Co. in 1911; September 6 (1886, Greensboro, W. C. Avery) to September 13 (1956, Marion, T. A. Imhof); winters at Marion (Lois McCollough and T. A. Imhof). *Lower Coastal Plain*: May 25, 1956 (McIntosh, T. A. Imhof and W. F. Colin); August 8, 1954 (Columbia, Henry Co., T. Z. Atkeson, Sr.); date unknown (Jackson, W. U. Harris). *Gulf Coast*: Permanent resident; common, July 30 (1959, Dauphin Island, H. M. Stevenson) to April 26 (1958, 4 birds, Spring Count, Mobile Bay Area); most seen, 34, October 6, 1956 (Fall Count, Mobile Bay Area).

TIME OF BREEDING. Data on 8 nestings: Eggs, Limestone Co., 5 nests, May 22, 1959 (T. A. Imhof, D. C. Hulse, and R. W. Skinner); Autauga Co., nest, April 23, 1911 (L. S. Golsan); Macon Co., nest, date unknown (J. L. Dusi); Mobile Co., nests, date unknown prior to 1955 (J. L. Dorn).

BANDING. Six of these night herons banded as nestlings have been recovered during the period September 18 to May 18 in Alabama: 1 in the Tennessee Valley, 3 in the Mountain Region, and 2 in the Lower Coastal Plain. One of them was 14 years old. For place of banding, see Map 6.

NEST OF YELLOW-CROWNED NIGHT HERON. Occasionally these herons nest in colonies with other herons.

Yellow-crowned Night Heron

Nyctanassa violacea (Linnaeus)   [203]   (Plate 5, facing page 88)
OTHER NAMES: Gros-bec, Quak

Although it is much like the Black-crowned Night Heron, this species can be distinguished by its shorter, heavier bill, and *longer legs*—so much longer that when the bird is in flight they show beyond the tail. The *adult* is *purplish-gray* with a *black head* marked with *yellowish-white crown* and *cheeks.* The *immature* bird differs from immatures of the black-crowned species in being more *slaty-brown* and more *finely spotted.* The call of this bird is pitched higher than that of the other night heron.

In Alabama Yellow-crowned Night Herons are fairly common summer residents, becoming more local north of the Coastal Plain, but nevertheless breeding in small groups in the Tennessee Valley. A few winter in the state, usually near their breeding places, both inland and on the coast. (See Map 11.) The species generally frequents the same haunts as other herons, but isolated pairs often

[98]

occur in timbered river bottoms where other herons are scarce. Few birds breed within thirty miles of the coast, but the species is common there in late summer and fall.

NESTING. In this state this species breeds in single pairs or in small or large groups by themselves, and also in small and large numbers in colonies of other herons. They build a nest of loosely-bound twigs which is fairly sturdy for a heron nest and frequently line it with Spanish moss. They may place it in a bush over water or high in a tall tree in bottomlands. In Alabama a clutch consists of three to six dull bluish eggs.

FOOD. Besides fish, the diet consists of crabs, snails, crawfish, mussels, small mammals, lizards, and snakes.

DISTRIBUTION. This night heron breeds from Lower California, Kansas, the Ohio Valley, and Massachusetts south to Peru and Brazil. It wanders northward after the breeding season and winters from Lower California, the northern Gulf Coast, and South Carolina southward.

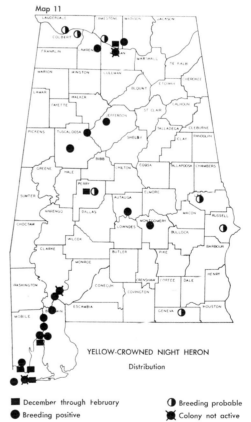

Map 11

YELLOW-CROWNED NIGHT HERON

Distribution

■ December through February
● Breeding positive
◑ Breeding probable
✶ Colony not active

OCCURRENCE IN ALABAMA. (Throughout the year.) *Tennessee Valley*: March 20 (1902, Leighton, F. W. McCormack) to at least August 9 (1941, Wheeler Refuge, T. Z. Atkeson, Jr.); also December 8, 1949 (1 adult, Wheeler Refuge, H. H. Grammer); most seen, 25, April 8, 1960 (Triana, Madison Co., W. M. Depreast and T. Z. Atkeson, Jr.). *Mountain Region*: April 5 (1949, Short Creek, Jefferson Co., T. A. Imhof) to September 23 (1954, 5 birds, Birmingham, T. A. Imhof). *Piedmont*: May 18, 1954 (2 birds, Auburn, H. G. Good). *Upper Coastal Plain*: March 16 (1951, 2 birds, Catoma Creek, Montgomery Co., C. W. Summerour) to November 1 (1956, Marion, Lois McCollough); also January 20, 1955 (Marion, Lois McCollough); most seen, 8, July 3, 1956 (Autaugaville, J. E. Keeler). *Lower Coastal Plain*: March 16 (1959, Camden, Lovett Williams) to October 13 (1949, Andalusia, W. R. Middleton); most seen, 75 pairs breeding, June 1956 (Choctaw Bluff, M. W. Gaillard). *Gulf Coast*: Permanent resident; common, March 17 (1957, 400 birds, Tensaw, R. W. Skinner) to November 7 (1959, Dauphin Island, J. L. Dorn and others); young of year reach coast, June 27; most seen, fall, 26, October 6, 1956 (Fall Count, Mobile Bay Area).

TIME OF BREEDING. Data on 88+ nestings: Eggs, April 5 to May 20;

dependent young, May 12 to July 13; flying by June 20.

BANDING. One bird banded as a nestling at Wheeler Refuge June 23, 1940 was recovered at Ciudad del Carmen, Campeche, Mexico, October 20, 1940; see Map 6.

SUBFAMILY BOTAURINAE: BITTERNS

These birds differ from other herons in that they are largely brownish, perch in trees only rarely, and are solitary in habit. Bitterns live in marshes and when threatened with discovery they point their bills upward and remain motionless, thus resembling a reed. For this reason they are called "sungazers" in Alabama.

Least Bittern

Ixobrychus exilis (Gmelin)   [191]   (Plate 15, facing page 216)
OTHER NAME: Sungazer

This miniature bird is the brighter-colored of Alabama's two bitterns. It has a *black back* and *crown* and *large, buffy wing patches,* and is whitish beneath. Usually it flushes close at hand, flies weakly over the marsh, and drops quickly in again. Because of this habit and its size, it is frequently mistaken for a rail. But the Least Bittern has a heron flight and shape, rarely dangles its legs,

NEST OF LEAST BITTERN.   Usually located in reeds one to three feet from the water, the nest is a compact platform of plant stems.

E. E. and L. E. Foote

and is apt to perch high on reeds. Its call is low and soft, somewhat like that of a cuckoo but not as prolonged.

In Alabama, the Least Bittern is a common, breeding, summer resident in fresh and salt marshes. It is abundant on the coast in fresh marshes, but inland, where its distribution is limited by lack of suitable marshes, it is much more rare. In winter, it has been recorded only once on the coast. The Least Bittern tries to remain out of sight, and is therefore often overlooked.

NESTING. This bird builds a compact platform of reeds or other marsh grasses, often over a loose foundation of small twigs, and lays three to six pale blue eggs in it. The nest is placed close to or directly over water. The Least Bittern is a close sitter, and will often allow an intruder to approach very near the nest, or even to step on it when the nest is low in thick grass. Where nesting habitat is limited, several pairs sometimes build close to each other.

FOOD. Its food consists of small fish, snails, frogs, tadpoles, small shrews, mice, insects, and lizards.

DISTRIBUTION. The Least Bittern breeds from Oregon, Minnesota, and New Brunswick south to Paraguay and Brazil. It winters from California, coastal Texas, and central Florida southward.

OCCURRENCE IN ALABAMA. (Normal: March 29 to November 1. Out-of-season: December 31.) *Tennessee Valley*: April 20 (1951, Wheeler Refuge, D. C. Hulse) to October 4 (1952, Wheeler Refuge, D. C. Hulse). *Mountain Region*: April 3 (1957, Fairfield, T. A. Imhof) to August 23 (1957, Fairfield, T. A. Imhof); most seen, 5, April 12, 1957 and June 20, 1955 (Fairfield, T. A. Imhof). *Piedmont*: Spring 1928 (Auburn, W. A. Rosene). *Upper Coastal Plain*: May 1 (1956, Marion, Lois McCollough) to August 8 (1957, Lowndes Co., J. E. Keeler). *Lower Coastal Plain*: Late March 1936 (Columbia, T. Z. Atkeson, Jr.); August 21, 1956 (specimen in Dept. of Conservation collection, Barbour Co., J. E. Keeler); September 10, 1941 (remains found in stomach of fox, Butler Co., Sam Sellers). *Gulf Coast*: March 29 (1952, Bear Point, H. M. Stevenson) to November 1 (1958, Cochrane Causeway, Lois McCollough, R. W. Skinner, and Lynn Green); also December 31, 1960 (Cochrane Causeway, J. L. Dorn and M. W. Gaillard); most seen, 15, April 21, 1956 (Spring Count, Mobile Bay Area).

TIME OF BREEDING. Data on 10 nestings: Eggs, May 16 to July; dependent young, June 9 to July 17.

American Bittern
Botaurus lentiginosus (Rackett)   [190]   (Plate 15, facing page 216)
OTHER NAME: Sungazer

The American Bittern is a streaked brown heron with a *black whisker mark* and a clear buffy throat. Its flight is more rapid than that of most herons, and its wings are not arched. Its *dark wing tips* set it apart from the brownish immature night herons. During the mating season this bittern has an odd call which resembles the noise made by driving a stake into the ground.

This bird is fairly common throughout Alabama on migration and uncommon in winter, occurring mostly on the coast. It is not known to breed in this state. Inland on migration it may be found in various wet locales—grassy pond borders and flooded fields, for example. On the coast it frequents both salt and fresh marshes.

NESTING AND FOOD. This bittern lays three to five brownish eggs in a nest of rushes in the marsh. It eats crawfish, lizards, frogs, snakes, small fish, spiders, and large insects.

DISTRIBUTION. The American Bittern breeds from British Columbia and northern Ontario south to southern California, the Ohio Valley, and New Jersey (and less frequently in the southeastern United States). It winters from British Columbia, the Ohio Valley, and Delaware south to Panama and Puerto Rico.

OCCURRENCE IN ALABAMA. (July 16 to May 28.) *Tennessee Valley*: March 15 (1943, Wheeler Refuge, H. H. Grammer) to May 24, 1961 (Wheeler Refuge, H. H. Grammer); July 30 (Wheeler Refuge, *fide* T. Z. Atkeson, Jr.) to November 24 (1952, Wheeler Refuge, L. S. Givens and others); also February 6, 1951 (1 dead bird, Wheeler Refuge, E. L. Humphries). *Mountain Region*: March 9 (1952, Birmingham, T. A. Imhof) to May 5 (1955, Fairfield, T. A. Imhof); also October 4, 1955 (Fairfield, T. A. Imhof). *Piedmont*: March 27 (1953, Auburn, H. G. Good) to May 18 (1954, Auburn, H. G. Good); also July 16, 1936 (specimen, Auburn, H. S. Swingle). *Upper Coastal Plain*: March 28 (1891, specimen in Avery collection, Uniontown, W. C. Avery; 1958, Livingston, Jenkins Jackson; and 1959, 1 dead on road,

Lowndes Co., J. E. Keeler) to May 28 (Autaugaville, L. S. Golsan); August 26 (1946, Marion, T. A. Imhof) to November 15 (1911, specimen in U. S. National Museum, Barachias, E. G. Holt); also January 31, 1939 (Booth, Autauga Co., L. S. Golsan). *Lower Coastal Plain*: March 24, 1958 (Camden, Lovett Williams); April 11, 1912 (specimen in U.S. National Museum, Thomasville, E. G. Holt); October 16, 1948 (Columbia, T. Z. Atkeson, Sr.). *Gulf Coast*: August 26 (1911, Bayou La Batre, J. S. Gutsell) to May 1 (1954, Gulf Shores, T. A. Imhof).

BANDING. Three birds have been recovered in Alabama: Coosa Co., December 26, 1955; Opp, April 11, 1938; and Goodwater, April 4, 1944. For place of banding, see Map 6.

FAMILY CICONIIDAE: STORKS AND WOOD IBISES

SUBFAMILY MYCTERIINAE: WOOD IBISES

Wood Ibis
Mycteria americana Linnaeus   [188]   (Plate 6, facing page 96)
OTHER NAMES: Gourdhead, Wood Stork

This great white bird is almost as tall as the Great Blue Heron and is heavier.

It has a *naked, dark brown head,* and its wings show extensive black areas, including the trailing edge. It flies with its neck outstretched and often soars at a great height. Its manner of flight and its shape set it apart from the White Pelican and white herons, and the size, naked head, and partly naked neck, and *large, black wing patches* distinguish it from the White Ibis. The young bird is duller, and the head and neck are partially feathered, but it is easily recognized.

The Wood Ibis is fairly common in the Coastal Plain of Alabama in summer and fall, and farther north it is rare to uncommon, occurring mostly in the Tennessee Valley. (See Map 12.) In Alabama the species chooses wet places. In swamps it often perches in dead treetops or soars high overhead for long periods of time. It forages in shallow ponds, on the shores of deeper fresh water, in river bottom sloughs, and sometimes on marshes or wet meadows. Thus far it has not been recorded in this state near salt or brackish water, nor has it been known to breed here.

NESTING. Many hundreds of Wood Ibises nest together in south Florida, and they also nest farther north, but in smaller numbers. The nests are built high in the trees and consist of rather bulky platforms of sticks, to which the birds add each year. The females lay two or three, sometimes five, white eggs which are regularly stolen by Fish Crows.

FOOD. These birds feed by stirring up the bottom of shallow ponds, forcing aquatic animals to the surface, and then spearing them. Young alligators, fish, frogs, and other water animals are the main items of food.

DISTRIBUTION. Wood Ibises are resident from Sonora, coastal Texas, and South Carolina south to Argentina and Peru. In summer and fall they wander north regularly to California, Arizona, and Tennessee, and irregularly even to southern Canada.

OCCURRENCE IN ALABAMA. (Normal: May 25 to November 1; Out-of-season: February 8 and March 16.) *Tennessee Valley*: June 27 (1955, Wheeler Refuge, E. A. Byford) to October 15 (1951, Wheeler Refuge, E. A. Byford and others); most seen, 32, July and August 1955 (Wheeler Refuge, *fide* T. Z. Atkeson, Jr.). *Mountain Region*: July 24, 1935 (Lake Purdy near Birmingham, H. M. Stevenson); about September 24, 1959 (Easonville, St. Clair Co., Ralph Allen). *Piedmont*: No record. *Upper Coastal Plain*: June 12 (1956, 40 to 50 birds, Demopolis Lake, W. W. Beshears) to November 1 (1956, flock of 10, Marion, Lois McCollough); most seen, 100, September 18, 1956 (Demopolis Lake, W. W. Beshears). *Lower Coastal Plain*: May 25 (1956, 18 birds, McIntosh, T. A. Imhof and W. F. Colin) to October 19 (1956, 9 birds, Andalusia, T. A. Imhof and L. C. Crawford); also March 16, 1958 (Jackson, W. U. Harris); most seen, 22, October 17, 1957 (Shipp's Pond, Covington Co., L. C. Crawford). *Gulf Coast*: May 26 (1956, 7 birds, Mt. Vernon, T. A. Imhof and W. F. Colin) to at least June 27 (1957, Tensaw, R. W. Skinner); also February 8, 1959 (Bridge Creek Reservoir, J. L. Dorn).

BANDING. A bird banded as a nestling at Cape Sable, Fla., March 17, 1938 was found wounded at Little River, Baldwin Co., July 20, 1938.

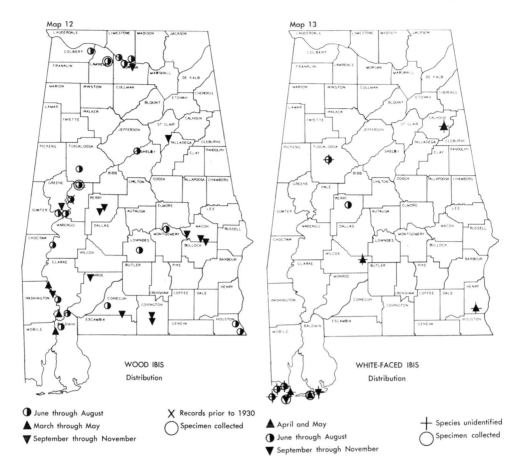

Map 12

WOOD IBIS
Distribution

◐ June through August   X Records prior to 1930
▲ March through May   ○ Specimen collected
▼ September through November

Map 13

WHITE-FACED IBIS
Distribution

▲ April and May   ✝ Species unidentified
◐ June through August   ○ Specimen collected
▼ September through November

FAMILY THRESKIORNITHIDAE: IBISES AND SPOONBILLS

These waders lack the sword-like bills and nuptial plumes of the herons. With these exceptions, they look very much like herons on the ground, and they feed in the same places. In flight, however, ibises and spoonbills extend their necks and fly on rapidly-beating wings, usually in long, irregular lines either tandem or abreast. They frequently soar between strokes.

SUBFAMILY THRESKIORNITHINAE: IBISES

The bills of these birds are narrow and curved downward.

[104]

White-faced Ibis

Plegadis chihi (Vieillot)   [187]   (Plate 6, facing page 96)
OTHER NAMES: Black Curlew, Glossy Ibis

Adult White-faced Ibises are dark throughout, iridescent, largely coppery-brown and green, and in winter the head and neck become streaked dark brown on gray. Immature birds have the streaked head and neck of the winter adult, but the back is iridescent green. *Adults* and *young* look *wholly dark at a distance* at all seasons, and the adult is a bit smaller than the White Ibis. The bare face has a white border going behind the eye, which usually distinguishes breeding adults of this ibis from those of the more eastern Glossy Ibis. But all immature and many adult White-faced Ibises lack the white face. Thus, separation of the two forms in the field is usually impossible.

In Alabama, dark ibises are rare visitors in the Coastal Plain and occur most often in summer and near salt water. They are not known to breed here. (See Map 13.) These birds frequent marshes, mudflats, and the shores of large bodies of water, usually in small numbers by themselves but occasionally in larger flocks of White Ibises or herons.

NESTING AND FOOD. The nest is a loose platform of sticks in shrubs or small trees usually within ten feet of the water. Sometimes the species breeds in small numbers in colonies of herons or other ibises; at other times, in large, pure colonies. The female lays three or four pale bluish-green eggs. Aquatic animals constitute the major food, including crawfish, other crustaceans, water insects, earthworms, frogs, small snakes, grasshoppers, and leeches.

DISTRIBUTION. The White-faced Ibis breeds from Oregon and Nebraska south, excluding Central America, to Chile and Argentina, and east to Louisiana and rarely Florida. After the breeding season it wanders casually north to British Columbia, North Dakota, and New York, and regularly east to Alabama. It winters north to California, Arizona, and Louisiana, and in Central America.

OCCURRENCE IN ALABAMA. (April 18 to November 6; all records of the genus *Plegadis* are included for the sake of completeness, but only the 3 records mentioned in the Note below definitely refer to the present species.) *Tennessee Valley*: No record. *Mountain Region*: April 21, 1961 (1 adult at close range, White Plains, Calhoun Co., R. W. Skinner and J. E. Keeler). *Piedmont*: No record. *Upper Coastal Plain*: Frequent in summer with White Ibis (Tuscaloosa R. L. Chermock and B. C. Williams); summer of 1956 (definite adult White-faced Ibis, Marion, R. Snow). *Lower Coastal Plain*: April 29, 1952 (Furman, Wilcox Co., J. E. Keeler); May 9, 1958 (Headland, Henry Co., T. A. Imhof). *Gulf Coast*: April 18 (1959, Dauphin Island, H. A. J. Evans) to November 6 (1948, Gulf Shores, F. M. Weston and M. W. Gaillard).

NOTE. Two specimens, one in the L. S. U. collection (May 30, 1956, Gulf Shores, B. L. Monroe, Jr.) and one in the Univ. of Ala. collection (October 5, 1956, Dauphin Island, T. A. Imhof and Lois McCollough) are both *Plegadis chihi*. Among over a dozen sight records, only one reports white behind the eye (summer 1956, Marion, R. Snow). These three are the only positive records of the species in Alabama. No specimens of the Glossy Ibis (*Plegadis falcinellus*) are known from Alabama, but the geographic position of this state makes the occurrence of this form highly possible. Except for adult White-faced Ibises showing the white border running behind the eye, identification of dark ibises (genus *Plegadis*) in the field in Alabama is highly risky and not recommended.

White Ibis

Eudocimus albus (Linnaeus)   [184]   (Plate 6, facing page 96)

OTHER NAMES: White Curlew, Spanish Curlew, Pond Guinea, Bec-croche (Hook-bill)

This almost all *white* bird has red legs, red face, and a long, *down-curved red bill*. In flight, its *black-tipped wings,* rapid wing beat, frequent sailing, and outstretched neck make it simple to identify. On the ground, it resembles a heron, but it flies much like a large shorebird and often in close formation. The brown immature bird is often mistaken for a curlew because of the down-curved bill. But the young White Ibis has a rather *sharply-defined white belly* and *rump* and much red at the base of the bill which is zoned with brown and dull yellow.

A NESTING WHITE IBIS. At this stage of its life this bird is brown streaked with white.

J. L. Dusi

Like herons, this bird frequents swamps, marshes, and pond shores. In Alabama it breeds locally in swamps south of the Black Belt, and in summer and fall spreads out over most of the Coastal Plain and sometimes north to the Tennessee Valley. It has been noted in winter on the coast. (See Map 14.) It is common, or sometimes locally abundant, in the Coastal Plain, particularly on the coast and in the larger river valleys. Above the Fall Line it is rare to uncommon.

NESTING. Ordinarily large numbers of this bird nest together, but occasionally small numbers nest in heron colonies. The compact stick nests are often close together in low bushes or small trees over water. There are three to five pale grayish-blue eggs with brown, yellow, and rufous spots. Although Fish Crows eat many of these eggs, female ibises continue to lay until young hatch successfully.

FOOD. White Ibises eat small water animals including mammals, reptiles, insects, fish, and crustaceans. One specimen from Alabama had a stomach full of maggots of tabanid (blood-sucking) flies.

DISTRIBUTION. White Ibises breed from Lower California, Texas, and North Carolina south to Peru, Venezuela, and the West Indies. They winter north to central Mexico, Louisiana, and Florida, and wander casually north in late summer to California, South Dakota, and southern New England.

ADULT WHITE IBISES IN NESTING COLONY. In this rookery on an island in Southfield Lake, Baldwin County, nestlings are banded.

J. E. Keeler

OCCURRENCE IN ALABAMA.
(Normal: February 8 to November 11; Out-

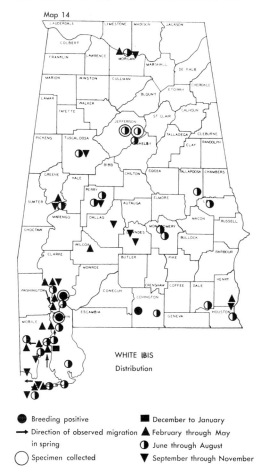

Map 14

WHITE IBIS
Distribution

● Breeding positive
➡ Direction of observed migration in spring
◯ Specimen collected
■ December to January
▲ February through May
◐ June through August
▼ September through November

of-season: December 31.) *Tennessee Valley*: June 26 (1951, Wheeler Refuge, E. A. Byford and L. S. Givens) to September 18 (1951, Wheeler Refuge, E. Collier, E. L. Humphries, and T. Z. Atkeson, Jr.); also April 17, 1951 (Wheeler Refuge, *fide* T. Z. Atkeson, Jr.) and May 7, 1957 (2 adults, Wheeler Refuge, D. C. Hulse). *Mountain Region*: June 30, 1951 (10 immature birds, Birmingham, F. B. Daniel, M. H. Perry, and Mims Williamson); summer of 1951 (immature specimen, C. L. Christy); July 28, 1960 (immature specimen found dead, J. B. Sullivan). *Piedmont*: June 22, 1950 (specimen, Auburn, Malcolm Johnson); July 12, 1951 (immature specimen in Auburn collection, Camp Hill, F. W. Fitch). *Upper Coastal Plain*: April 30 (1956, 150 birds, Demopolis Lake, W. W. Beshears) to second week in October (1953 and 1954, Hayneville, J. M. Rice). *Lower Coastal Plain*: March 25 (1958, Camden, Lovett Williams) to November 11 (1957, 4 birds, Jackson, W. U. Harris); most seen, 500+, June 31, 1956 (Choctaw Bluff, Elwood Overstreet). *Gulf Coast*: February 8 (1959, Bridge Creek Reservoir, J. L. Dorn) to November 7 (1959, Dauphin Island, J. C. and Margaret Robinson); also December 31, 1960 (15 birds, Cochrane Causeway, Paul Feldhaus); most seen, 10,000, summer of 1956 (Tensaw, Perry Prescott and others).

TIME OF BREEDING. Data on over 5200 nests in 4 colonies: Eggs, May 22 to July 22; young of all ages, May 22 to July 22.

BANDING. For place of recovery of 31 birds banded as nestlings in northern Baldwin Co., by J. E. Keeler and others, see Map 15.

[Scarlet Ibis]
Eudocimus ruber (Linnaeus)   [185]

Since the plumage of the Scarlet Ibis is brown when the bird is immature, it closely resembles the immature White Ibis. Its bill is dissimilar, being a solid dull yellow without the dark gray banding, and this and its paler crown may possibly distinguish it. But as the White Ibis approaches maturity, this banding disappears from its bill also. The Scarlet Ibis is slightly smaller than the White Ibis, and the adult bird, of course, has *brilliant scarlet plumage.*

This species was formerly accidental in Alabama. It is doubtful that new definite sight records will be obtained because the immature birds, which are the great wanderers, are virtually impossible to distinguish from immature White Ibises.

NESTING AND FOOD. This ibis nests in deltaic islands of mangroves and other shrubs, or in plains flooded during the rainy season. It builds a nest similar to that of the White Ibis but lays only two eggs. The food includes crustaceans, mollusks, fish, and other small water animals.

DISTRIBUTION. The Scarlet Ibis breeds from Venezuela to southeastern Brazil and wanders to shores of the Caribbean Sea and accidentally to those of the Gulf of Mexico, including Florida, Texas, and Louisiana.

OCCURRENCE IN ALABAMA. This species is included in the Alabama list on the basis of Thomas Nuttall's statement (*Manual of Ornithology, the Water Birds,* 1834:84-85) that "they migrate in the course of the summer (about July and August) into Florida, Alabama, Georgia, and South Carolina."

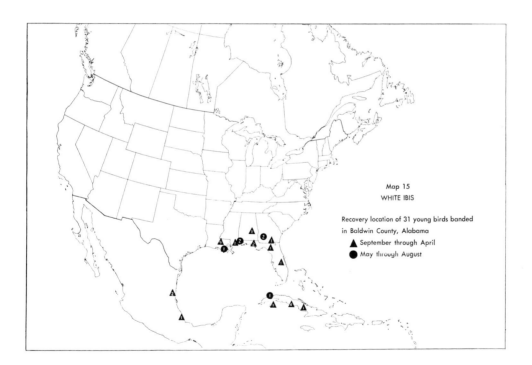

Map 15
WHITE IBIS

Recovery location of 31 young birds banded in Baldwin County, Alabama

▲ September through April
● May through August

SUBFAMILY PLATALEINAE: SPOONBILLS

Roseate Spoonbill

Ajaia ajaja (Linnaeus)   [183]   (Plate 6, facing page 96)
OTHER NAME: Pink

The Roseate Spoonbill has the look of a prehistoric curiosity. The greenish, spoon-shaped bill and naked brownish head are incongruous on the white body with its red legs and rosy-pink wings and under parts. In flight and actions this bird resembles an ibis, and it usually associates with ibises. The young bird is whiter than the adult and has a yellow bill.

From 1865 to 1920 the Roseate Spoonbill was confined to small areas in Texas, Louisiana, and Florida and seemed doomed to extinction. Thanks to the National Audubon Society and more intelligent conservation attitudes, it is now increasing in numbers. In Alabama it is a casual visitor to the Gulf Coast, and there is one record of occurrence inland, but it is not known to nest here. Possibly with the gradual increase in numbers, the state will see it more often in the future.

NESTING AND FOOD. The Roseate Spoonbill often nests in ibis colonies in dense mangroves or cypress, where it lays three or four whitish, brown-spotted eggs on a platform of sticks. Young birds thrust their heads into the parents' mouths to receive food. Minnows and other small fish form the major part of the diet, but the bird also eats water insects, crustaceans, and occasionally mollusks and plants. It feeds in shallow water subject to little tidal action and swings its partly-opened bill from side to side, trapping small animals therein.

DISTRIBUTION. The Roseate Spoonbill breeds locally from northern Sinaloa, Texas, Louisiana, and southern Florida south through Mexico, Cuba, and the Bahamas to Argentina and Chile. It winters in the same area, and formerly ranged casually northward to Utah, southern Indiana, and Pennsylvania.

OCCURRENCE IN ALABAMA. (June 1, September 17 and 18 the only dated records.) *Tennessee Valley*: No record. *Mountain Region*: No record. *Piedmont*: No record. *Upper Coastal Plain*: September 17 and 18, 1958 (specimen in the Auburn Univ. collection, Montgomery, 18 miles southeast, Archie Hooper, J. E. Keeler, and J. L. Dusi). *Lower Coastal Plain*: No record. *Gulf Coast*: About 1897 (2 birds killed, Dauphin Island, Capt. W. M. Sprinkle); June 1, 1930 (specimen, probably now in Russia, Oliver Ladnier). Nuttall (1834) says, "They are also occasionally met with on the river shores of the Alabama, and in other parts of that state."

FAMILY PHOENICOPTERIDAE: FLAMINGOS

[American Flamingo]
Phoenicopterus ruber Linnaeus   [182]

The brilliant, reddish-pink American Flamingo is a lanky, crane-sized, black-winged wader. The neck and legs are fantastically long and thin, and the white and black bill is thick and bent downward to make feeding in shallow water easy. Immature birds are paler, almost white, as are birds kept in captivity, for apparently adults require certain seafoods to maintain their color.

NESTING AND FOOD. This flamingo breeds in large colonies on extensive, rarely disturbed, shallow, coastal mudflats. It lays a single chalky-white egg on a foot-high mound of mud. The adult feeds almost entirely on a small snail-like mollusk of the genus *Cerithium*, which is abundant in southern Florida.

DISTRIBUTION. The American Flamingo breeds in Yucatan, the Bahamas, the West Indies, the Galapagos Islands, and northern South America. It wanders rarely to southern Florida and accidentally to Texas and North Carolina.

OCCURRENCE IN ALABAMA. According to Audubon (1839, 5:256), "The western coast of Florida and some portions of that of Alabama in the neighborhood of Pensacola, are the parts to which they mostly resort." This is the only known basis for the inclusion of the American Flamingo on the Alabama list.

ORDER ANSERIFORMES: SCREAMERS, SWANS, GEESE, AND DUCKS

FAMILY ANATIDAE: SWANS, GEESE, AND DUCKS

This family includes all the birds we know as waterfowl: one subfamily of swans, another of geese, and five of ducks. All members of this family have webbed feet and a hooked bill that is either flat, with plate-like processes, or cylindrical, with saw-like processes. Other swimming birds are often called ducks, but true waterfowl generally have rather large heads, long necks, and well-developed tails, as well as the webbed feet and hooked bill.

Waterfowl occur on all bodies of water, from marshes to the ocean, but they are less frequent on rivers and streams and most frequent on ponds, lakes, and bays. Most of these birds breed in marshy areas in the north. The majority nest on the ground, but some choose tree cavities. The nest is lined with down from the breast of the female and the young can swim and dive almost as soon as hatched. Few waterfowl breed in Alabama, but scattered individuals of most species, very likely hunting season casualties, may summer in areas where the species is abundant in winter. Waterfowl winter in large flocks along the coasts, and inland where food is abundant, hunting pressure not too severe, and the water rarely freezes over. In Alabama the bulk of the waterfowl winter in the Tennessee Valley, on upper Mobile Bay, and on Mississippi Sound.

Waterfowl are probably our most important group of game birds. Most of them are edible, but sea ducks and fish-eating ducks are rarely tasty. They provide good sport because hunting them requires a knowledge of their habits and the ability to hit a fast-moving target. Unfortunately many of the marshes where these birds nest have been destroyed by the demand for additional cultivable land.

SUBFAMILY CYGNINAE: SWANS

Unlike other waterfowl these birds have bare lores and their necks are longer than their bodies. Because of their esthetic value, swans are not legal game, but Eskimos and certain northern Indians may hunt them because their meat is an important winter food.

[Mute Swan]
Cygnus olor (Gmelin)   [178.2]

The Mute Swan is all white and somewhat larger than the Whistling Swan. It *holds its neck in a graceful* S-*curve* with its *knobbed orange bill* pointed downward and its wings often arched over the back. The bird is usually silent.

A European species, the Mute Swan was introduced into the United States and now exists in the wild state from southern New England to New Jersey and in Ohio, West Virginia, and Pennsylvania.

NESTING. This bird builds a large nest of sticks, roots, and marsh vegetation near the shore of a pond and lays five to seven greenish-blue eggs.

FOOD. This bird feeds almost exclusively on underwater vegetation.

OCCURRENCE IN ALABAMA. Semi-captive birds occur throughout the year and occasionally nest on ponds near Fort Payne, Cullman, Birmingham, Oxford, Hayneville, Dothan, and Bellingrath Gardens.

TIME OF BREEDING. Data on 2 nestings: Eggs, April 26; dependent young, early June.

Whistling Swan
Olor columbianus (Ord)   [180]   (Plate 7, facing page 112)
OTHER NAME: Wild Swan

This beautiful all-white waterfowl is an unforgettable sight. The Whistling Swan holds its *neck straight* and *black bill horizontal,* and can thus be distinguished from the Mute Swan, which arches its neck and has a knobbed orange bill. Young birds are brownish on the head and neck but are otherwise like the adults. The larger size, longer neck, and lack of black wing tips set this swan apart from other large white water birds, especially the Snow Goose. The Whistling Swan has a cooing call vaguely suggesting the call of the Canada Goose but more musical and wilder-sounding. These swans call in flight like geese and during winter nights they keep up a constant musical cooing.

The Whistling Swan occurs in shallow, often brackish, water, on bays, estuaries, and larger ponds, especially where much underwater vegetation grows. In the Tennessee Valley of Alabama it is a rare transient which occasionally winters, and elsewhere in the state it is casual. It is not known to nest here.

NESTING AND FOOD. The female lays two to seven dull white eggs. Usually there are four or five in a huge nest of grasses, seaweeds, and moss on the tundra near water. It covers the eggs when leaving the nest so that they will be warm and concealed. Pairs of Whistling Swans remain mated for life and are said to be much attached to each other. The principal foods are foxtail grass and underwater plants such as wild celery, of which this bird eats roots, seeds, stems, and leaves. It feeds in shallow waters by submerging its long neck.

DISTRIBUTION. The Whistling Swan breeds mainly north of the Arctic Circle from Alaska and Baffin Island south to the Barren Grounds of Canada. It winters on the Pacific Coast from southern Alaska to Lower California, on the Atlantic Coast from Chesapeake Bay to Currituck Sound, rarely Maine to Florida, and rarely Michigan, Lake Erie, and the Gulf Coast from Texas to Florida.

OCCURRENCE IN ALABAMA. (November 3 to March 25.) *Tennessee Valley*: November 3 (1957, Wheeler Refuge, C. M. Parker and others) to March 25 (1950, 4 birds, Wheeler Refuge, Clarence Cottam). *Mountain Region*: No record. *Piedmont*: No record. *Upper Coastal Plain*: No record. *Lower Coastal Plain*: February 1931 (2 birds, Columbia, Henry Co., T. Z. Atkeson, Jr. and Robert McKemie). *Gulf Coast*: Mississippi Sound, "rare winter resident," and Polecat Bay near Mobile, early December, 1916 (*fide* A. H. Howell).

NOTE. Although no specimen of this species is known from Alabama, Chester R. Markley of the U. S. Fish and Wildlife Service has in his possession a roll of 16 mm. movie film taken with a telephoto lens of 2 swans observed at Wheeler Refuge, November 16 and 17, 1942.

SUBFAMILY ANSERINAE: GEESE

Geese are larger and heavier than ducks and have longer necks. They are usually gray with much black and white, and the sexes are alike at all seasons. All local geese have white upper and under tail coverts. The feet of geese are set close enough to the center of the body so that they can feed on dry land, for example, in grain and stubble fields. In the water they tip up the body and submerge the foreparts to feed on underwater vegetation. They do not dive.

Geese are noisy in flight and string out in loose lines or V's. They look much like cormorants in the air, but the wing beat is slower. Geese frequent ponds and bays and graze on nearby fields, especially after dark.

Canada Goose
Branta canadensis (Linnaeus)   [172]   (Plate 7, facing page 112)
OTHER NAMES: Canadian Goose, Honker, Wild Goose

This big, gray goose with a white belly and *black head* and *neck* has a *white triangle* on the *cheeks.* Its call is a far-carrying honk heard often over Alabama on cold or overcast nights.

The Canada Goose is common on migration almost throughout Alabama, but especially in the Tennessee Valley and the eastern half of the state. The bird remains for the winter on the wider expanses of the Tennessee River, the area in which it is most abundant in this state. It also winters on smaller ponds and lakes, particularly in the Coosa, Tallapoosa, and Chattahoochee valleys, or wherever it is given sufficient protection and food. While Alabama is a thousand miles south of the breeding range, some half-wild birds do breed in the state, especially in the Tennessee Valley.

TVA reservoirs in the Tennessee Valley have great fluctuation in water level, partly as a malaria control measure, and so natural water plants are scarce. Waterfowl there must depend instead on grain left in fields and sown on dry

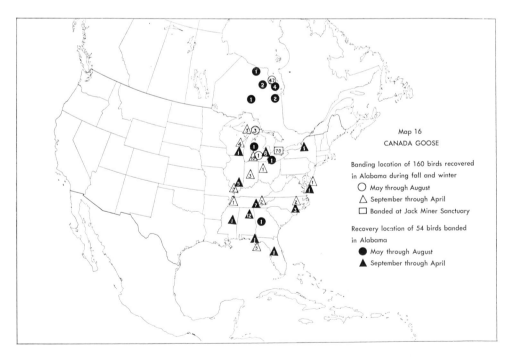

Map 16
CANADA GOOSE

Banding location of 160 birds recovered
in Alabama during fall and winter
○ May through August
△ September through April
☐ Banded at Jack Miner Sanctuary

Recovery location of 54 birds banded
in Alabama
● May through August
▲ September through April

sloughs in summer. Some species of waterfowl, notably Canada Geese, thrive on this program, which, according to population figures, is an admirable substitute for their natural food and cover.

NESTING. The female generally lays five or six dull white eggs in a fairly large mound which may be on the marsh or on an island in a lake. In certain areas of the northwest, it may select an abandoned eagle or osprey nest in a tree. The nest is made of grasses, reeds, and leaves and is lined with down. Pairs mate for life and families are said to remain together throughout the winter.

FOOD. This goose eats roots, stems, leaves, and seeds of a variety of water plants such as wild rice and sedges. It also eats waste grain from stubble fields, tender shoots of various grasses, and occasionally insects, crustaceans, and mollusks.

DISTRIBUTION. The Canada Goose breeds from Alaska and Labrador south to northern California, Kansas, and Massachusetts. It winters from southeastern Alaska, southern Ontario, and Nova Scotia south to Mexico and the Gulf states.

OCCURRENCE IN ALABAMA. (Mid-September to early April; summers in small numbers.) *Tennessee Valley*: Migration peaks at Wheeler Refuge, mid-September to early December and mid-February to early April; maximum there in winter, about 30,000; migration, 25,000, early October 1960 (*fide* T. Z. Atkeson, Jr.), summers almost annually and occasionally breeds; semi-wild descendants of captive birds breed at Stevenson. *Mountain Region*: September 13 (1952, flock of 7, Gadsden, Edith Clark) to March (Birmingham, numerous observers). *Piedmont*: October 10 (1950, Auburn, F. W. Fitch) to at least March 5 (1928, 50 birds, Auburn, J. M. Robertson); most seen, 150, November 16, 1953 (Tallapoosa River Management Area, W. B. Traylor). *Upper Coastal Plain*: October 11 (1957, Montgomery, J. E. Keeler) to April 11 (1958, Montgomery, R. W. Skinner). *Lower Coastal Plain*: October (Columbia, T. Z. Atkeson, Sr.) to April 6 (1954, Barbour County Lake, R. W. Thrasher). *Gulf Coast*: October 19 (1957, Cochrane Causeway, H. G. Loftin) to March 20 (1912, Bayou La Batre, *fide* A. H. Howell); most seen, many thousands, November 6-7, 1921 (Mobile, W. H. Hoffman).

TIME OF BREEDING. Data are available on 1 nesting: Full-grown young, June 29, 1953 (Swan Creek, J. H. Heflin).

BANDING. See Map 16.

[White-fronted Goose]
Anser albifrons (Scopoli) [171] (Plate 7, facing page 112)

The White-fronted Goose is a gray-brown bird similar in color and size to the immature Blue Goose, which is much more common in Alabama. The *adult* White-fronted Goose has a *pink bill,* a *white area* on the *front* of the *face,* a variable amount of *black barring* on the *belly,* and yellow or orange feet. When immature, the bird is dusky and has a *pale bill* and *feet,* whereas the immature Blue Goose has a dark bill and feet and white in the wing linings near the body. In Alabama, the White-fronted Goose should be identified with care and only at close range.

The White-fronted Goose is casual on migration in Alabama in the Tennessee Valley and on the Gulf Coast. It occurs in about the same places as does the Blue Goose, and of course it is not known to nest here.

NESTING AND FOOD. This bird lays four to seven creamy-white eggs in a shallow depression in the ground, usually on the tundra near a lake. The nest is lined with grass, feathers, and down. Like other geese, it feeds on underwater vegetation, on grain and sprouting grasses, and occasionally on insects and snails. Audubon says it also eats beechnuts, acorns, and snails in winter. In the far north it eats berries.

DISTRIBUTION. The White-fronted Goose breeds in a circumpolar belt from western Greenland eastward to Mackenzie. In this hemisphere it winters from southern British Columbia and southern Illinois south to southern Mexico and the northern Gulf Coast. It is casual east of the Mississippi Valley.

OCCURRENCE IN ALABAMA. (November; February 16 and 17; March 11 to 15; and March 17.) *Tennessee Valley*: February 16 and 17, 1961, an adult on headquarters lawn with a small flock of Canada Geese (Wheeler Refuge, W. M. Depreast, G. C. Bishop, and E. A. Byford) and March 11 to 15, 1942 (a flock of 27 birds, Wheeler Refuge, T. Z. Atkeson, Jr. and many others). *Mountain Region*: No record. *Piedmont*: No record. *Upper Coastal Plain*: No record. *Lower Coastal Plain*: No record. *Gulf Coast*: November 1953 (an adult shot at Coden, Eugene Collier) and March 17, 1960 (2 adults, Delchamps, J. L. Dorn).

Snow Goose
Chen hyperborea (Pallas)   [169]   (Plate 7, facing page 112)
OTHER NAMES: Wavy, White Wavy, White Brant

The Snow Goose is a medium-sized *white goose* with *black wing tips*. The young bird is duskier but still easy to recognize. The Snow, Blue, and White-fronted Geese are all about the same size, smaller than a Canada Goose. The Snow Goose has a high-pitched, honking call which is sometimes likened to the distant barking of a dog.

This goose is common on migration and fairly common in winter at Wheeler Refuge, but elsewhere in Alabama it is a rare transient except on the Gulf Coast, where it is fairly common in fall. It is not known to nest in the state. Usually it flocks with Blue Geese to such an extent that records of Snow Geese without Blue Geese in Alabama are almost unknown.

NESTING AND FOOD. The nest is on dry ground near the edge of a lake on the tundra and is composed of grasses, moss, and a lining of down. In it the Snow Goose lays anywhere from four to eight creamy-white eggs, the usual clutch being six. The bird eats waste grain, sprouting grasses (including rushes, sedges, and horsetail) and other aquatic vegetation, especially the bulbous roots.

DISTRIBUTION. The Snow Goose breeds on Arctic islands from northeastern Siberia to Greenland, particularly on Southampton, Baffin, and Ellesmere islands. It winters from southern British Columbia, southern Colorado, and southern Illinois south to central Mexico and the Gulf Coast from Mexico to Florida and also along the Atlantic Coast from Delaware to North Carolina and rarely in Korea and Japan. It migrates with the Blue Goose and sometimes with other geese, generally following the same route each year and usually making the same stopovers.

OCCURRENCE IN ALABAMA. (September 30 to April 28.) *Tennessee Valley*: Prior to 1937 a rare transient, 1937 to 1949 a common transient, since 1949 regular in winter at Wheeler Refuge; transients September 30 to mid-November and late February to April 28 (Wheeler Refuge, *fide* T. Z. Atkeson, Jr.); most seen in winter, 60, 1958-59 (*fide* T. Z. Atkeson, Jr.); fall, 200 (*fide* T. Z. Atkeson, Jr.); spring, 74, April 7, 1936 (Wheeler Reservoir, A. R. Cahn). This species makes up about 5% to 10% of the Blue-Snow flocks (T. Z. Atkeson, Jr.). *Mountain Region*: October 25, 1949 (2 birds, Fairfield, C. H. Winfield and T. A. Imhof); October 28, 1955 (4 birds, Bangor, Blount Co., T. A. Imhof); and late October 1955 (1 bird, Cardiff, Jefferson Co., Barto Country). *Piedmont*: No record. *Upper Coastal Plain*: Livingston, October 21 (1957, Jenkins Jackson) to November 13 (1958, Jenkins Jackson) and Montgomery, October 19, 1959 (4 birds, R. W. Skinner). *Lower Coastal Plain*: No record. *Gulf Coast*: October 13 (1960, Dauphin Island, J. C. Robinson and others) to November 11 (1931, Fairhope, Helen Edwards); also February 21, 1959 (Cochrane Causeway, F. M. Weston and A. M. McMillan); specimen in Dept. of Conservation, October 13, 1960 (Dauphin Island, R. W. Skinner).

Blue Goose

Chen caerulescens (Linnaeus) [169.1] (Plate 7, facing page 112)
OTHER NAMES: White-headed Goose, White-head, Wavy

The adult of this species is a handsomely-marked, medium-sized, *blue-gray* bird with a *white head* and *neck*. In this plumage it is easy to identify. But the young bird is *dusky*, with a *dusky head, dark bill* and *feet*, and wings which are lighter-colored than the body. From below it shows a tuft of white feathers where the wings join the body. Thus, the immature bird is not so readily recognizable. The call of the Blue Goose, like that of the Snow Goose with which it commonly flocks, is a high-pitched honk.

[119]

PLATE 8

MALLARD
Adult Male
Page 123

MALLARD
Adult Female
Page 123

PINTAIL
Adult Male
Page 131

MOTTLED DUCK
Adult, Sexes Alike
Page 127

FULVOUS TREE DUCK
Adult, Sexes Alike
Page 122

PINTAIL
Adult Female
Page 131

GADWALL
Adult Male
Page 130

GADWALL
Adult Female
Page 130

BLACK DUCK
Adult, Sexes Similar
Page 125

[120]

At one time rare in Alabama, the Blue Goose has increased considerably here since the impoundment of the Tennessee River lakes. On migration, especially in late October, it is now common to abundant in the Tennessee Valley, fairly common in the western half of the state, uncommon in the eastern half, and sometimes in fall abundant on the Gulf Coast. It winters commonly and regularly at Wheeler Refuge and sometimes in small numbers in the western half of Alabama. It is not known to nest in this state.

NESTING AND FOOD. The bulky tundra nest of shredded moss lined with grass and down usually holds three to five whitish eggs. This goose eats the roots and shoots of grasses—tundra grass in the far north and Johnson and flag grass in the south. At Wheeler Refuge it grazes on rye grass and waste grain. Where large numbers of geese dig out the roots of grasses, the ground looks as if it had been plowed. But the next year the grass reappears, so apparently no permanent damage is done.

DISTRIBUTION. The Blue Goose breeds on islands of the Arctic Ocean and nearby areas. It migrates through Hudson and James bays and the Mississippi Valley to winter on the Gulf coast of Texas and Louisiana, rarely to Mexico and Florida, and also on lakes in the lower Mississippi Valley, especially TVA reservoirs, and rarely on the Atlantic Coast from Maine to Georgia.

OCCURRENCE IN ALABAMA. (September 4 to May 8; summers rarely.) *Tennessee Valley*: Prior to 1937, 1 record near Muscle Shoals, 4 birds in May 1912 which remained to the 8th (F. R. King); since 1937, September 4 (1951, Wheeler Refuge, D. C. Hulse) to May 1 (1948, Wheeler Refuge, T. A. Imhof and others); began wintering in 1948-49; most seen, migration, 5000, fall 1945 (Wheeler Refuge, *fide* T. Z. Atkeson, Jr.), winter, 800, 1954-55 (E. A. Byford and C. M. Parker); (T. Z. Atkeson, Jr., 1954, *Wilson Bull.* 66:63-64). *Mountain Region*: October 15 (1956, Oak Mountain Public Lake, J. B. Owens) to April (1956, Gadsden, *fide* Edith Clark); 1958 (1 bird summered at Lake Mac, Talladega, T. A. Imhof and C. T. Hornady); most seen, 88, October 28, 1955 (Bangor, Blount Co., T. A. Imhof). *Piedmont*: October 23 (1948, Lake Martin, an adult female found dead, *fide* H. G. Good) to March 17 (1951, Lake Martin, another bird found dead, J. S. Dendy). *Upper Coastal Plain*: October 15 (1959, Marion, T. A. Imhof and A. J. Murphy) to April 15 (1955, Davis Lake, Montgomery Co., R. W. Thrasher); most seen, 750, October 20, 1959 (Montgomery, R. W. Skinner). *Lower Coastal Plain*: October 25 (1957, Jackson, W. U. Harris) to at least January 1957 (Florala, L. C. Crawford). *Gulf Coast*: October 7 (1956, Dauphin Island, J. L. Dorn and others) to April 21 (1956, Cochrane Causeway, H. M. Stevenson); most seen, 100,000+, November 15, 1956 (flying west all day over Mississippi Sound and the Gulf, numerous observers including M. W. Gaillard).

BANDING. One Wheeler-banded Blue Goose was captured in Missouri, and another banded in Louisiana in winter was shot on Mon Luis Isle, Mobile Co.

Fulvous Tree Duck

Dendrocygna bicolor (Vieillot) [178] (Plate 8, facing page 120)
OTHER NAME: Squealer

The Fulvous Tree Duck has very long legs and an erect stance. It is a rich *chestnut-brown* on the *head* and *under parts*. Separating the brown of the under parts from the dark brown of the back and wings is a *prominent white line* on the *flanks,* a white line made even more noticeable by the dark under surface of the wings. The duck's tail is black with white upper and under tail coverts and its bill and feet are dark. For a duck this bird has a very slow wing beat. Its call is a high-pitched, squealing whistle of two notes.

In Alabama the Fulvous Tree Duck is accidental in Gulf Coast marshes in the fall and is not known to nest here. It seldom inhabits trees, but prefers dense marshes, rice fields, and the like. It is active at night.

NESTING AND FOOD. The usual nest is a grassy basket set in dense marshy vegetation and holding about twelve creamy-white eggs. Occasionally there are as many as thirty eggs in one nest when several females lay together. This duck feeds mostly on dry land and prefers seeds, waste grain, and the foliage of grass and alfalfa.

DISTRIBUTION. The Fulvous Tree Duck breeds in coastal Louisiana and Texas, central California to central Mexico, South America, East Africa, and India, and it wanders to nearby areas outside of the breeding season.

OCCURRENCE IN ALABAMA. *Gulf Coast only*: November 7, 1956 (specimen in the Dept. of Conservation collection, Chuckfee Bay, Roy Gaisser).

SUBFAMILY ANATINAE: SURFACE-FEEDING DUCKS

All ducks in this subfamily (Tip-up, Pond, Puddle, or Marsh Ducks) feed by dabbling or tipping up as do geese and swans. They often feed in marshes and have developed the ability to spring directly into the air when taking flight. The drakes are brightly-colored and the females generally dull brownish, streaked birds. Both sexes have the same general wing pattern including the speculum of iridescent color on the trailing edge of the wing near the body, so that the female is usually easier to identify in flight. All of them have broad bills and well-developed tails which they hold clear of the water. They feed of necessity in very shallow water, but most of them can dive when hard pressed.

Since water plants are the staple diet of these ducks, they are better tasting than most diving ducks, which often eat water animals. Tip-up ducks are more at home on land because their legs are set closer to the center of their bodies. They prefer to feed at night or in cloudy weather, choosing marshes and similar spots, and then to spend the day dozing or preening on open water, on sand bars, or in another safe place.

Mallard

Anas platyrhynchos Linnaeus   [132]   (Plate 8, facing page 120)
OTHER NAMES: Mallard Duck, Green-head, English Duck

The Mallard, ancestor of our common barnyard duck, is easily recognized. The *drake* has a yellow bill, a glossy *green head* and neck, and a *reddish chest* separated from the neck by a *white ring*. The rest of the body is largely whitish or pale gray. The *female* is light *brown streaked* with dark brown but has a *dark-spotted orange bill* and a *whitish tail*. Both sexes have a *white-bordered blue speculum*.

The Mallard is Alabama's commonest tip-up duck. In suitable habitat it is abundant in winter and on migration, and on migration it is still common and widespread even in less favorable areas—deep lakes, for example. It remains here to breed in the Tennessee Valley (an estimated 25 pairs stay at Wheeler Refuge), and occasionally in a few scattered localities southward (possibly feral or injured birds). (See Map 17.) It frequents the shallower ponds, lakes, and rivers of all sizes, and also swamps, timbered bottomlands, and most marshes.

NESTING. The Mallard builds a nest of fine reeds, grass, or leaves lined with down in a clump of grass on the ground, and generally chooses a spot well hidden under shrubs and near water. The female lays from eight to ten light greenish-buff eggs.

FOOD. The edible parts of most fresh-water plants and many cereals form the bulk of the Mallard's food. The diet includes sour gum, grape, acorn, bayberry, and dogwood. This duck also eats most of the larger insects found around and in the water, as well as frogs, toads, small fish, mollusks, earthworms, crustaceans (especially crawfish), lizards, and other small animals, and occasionally even mice.

DISTRIBUTION. The Mallard breeds in the Western Hemisphere from Alaska and southern Ontario south to Lower California, southern New Mexico, and from the Mississippi-Ohio Valley east to Virginia. It breeds rarely in southeastern Canada and southeastern United States. It winters from the Aleutian Islands and southern Canada south to southern Mexico, Panama, and the Lesser Antilles.

OCCURRENCE IN ALABAMA. (Throughout the year.) *Tennessee Valley*: Abundant, October to March, peak Wheeler Refuge winter population, 30,000 to 50,000 (*fide* T. Z. Atkeson, Jr.); population of the whole valley often estimated at over 90,000 (state and federal game personnel). *Mountain Region*: October 15 (1952, Blount Co., Loggins) to March 29 (1959, Piedmont, Maxie gins) to March 29 (1959, Piedmont, Maxie

Swindell); also September 15, 1955 (Legarde Lake, Cherokee Co., E. L. Humphries); most seen, 240, December 27, 1942 (Lake Purdy, M. F. Prather). *Piedmont*: October 1 (1952, Lake Martin, W. T. Meadows and J. R. Beam) to March 29 (1954, Auburn, D. W. Speake); most seen, 2000, December 1, 1952 (Opelika City Lake, Ellis). *Upper Coastal Plain*: October 1 (1952, Tombigbee River, Pickens Co., H. A. Speed) to April 7 (1935, Fitzpatrick, Bullock Co., R. W. Thrasher); also May 26, 1957 (Livingston, Jenkins Jackson); May 27, 1954 (Aliceville, F. X. Lueth and H. A. Speed); and June 1, 1956 (Marion, Lois McCollough); breeds rarely in Elmore Co., and Montgomery Co. (numerous sources); most seen, 3000, January 15, 1953 (Tombigbee River, Pickens Co., H. A. Speed). *Lower Coastal Plain*: October 1 (1952, Geneva, Gramble and Chattahoochee State Park, Hughes) to March 15 (1953, Washington Co., Newsom); also April 19, 1958 (Alabama River Cutoff, Clarke Co., T. A. Imhof, J. R. Davis, and W. U. Harris) and June 8, 1954 (a pair, Comer Lake, Barbour Co., R. W. Thrasher); most seen, 350, February 1, 1953 (Salt Springs Sanctuary, Clarke Co., H. L. Dykes). *Gulf Coast*: October 20 (1952, Mobile Delta, W. F. Colin) to April 12 (1957, Dauphin Island, J. L. Dorn and T. A. Imhof); most seen, 8900, November 17, 1952 (Mobile Delta, W. F. Colin); several records from April to October for the outer islands and peninsulas are possibly referable to the Mottled Duck.

TIME OF BREEDING. Data on about 50 nestings: Eggs, early April to May 20; small young, April to early July.

BANDING. Of 161 banded Mallards reported from Alabama, 28 were banded in Alabama at Wheeler and North Sauty refuges. They were recaptured as follows: Tennessee Valley, 110; Mountain Region, 13; Piedmont, 2; Upper Coastal Plain, 8; Lower Coastal Plain, 11; and Gulf Coast, 17. For place of recovery of 281 Alabama-banded birds and place of banding of 133 Alabama-recovered birds, see Map 18.

Map 17

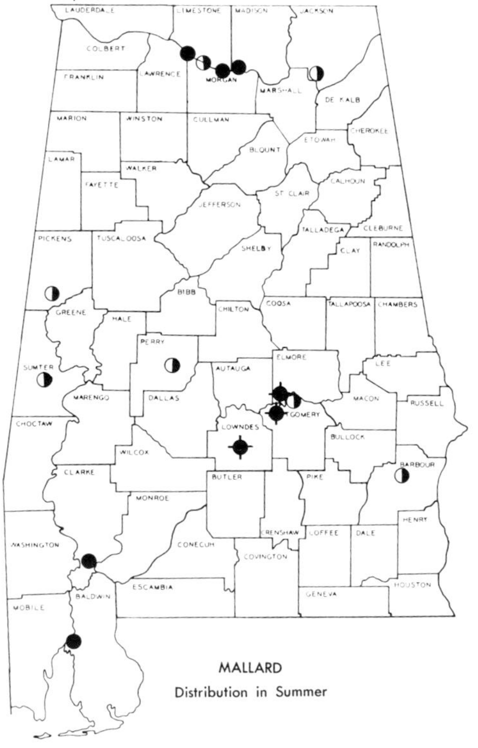

MALLARD
Distribution in Summer

◗ May 1 to July 31

● Breeding positive

+ Probable escapes from domestic stock

Black Duck

Anas rubripes Brewster   [133a]   (Plate 8, facing page 120)
OTHER NAME: Black Mallard

The Black Duck is a *dark brown,* streaked duck with a lighter brown head and neck. Alabama hunters are evidently well aware that it closely resembles the Mallard in size, shape, and actions, since they call it the Black Mallard. The *speculum* of this duck is *purple,* without the white border of the Mallard. In flight the white under surface of the wings is a good mark at a considerable distance. This duck's quack is much like that of the Mallard.

The species is common to abundant on migration and in winter in Alabama. It occurs in about the same places as does the Mallard, but the Black Duck likes salt marshes and bays also. It is especially numerous in the eastern half of the Tennessee Valley—the only place in the state where it is known to breed. There are an estimated twelve pairs at Wheeler Refuge. It is common in the Tennessee Valley, the Chattahoochee Valley, and the Gulf Coast, and uncommon elsewhere in the state. It prefers to feed at night on the marshes and to spend its days on open water.

The Black Duck is wary. It is usually hard to decoy and will generally make several passes over a spot before landing. In a mixed flock it is apt to be the

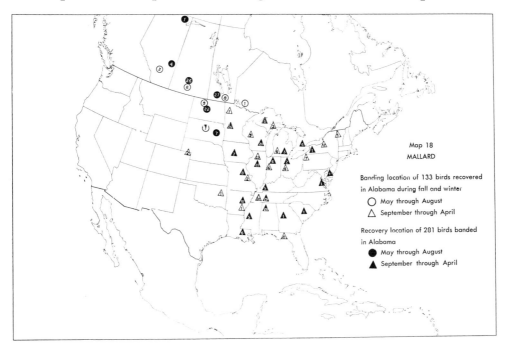

Map 18
MALLARD

Banding location of 133 birds recovered in Alabama during fall and winter

○ May through August
△ September through April

Recovery location of 281 birds banded in Alabama

● May through August
▲ September through April

farthest from shore and the first to flush. In the breeding season the female and young are adept at remaining hidden.

NESTING. For its nest the Black Duck chooses a shrubby, brushy, or grassy spot on the ground near water. The large, well-built nest of grasses and weeds is deeply cupped and lined with down and feathers. It usually contains six to twelve pale buff or pale greenish eggs.

FOOD. This bird eats many water plants—pondweeds, eelgrass, and wild celery, for instance—and also grasses, sedges, wild rice, and other grains, and many kinds of seeds, nuts, and berries. In addition, it feeds on many mollusks, especially the blue mussel, and small water animals such as snails, shrimp, frogs, toads, insects, other crustaceans, and occasionally fish.

DISTRIBUTION. The Black Duck breeds from northern Manitoba and northern Quebec south to North Dakota, Indiana, northern Alabama, and North Carolina but chiefly along the Atlantic Coast. It winters from as far north as it can find open water, usually the Great Lakes and New England, south to southern Texas, Florida, and Bermuda.

OCCURRENCE IN ALABAMA. (Throughout the year.) *Tennessee Valley*: Abundant, mid-October to mid-March; usual Wheeler Refuge winter population, 2500 with peaks of 8000 (*fide* T. Z. Atkeson, Jr.). *Mountain Region*: October 15 (1954, Legarde Lake, Cherokee Co., E. L. Humphries) to March 30 (1954, Birmingham, T. A. Imhof);

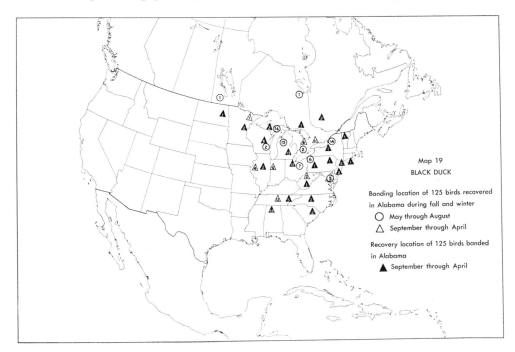

Map 19
BLACK DUCK

Banding location of 125 birds recovered in Alabama during fall and winter

○ May through August
△ September through April

Recovery location of 125 birds banded in Alabama

▲ September through April

also April 23, 1961 (Hammondville, DeKalb Co., T. A. and James Imhof); most seen, 63, November 15, 1954 (Fink's Lake, Calhoun Co., J. L. Herring). *Piedmont*: October 15 (1954, Edmond's Lake, Cleburne Co., E. L. Humphries) to March 1 (1954, Auburn, D. W. Speake). *Upper Coastal Plain*: October 19 (1953, Davis No. 1 Lake, Montgomery Co., R. W. Thrasher) to March 25 (1960, Livingston, Jenkins Jackson); most seen, 50, January 13, 1954 (Sumter Farms Lake, W. W. Beshears). *Lower Coastal Plain*: October 14 (1955, 5 birds, Open Pond, L. C. Crawford and J. R. Stinson) to March 15 (1954, Club Pond, Conecuh Co., L. C. Crawford). *Gulf Coast*: October 20 (1952, Mobile Delta, W. F. Colin) to April 13 (1957, Cochrane Causeway, Karl and Marion Zerbe); several summer records in the Mobile-Tensaw

delta and along the outer islands and peninsulas may refer to the Mottled Duck.

TIME OF BREEDING. Data on about 20 nestings, all Wheeler Refuge: Eggs, May 1; small young, May 13 to June 7.

BANDING. Of 153 recovered Black Ducks banded in Alabama at Wheeler and North Sauty refuges, 63 have been recovered in Alabama. Of those banded outside Alabama, 94 have been recovered in this state. The distribution of the 157 state recoveries: Tennessee Valley, 133; Mountain Region, 5; Piedmont, 2; Upper Coastal Plain, 6; Lower Coastal Plain, 5, and Gulf Coast, 6; is a good indication of the relative abundance of the species. For place of banding and recovery of Alabama-recovered and Alabama-banded birds outside this state, see Map 19.

Mottled Duck

Anas fulvigula Ridgway   [134]   (Plate 8, facing page 120)

OTHER NAMES: Summer Black Mallard, Summer Black Duck, Summer Duck

This duck resembles the Black Duck in pattern, but it is paler in color. The Mottled Duck is *buffy* throughout with a *rich, buffy, unstreaked throat* and a

NEST OF MOTTLED DUCK.   This is the first nesting record of the Mottled Duck in Alabama.

C. W. Summerour

[128]

prominent *white border* behind the *bluish speculum.* It differs from the female Mallard in that the female Mallard has a blotched bill, a whitish tail, and a white border on front and rear of the bluer speculum. The field marks of the Mottled Duck are not easy to see, especially in poor light, so that considerable care should be exercised in identifying this species.

The Mottled Duck is a local and uncommon permanent resident on the Gulf Coast of Alabama. In summer it nests on the outer islands and peninsulas and their sheltered bays. During the remainder of the year it is more widespread, and it often winters at the head of Mobile Bay. In these places it frequents salt and brackish water areas, especially marshes. (See Map 20.)

NESTING. The only Alabama nest so far recorded held eight bluish-green eggs and was a low, neat mound of fine bits of grass, lined with down. It had been well concealed in dense *Spartina* grass on a dry point of a small meandering tidal stream. This record conforms well with those of nests in Louisiana and Florida.

FOOD. Mollusks, particularly the snails, form more than half of the food the Mottled Duck eats. It also takes water bugs, water beetles, and larvae and nymphs of dragonflies, caddis flies, and horseflies. It varies this diet with crustaceans, a few fish, and the roots, stems, and especially the seeds of bulrush, spikerush, wild rice, pickerelweed, and naiad.

DISTRIBUTION. This species is resident on the Gulf Coast from southern Texas to southern Florida and inland in the states of Florida, Texas, and Louisiana.

OCCURRENCE IN ALABAMA. *Gulf Coast only:* Dauphin Island, March 24 (1961, Ava Tabor and others) to September 23 (1955, specimen in Univ. of Ala. collection, W. W. Beshears and T. A. Imhof); specimen in Auburn Wildlife collection (April 26, 1959, Lovett Williams); Grand Bay, Mobile Co., July 12, 1944 (J. L. Dorn) and October 11, 1941 (J. L. Dorn); West Fowl River, June

Map 20

MOTTLED DUCK
Distribution

■ December through February
▲ March and April
◑ May through August
▼ September through November

● Breeding positive
+ Probable records
○ Specimen collected

16, 1956 (O. L. Austin, Jr.); Cochrane Causeway, December 3, 1939 (J. L. Dorn); December 28, 1959 (J. L. Dorn); and December 29, 1954 (J. L. Dorn); most seen, 13, September 16, 1960 (Dauphin Island, J. L. Dorn). Probable records from Gulf Shores (April and October), lower Tensaw River (July),

and Chuckfee Bay (August) may indicate more widespread coastal distribution.

TIME OF BREEDING. Data on 2 Dauphin Island nestings: Eggs, May 16, 1960 (C. W. Summerour, Jr.); downy young (15, probably 2 broods), May 1955 (Eugene Collier).

Gadwall

Anas strepera Linnaeus   [135]   (Plate 8, facing page 120)
OTHER NAMES: Chickcock, Gray Duck

The Gadwall is a *slim duck,* smaller than the Mallard, with a black-bordered *white speculum.* The male is largely dark gray with a lighter-colored head, a black bill, and black upper and under tail coverts. The female, a streaked brown bird with a black-spotted yellow bill, and the same white speculum, is best identified by the speculum.

On migration this bird occurs fairly commonly throughout the state. It also winters commonly in many places here. In the Tennessee Valley and on the Gulf Coast it is often abundant in winter and during migration, and it occasionally summers. It is not known to breed anywhere in Alabama. It inhabits mostly

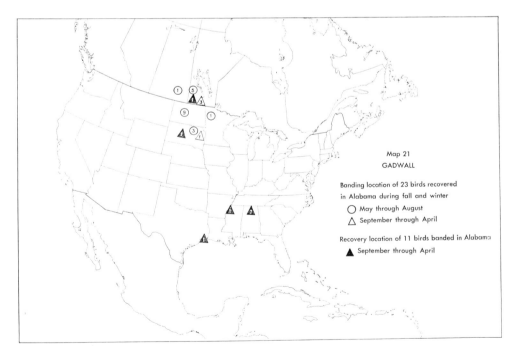

Map 21
GADWALL

Banding location of 23 birds recovered in Alabama during fall and winter

○ May through August
△ September through April

Recovery location of 11 birds banded in Alabama
▲ September through April

fresh or brackish water and feeds in marshes, swamps, pond borders, and brackish mudflats.

NESTING AND FOOD. The female lays seven to thirteen creamy to buffy-white eggs in a grassy, down-lined nest often far from water. The Gadwall's food is preponderantly plant life, especially the leaves and stems of water plants, but sometimes the buds and tubers as well. Most often it eats pondweeds, algae, many wild grasses, sedges, arrowhead, and wild celery. The few animals it eats include snails and water insects. Occasionally this duck dives for food, whereas other tip-up ducks dive only in an emergency.

DISTRIBUTION. The Gadwall breeds from southern Alaska and the Hudson Bay south to interior California, northern Texas, northern Iowa, and on the Atlantic Coast to North Carolina. It winters from southern Alaska, Colorado, the Ohio Valley, and Chesapeake Bay, rarely Long Island, south to Mexico and northern Florida.

OCCURRENCE IN ALABAMA. (September 2 to May 29; occasional in summer.) *Tennessee Valley*: September 2 (1955, Guntersville Lake, Jackson Co., C. C. Harrison) to May 29 (1946, Wheeler Refuge, L. S. Givens); occasional in June, especially at Harris Station (D. C. Hulse and others); also July 18, 1947 (2 birds, Elk River Hatchery, L. S. Givens); most seen, 6000, November 15, 1955 (Wheeler Refuge, E. A. Byford and C. M. Parker). *Mountain Region*: October 15 (1952, 16 birds, Blount Co., Loggins) to April 3 (1957, Birmingham, T. A. Imhof); most seen, 25, December 20, 1947 (Lake Purdy, T. A. Imhof). *Piedmont*: October 15 (1954, Cleburne Co., E. L. Humphries) to February 27 (1941, specimen in the Auburn Univ. collection, F. E. Guyton). *Upper Coastal Plain*: September 4 (1955, 48 birds, Marion, Lois McCollough) to April 12 (1957, Livingston, Jenkins Jackson); most seen, 250, February 14, 1955 (Demopolis Lake, W. W. Beshears). *Lower Coastal Plain*: October 14 (1955, 66 birds, Open Pond and vicinity, L. C. Crawford and J. R. Stinson) to March 23 (1957, "L" Pond, Conecuh Co., T. A. Imhof and L. C. Crawford). *Gulf Coast*: October 11 (1949, Mobile Delta, F. X. Lueth) to May 2 (1959, 15 birds, Cochrane Causeway, H. M. Stevenson); occasional in summer near Cochrane Causeway (F. M. Uhler, M. W. Gaillard, T. A. Imhof, and others); most seen, 13,500, November 16, 1954 (Mobile Delta, W. F. Colin).

BANDING. Of 23 birds banded outside the state and recovered in Alabama, 16 were recovered on the Gulf Coast, 5 in the Tennessee Valley, 1 in St. Clair Co., and 1 in Sumter Co. For further information, see Map 21.

Pintail

Anas acuta Linnaeus   [143]   (Plate 8, facing page 120)
OTHER NAMES: Picket-tail, Sprig, Sprig-tail

This is a rather large, handsome duck. Its long, pointed tail and long neck give it a distinctive shape, especially when it is in flight. The drake is grayish with a *white area* extending from the breast to a *point* behind the eye, and the *head* is *reddish-brown*. Except for the chunky, heavy-billed Shoveler, this is the only local tip-up duck with a white breast, a good mark that can be seen far away. The female is a streaked brown duck, which can be identified by its *slim proportions* and small, *blue-gray bill*. The Pintail is a strong, rapid flyer.

In winter and on migration the Pintail is common in Alabama and often abundant in the Tennessee Valley and on the Gulf Coast. It is not known to nest here. It winters in suitable habitat, provided there is little hunting pressure. It frequents the same places as other tip-up ducks, and sometimes occurs in deeper water as well.

NESTING AND FOOD. The Pintail builds a nest of dry grass lined with down usually in tall prairie grass near water, preferring small islands. A clutch consists of six to twelve pale greenish to olive-buff eggs. Most of its food is vegetable matter, with seeds of pondweeds and sedges its favorites. It eats the seeds, stems, and leaves of many other water plants, such as wild grasses, wild rice, arrow grass, glasswort, and waterlilies. It also eats a few mollusks, crustaceans, and insects.

DISTRIBUTION. The Pintail breeds in the Western Hemisphere from northwestern Alaska and New Brunswick south to southern California and Iowa. It winters from southern British Columbia, Colorado, the Ohio Valley, and Massachusetts south to Hawaii, Colombia, and the West Indies.

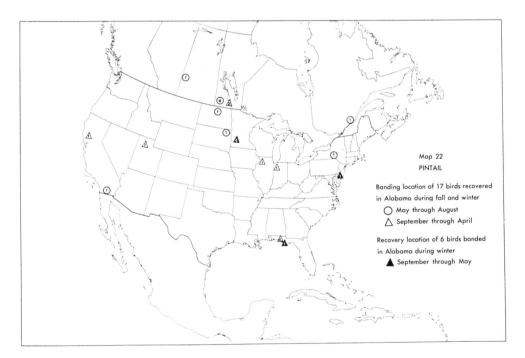

Map 22
PINTAIL

Banding location of 17 birds recovered
in Alabama during fall and winter
○ May through August
△ September through April

Recovery location of 6 birds banded
in Alabama during winter
▲ September through May

OCCURRENCE IN ALABAMA. (September 6 to May 4.) *Tennessee Valley*: September 6 (Wheeler Refuge, Leo Martin) to May 4 (1949, Wheeler Refuge, W. T. Meadows); most seen, 8000, mid-December (Wheeler Refuge, *fide* T. Z. Atkeson, Jr.). *Mountain Region*: October 27 (1956, Fort Payne, Ala. Orn. Soc.) to March 20 (1950, Birmingham, T. A. Imhof); most seen, 250, December 27, 1942 (Lake Purdy, M. F. Prather). *Piedmont*: November 14 (1952, Opelika, F. W. Fitch and W. W. Beshears) to March 16 (1953, Opelika, Ellis) *Upper Coastal Plain*: October 19 (1956, Livingston, Jenkins Jackson) to March 22 (1958, Marion, Lois McCollough and others); most seen, 150+, March 7, 1912 (Montgomery, C. N. Hinderer). *Lower Coastal Plain*: September 17 (1956, Covington Co., and Coffee Co., J. R. Stinson and L. C. Crawford) to March 22 (1957, Florala, T. A. Imhof); most seen, 25, November 7, 1958 (Camden, Lovett Williams). *Gulf Coast*: September 24 (1955, 11 birds, Fort Morgan, T. A. Imhof and others) to April 12 (1957, Dauphin Island, T. A. Imhof); most seen, 3600, December 15, 1952 (Mobile Delta, W. F. Colin).

BANDING. Of 17 birds banded in other states and recovered in Alabama, 8 were recovered in the Tennessee Valley, 7 on the Gulf Coast, and 1 each in Cherokee Co. and Dallas Co. See Map 22 for further information.

Green-winged Teal
Anas carolinensis Gmelin   [139]   (Plate 9, facing page 128)
OTHER NAME: Teal

This Lilliputian duck, hardly half the size of the Mallard, is set apart from all other ducks except the Blue-winged Teal by its diminutive size. The Green-winged Teal has a *dark wing* with a green speculum. The male is dark gray and brown, its breast ruddy and its head a reddish-brown with a green patch behind and around the eye. The female, a streaked brown duck rather difficult to distinguish on the water, shows a wing like that of the male when in flight. On the water males whistle and females quack softly, and in flight both give a creaking sound.

In Alabama the Green-winged Teal is common in winter and on migration, but it is not known to breed here. Probably because it is so small, it often feeds in shallower waters and smaller pools than other ducks, but it frequently flocks with larger ducks in deeper waters. This teal is a fast flyer.

NESTING AND FOOD. The nest of dry grasses and leaves lined with down is well hidden in a dry, brushy place usually far from water. The ordinary clutch is eight to twelve dull whitish eggs. Plants form the major part of this duck's food. Favorites are seeds, especially those of sedges, pondweeds, grasses, smartweeds, algae, duckweeds, wild oats, wild millet, and wild rice. Other food items are water milfoil, acorns, chestnuts, grapes, berries, and some insects, snails, and small crustaceans.

ANSERIFORMES: ANATIDAE: GREEN-WINGED TEAL

DISTRIBUTION. The Green-winged Teal breeds from northern Alaska, southeastern Quebec, and Newfoundland south to central California, northern New Mexico, southern Minnesota, and Nova Scotia. It winters from southern British Columbia, Wisconsin, the Ohio Valley, and Nova Scotia south to Honduras and the West Indies.

OCCURRENCE IN ALABAMA. (September 19 to April 21.) *Tennessee Valley*: September 19 (1954, Wheeler Refuge, C. M. Parker and E. A. Byford) to April 5 (1938, Wheeler Refuge, Paul Bryan); most seen 6500, December 22, 1954 (Wheeler Refuge, E. A. Byford and C. M. Parker). *Mountain Region*: October 3 (1952, Birmingham, T. A. Imhof) to April 2 (1936, Birmingham, H. M. Stevenson). *Piedmont*: October 15 (1952, Mitchell Lake, Alton Boulware) to March 1 (1953, Mitchell Lake, Alton Boulware). *Upper Coastal Plain*: October 19 (1956, Livingston, Jenkins Jackson) to March 26 (1955, Marion, Lois McCollough); also September 19, 1955 (White Oak Lake, Bullock Co., J. M. Fleming); most seen, 150, January 8, 1956 (Marion, Lois McCollough). *Lower Coastal Plain*: October 14 (1955, Butler County Lake, J. R. Colquitt) to at least February 25 (1955, Open Pond, T. A. Imhof); most seen, 75, November 15, 1954 (Lake Tholloco, L. C. Crawford). *Gulf Coast*: October 6 (1956, Dauphin Island, S. M. Russell and E. O. Willis) to April 21 (1956, Cochrane Causeway, H. M. Stevenson); most seen, 2500, December 1, 1952 (Mobile Delta, W. F. Colin).

BANDING. Of 12 banded Green-winged Teal reported from Alabama, 8 were recovered in the vicinity of Mobile, 1 on Chewacla Creek, Lee Co., 1 at Scottsboro, 1 at Jackson, and 1 near Opp. See Map 23 for place of banding.

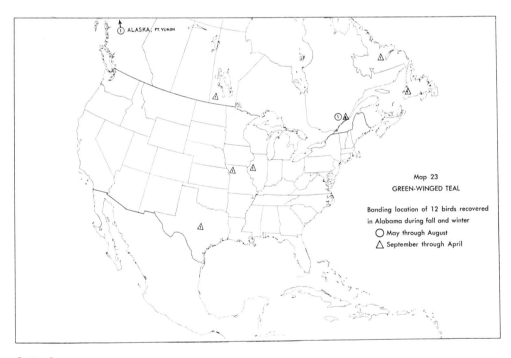

Map 23
GREEN-WINGED TEAL

Banding location of 12 birds recovered in Alabama during fall and winter
○ May through August
△ September through April

Blue-winged Teal

Anas discors Linnaeus   [140]   (Plate 9, facing page 128)
OTHER NAME: Teal

The *male* of this small-sized duck has a ruddy body, a dark belly, and a *large white crescent* in *front* of the *eye*. The female is streaked brown. The slightly larger size, the bigger bill, and the large patch of *pale blue* on the *fore edge* of the *wing* distinguish it from the Green-winged Teal. The Shoveler has the same patch of blue, but its bill is tremendous, longer than its head and very wide, so that it should not be confused with the Blue-winged Teal. In addition, the female Shoveler's tail contains much white.

The Blue-winged Teal is common to abundant on migration throughout Alabama. It winters rarely north of the Fall Line, and uncommonly in the Coastal Plain, and it breeds rarely in several well-scattered places. (See Map 24.) It is more widespread than other ducks, for it often occurs on migration in very small ponds, mud holes, and rain pools. It frequents marshes, mudflats, sandbars, and the shallower parts of ponds, and it feeds by dabbling more often than not.

NESTING. The Blue-winged Teal prefers prairie country for nesting and often chooses to build its nest close to places frequented by man, concealing it well. It is made of grasses, lined with down, and usually covered over with down when the female is absent. This bird lays ten to thirteen dull white, creamy-white, or pale olive-white eggs.

FOOD. Seeds of sedges and the seeds, stems, and leaves of pondweeds are this duck's favorite food. It also eats wild grasses, wild rice, smartweeds, algae, waterlilies, snails, tadpoles, crustaceans, and insects, especially immature forms of caddis flies, dragonflies, and beetles.

DISTRIBUTION. This duck breeds from British Columbia, southern Quebec, and Nova Scotia south to southern California, southern New Mexico, and the northern Gulf Coast. It winters from southern California, Texas, and North Carolina, south through Central America and the West Indies to Peru and Brazil. Less commonly it winters north to the Ohio Valley and the Chesapeake Bay.

OCCURRENCE IN ALABAMA. (Throughout the year.) *Tennessee Valley*: March 1 (1953, Seven-mile Island, J. H. Parsons) to May 25 (1951, Wheeler Refuge, D. C. Hulse) and August 11 (1954, Wanville, J. H. Heflin) to November 18 (1949, Wheeler Refuge, D. C. Hulse); summers, breeds, and winters in milder years; most seen, migration, 2500, October 4, 1950 (Wheeler Refuge, D. C. Hulse), winter, 35, December 31, 1954 (Christmas Count, Wheeler Refuge). *Mountain Region*: March 14 (1937, Birming-

[135]

ham, H. M. Stevenson) to May 20 (1937, Birmingham, H. M. Stevenson) and August 19 (1936, Birmingham, H. M. Stevenson) to October 28 (1956, Birmingham, T. A. Imhof and M. W. Gaillard); also June 5, 1950 (Birmingham, T. A. Imhof); winters occasionally; most seen, 250, September 17, 1955 (Lake Purdy, T. A. Imhof, F. B. Daniel, and M. H. Perry). *Piedmont*: March 15 (1954, Lee Co., D. W. Speake) to May 18 (1954, Auburn, D. W. Speake) and August 30 (1954, Lee Co., D. W. Speake) to October 27 (1950, Auburn, W. W. Beshears); summered in Lee Co., in 1953 (W. F. Helms) and 1954 (D. W. Speake). *Upper Coastal Plain*: August 9 (1960, Livingston, Jenkins Jackson) to May 31 (1957, Marion, Lois McCollough); winters sparingly and breeds rarely; most seen, 500, September 18, 1956 (Demopolis Lake, W. W. Beshears). *Lower Coastal Plain*: September 17 (1956, Covington Co., J. R. Stinson) to May 11 (1956, Choctaw Bluff, Clarke Co., T. A. Imhof, G. A. Carleton, and M. W. Gaillard); winters sparingly and breeds rarely. *Gulf Coast*: Common, August 24 (1956, Dauphin Island, T. A. Imhof and others) to May 25 (1957, Dauphin Island, T. A. Imhof and others); most seen, spring, 600, March 15, 1953 (Mobile Delta, W. F. Colin), fall, 1400, September 19, 1955 (Mobile Delta, W. F. Colin), winter, 195, December 29, 1954 (Mobile, J. L. Dorn); frequent in June; breeds rarely.

TIME OF BREEDING. Data on 7 nestings: Eggs, April 8 to June 1; dependent young, May 20 to June 12.

BANDING. Of 28 banded birds reported from Alabama, 7 were from the Mountain Region, 5 each from the Tennessee Valley, Lower Coastal Plain, and the Gulf Coast, 4 from the Upper Coastal Plain, and 2 from the Piedmont. (See Map 25.) Only 4 of these birds were obtained in December, January, or February. Two immature females held at Springfield, Illinois beyond their normal fall departure date were both shot by the same hunter near Mobile 2 days after release. They traveled 635 straight line miles!

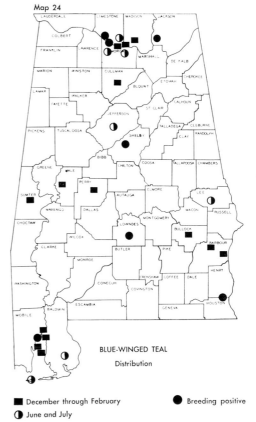

Map 24

BLUE-WINGED TEAL

Distribution

■ December through February ● Breeding positive
◑ June and July

[European Widgeon]

Mareca penelope (Linnaeus) [136] (Plate 9, facing page 128)

The European Widgeon has a *gray body, reddish head* with *pale yellow crown*, a ruddy breast, and a large white patch on the fore edge of the wing. It closely

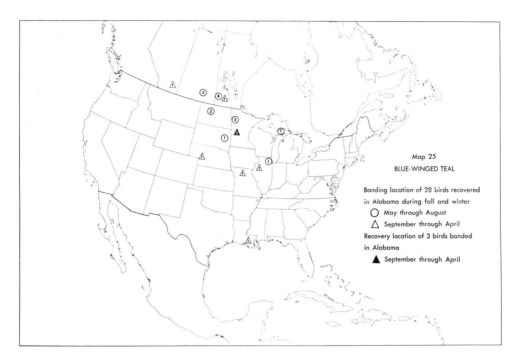

Map 25
BLUE-WINGED TEAL

Banding location of 28 birds recovered
in Alabama during fall and winter
O   May through August
△   September through April
Recovery location of 3 birds banded
in Alabama
▲   September through April

resembles the American Widgeon, but the American bird has a ruddy-brown body, green and gray head, and a white crown. The European female's dusky wing linings distinguish it from the American female. Although it lacks the black breast, the male European Widgeon is so strikingly similar to the Redhead, with which it associates, that it is very difficult to spot.

This duck has been recorded once in Alabama, in spring. Strangely, it has not so far been recorded where the American Widgeon is abundant, and yet it frequents the same types of habitat.

NESTING AND FOOD. These are similar to the habits of the American Widgeon.

DISTRIBUTION. The European Widgeon breeds from Iceland eastward to Kamchatka, and winters in much of Europe, Asia, and North Africa. It is frequent in winter on the Pacific Coast of Canada and the United States, uncommon along the Atlantic Coast in the fall, and rare but regular in the upper Mississippi Valley in spring.

OCCURRENCE IN ALABAMA. (a male at close range, Tuscaloosa, H. M. *Upper Coastal Plain only*: March 30, 1939 Stevenson).

[137]

American Widgeon

Mareca americana (Gmelin)   [137]   (Plate 9, facing page 128)
OTHER NAMES: Baldpate, Robber Duck

The *male* American Widgeon is a ruddy-brown, medium-sized duck with a reddish breast, *gray* and *green head,* and a prominent *white crown.* The *female* is *plain reddish-brown* with *gray head* and *neck.* In flight the large white patch on the fore edge of the wing is a good mark for both sexes if it is not confused with the pale blue wing patches of the big-billed Shoveler and the small Blue-winged Teal. The call of the American Widgeon is a short whistle which can be easily imitated by squeezing a rubber toy.

This duck is common to abundant in winter and on migration in Alabama. Although it occasionally lingers until late May and June, it is not known to nest here. It is a typical pond and lake duck, but it is apt to spend time also in fairly deep water where, because it cannot dive well, it snatches food from the American Coot, Redhead, Canvasback, and others, and so is called "Robber Duck." On the coast it often frequents brackish water and at times even salt water.

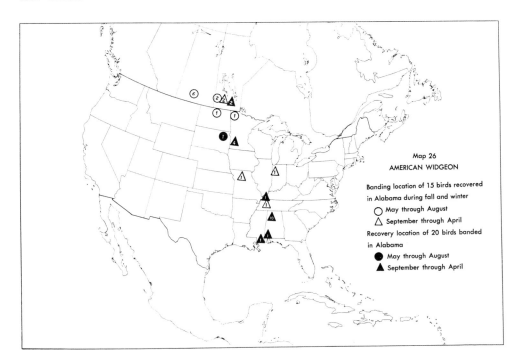

Map 26
AMERICAN WIDGEON

Banding location of 15 birds recovered
in Alabama during fall and winter
○ May through August
△ September through April
Recovery location of 20 birds banded
in Alabama
● May through August
▲ September through April

[138]

NESTING AND FOOD. The nest is a neat one, built on dry ground, of grasses lined with down. It usually contains six to twelve creamy-white eggs. The American Widgeon feeds on pondweeds, grasses, algae, sedges, wild celery, water weeds, water milfoil, duckweeds, and smartweeds, and occasionally it consumes small mollusks and insects.

DISTRIBUTION. The American Widgeon breeds from northwestern Alaska and Hudson Bay south to northeastern California and northern Nebraska. It winters from southeastern Alaska, Utah, the Ohio Valley, and the Chesapeake Bay, rarely farther north, south to Panama and the West Indies.

OCCURRENCE IN ALABAMA. (September 21 to June 6.) *Tennessee Valley*: September 21 (1960, Wheeler Refuge, D. C. Hulse) to April 23 (1951, Wheeler Refuge, D. C. Hulse); most seen, 1500, January 2, 1954 (Wheeler Refuge, T. A. Imhof). *Mountain Region*: October 16 (1949, Birmingham, T. A. Imhof) to April 11 (1936, Birmingham, H. M. Stevenson); also June 6, 1956 (Hammondville, DeKalb Co., T. A. Imhof and G. M. Kyle); most seen, 18, April 3, 1949 (Birmingham, T. A. Imhof). *Piedmont*: October 28 (1953, Auburn, D. W. Speake) to March 23 (1953, Opelika, F. W. Fitch). *Upper Coastal Plain*: October 16 (1956, Marion, R. T. Gaisser) to May 11 (1957, Marion, Lois McCollough); also May 24, 1956 (Marion, T. A. Imhof); most seen, 400+ March 19, 1960 (Marion, T. A. Imhof and others). *Lower Coastal Plain*: November 2 (1954, Barbour County Lake, J. E. Keeler) to April 5 (1957, Jackson, T. A. Imhof and W. U. Harris); also May 25, 1958 (Camden, Lovett Williams). *Gulf Coast*: October 15 (1956, Cochrane Causeway, W. F. Colin) to April 20 (1958, Spring Count, Mobile Bay Area); also May 17, 1958 (Cochrane Causeway, T. A. Imhof and M. W. Gaillard); most seen, 8500, January 1, 1953 (Mobile Delta, W. F. Colin).

BANDING. Of 21 Wheeler-banded birds, 20 were recovered in the vicinity, and 1 from the Gulf Coast. Of 15 others banded outside the state, 11 are reported from the Gulf Coast, 2 in the Tennessee Valley, and 1 each in Jefferson and Lowndes counties. For further information, see Map 26.

Shoveler

Spatula clypeata (Linnaeus) [142] (Plate 9, facing page 128)

OTHER NAMES: Spoonbill, Scooper

This medium-sized duck has a *tremendous bill,* longer and wider than its head, and usually held pointed downward at an angle. The *fore edge* of its *wing* is marked with a *large, light blue patch.* The *male* has a glossy green head, white breast, *reddish-brown belly,* and black back and tail coverts. The female is mottled brown with a whitish tail, and is easily distinguished by the very large bill.

In Alabama this duck is common and local in winter and on migration, and in spring it becomes especially common. It occurs in the same places as other tip-up ducks, but it also frequents the shallower margins of ponds, lakes, and swamps, where it feeds by dabbling with its huge bill in muddy places. In 1937 and 1938 the species nested in the Tennessee Valley, but these are the only known breeding records for the state.

NESTING. The nest is either in marshy or dry places, most frequently near sloughs on the prairies, and is made of grasses and leaves lined with feathers and down. The female lays six to eleven pale olive-buff to pale greenish-gray eggs.

FOOD. The Shoveler feeds on many small aquatic animals, especially snails and other mollusks, insects, crustaceans, tadpoles, worms, and occasionally small fish. It also eats the seeds, stems, and bulbs of many water plants such as grasses, sedges, ditchgrass, pondweeds, sawgrass, algae, duckweeds, smartweeds, and waterlilies. It works its large bill through the mud and shallows, draining debris and water out the side and retaining food particles. It eats more animal matter than any other tip-up duck with the possible exception of the Mottled Duck.

DISTRIBUTION. This duck breeds from northwestern Alaska, Great Slave Lake, southern Ontario, and Delaware south to southern California, Nebraska, and North Carolina. It winters from British Columbia, Arizona, the lower Mississippi Valley, and South Carolina south to Hawaii, Colombia, and the West Indies, and occasionally north to Minnesota, Illinois, and New York.

OCCURRENCE IN ALABAMA. (October 3 to June 4; bred in 1937 and 1938.) *Tennessee Valley*: October 3 (1949, Wheeler Refuge, W. E. Jernigan) to May 13 (Wheeler Refuge, L. S. Givens); bred 2 years; most seen, 100, April 14, 1937 (Wheeler Reservoir, Paul Bryan and A. R. Cahn). *Mountain Region*: October 31 (1936, Birmingham, H. M. Stevenson) to April 2 (1936, Birmingham, H. M. Stevenson); also June 4, 1954 (Hammondville, DeKalb Co., H. M. Stevenson and others); most seen, 7, November 15, 1954 (Fink's Lake, Calhoun Co., J. L. Herring). *Piedmont*: October 13 (1954, Auburn, D. W. Speake) to October 31 (1953, Auburn, D. W. Speake) and February 8 (1935, Auburn, F. S. Arant) to April 26 (1954, Cleburne County Lake, J. L. Herring). *Upper Coastal Plain*: October 6 (1952, Payne Lake, F. X. Lueth and L. Snipes) to March 27 (1959, Livingston, Jenkins Jackson); most

seen, 25, March 19, 1960 (Marion, T. A. Imhof and others). *Lower Coastal Plain*: "Uncommon transient at Columbia" (the T. Z. Atkesons); no dates available. *Gulf Coast*: October 19 (1957, Cochrane Causeway, H. G. Loftin) to May 2 (1959, Little Dauphin Island, T. A. Imhof and Talmadge Lundy); most seen, 250, December 1, 1952 (Mobile Delta, W. F. Colin).

TIME OF BREEDING. Data on 3 nestings from Harris Station, Limestone Co. (Alvin R. Cahn and Paul Bryan, *Auk* 55: 271-272): May 4, 1937, 2 broods, 9 and 11 young about 3 or 4 days old, and May 31, 1938, 1 brood of 6 young.

BANDING. The only banded Shoveler reported from Alabama is 1 shot at Dawson, DeKalb Co., during the fall 1954 hunting season which had been banded in Saskatchewan, July 17, 1953.

Wood Duck

Aix sponsa (Linnaeus)   [144]   (Plate 9, facing page 128)
OTHER NAME: Summer Duck

This is one of the handsomest species in a family of brightly-colored birds. Both sexes are *dark, crested* ducks with *dark wings,* a long, *dark tail,* and a white belly. Most ducks appear to have their wings set well to the rear because of their long necks and short tails, but the short neck and long tail of the Wood Duck give it a distinctive shape. The *male* is *highly-colored,* with dark, iridescent back and head, buffy sides, chestnut neck, white markings on the face, and other highly-colored areas. The *female* is rather plain dark brown, but with a *white area around the eye.*

The Wood Duck is a common, breeding, permanent resident in most of Alabama; it is uncommon south of Mobile, in the eastern half of the Lower Coastal Plain, and in winter in the Mountain Region. It frequents swamps and other bottomlands, especially beaver ponds and other ponds with wooded borders. Seldom does it occur with other ducks, and in winter it usually roosts in large flocks in swamps.

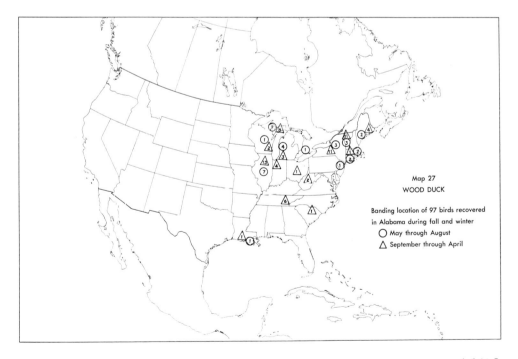

Map 27
WOOD DUCK

Banding location of 97 birds recovered
in Alabama during fall and winter
○ May through August
△ September through April

NESTING. This duck nests in a hole from ten to forty feet up in a tree. Usually it finds a natural cavity, but it will use a nest box with dimensions as follows: floor, ten by eighteen inches; height, two feet; entrance hole, one foot above the floor and about four inches wide and three inches high. The nest tree may be over water or as much as half a mile away from it. The female lays eight to fourteen creamy-white eggs in a nest of down. When the young are one or two days old, they flutter to the ground as best they can, and the female then leads them to water.

FOOD. The Wood Duck eats large amounts of duckweeds, cone scales and galls from cypress, and the seeds of sedges, rushes, and grasses, especially those of wild rice, smartweeds, pondweeds, and waterlilies. It eats the fruit of many trees and shrubs, such as water elm, water hickory, wild grape, swamp privet, buttonbush, oaks, other hickories, beech, and tupelo gum. A small amount of its food consists of small water animals, especially large insects, spiders, and crustaceans. Most of this food it obtains by dabbling in the water or by foraging on the ground in swampy woods.

DISTRIBUTION. The Wood Duck breeds locally in almost all the continental United States and southern Canada but is uncommon in the Rocky Mountains and the Plains. It winters from southern British Columbia (rarely), central Missouri, southern Illinois, and eastern Maryland south to central Mexico and Cuba.

TIME OF BREEDING. Data on about 20 nestings: Eggs, late February to May. Data on over 197 broods: Downy young, April 9 to July 1; partly-feathered young, May 3 to July 21; fully-feathered young, May 25 to August 18; flying young (short distance), May 18 to August 18.

BANDING. No Alabama-banded Wood Ducks have been recovered for the simple reason that the birds are difficult to trap in the South and few have been banded here. Of 97 Wood Ducks recovered in Alabama, 33 were reported from the Lower Coastal Plain, 32 from the Upper Coastal Plain, 11 from the Tennessee Valley, 9 from the Mountain Region, 6 from the Gulf Coast, and 5 from the Piedmont. See Map 27 for approximate location in state of banding.

SUBFAMILY AYTHYINAE: DIVING DUCKS

These ducks (also called Bay Ducks and Sea Ducks) feed by diving in deep water. Most of them must paddle along the surface of the water for some distance before they can take flight. On the whole, diving ducks are less brightly-colored than tip-up ducks, but they do show a large amount of white, especially in the wings. In the hand these birds can be distinguished from tip-up ducks by the well-developed lobe on the hind toe.

In winter, diving ducks frequent bays, estuaries, deep lakes, and other deeper and wider expanses of water, even the sea. They are more northerly and more coastwise in distribution. Many of them winter almost exclusively on salt water, where they occur in very large, dense flocks called rafts. On land they are clumsier than the surface-feeders, and they feed more often during the day. Many of them eat mollusks, crustaceans, and other seafood, but members of the scaup genus (*Aythya*) usually feed on underwater vegetation. No member of this subfamily is known to breed in Alabama, but sick, crippled, or old birds often summer here.

Redhead
Aythya americana (Eyton)   [146]   (Plate 10, facing page 144)

The *male* Redhead is a gray duck with a black chest and tail, a *rounded, rufous-red head,* and a blue bill. The *female* is a very plain, grayish-brown duck with an *ill-defined whitish eye ring,* and an *ill-defined whitish* area at the *base* of the *blue bill.* This species, with its gray wing stripe, is the most evenly-colored diving duck, and this very plainness is a help in identifying the female.

In most of Alabama the Redhead is uncommon in winter and on migration, but on the Gulf Coast it is locally abundant. It is not known to breed in this

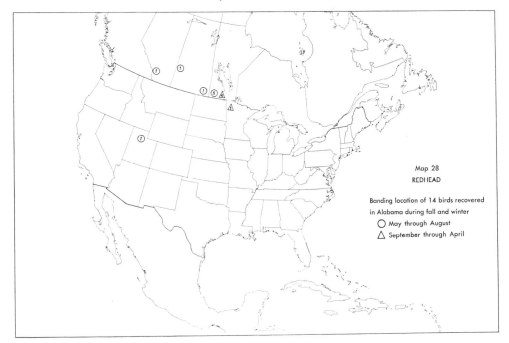

Map 28
REDHEAD

Banding location of 14 birds recovered
in Alabama during fall and winter
◯ May through August
△ September through April

PLATE 10

GREATER SCAUP
Adult Male
Page 149

LESSER SCAUP
Adult Female
Page 150

RING-NECKED DUCK
Adult Male
Page 145

LESSER SCAUP
Adult Male
Page 150

RING-NECKED DUCK
Adult Female
Page 145

CANVASBACK
Adult Male
Page 147

CANVASBACK
Adult Female
Page 147

REDHEAD
Adult Male
Page 143

REDHEAD
Adult Female
Page 143

COMMON GOLDENEYE
Adult Female
Page 153

BUFFLEHEAD
Adult Male
Page 154

BUFFLEHEAD
Adult Female
Page 154

COMMON GOLDENEYE
Adult Male
Page 153

RUDDY DUCK
Adult Female, Winter
Page 158

RUDDY DUCK
Adult Male, Winter
Page 158

[144]

D.Hulse

state. It occurs on the deeper lakes, rivers, and bays in fresh, brackish, or salt water. Usually it associates with others of the scaup genus.

NESTING AND FOOD. This duck builds a bulky nest of grasses lined with down and hides it well in marsh vegetation or on the prairie near water. The usual clutch is ten to fifteen pale olive-buff or creamy-buff eggs. The Redhead eats principally water plants, such as wild rice, wild celery, pondweeds, muskgrass, sedges, smartweeds, coontail, and ditchgrass, and secondarily acorns, beechnuts, mollusks (especially snails), tadpoles, and small fish.

DISTRIBUTION. This species breeds from British Columbia, Great Slave Lake, and Minnesota south to southern California, central Nebraska, and southern Wisconsin, rarely east to New Brunswick. It winters from southern British Columbia, southern Illinois, and the Chesapeake Bay, rarely farther north, south to Mexico and the West Indies.

OCCURRENCE IN ALABAMA. (October 17 to May 19.) *Tennessee Valley*: October 21 (1949, Wheeler Refuge, W. E. Jernigan and T. Z. Atkeson, Jr.) to April 15 (1951, Wheeler Refuge, D. C. Hulse and E. A. Byford); most seen, 100, mid-winter (Wheeler Refuge, *fide* T. Z. Atkeson, Jr.). *Mountain Region*: November 11 (1956, Birmingham, Adele West) to April 5 (1952, Birmingham, T. A. Imhof); most seen, 23, December 15, 1954 (Weaver Lake, Calhoun Co., J. L. Herring). *Piedmont*: October 30 (1953, Auburn, D. W. Speake) to April 8 (1953, Auburn, H. G. Good). *Upper Coastal Plain*: October 27 (1957, Marion, Lois McCollough) to April 7 (1956, Hayneville, J. M. Rice); most seen, 12, January 13, 1954 (Sumter Farms, W. W. Beshears). *Lower Coastal Plain*: November 1 (1957, 6 birds, Jackson, T. A. Imhof and W. U. Harris) to at least December 21 (1953, 11 birds, "L" Pond, Conecuh Co., L. C. Crawford). *Gulf Coast*: October 17 (1931, Cochrane Causeway, Helen Edwards) to April 10 (1959, Dauphin Island, T. A. Imhof and A. J. Murphy); also May 6 and 19, 1956 (Cochrane Causeway, M. W. Gaillard); most seen, 3000, January 19, 1956 (Mississippi Sound, T. A. Imhof and others).

BANDING. Of 14 banded Redheads recovered in Alabama, 8 were reported from the Gulf Coast, 2 from Jefferson Co., and 1 each from Limestone, Calhoun, Sumter, and Washington counties. For place of banding, see Map 28. Note that although many Redheads are banded in Michigan, and many other banded ducks from Michigan reach Alabama, no Michigan-banded Redheads are reported from Alabama.

Ring-necked Duck

Aythya collaris (Donovan) [150] (Plate 10, facing page 144)
OTHER NAMES: Black Duck, Black Jack

The Ring-necked Duck is a *black-backed scaup* with a gray wing stripe. Around the *tip* and *base* of their *blue bills*, both sexes have a *white ring*. In fact, this bird might well be called the "Ring-billed Duck," for the neck ring is dark brown and difficult to see, while the bill ring is conspicuous. The *male* has a black head and chest as well as a black back, and its sides are gray. In

[145]

front of the *wing* is a very noticeable *white crescent*. The *female* is a dark brown duck, darkest on top of the head and on the back, with an ill-defined white area at the base of the bill and a *white line around and behind the eye*. Both sexes have a rather triangular head shape.

In winter, the Ring-necked Duck and the Lesser Scaup occur over a more widespread area of Alabama than any other ducks, but they are often out-numbered locally by other ducks, especially in the Tennessee Valley and on the Gulf Coast. Although the Ring-necked Duck sometimes lingers until May and occasionally even summers in the state, it is not known to nest here. The deeper artificial lakes and ponds, particularly those with wooded shores, are ideal for this duck. It is well distributed in small flocks instead of concentrated in a few favored places, but sometimes the Ring-necked Duck is abundant locally in Alabama.

NESTING AND FOOD. This bird uses grass lined with down for its nest and places it on the ground in a marsh, preferring one near a small, tree-bordered lake. The female usually lays from six to twelve dark olive-buff eggs. The Ring-necked Duck eats the seeds and foliage of such water plants as pondweeds, waterlilies, ditchgrass, sedges, smartweeds, muskgrass, delta potato, wild rice, hornwort, and purple watershield. It also feeds on the seeds of dogwood and

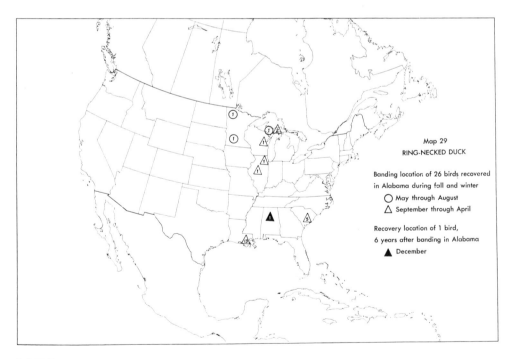

Map 29
RING-NECKED DUCK

Banding location of 26 birds recovered
in Alabama during fall and winter
○ May through August
△ September through April

Recovery location of 1 bird,
6 years after banding in Alabama
▲ December

tupelo gum, quite a few snails, and a few other water animals—for instance, tadpoles, insects, crawfish, and an occasional minnow.

DISTRIBUTION. This species breeds from central British Columbia, Quebec, and Newfoundland south to California, northern Nebraska, and the Canadian Maritime Provinces. It winters from southern British Columbia, the Ohio Valley, and Massachusetts south to Panama and the Greater Antilles.

OCCURRENCE IN ALABAMA. (September 10 to May 29; occasionally summers.) *Tennessee Valley*: September 10 (1948, Wheeler Refuge, J. H. Heflin) to May 29 (1951, Wheeler Refuge, D. C. Hulse); most seen, 1500, December 22, 1954 (Wheeler Refuge, E. A. Byford and C. M. Parker). *Mountain Region*: September 26 (1959, Lake Mac, Talladega Co., T. A. Imhof and others) to May 8 (1949, Birmingham, T. A. Imhof); summered at East Lake in 1955 (T. A. Imhof); most seen, 1100, December 21, 1941 (Lake Purdy, M. F. Prather). *Piedmont*: November 2 (1953, Lee Co., D. W. Speake) to April 19 (1958, Auburn, R. W. Skinner and others); summered at Whatley's Lake in 1953 and 1954 (D. W. Speake); most seen, 1450+, January 22, 1955 (Lake Ogletree and Whatley's Lake, D. W. Speake). *Upper Coastal Plain*: September 13 (1956, Speigner Lake, R. W. Thrasher) to May 14 (1954,

Hall's Pond, Macon Co., R. W. Thrasher); most seen, 400, January 13, 1954 (Sumter Farms Lake, W. W. Beshears). *Lower Coastal Plain*: October 15 (1954, "L" Pond, Conecuh Co., L. C. Crawford) to March 23 (1957, Covington Co., L. C. Crawford and T. A. Imhof); most seen, 350, March 15, 1954 (Open Pond, T. C. Hattaway). *Gulf Coast*: October 20 (1952, Mobile Delta, W. F Colin) to April 29 (1960, Big Creek Reservoir, J. L. Dorn); also May 26, 1956 (Stockton, T. A. Imhof and W. F. Colin); most seen, 1900, November 4, 1952 (Mobile Delta, W. F. Colin).

BANDING. Of 27 banded Ringnecked Ducks recovered in Alabama, 1 was a Wheeler-banded bird shot in Jefferson Co. Twenty others were reported from the Gulf Coast, and 1 each in Colbert, St. Clair, Talladega, Lee, Chilton, and Sumter counties. For place of banding, see Map 29.

Canvasback

Aythya valisineria (Wilson)   [147]   (Plate 10, facing page 144)

OTHER NAME: Horse Duck

The Canvasback is aptly named, for the most prominent feature of the *male* is its *white back* and sides. The male also has the black chest and black tail typical of the scaup genus. Its head is reddish-brown, not as bright as that of the Redhead. The female is a little darker on the back and sides but still easily recognizable. Both sexes have a *long, low-sloping forehead* and a *large, black bill*.

The bird is fairly common in winter and on migration in Alabama and is quite regular and sometimes numerous in favored places. Although it has been noted once in summer, it has not been known to breed here. It occurs on the same ponds, lakes, and bays as other scaup but prefers the wider expanses of not-too-deep water in the Tennessee River and Mobile Bay. Inland it occurs in small flocks. It is abundant only on the coast.

ANSERIFORMES: ANATIDAE: CANVASBACK

NESTING AND FOOD. The Canvasback hides its nest carefully in a clump of prairie marsh vegetation. A basket of reeds and grasses lined with down, the nest usually holds seven to nine or more grayish-olive eggs. This duck likes to feed on wild celery, and when it does, is reputed to be one of the tastiest of ducks. Its specific name, *valisineria*, comes from the generic name of the wild celery plant. It also eats pondweeds, wild potato, sedges, widgeon grass, foxtail grass, coontail, banana waterlilies, and nutgrass or chufa. Occasionally it takes waste grain, especially wheat, and mollusks, insects, and fish.

DISTRIBUTION. The Canvasback breeds from Alaska and central Manitoba south to northern California and northern Minnesota. It winters from southern British Columbia, southern Illinois, and Massachusetts south to central Mexico and Florida.

OCCURRENCE IN ALABAMA. (Normal: October 17 to May 15; Out-of-season: June 5.) *Tennessee Valley*: October 28 (1955, Wheeler Refuge, T. A. Imhof) to May 15 (1952, Wheeler Refuge, H. H. Grammer); most seen, 200, January or February 1954 (Wheeler Refuge, D. C. Hulse). *Mountain Region*: November 11 (1956, Birmingham, Adele West) to March 27 (1957, Birmingham, Harriett Wright and Marjorie Ayres); also June 5, 1956 (Birmingham, T. A. Imhof); most seen, 78, December 20, 1958 (Christmas Count, Birmingham). *Piedmont*: October 28 (1953, Lee Co., D. W. Speake) to April 8 (1953, Auburn, H. G. Good); most seen, 63, December 19, 1955 (Delta Lake, Clay Co., E. L. Humphries). *Upper Coastal Plain*: October 17 (1955, Marion, W. W. Beshears) to March 26 (1955, Marion, T. A. Imhof, Lois McCollough, and

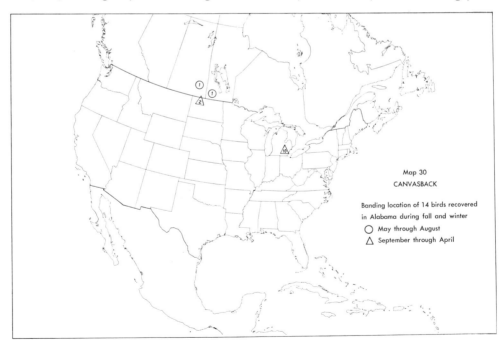

Map 30
CANVASBACK

Banding location of 14 birds recovered in Alabama during fall and winter
○ May through August
△ September through April

[148]

Idalene Snead); most seen, 25, January 13, 1954 (Sumter Farms Lake, W. W. Beshears). *Lower Coastal Plain*: October 19 (1953, Barbour County Lake, J. M. Fleming) to at least January 12 (1957, Florala, L. C. Crawford and J. R. Stinson); most seen, 75, December 16, 1955 (Coffee County Lake, L. C. Crawford). *Gulf Coast*: November 1 (1958, Gulf

Shores, H. M. Stevenson and Lovett Williams) to April 21 (1956, Cochrane Causeway, H. M. Stevenson); most seen, 7600, January 7, 1955 (Mobile Delta, W. F. Colin).

BANDING. All 14 banded Canvasbacks reported from Alabama are from the Mobile area. For place of banding, see Map 30.

Greater Scaup

Aythya marila (Linnaeus) [148] (Plate 10, facing page 144)
OTHER NAMES: Big Bluebill, Broadbill, Grayback, Dos-gris, Dogs, Blackhead, Bullhead

This duck is like a larger Lesser Scaup, for both males have a white back and sides and a black head, chest, and tail. In strong light at close range, the head of the male Greater Scaup shows a greenish gloss, while that of the Lesser Scaup is purplish. Females of both species are dark brown with a reddish tinge and a large, well-defined white area at the base of the bill. These two scaup are best distinguished by their wing stripes. The white on the Greater Scaup includes all but a few of the outermost primaries, while that on the Lesser Scaup rarely if ever extends beyond the bend of the wing into the primaries.

The Greater Scaup is locally common in winter on the Gulf Coast of Alabama, rare in late fall in the Tennessee Valley, and has been recorded once in the intervening area. Although a pair has been noted once in summer on the coast, there is no indication that the species breeds in Alabama. On the coast, the species occurs on the outermost bays, this being a salt-water duck in winter. Inland it should be identified only with extreme care because it so closely resembles the Lesser Scaup.

NESTING AND FOOD. For nesting this duck chooses marshy ground or ground near a small pond. It builds with weeds and grass, lines the whole with down, and lays seven to ten buffy-olive eggs. About half of the food of the Greater Scaup is plant life. It eats the stems, leaves, and roots of pondweeds, ditchgrass, muskgrass, water milfoil, sedges, wild celery, eelgrass, and other water plants. It also feeds on many mollusks, especially snails, oysters, and mussels, depending on what is locally available, and also some crustaceans and water insects.

DISTRIBUTION. The Greater Scaup breeds on the Arctic coasts of Alaska and Canada south to North Dakota and Michigan. It winters on the Pacific

Coast from the Aleutian Islands to Lower California, on the Atlantic Coast from Quebec to Florida, on the Great Lakes, and on the Gulf Coast from Texas to Florida, rarely farther south.

OCCURRENCE IN ALABAMA. (Normal: November 4 to April 13; Out-of-season: June 16.) *Tennessee Valley*: Wheeler Refuge and vicinity, November 17, 1954 (female shot by a hunter and examined by F. X. Lueth); November 22, 1954 (female killed by D. C. Hulse, wing preserved at Wheeler Refuge); November 30, 1944 (male trapped and banded by J. H. Steenis); December 2 and 9, 1958 (2 birds shot by D. C. Hulse and J. Ross Williams); December 20, 1942 (male shot by D. C. Hulse). *Mountain Region*: No record. *Piedmont*: No record. *Upper Coastal Plain*: November 27, 1959 (specimen in the Dept. of Conservation collection, Mt. Meigs, Montgomery Co., R. W. Skinner). *Lower Coastal Plain*: No record. *Gulf Coast*: November 4 (1955, Cedar Point, T. A. Imhof and others) to April 13 (1957, Gulf Shores, H. M. Stevenson and Lovett Williams); also June 16, 1956 (Dauphin Island, a pair identified at close range in flight, T. A. Imhof and J. L. Dusi); most seen, 600+, January 19, 1957 (Grand Bay, Mobile Co., T. A. Imhof and others); in 1947 F. X. Lueth identified 23 birds in game bags at the head of Mobile Bay, and in 1948 he identified 15 more.

Lesser Scaup
Aythya affinis (Eyton)   [149]   (Plate 10, facing page 144)

The Lesser Scaup is called by all the common names of the Greater Scaup, except that each one is usually prefaced by "Little." This duck differs from the slightly larger Greater Scaup in that the male's glossy black head has a purplish tinge at close range and in good light, and the white wing stripes are shorter in length, usually including only the secondaries. The male Lesser Scaup has a *black head, neck, chest,* and *tail,* a *white back, sides,* and *belly,* and a *blue bill.* The female is a plain *dark brown bird* with a *well-defined white area* at the *base* of its *blue bill.* All black-headed, white-backed scaup seen inland in Alabama can be quite safely assumed to be Lesser Scaup.

This duck is abundant in winter and on migration in Alabama, and occasionally it summers here. With the Ring-necked Duck it shares the distinction of being the state's most widespread duck in winter. It prefers the deeper inland lakes and ponds. On the coast it occurs in salt, brackish, or fresh water, and it rafts in large numbers over beds of mussels and other mollusks or dabbles in shallows. Usually it associates with others of its genus, but at times it forms pure flocks. It is not known to breed here.

NESTING AND FOOD. The Lesser Scaup builds a grassy, down-lined nest in a tussock of prairie grass on the shore of a small slough. The clutch is usually nine to twelve olive eggs. Most of its food is plant life—the foliage and seeds of such water plants as pondweeds, water milfoil, wild celery, muskgrass, coontail, smartweeds, hornwort, waterlilies, and sedges. It also eats snails, mussels, other mollusks, crabs, and aquatic insects.

DISTRIBUTION. This scaup breeds from central Alaska and the west coast of Hudson Bay south to southern Alaska, Colorado, and Ohio. It winters from southern British Columbia, Colorado, southern Illinois, and the Chesapeake Bay, occasionally farther north, south to Colombia, Ecuador, and Trinidad.

OCCURRENCE IN ALABAMA. (October 7 to June 7; occasionally summers.) *Tennessee Valley*: October 15 (1949, Wheeler Refuge, T. A. Imhof and others) to June 7 (1955, Wheeler Refuge, D. C. Hulse); also June 20, 1951 (Wheeler Refuge, D. C. Hulse); most seen, 50,000 to 75,000, April 7, 1936 (Wheeler Refuge, A. R. Cahn), more recent, 1000, December 22, 1954 (Wheeler Refuge, E. A. Byford and C. M. Parker). *Mountain Region*: October 27 (1949, Birmingham, T. A. Imhof) to June 6 (1953, Birmingham, T. A. Imhof); also July 3, 1936 (Lake Purdy, H. M. Stevenson) and August 20, 1954 (Lake Purdy, F. X. Lueth); most seen, 802, December 27, 1942 (Christmas Count, Birmingham). *Piedmont*: October 28 (1953, Lee Co., D. W. Speake) to April 28 (1953, Auburn, H. G. Good); 2 summered at Lake Ogletree in 1953 (W. F. Helms). *Upper Coastal Plain*: October 7 (1890, Greensboro, W. C. Avery) to June 2 (1955, 12 birds, Greene Co., Ralph Allen); most seen, 150, November 16, 1953 (Marion, W. W. Beshears). *Lower Coastal Plain*: No fall dates to April 5 (1957, Jackson, T. A. Imhof and W. U. Harris); most seen, 32, February 26, 1955 (Florala, T. A. Imhof). *Gulf Coast*: October 7 (1956, Dauphin Island, S. A. Gauthreaux and others) to May 25 (1957, Dauphin Island, T. A. Imhof and H. C. Loesch); also June 20, 1932 (Cochrane Causeway, Helen Edwards) and July 31, 1959 (Cochrane Causeway, H. M. Stevenson); most seen, 10,000, November 7, 1931 (Daphne, M. Busby).

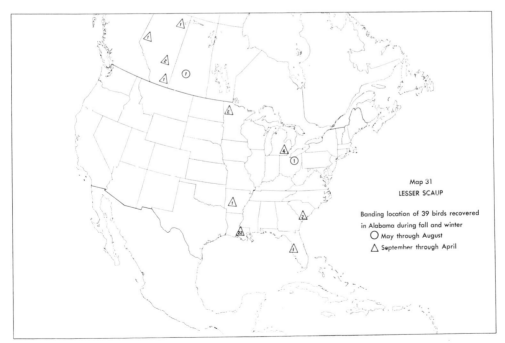

Map 31
LESSER SCAUP

Banding location of 39 birds recovered
in Alabama during fall and winter
○ May through August
△ September through April

PLATE 11

SURF SCOTER
Adult Female
Page 157

SURF SCOTER
Adult Male
Page 157

COMMON SCOTER
Adult Male
Page 158

COMMON SCOTER
Adult Female
Page 158

COMMON MERGANSER
Adult Female
Page 161

COMMON MERGANSER
Adult Male
Page 161

HOODED MERGANSER
Adult Female
Page 160

RED-BREASTED MERGANSER
Adult Female
Page 162

HOODED MERGANSER
Adult Male
Page 160

RED-BREASTED MERGANSER
Adult Male
Page 162

OLDSQUAW
Adult Male, Winter
Page 155

WHITE-WINGED SCOTER
Adult Female
Page 156

OLDSQUAW
Adult Female, Winter
Page 155

WHITE-WINGED SCOTER
Adult Male
Page 156

D. Hulse

BANDING. Of 39 banded Lesser Scaup reported from Alabama, 28 are from the Gulf Coast, 5 from the Tennessee Valley, 2 from Montgomery Co., and 1 each from Marion, Escambia, Covington, and Houston counties. For place of banding, see Map 31.

Common Goldeneye

Bucephala clangula (Linnaeus)   [151]   (Plate 10, facing page 144)
OTHER NAMES: Fiddler Duck, Whistler

The *male* Common Goldeneye is a white duck with black back and tail, a glossy, dark green head, and a large, round, *white spot* between the *eye* and the *bill*. The *female*, a gray duck with a *brown head*, wears a *white collar* high around the neck. Both sexes sport a large white patch that covers nearly all the inside half of the wing. This duck has a short neck and cheeks so puffy that they give the head a triangular shape, the head and puffy cheeks being useful in identification at a considerable distance. Its color pattern is nearly the same as that of the Red-breasted Merganser, yet the goldeneye is so chunky, and the merganser so long and thin, that the two are rarely confused—a fine illustration of the effectiveness of shape and proportion in identifying birds.

This duck is uncommon in winter and on migration in interior Alabama but locally common in the Tennessee Valley and on the Gulf Coast, especially on Mississippi Sound and Bon Secour Bay. It is not known to breed in this state. In the North it is common on fresh water and often remains until a hard freeze forces it to the coast, but in Alabama, even though fresh water remains open except in unusual circumstances, most of the birds pass on to the coast. Here the species becomes common on salt-water bays along with the Greater Scaup, Bufflehead, and Oldsquaw.

NESTING AND FOOD. For its nest this duck chooses a hollow tree near water, building with grass, leaves, and moss. Eight to twelve light greenish eggs are laid. The Common Goldeneye eats small crabs (including fiddlers), other crustaceans, insects, snails, mussels, crawfish, and small fish. It also eats wild celery, pondweeds, eelgrass, spatterdocks, and muskgrass.

DISTRIBUTION. The Common Goldeneye breeds from central Alaska, northern Labrador, and Newfoundland south to British Columbia and the northern parts of our northern tier of states. It winters from the Aleutian Islands, Montana, the Great Lakes, and Quebec south to Lower California, Texas, and Florida.

OCCURRENCE IN ALABAMA. (November 18 to April 24.) *Tennessee Valley*: November 18 (1949, 6 birds, Wheeler Refuge, W. E. Jernigan) to April 24 (1950, Wheeler Refuge, T. A. Imhof and W. E. Jernigan). *Mountain Region*: December 6

(1952, Birmingham, T. A. Imhof) to April 24 (1937, Lake Purdy, H. M. Stevenson). *Piedmont*: November 29 (1952, Auburn, F. W. Fitch) to March 20 (1953, Auburn, H. G. Good). *Upper Coastal Plain*: November 27 (1954, Marion, Lois McCollough) to April 19 (1956, Marion, T. A. Imhof); most seen, 8, December 16, 1955 (Marion, W. W. Beshears). *Lower Coastal Plain*: No record. *Gulf Coast*: November 23 (1915, specimen in the U. S. National Museum, Coffee Island, A. H. Howell) to April 10 (1937, Gulf Shores, H. G. Good); most seen, 435, December 30, 1960 (Christmas Count, Dauphin Island).

Bufflehead

Bucephala albeola (Linnaeus)   [153]   (Plate 10, facing page 144)
OTHER NAMES: Marionette, Butterball

This diminutive duck looks like a teal-sized goldeneye with different head markings. The *male* Bufflehead is largely white with a black back and head. A *large, white area* behind its *eye* covers more of its head than the glossy black. The *female* is a plain, dark brown duck which resembles a miniature female Common Goldeneye except for a *small, white patch* below and behind the *eye*. The drake has a white wing patch almost exactly like that of the goldeneye, but the wing patch of the female Bufflehead is small and on the trailing edge of the wing. This little duck is a rapid flyer which only rarely needs to patter across the water to gain flight.

The Bufflehead is uncommon in winter in most of Alabama, but locally common on deeper waters in the Tennessee Valley, on some of our larger lakes, and on the outermost bays of the Gulf Coast. It is not known to nest here. It seems to be about equally common on fresh and salt water in this state.

NESTING AND FOOD. This species nests near water in a natural tree cavity or in a deserted woodpecker hole and lays ten to twelve cream-colored eggs. On the coast in winter it eats shrimp, small fish, and several kinds of mollusks. On fresh water it feeds on small crawfish, leeches, snails, and large insects, especially grasshoppers. This diet is supplemented with wild celery, wild rice, and pondweeds.

DISTRIBUTION. The Bufflehead breeds from Alaska, Hudson Bay, and James Bay south to British Columbia and Montana, and rarely farther east and south. It winters from the Aleutian Islands to central Mexico and from western Montana, the Great Lakes, and New Brunswick south to the Gulf Coast.

OCCURRENCE IN ALABAMA. (October 26 to April 22.) *Tennessee Valley*: October 26 (1956, North Sauty Refuge, T. A. Imhof and M. W. Gaillard) to April 20 (1961, Wheeler Refuge, D. C. Hulse); most seen, about 250 (Wheeler Refuge, *fide* T. Z. Atkeson, Jr.). *Mountain Region*: November 22 (1947, Birmingham, T. A. Imhof) to April 4 (1949, 5 birds, Birmingham, T. A. Imhof). *Piedmont*: November 26 (1953, Lee Co., D. W. Speake) to April 18 (1953, Auburn, H. G. Good). *Upper Coastal Plain*:

November 15 (1957, Marion, Lois McCollough) to April 4 (1957, Marion, T. A. Imhof); most seen, 10, December 22, 1953 (Marion, W. W. Beshears). *Lower Coastal Plain*: No record. *Gulf Coast*: November 6 (1959, 4 birds, Dauphin Island, T. A. Imhof and F. B. Daniel) to April 22 (1957, Cedar Point, S. A. Gauthreaux, J. L. Dorn, and T. J. Hatrel); most seen, 215, February 8, 1957 (Bon Secour Bay, T. A. Imhof).

Oldsquaw
Clangula hyemalis (Linnaeus)   [154]   (Plate 11, facing page 152)

The Oldsquaw is a *dark-winged* sea duck with a *white belly, a dark brown back,* and a *head* with *dark brown* and *white* plumage the pattern of which varies with the season. In flight the dark wings and dark Y of the breast, center of the back, and tail make a contrasting pattern with the white scapulars and other white areas. The male has long, black, pointed, central tail feathers and a dark brown breast. In winter, the head is white with a two-toned brown spot over the eye and ear. In summer, it is dark brown with a large white circular area around the eye from bill to ear. The female lacks the long tail feathers, has a white breast and head and a dark brown lower neck, crown, bill, and patch below the eye. In summer it is darker, especially on the head and chest. The chattering of these birds when they are on the water has inspired many colorful local names, including "Oldsquaw."

On the Gulf Coast of Alabama this bird is uncommon but regular in winter in small numbers, especially in the deeper waters of Bon Secour Bay, Mobile Bay, and the Gulf. Inland on deeper waters in mid-winter it is erratic and rarely remains long or occurs annually in any one locality, although it occurs rather frequently in and near Wheeler Refuge. It is not known to breed in Alabama. Specimens caught in fish nets have proved that the Oldsquaw can dive to a depth of 180 feet.

NESTING AND FOOD. The female lays five to seventeen olive-buff eggs in a grass and weed nest placed under grass and bushes near water on the tundra. This duck lives chiefly on shellfish and crustaceans, and in winter it feeds extensively on mussels. Only a small portion of its food is plant life, particularly grasswrack and eelgrass. This diet does not make it very tasty, and so most experienced hunters do not take it.

DISTRIBUTION. The Oldsquaw breeds on Arctic coasts south to the Aleutian Islands, southern Yukon, Hudson Bay, and the mouth of the St. Lawrence River. It winters on the Great Lakes and coastally south to California, Colorado, the northern Gulf Coast, and Florida.

OCCURRENCE IN ALABAMA. (October 24 to April 11.) *Tennessee Valley*: October 24 (1952, Wheeler Refuge, D. C. Hulse) to April 11 (1961, Wheeler Refuge, W. M. Depreast, Philip Kyle, and T. Z. Atkeson, Jr.); specimen at Wheeler Refuge of a male of a pair seen January 15, 1957 (Wheeler Refuge, D. C. Hulse); most seen, 26, January 1961 (Wheeler Refuge, D. C. Hulse). *Mountain Region*: January 25 (1935, Birmingham, H. M. Stevenson) to March 2 (1947, 3 birds, Lake Purdy, T. A. Imhof). *Piedmont*: No record. *Upper Coastal Plain*: November 11 (1952, Montgomery, J. E. Keeler) to March 7 (1954, Marion, Harriett Wright); specimen from Marion, date unknown (C. A. Wiant); most seen, 3, about December 15, 1958 (Livingston, Juanita Ennis and Jenkins Jackson). *Lower Coastal Plain*: No record. *Gulf Coast*: November 5 (1955, Heron Bay, T. A. Imhof and others) to March 12 (1955, flock of 8, Bon Secour Bay, T. A. Imhof and others and 1960, Mobile Bay, J. L. Dorn); most seen, 65, January 9, 1961 (Fort Morgan, J. L. Dorn) and 30, January 25, 1947 (Bon Secour Bay, T. A. Imhof and others); December 30, 1955 (specimen in the Dept. of Conservation collection, Mobile Bay, W. W. Beshears and W. F. Colin).

White-winged Scoter

Melanitta deglandi (Bonaparte) [165] (Plate 11, facing page 152)

OTHER NAMES: White-winged Coot, Sea Coot

This bird is a *chunky, black* sea duck with a *white patch* on the inside rear edge of the *wing*. When the bird rests on the water this patch may be hidden. The male has a small, irregular white line under the eye and a black knob at the base of the bill. The female, almost as dark as the male, has two light patches, one before and one behind the eye, and young birds of both sexes have the same patches. The flight of this species is rather slow and heavy for a duck.

Scoters usually occur in winter on the open ocean near shore or on coastal bays. In Alabama the White-winged Scoter is rare in winter and so far has been recorded only near Decatur and in the Gulf of Mexico just off the beaches. It is not known to breed here.

NESTING AND FOOD. The female selects a depression in the ground usually near water and lines it with grass, sticks, leaves, rubbish, and down. This bird lays nine to fourteen salmon-buff eggs, buries them, and then digs them out when the clutch is nearly complete. For its food this scoter prefers mollusks, especially clams, mussels, oysters, scallops, and periwinkles. In addition it eats hermit crabs, other crustaceans, some caddis fly larvae, bur-reed, and algae.

DISTRIBUTION. The White-winged Scoter breeds from northwestern Alaska and Labrador south to northeastern Washington, southern Manitoba, and central North Dakota. It winters on the Pacific Coast from the Aleutian Islands to Lower California, inland in British Columbia, Colorado, and the Great Lakes, on the Atlantic Coast from the Gulf of St. Lawrence to South Carolina, and rarely on the northern Gulf Coast.

OCCURRENCE IN ALABAMA. (November 2 to April 13.) *Tennessee Valley*: Decatur and vicinity, November 2, 1954 (a female, D. C. Hulse); December 2, 1942 (1 bird in a game bag, Paul Bryan and J. H. Steenis); December 12, 1960 (specimen in Dept. of Conservation collection, James Call); and December 21, 1942 (1 seen, Ernest Holland). *Mountain Region*: No record. *Piedmont*: No record. *Upper Coastal Plain*: No record. *Lower Coastal Plain*: No record. *Gulf Coast*: November 29, 1957 (15 birds flying west at Fort Morgan, B. L. Monroe, Jr. and H. M. Stevenson); December 27, 1947 (a female or immature in the surf at Gulf Shores, T. A. Imhof); February 28, 1959 (9 birds flying west off Dauphin Island, S. A. Gauthreaux, J. P. Gee, Dorothy Howerton, and Mary Lewis); and April 13, 1957 (3 birds at Gulf Shores, F. M. Weston, B. L. Monroe, Jr., and L. E. Goodnight).

Surf Scoter

Melanitta perspicillata (Linnaeus)   [166]   (Plate 11, facing page 152)
OTHER NAMES: Skunkhead Coot, Sea Coot

The Surf Scoter is a stocky duck. The *male* is black with *two white patches* on the *top* of its *head,* while the *female* is very dark brown and has *two light areas on the sides of the head.* It looks much like the female White-winged Scoter but the *Surf Scoter's wings* are entirely *dark.*

This is the commonest scoter in Alabama, yet it has been recorded inland only once, in the Tennessee Valley. The Surf Scoter is uncommon but regular in winter in Mississippi Sound and nearby waters in Alabama where it flocks with Greater and Lesser Scaup and occasionally with the Common Scoter. It is not known to nest here.

NESTING AND FOOD. The usual clutch is five to nine pinkish or buffy-white eggs, laid in a grass and weed nest on the ground, ordinarily in a clump of marsh grass. This duck lives principally on mussels, but it also eats other mollusks, small crabs, insects, fish, algae, pondweeds, and eelgrass.

DISTRIBUTION. The Surf Scoter breeds from northwestern Alaska and Labrador south to James Bay and the Gulf of St. Lawrence. It winters on the Pacific Coast from the Aleutian Islands to Lower California, on the Great Lakes, on the Atlantic Coast from the Bay of Fundy to Florida, on the northern Gulf Coast, and rarely inland from British Columbia and Minnesota to Arizona and Kentucky.

OCCURRENCE IN ALABAMA. (November 8 to April 13.) *Tennessee Valley*: January 23, 1961 (Wheeler Refuge, D. C. Hulse and James Call). *Mountain Region*: No record. *Piedmont*: No record. *Upper Coastal Plain*: No record. *Lower Coastal Plain*: No record. *Gulf Coast*: November 8 (1957, Cochrane Causeway, J. E. Keeler) to April 13 (1957, Coffee Island, T. A. Imhof and others); most seen, 50 to 75 near Coffee Island (*fide* A. H. Howell, 1928:65), recent, 3, November 20, 1959 (Dauphin Island, Ava Tabor and Electa Levi); specimens, 1, November 13, 1915 (Pointe aux Pines, A. H. Howell) and another February 8, 1916 (in U. S. National Museum, Grand Bay, Mobile Co., W. L. Bryant).

[Common Scoter]
Oidemia nigra (Linnaeus)   [163]   (Plate 11, facing page 152)
OTHER NAMES: American Scoter, Black Scoter, Coot

The *male* Common Scoter is all *black* except for a bright *yellowish-orange knob* at the *base* of its *bill*. It has a slightly longer tail and a higher forehead than our other scoters. The *female* is plain dark brown with the whole *side* of the *head* and *upper neck light-colored*. Immature birds resemble the female.

This duck is rare to casual in winter on the Alabama Gulf Coast where it has so far been found in Mississippi Sound and upper Mobile Bay in small flocks usually with Surf Scoters and Greater and Lesser Scaup. It is not known to breed in this state.

NESTING AND FOOD. The nest is well hidden in a low place sheltered by foliage and near water. It is made of coarse grass lined with fine grass, feathers, and down, and usually holds six to ten light-buffy eggs. The Common Scoter feeds on the blue mussel, clams, oysters, barnacles, limpets, starfish, periwinkles, and other invertebrate sea animals.

DISTRIBUTION. This species breeds from Alaska and Labrador south to the Aleutian Islands and James Bay. It winters from the Aleutian Islands to southern California, on the Great Lakes, from Newfoundland to South Carolina, and irregularly on the northern Gulf Coast and in Florida.

OCCURRENCE IN ALABAMA. *Gulf Coast only*: Upper Mobile Bay, 3 immature or female specimens (not preserved) examined in hunters' bags between November 26 and December 25, 1948 (F. X. Lueth); Mississippi Sound, December 21, 1957 (flock of 8, T. A. Imhof); December 27, 1958 (a female or immature, T. A. Imhof and R. W. Skinner); and April 13, 1957 (4 birds, T. A. Imhof, M. W. Gaillard, and Freddie Bosarge).

SUBFAMILY OXYURINAE: RUDDY AND MASKED DUCKS

Ruddy Duck
Oxyura jamaicensis (Gmelin)   [167]   (Plate 10, facing page 144)
OTHER NAME: Sleeper

The Ruddy Duck is a *small, grayish* duck with *white cheeks, dark wings*, a slightly upturned bill, and a well-developed tail which it frequently holds at an angle, as a wren does. In spring, males become reddish-brown and have a bright blue bill. *Females* have a brown bill and a *dark line on the cheeks*. On land this species is very awkward because its feet are set far to the rear, but in the water it is completely at home. When alarmed it prefers diving to taking flight, and it is also able to sink slowly out of sight beneath the surface like a grebe.

Fairly common as a transient and in winter in Alabama, this duck occurs in the shallower parts of the fairly deep ponds—the same ponds as those frequented by the American Coot and members of the scaup genus. Although it has summered a few times around Marion, it is not known to breed anywhere in the state.

NESTING. The nest is a floating, arched basket of reeds and other nearby vegetation. It is carefully concealed and firmly anchored on a prairie slough near the shore. The eggs are very large for so small a duck, dull white or creamy-white, and usually there are six to ten of them. This is the only North American duck that raises two broods a season, and the only one in which the male invariably assists in rearing the young.

FOOD. In fresh water the Ruddy Duck lives on the roots, leaves, and seeds of water plants such as wild rice, wild celery, bulrushes, pondweeds, arrowhead, and waterlilies. On salt water it eats mollusks, snails, fiddler crabs, young crabs, and small fish.

DISTRIBUTION. The Ruddy Duck breeds from central British Columbia and northern Manitoba south to Guatemala and the West Indies, and also in the Great Lakes region and rarely farther east. It winters from southern British Columbia, southern Illinois, and Massachusetts south to Costa Rica and the West Indies.

OCCURRENCE IN ALABAMA. (September 29 to May 11; occasionally summers.) *Tennessee Valley*: October 10 (1959, Wheeler Refuge, T. A. Imhof) to April 22 (1951, Wheeler Refuge, D. C. Hulse). *Mountain Region*: October 27 (1949, Birmingham, T. A. Imhof) to April 5 (1952, Birmingham, T. A. Imhof and others); most seen, 150, December 27, 1942 (Birmingham, M. F. Prather). *Piedmont*: November 11 (1954, Auburn, D. W. Speake) to April 19 (1958, Auburn, R. W. Skinner and others). *Upper Coastal Plain*: September 29 (1955, Marion, Lois McCollough) to May 11 (1957, Marion, Lois McCollough); summered several times at Marion (Lois McCollough); most seen, 75, November 16, 1953 (Marion, W. W. Beshears). *Lower Coastal Plain*: October 21 (1958, Camden, Lovett Williams) to at least February 26 (1955, 83 birds, Florala, T. A. Imhof). *Gulf Coast*: November 1 (1958, Bayou La Batre, T. A. Imhof) to April 10 (1937, Gulf Shores, H. G. Good); most seen, 250, November 17, 1952 (Mobile Delta, W. F. Colin).

BANDING. The single banding recovery from Alabama is that of a bird shot on Mobile Bay, November 21, 1953, that had been banded in North Dakota, August 21, 1950.

SUBFAMILY MERGINAE: MERGANSERS

The three American birds in this subfamily (called Sawbills, Bec-scies, Bexies, Sheldrakes, or Fish Ducks) have a narrow, toothed bill for seizing the fish which are their principal food. With the exception of the Common Merganser drake, all mergansers are crested and all have long necks. In flight the rapid wing beat and the long body held perfectly straight from bill to tail are characteristics which make them easy to distinguish from other ducks. These are diving ducks, and before taking flight they patter across the water.

Hooded Merganser
Lophodytes cucullatus (Linnaeus) [131] (Plate 11, facing page 152)
OTHER NAMES: Summer Duck, Sawbill, Bec-scie, Bexie, Sheldrake, Fish Duck

This is the darkest, chunkiest, and smallest merganser. The *male* has a black head with a *black-bordered, white, fan-like crest.* Two black crescents separate the white of the breast from the ruddy color of the sides. The bill, neck, and back are also black, and the wings have a small patch of white. The *female,* largely dark gray, has a white belly, a dark bill, and a *rufous-red crest* and in flight shows a little white on the rear of the wing near the body. This pattern closely resembles that of a Gadwall, but the long, thin shape and the rapid wing beat readily distinguish the merganser.

The Hooded Merganser is common to abundant in winter and on migration in much of Alabama. In summer a few remain to breed in swamps and timbered sloughs in the Tennessee Valley and south at least to Clarke County. (See Map 32.) In winter this duck is most numerous in the Tennessee Valley. While most of the birds remain on fresh water, a few occur on the brackish and salt waters of the coast.

NESTING. This species builds in a hollow tree near water. The nest is made of grasses, leaves, feathers, and down, and holds from six to twelve ivory-white eggs.

FOOD. The Hooded Merganser feeds on crabs, shrimp, crawfish, small fish, frogs, tadpoles, aquatic insects, and tupelo gum seeds.

DISTRIBUTION. This species breeds locally from southern Alaska and New Brunswick south to Oregon, Nebraska, southern Alabama, and central Florida. It winters from southern British Columbia, Colorado, Lake Michigan, and Massachusetts south to east-central Mexico and Florida, rarely Cuba.

[160]

OCCURRENCE IN ALABAMA. (Throughout the year, dates below apply to birds not breeding locally.) *Tennessee Valley*: November 3 (1915, specimen in U. S. National Museum, Leighton, A. H. Howell) to April 3 (1912, specimen in U. S. National Museum, Town Creek, A. H. Howell); most seen, 750, December 11, 1954 (Wheeler Refuge, E. A. Byford and C. M. Parker), breeding, 3 to 5 pairs (Wheeler Refuge, *fide* T. Z. Atkeson, Jr.); specimen in Auburn Wildlife collection, mature male in eclipse plumage found dead at Wheeler Refuge, June 15, 1959 (*fide* T. Z. Atkeson, Jr.). *Mountain Region*: October 16 (1956, Talladega, Bill Kelly) to April 18 (1950, Birmingham, T. A. Imhof); most seen, 24, January 2, 1949 (Birmingham, T. A. Imhof). *Piedmont*: November 15 (1954, Auburn, D. W. Speake) to April 18 (1953, Auburn, D. W. Speake); most seen, 34, December 15, 1954 and January 11, 1955 (Auburn, Bill Kelly). *Upper Coastal Plain*: October 9 (1954, Marion, Lois McCollough) to April 16 (1955, Marion, Lois McCollough); most seen, 22, January 26, 1957 (Marion, Harriett Wright and Lois McCollough). *Lower Coastal Plain*: November 5 (1953, Barbour County Lake, J. E. Keeler and others) to April 19 (1958, McIntosh, T. A. Imhof and others); most seen, 22, January 11, 1958 (McIntosh, T. A. Imhof and others). *Gulf Coast*: November 12 (1915, specimen in U. S. National Museum, Bayou La Batre, A. H. Howell) to April 10 (1937, Gulf Shores, H. G. Good); also July 15, 1953 (Cochrane Causeway, J. L. Dorn); most seen, 23, December 28, 1959 (Cochrane Causeway, J. L. Dorn).

TIME OF BREEDING. Data on 7+ nestings: Eggs, April 19; flightless young, April 27 to May 25.

BANDING. An injured bird found near Huntsville, June 11, 1933, wore a band placed on it in Wisconsin, April 10, 1931.

Map 32

HOODED MERGANSER
Distribution

◑ May through August   ◯ Specimen collected
● Breeding positive

Common Merganser

Mergus merganser Linnaeus   [129]   (Plate 11, facing page 152)

OTHER NAMES: American Merganser, Sawbill, Bec-scie, Bexie, Sheldrake, Fish Duck

The *male* of this Mallard-sized duck is *largely white*, but it has a dark green, *uncrested* head, black on the outer half of its wing, black on the center of its back, black tail, red bill, and a faint rosy wash on its breast. The slightly smaller and paler *female* is a gray, *crested* merganser with a bright rufous-red head and neck, and the white in the wings confined to the trailing edge. It has a

[161]

sharply-defined white chin patch which distinguishes it from the female Red-breasted Merganser. In flight the Common Merganser usually follows the water and rarely cuts across stream bends or headlands.

This merganser is fairly common to uncommon in winter in the Tennessee Valley and rare and irregular elsewhere in the state. Its abundance is probably determined by ice conditions farther north, for in winter it remains on deeper fresh water as late as possible. Thus it is more common inland in Alabama and seldom frequents salt water as do other northern ducks. It is not known to nest in Alabama.

NESTING AND FOOD. The nest of grass and moss usually contains nine to twelve buffy eggs, and is most often found in a hollow tree but sometimes it is in a crevice in rocks. This duck subsists largely on small rough fish such as minnows, chubs, and suckers, varied with crawfish, frogs, aquatic insects, and water plants. When it visits salt water it also eats crustaceans and mollusks.

DISTRIBUTION. The Common Merganser breeds from southern Alaska, central Quebec, and Newfoundland south to central California, Chihuahua, South Dakota, central New York, and Nova Scotia. It winters from the Aleutian Islands, southern British Columbia, the Great Lakes, and the St. Lawrence Valley south to northern Mexico and the Gulf states.

OCCURRENCE IN ALABAMA. (November 1 to April 18.) *Tennessee Valley*: November 1 (1951, Wheeler Refuge, H. H. Grammer, D. C. Hulse, and T. Z. Atkeson, Jr.) to March 25 (1950, Wheeler Refuge, Clarence Cottam); most seen, 200, January 1951 (Wheeler Refuge, *fide* T. Z. Atkeson, Jr.). *Mountain Region*: December 19 (1943, 5 birds, Birmingham, M. F. Prather) to April 3 (1937, Birmingham, H. M. Stevenson). *Piedmont*: November 29, 1954 (Lake Ogletree, D. W. Speake); December 26, 1959 (Auburn, J. L. Dusi and others) and an undated specimen in the Auburn Wildlife collection (Auburn, F. E. Guyton). *Upper Coastal Plain*: December 21, 1956 (a female, Marion, Lois McCollough) and February 27, 1954 (a female, T. A. Imhof and others). *Lower Coastal Plain*: Point A Lake, Covington Co., January 12, 1957, 2 males and 7 females (L. C. Crawford and J. R. Stinson). *Gulf Coast*: Cochrane Causeway, between November 20 and December 25, 1952 (1 in a hunter's bag, *fide* F. X. Lueth); Bon Secour Bay, February 3, 1943 (6 birds, J. L. Dorn); and Dauphin Island and vicinity, March 22, 1958 (a pair, S. A. Gauthreaux and others); a flock of 10, December 27, 1958 (Blanche Chapman and Blanche Dean), 5 still present, April 9, 1959 (Owen Davies) and 1, April 18, 1959 (H. A. J. and Cora Evans) and a male, January 2, 1960 (T. A. and Joseph Imhof).

Red-breasted Merganser

Mergus serrator Linnaeus   [130]   (Plate 11, facing page 152)
OTHER NAMES: Sea Sawbill, Sea Bec-scie, Sea Bexie, Sheldrake, Fish Duck

The Red-breasted Merganser is slightly smaller than the Common Merganser and shows less white, both when it is on the water and when it is in flight. The *male* differs from the male Common Merganser in being *crested* and having a reddish-brown breast and darker flanks. The *white chin patch* of the *female* is *ill-defined,* in contrast to the chin patch of the female Common Merganser, which is sharply-defined. The females of both species have a rufous-red head but the head of this duck is *paler* and *shades gradually* into the white of the breast.

In winter and on migration, the Red-breasted Merganser is abundant on the Alabama Gulf Coast and fairly common inland, especially in the Tennessee Valley. On the coast this salt-water merganser is widespread but occurs most often on the Gulf itself. In summer it has been noted once inland, and on the coast a few are recorded almost every summer, but it has not been known to nest in the state.

NESTING AND FOOD. The female lays eight to ten olive-buff eggs in a nest of grass, leaves, and moss on the ground in rock crevices or in brush near water. Except for the Ruddy Duck, this male takes a more active part in raising the young than any other North American duck. The Red-breasted Merganser eats fish, shrimp, and shellfish. The fish taken are almost always trash fish because they are so much easier to obtain. Fishermen fail to appreciate this weeding-out process, and deplore the fact that groups of mergansers often dive in unison into a school of fish.

DISTRIBUTION. This merganser breeds in the Western Hemisphere from the Arctic Coast of Alaska, Baffin Island, and central Greenland south to northern British Columbia, central Minnesota, and Newfoundland. It winters from southeastern Alaska, the Great Lakes, and Nova Scotia south to Lower California, Texas, and Florida.

OCCURRENCE IN ALABAMA. (October 18 to May 26; summers often.) *Tennessee Valley*: November 11 (Wheeler Refuge, *fide* T. Z. Atkeson, Jr.) to May 26 (1949, Wheeler Refuge, L. S. Givens); summered in 1940 (Wheeler Refuge, T. Z. Atkeson, Jr. and Green); most seen, 25, February 5, 1955 (Preston, Marshall Co., T. A. Imhof and others). *Mountain Region*: October 28 (1960, Birmingham, T. A. Imhof and Rosemary Gaymer) to May 8 (1953, Birmingham, T. A. Imhof). *Piedmont*: November 12, 1928 (Auburn, W. A. Ruffin) and April 18, 1953 (Auburn, H. G. Good). *Upper Coastal Plain*: November 1 (1957, Marion, Lois McCollough) to December 4 (1954, Marion, Lois McCollough); most seen, 16, November 15, 1954 (Sumter Farms, W. W. Beshears). *Lower Coastal Plain*: "Rare transient," no dates (Columbia, the T. Z. Atkesons). *Gulf Coast*: Non-summering birds, October 18 (1957, Dauphin Island, T. A. Imhof and others) to May 16 (1960, Dauphin Island, J. L. Dorn); most seen, 2850+, December 27, 1947 (Fort Morgan Peninsula, T. A. Imhof).

[163]

ORDER FALCONIFORMES: VULTURES, HAWKS, AND FALCONS

These generally large birds, powerful in flight, are usually able to soar, dive in the air, and course with great speed. Their nostrils open in a cere (a soft, swollen process) on powerful, hooked bills. The feet are strong, armed with sharp, curved claws for grasping prey, and the eyes are exceptionally keen. As a rule these birds perch high in exposed places—dead treetops, cliffs, tall man-made structures, and the like.

FAMILY CATHARTIDAE: AMERICAN VULTURES

The vultures, called buzzards in Alabama, are large, chiefly black, soaring birds of prey, with few if any feathers on the head. Because they feed on dead or dying animals, their bills and feet do not need great power, and their hind toes are small. Their nostrils are perforate, that is, undivided by a wall or septum.

Turkey Vulture

Cathartes aura (Linnaeus)   [325]   (Plate 12, facing page 168)
OTHER NAMES: Turkey Buzzard, Buzzard

The *big, black* Turkey Vulture has a *long tail* and a *bare, red head*; so when it is seen on the ground it somewhat resembles a turkey. Immature birds, however, have black heads. The paleness of the rear half of the wings and the posture of the wings in flight (somewhat like the shallow V of the Marsh Hawk wings) distinguish this species from the Black Vulture. The Turkey Vulture is almost as long as an eagle, but eagles are heavier and have larger heads and bills, longer wings, and shorter tails.

In Alabama the Turkey Vulture is a common to abundant, breeding, permanent resident. This widely-distributed species seems to be most common in wooded, mountainous country and least common over coastal marshes and beaches. Usually it is abroad on sunny, windy days when thermal updrafts develop and it can soar on motionless wings over ridge and woodland. On rainy or cloudy days it seldom flies. It roosts, sometimes in large groups, in dead treetops in a secluded, sheltered place, often on a mountain.

NESTING. This bird does not build a nest for its one or two creamy-white, lavender-spotted eggs, but in bottomlands it uses hollow trees, stubs and fallen logs, and in the highlands it hides or completely conceals the eggs on the ground between rocks, in crevices, or on ledges in cliffs. The dependent young are buffy-white, downy, quite ugly, and they are fed by disgorging.

FOOD. The Turkey Vulture is a carrion-eater. Birds come from many miles to feast on any dead animal. They often feed along roads on animals killed by passing automobiles. The value of this bird as a scavenger is well established; furthermore, it rarely disturbs livestock as the Black Vulture does.

DISTRIBUTION. This species breeds from British Columbia, southern Ontario, central New York, and Connecticut south to the southern tip of South America. It winters from California, Nebraska, the Ohio Valley, and Connecticut southward.

ABUNDANCE IN ALABAMA (*most seen in a day*). Wheeler Refuge 25+, May 1, 1948 (T. A. Imhof); Weaver, Calhoun Co., 35, December 21, 1943 (David Kemp); Birmingham, 16, December 20, 1947 (Christmas Count); Tuscaloosa, 38, December 23, 1940 (H. M. Stevenson); Marion, 30, February 27, 1954 (T. A. Imhof and others); Montgomery Co., 60+, October 20, 1956 (T. A. Imhof); Covington Co., and Geneva Co., 31, February 26, 1955 (T. A. Imhof); Gulf Shores, 50, February 13, 1946 (T. A. Imhof).

TIME OF BREEDING. Data on 16 nestings: Eggs, March 31 to May 23; dependent young, May 23 to June 24.

BANDING. A banded bird found at Florence, November 18, 1944 had been banded at St. Mark's Refuge, Florida, February 1, 1938, over 6 years earlier. See Map 35.

Black Vulture

Coragyps atratus (Bechstein)   [326]   (Plate 12, facing page 168)
OTHER NAMES: Black Buzzard, Carrion Crow

Except for the *large, white areas* near the *tip* of *each wing*, this vulture is black, even to the skin on the bare head. It is quite different from the Turkey Vulture in shape. The Black Vulture has a longer neck, a *shorter tail,* and flies with its wings almost straight out. When the two are seen in flight together, the Black Vulture appears to have broader, shorter wings set in the center of the body, while the Turkey Vulture's wings are well forward. The Black Vulture is not so adept at soaring and must flap its wings often.

The Black Vulture is a common to abundant, breeding, permanent resident in this state. Although not as widely distributed as the Turkey Vulture, it occurs in large flocks, particularly southward, so that in numbers the two are

[165]

about equal. The Black Vulture is more prevalent in agricultural regions, especially where livestock is raised. It often loiters around pigsties or any place where it can obtain garbage, dead animals, or other offal.

NESTING. The one or two greenish-white or bluish-white eggs marked with dark brown or brownish-purple are laid without any nest material in a hollow tree, stump, or log on the ground, in rocky places, small caves, swampy bottomlands, or dense vine thickets. The young are quite similar to those of the Turkey Vulture, and they feed on the stomach contents of their parents which are disgorged on the ground in front of them.

FOOD. The Black Vulture will eat any kind of dead or decaying animal matter, including sewage, garbage, or carcasses. It sometimes kills newly-born livestock, and it often stays around heronries, feeding on anything that falls from the nests, whether young heron or dead fish.

DISTRIBUTION. This vulture is resident from southern Arizona, the Ohio Valley, and Delaware south to Chile and Argentina.

ABUNDANCE IN ALABAMA (*most seen in a day*). Wheeler Refuge, 50, May 1, 1948 (T. A. Imhof and others); Birmingham, 21, September 29, 1948 (T. A. Imhof); Auburn, 70, January 2, 1954 (Christmas Count); Marion, 175, January 2, 1955 (Lois McCollough); Tuscaloosa, 107, December 23, 1940 (H. M. Stevenson); Autauga Co., 130+, December 16, 1955 (T. A. Imhof, J. E. Keeler, and G. M. Kyle); Grove Hill, 100, October 6, 1957 (W. U. Harris); Slocomb, 65, September 21, 1957 (T. A. Imhof and Lovett Williams); Foley, 49, December 27, 1947 (Christmas Count).

EGGS OF BLACK VULTURE. The base of a hollow tree is the nest site. The Turkey Vulture nests in similar situations.

C. W. Summerour

TIME OF BREEDING. Data on 25 nestings: Eggs, March 8 to May 25; flightless young, March 29 to August 5.

BANDING. All 4 banded Black Vultures reported from Alabama had been winter-banded in Louisiana by E. A. McIlhenny. *Banded*, Louisiana, Avery Island, March 15, 1946; *recovered*, Grove Hill, March 3, 1947; *banded*, Louisiana, Avery Island, February 8, 1941; *recovered*, Robertsdale, May 10, 1942; *banded*, Louisiana, Avery Island, November 21, 1936; *recovered*, Hobson, Calhoun Co., May 14, 1938; *banded*, Louisiana, Avery Island, November 21, 1936; *recovered*, Chatom, May 13, 1938. See Map 35.

FAMILY ACCIPITRIDAE: HAWKS, OLD WORLD VULTURES, AND HARRIERS

These birds are typical hawks with the characteristics of the order *Falconiformes* well developed in them.

SUBFAMILY PERNINAE: HONEY BUZZARDS AND SWALLOW-TAILED KITES

Swallow-tailed Kite

Elanoides forficatus (Linnaeus) [327] (Plate 12, facing page 168)
OTHER NAMES: Snake Hawk, Fish Hawk, Forked-tailed Hawk

This large, strikingly marked, black and white hawk resembles a swallow in shape and flight. It is *white* with *black upper parts,* black *forked tail,* and *black flight feathers* in its *long, pointed wings.* Its flight is light, graceful, and often fast, giving the impression that the bird has complete mastery of the air.

In Alabama the Swallow-tailed Kite is an uncommon to rare summer resident in the Coastal Plain and has been noted once in winter. (See Map 33.) Breeding data for Alabama are few, but this hawk probably nests wherever it occurs in late May and June. It inhabits river swamps and spends much of its time on the wing just over the treetops or over fields near the river. Sometimes it occurs in flocks.

NESTING. The nest of twigs and grass, usually with some Spanish moss, is in the top of a tall tree near water. The bird lays two or three eggs which are white or buffy and boldly and handsomely marked with rich chestnut brown and dark brown.

FOOD. This hawk feeds wholly on large insects and small reptiles such as snakes, frogs, treefrogs, lizards, wasps, beetles, cicadas, grasshoppers, cotton worms, dragonflies, and others. It captures its prey with a graceful swoop and devours it on the wing.

[167]

Richard A. Parks

FALCONIFORMES: ACCIPITRIDAE: SWALLOW-TAILED KITE

DISTRIBUTION. The Swallow-tailed Kite breeds locally from central Texas, central Alabama, and South Carolina south more generally to Bolivia and Argentina. It winters in Central and South America, rarely Florida, and is casual on migration in many states and southern Canadian provinces north and east of its breeding range.

OCCURRENCE IN ALABAMA. (March 2 to August 5; also January 26 and November 24.) *Tennessee Valley*: No record. *Mountain Region*: No record. *Piedmont*: No record. *Upper Coastal Plain*: Dallas Co., daily in small groups in July 1858 (P. H. Gosse, 1859); Greensboro, "Not common, Once Abundant. It may breed along the Warrior River where now occasionally seen." (W. C. Avery, 1890); Autaugaville, about 1889 and November 24, 1945 (L. S. Golsan); Prattville, June 9, 1939 (1 shot, Douglas Evers) and Montgomery, May 23, 1939 (H. W. Holden, Jr.). *Lower Coastal Plain*: March 23 (1957, Choctaw Bluff, M. W. Gaillard) to August 5 (1954, Salt Springs Sanctuary, Clarke Co., 5 birds, J. E. Keeler and others); also January 26, 1921 (specimen in Dept. of Archives and History, Hartford, Geneva Co., *fide* P. A. Brannon, *Auk* 38:464); most seen, 100+, April 1960 (Choctaw Bluff, M. W. Gaillard). *Gulf Coast*: March 2 (1960, Coden, R. W. Skinner) to at least June 27 (1957, 8 birds, Tensaw, R. W. Skinner).

TIME OF BREEDING. Baldwin Co., near Mt. Vernon, carrying Spanish moss, May 26, 1956 (T. A. Imhof and W. F. Colin).

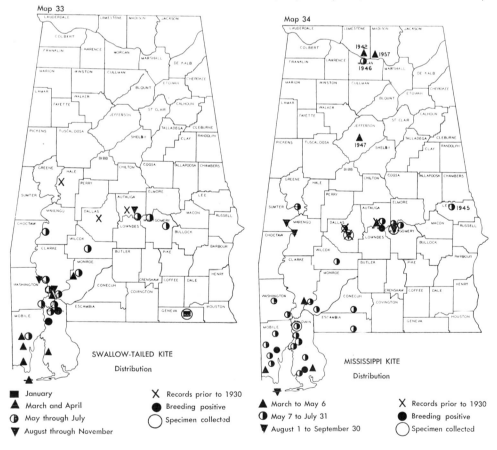

Map 33

Map 34

SWALLOW-TAILED KITE
Distribution

MISSISSIPPI KITE
Distribution

■ January
▲ March and April
◑ May through July
▼ August through November

✕ Records prior to 1930
● Breeding positive
○ Specimen collected

▲ March to May 6
◑ May 7 to July 31
▼ August 1 to September 30

✕ Records prior to 1930
● Breeding positive
○ Specimen collected

SUBFAMILY MILVINAE: TRUE KITES

Mississippi Kite
Ictinia misisippiensis (Wilson)   [329]   (Plate 12, facing page 168)

This kite is dark gray above and light gray below and is readily identified by its *pearly-gray head* and long, *black, square tail*. Its long, pointed wings have a whitish diagonal bar on the rear edge. The *young* bird is dark and streaked and has several bars on its tail, but the *tail* and wing tips are darker than those of other falcon-shaped birds.

The Mississippi Kite is an uncommon, breeding, summer resident and transient in Coastal Plain river and branch swamps, and it occurs occasionally north of the Fall Line in spring. (See Map 34.) It spends much of its time in the air, diving, swooping, and tumbling above the tall trees or over open fields, usually in river bottoms.

NESTING. This bird looks for an old nest abandoned by some other bird, selecting one in the top of a tall tree—usually a pine, sweetgum, or cottonwood. It renovates this nest with Spanish moss and green, leafy twigs, and then lays one or two pale bluish-white eggs which rarely have faint spots.

FOOD. This species feeds almost exclusively on large insects, especially cicadas, grasshoppers, locusts, dragonflies, and large beetles. Sometimes it also eats small snakes, frogs, and lizards. Its food is caught and consumed on the wing.

DISTRIBUTION. The Mississippi Kite breeds from northeastern Kansas, Iowa, and South Carolina south to Texas and northwestern Florida. It winters from southern Texas and Florida south to Mexico, rarely to Guatemala and Paraguay, and is casual on migration north and west of its breeding range.

OCCURRENCE IN ALABAMA. (March 26 to September 11.) *Tennessee Valley*: May 3, 1957 (Wheeler Refuge, T. A. Imhof, Edith Clark, and T. Z. Atkeson, Jr.); May 6, 1942 (J. H. Steenis) and June 3, 1946 (L. S. Givens). *Mountain Region*: March 29, 1947 (immediately after a tornado, Birmingham, T. A. Imhof). *Piedmont*: Late summer, 1945 (Auburn, Ralph Allen). *Upper Coastal Plain*: March 26 (1922, Booth, Autauga Co., L. S. Golsan) to September 1 (1958, 2 birds, Montgomery, R. W. Skinner); August 2, 1960 (specimen in Dept. of Con-servation collection, Montgomery, R. W. Skinner and J. E. Keeler); most seen, 7, May 13, 1958 (Montgomery, R. W. Skinner). *Lower Coastal Plain*: March 30 (1957, Choctaw Bluff, M. W. Gaillard) to August 7 (1958, 3 birds between Locks 2 and 3, Tombigbee River, Choctaw Co., Ralph Allen); most seen, 30+, June 1, 1951 (near Calvert, Washington Co., William J. Calvert). *Gulf Coast*: April 20 (1943, Spring Hill, J. L. Dorn) to September 11 (1960, Dauphin Island, Lovett Williams); most seen, 15, 1 a specimen in the Dept. of Conservation collection, May 7, 1958 (Tensaw, R. W. Skinner).

TIME OF BREEDING. Data on 3 Gulf Coast nestings: Copulation, May 31 (F. M. Weston); carrying food, July 22 (C. W. Summerour); large young, July (J. L. Dorn).

J. E. Keeler

NEST OF MISSISSIPPI KITE. This bird is rare in most sections of Alabama.

SUBFAMILY ACCIPITRINAE: BIRD HAWKS

These hawks have short, rounded wings and long tails. They are so skilled in flight that they can dart into dense cover to swoop up the birds which are their prey.

Sharp-shinned Hawk
Accipiter striatus Vieillot [332] (Plate 13, facing page 176)
OTHER NAMES: Little Blue Darter, Chicken Hawk, Bullet Hawk

The Sharp-shinned Hawk is a small hawk with short, rounded wings and a long tail. The adult male, much smaller than the female, is dark blue above and whitish, heavily barred with rufous, below. The female and the immature bird are dark brown above and heavily streaked with brown below. This species is similar in all plumages to the crow-sized Cooper's Hawk but the smaller Sharp-shinned Hawk's *tail* is *square when spread* and *notched when folded.* Size alone is not an adequate basis for field identification of these hawks.

[171]

FALCONIFORMES: ACCIPITRIDAE: SHARP-SHINNED HAWK

The Sharp-shinned Hawk is a locally common, permanent resident in the northern half of Alabama. Although we have but one positive instance of its nesting here, the species probably nests in June wherever it occurs. In winter it is common throughout the state, and on migration it is sometimes locally abundant. It occurs in almost any habitat, but in the breeding season usually frequents hilly, wooded districts, and on migration is most often noted along ridges or coastally along outer islands and peninsulas. (See Map 36.)

NESTING. This hawk builds a large nest of twigs, usually in a conifer 15 to 55 feet from the ground. The two or more dull bluish-white or greenish-white eggs are boldly and variously marked with brown.

FOOD. This is one of the two common Alabama hawks which prey on other birds. Other hawks eat birds only on rare occasions, but they are apparently mistakenly credited with the habits of the two bird-eating hawks, for many a hawk is shot on sight. The Sharp-shinned Hawk feeds on birds from the smallest to those larger than itself, like quail, dove, flicker, and small poultry. Occasionally it eats mice, other small mammals, frogs, lizards, and grasshoppers. It captures birds by a sudden swoop and a short dash, often through cover. Many birds seek safety in briars. The hawk's skill at hedge-hopping gives it the element of surprise it often needs.

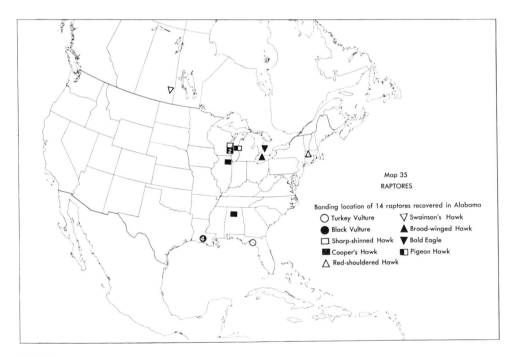

Map 35
RAPTORES

Banding location of 14 raptores recovered in Alabama

○ Turkey Vulture	▽ Swainson's Hawk
● Black Vulture	▲ Broad-winged Hawk
☐ Sharp-shinned Hawk	▼ Bald Eagle
■ Cooper's Hawk	◨ Pigeon Hawk
△ Red-shouldered Hawk	

DISTRIBUTION. The Sharp-shinned Hawk breeds from northwestern Alaska, southern Labrador, and Newfoundland south to California, Texas, central Alabama, and South Carolina, rarely farther south. It winters from British Columbia, the Great Lakes, and New England south to Panama.

OCCURRENCE IN ALABAMA. (Throughout the year.) *Tennessee Valley*: Permanent resident. *Mountain Region*: Permanent resident; most seen in Jefferson Co., 5, September 25, 1954 (Mulga Fire Tower, T. A. Imhof). *Piedmont*: Permanent resident. *Upper Coastal Plain*: Permanent resident. *Lower Coastal Plain*: September 17 (1958, Camden, Lovett Williams) to April 28 (1952, Andalusia, W. R. Middleton); also July 21, 1957 (Washington Co., W. U. Harris); summers in Barbour Co. (J. E. Keeler). *Gulf Coast*: September 14 (1958, Dauphin Island, H. A. J. and Cora Evans) to April 7 (1937, Gulf Shores, H. G. Good); most seen, 76, October 19, 1957 (Fall Count, Mobile Bay Area, 59 of these between Gulf Shores and Fort Morgan, F. M. Weston).

TIME OF BREEDING. Data on 1 nesting at Auburn: 2 fresh eggs, April 26, 1954 (C. W. Summerour).

BANDING. A bird banded at Cedar Grove, Wisconsin, September 21, 1954, was shot at Elba, Coffee Co., November 13, 1954. See Map 35.

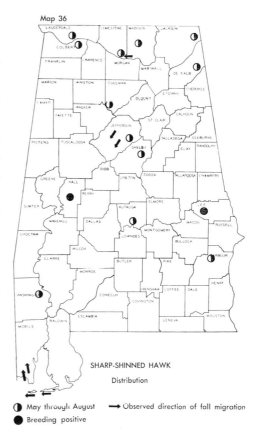

Map 36

SHARP-SHINNED HAWK

Distribution

◐ May through August   → Observed direction of fall migration

● Breeding positive

Cooper's Hawk

Accipiter cooperii (Bonaparte)   [333]   (Plate 13, facing page 176)

OTHER NAMES: Big Blue Darter, Chicken Hawk

This bird hawk is almost identical to the Sharp-shinned Hawk except that Cooper's Hawk is larger, being almost *crow-sized*, and has a *rounded tail*.

This species is a common, breeding, permanent resident throughout the state. Although not really numerous, it is widespread and wide-ranging, so that it is recorded commonly, especially in moderately-wooded areas. In many places it is more common in winter, when northern birds augment the local population.

[173]

NEST OF COOPER'S HAWK. This hawk nests uncommonly in Alabama so that this nest was an unusual find.

NESTING. Usually Cooper's Hawk builds its own nest, but it often appropriates a nest which another hawk or a crow has abandoned. The nest is from ten to fifty feet from the ground, near the trunk of a tree in secluded woods. Cooper's Hawk prefers a pine but sometimes takes a hardwood. The nest is built of sticks and twigs and is lined with a shallow bed of bark chips. Frequently it is occupied for several seasons and refurbished each year. The two to four pale bluish-white or greenish-white eggs are sometimes spotted with pale reddish-brown.

FOOD. Like the Sharp-shinned Hawk, this bird eats other birds, including those as large as robins, towhees, and meadowlarks. It is Cooper's Hawk which is the principal marauder of poultry yards. It will raid a yard daily in spite of the presence of humans, using the same hedge-hopping tactics as the Sharp-shinned Hawk. In addition to birds, it eats squirrels, rabbits, rats, mice, chipmunks, reptiles, amphibians, and insects.

DISTRIBUTION. Cooper's Hawk breeds from British Columbia across southern Canada to Nova Scotia and south to northern Mexico and Florida.

[174]

It winters from Washington, southern Michigan, and southern New England south to Costa Rica.

ABUNDANCE IN ALABAMA (*most seen in a day*). Birmingham, 5, December 28, 1957 (Christmas Count); Marion, 6, October 9, 1954 (Lois McCollough); Dauphin Island, 8, October 6, 1956 (S. M. Russell and E. O. Willis).

TIME OF BREEDING. Data on 9 nestings: Eggs, April 10 to 28; young in nest, June 2 to July 5.

BANDING. The 2 recoveries of this hawk from Alabama show its two-fold status here as permanent resident and winter visitor. One bird banded June 20, 1938 at Orland Park, Illinois was shot at Cherokee, Colbert Co., November 16, 1938. The other, banded at Wheeler Refuge, August 21, 1951, was shot at Priceville in the same county, October 25, 1952. See Map 35.

SUBFAMILY BUTEONINAE: HAWKS AND EAGLES

In Europe these birds are called Buzzards, which means a soaring bird, but in America this name has been given to the American Vultures. The birds of this subfamily have broad, rounded wings and tails, particularly suited to soaring and gliding. They are not capable of fast flight, for they cannot beat their great wings fast enough. Individual variation in plumage is frequent in these hawks, and many of them tend towards black.

These soaring hawks are not true bird-eaters. They eat birds only in severe winters when hard pressed for food, when this food is easy to obtain, or when satisfying the demands of hungry nestlings. Many of these hawks are shot at the sound of chickens squealing, but chickens will squeal whenever any large bird flies overhead. Many more are killed simply because they are hawks, but killing hawks indiscriminately is not a good policy. Soaring hawks have great value as mousers—a value equaled only by the owls. These birds, so often falsely blamed for nefarious habits, protect crops from rodents.

Red-tailed Hawk

Buteo jamaicensis (Gmelin) [337] (Plate 13, facing page 176)
OTHER NAMES: Hen Hawk, Chicken Hawk

This large hawk has broad, rounded wings and a rather short, rounded tail. The *adult* is dark brown above and white below, with a *rufous-red tail* and a broad zone of heavy streaks on the upper belly. The young bird lacks the red tail, its tail is generally unbarred, but it has a white chest and is usually rather heavily streaked on most of the under parts. When they are in flight, most Red-tailed Hawks can be identified from below by the combination of unbarred tail and black-bordered whitish wings. With much practice, birds of this family

[176]

Richard A. Parks

can be identified by relative proportions. This bird is heavier and has longer, broader wings and a shorter tail than the Red-shouldered Hawk. The call of the Red-tailed Hawk is a penetrating scream.

The Red-tailed Hawk breeds in heavily-wooded areas usually in hilly terrain, fairly commonly south to the Black Belt and uncommonly farther south. (See Map 37.) On migration and in winter (October to April) their number is increased by birds from the north, and this hawk is common throughout the state, particularly in hardwoods in valleys.

NESTING. The nest is a large and bulky affair of sticks, twigs, leaves, and moss. It is most often placed in the fork of a large tree, forty to eighty feet from the ground, but occasionally it is found well out on a limb near the top of a tall pine. The one to three dull whitish or bluish-white eggs are plain or variously marked with browns and reds.

FOOD. A large portion of the diet of this species consists of destructive rodents, in considerable variety but particularly rabbits and rats. The remainder includes grasshoppers, crickets, beetles, and, upon *rare* occasions, wild and domestic birds.

DISTRIBUTION. This hawk breeds from southeastern Alaska, Mackenzie, and Newfoundland south to Panama and the Greater Antilles. It winters from British Columbia, Minnesota, and central New England southward.

COLOR VARIATIONS OF RED-TAILED HAWKS. These museum specimens show the color variance of this species.

T. E. McKinney

T. E. McKinney

ALBINO RED-TAILED HAWK. This mounted specimen was collected in Autauga County in March, 1961.

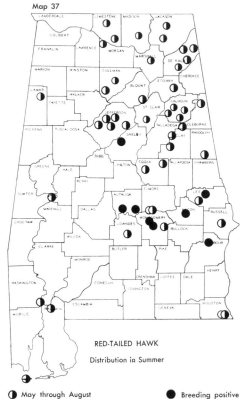

Map 37

RED-TAILED HAWK

Distribution in Summer

◑ May through August ● Breeding positive

OCCURRENCE IN ALABAMA. (Throughout the year.) *Tennessee Valley*: Permanent resident; most seen, 30, December 31, 1954 (Christmas Count, Wheeler Refuge). *Mountain Region*: Permanent resident; most seen, 14, December 26, 1953 (Christmas Count, Birmingham). *Piedmont*: Permanent resident. *Upper Coastal Plain*: Permanent resident; most seen, 20, February 27, 1959 (Montgomery, R. W. Skinner). *Lower Coastal Plain*: Uncommon and local permanent resident; no migration dates available. *Gulf Coast*: October 7 (1952, Foley, F. M. Weston) to April 23 (1960, 2 birds, Delchamps, J. L. Dorn and 1 bird, Dauphin Island, R. W. Skinner and others); also August 31, 1958 (Dauphin Island, S. A. Gauthreaux and others); most seen, 6, February 1, 1958 (southern Baldwin Co., T. A. Imhof and others).

TIME OF BREEDING. Data on 12 nestings: Eggs, February 28 to April 14; young in nest, April 12 to May 13.

SUBSPECIES. The very white, well-marked *Buteo jamaicensis kriderii* Hoopes of the Great Plains has been identified in Alabama as follows: Huntsville, October 1959, sketch made (J. C. and Margaret Robinson); Birmingham, April 17, 1953 (T. A. Imhof); Prattville, December 9, 1958 (R. W. Skinner); Montgomery Co., October 22 (1959, R. W. Skinner) to April 15 (1959, R. W. Skinner); November 16, 1958 (specimen, Dept. of Conservation collection, R. W. Skinner); most seen, 8, February 27, 1959 (R. W. Skinner); Livingston, January 11 (1959, Jenkins Jackson) to March 15 (1959, Jenkins Jackson); Union Springs, March 1959, most seen, 4 (R. W. Skinner and Lovett Williams); Coffeeville, Clarke Co., February 22, 1959 (Lovett Williams); and Alabama Port, December 27, 1958 (R. W. Skinner and T. A. Imhof).

BANDING. The 7 banded Red-tailed Hawks reported from Alabama were recovered during December, January, and February from points between Albertville

[178]

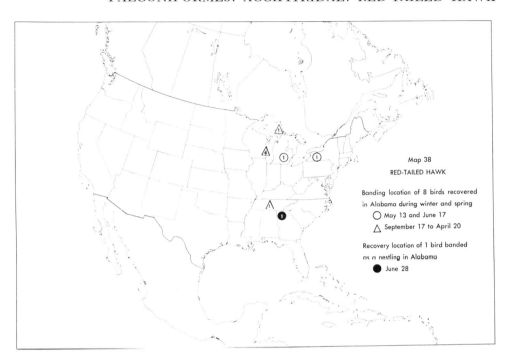

Map 38

RED-TAILED HAWK

Banding location of 8 birds recovered
in Alabama during winter and spring

○ May 13 and June 17

△ September 17 to April 20

Recovery location of 1 bird banded
as a nestling in Alabama

● June 28

YOUNG RED-TAILED HAWK IN PINE TREE. These hawks seldom nest in the Lower Coastal
Plain.

C. W. Summerour

and Mobile. See Map 38 for place of banding. One nestling banded by J. E. Keeler in Barbour Co., in May 1953 was recovered in Pickens Co., Georgia in June 1954. Another banded at Murfreesboro, Tennessee, December 18, 1942 was recovered at Elkmont, 70 miles south, on May 26, 1943.

[Harlan's Hawk]

Buteo harlani (Audubon)   [337d]   (Plate 13, facing page 176)

Harlan's Hawk closely resembles a dark-phased Red-tailed Hawk, but its *tail* is *whitish* at the *base,* sometimes extensively white, finely *mottled* with *black* with a *thin, broken black line* near the *tip.* Occasionally the tail is slightly red. Except for the tail, this bird's plumage varies considerably, from almost black to much white. Some have light areas on the head, under parts, and under surface of the flight feathers.

This hawk is casual in winter in Alabama, chiefly in the central part of the state. It is not known to nest here. It frequents the same places as does the Red-tailed Hawk, but appears to be a more active bird.

NESTING AND FOOD. So far as is known, the nest is made of sticks and placed rather high in a conifer. The eggs are yet to be described. This hawk's food is like that of the Red-tailed Hawk.

DISTRIBUTION. Harlan's Hawk breeds in eastern Alaska, Yukon, and northern British Columbia, and probably east to Manitoba. It winters from Kansas, southern Mississippi, and rarely southeastern Tennessee south to southern Texas and the northern Gulf Coast.

OCCURRENCE IN ALABAMA. (Late November to late February.) *Tennessee Valley*: No record. *Mountain Region*: Birmingham, December 26, 1955 (T. A. Imhof) and December 27, 1954 (Adele West). *Piedmont*: No record. *Upper Coastal Plain*: Montgomery, December 16, 1958 through February 1959 (R. W. Skinner) and late November 1959 (R. W. Skinner). *Lower Coastal Plain*: Thomaston, Marengo Co., December 15, 1959 (J. E. Keeler). *Gulf Coast*: No record.

Red-shouldered Hawk

Buteo lineatus (Gmelin)   [339]   (Plate 13, facing page 176)
OTHER NAMES: Hen Hawk

The *adult* Red-shouldered Hawk is dark above with *reddish-brown shoulders* and *whitish under parts* narrowly *barred* with *reddish brown.* Its *tail* is *black* with *narrow white bars,* a mark often evident in young birds as well. In flight this bird shows dark under wing coverts, a large ill-defined area of white at the base of the outermost primaries, and a proportionately longer tail than other *Buteos.* The immature bird, either at rest or in flight can usually be distinguished from the Red-tailed Hawk by its slimmer proportions and longer tail. The penetrating call is so ably imitated by the Blue Jay that it is useful in identification only when the bird making the sound can be seen.

This bird is the most common and most widespread of all soaring hawks in Alabama. It is a permanent resident, breeding throughout the state, and in winter its numbers are increased by an influx of northern birds. At least one pair occupies almost every large-sized tract of woodland, with more pairs in tracts of bottomland hardwood, and fewer in mountainous areas.

NESTING. The large and bulky nest is, in Alabama, usually twenty to one hundred feet above ground in a hardwood or a pine. It is composed of sticks and grasses with a lining of softer materials such as green leaves, pine needles, and Spanish moss. The one to three dull white or bluish-white eggs vary in color, ranging from dirty white to those marked heavily with brown, gray, and lavender spots and blotches.

FOOD. This highly valuable hawk eats destructive insects and rodents. Roughly one percent of its diet is poultry and game. Its food includes many rats, rabbits, shrews, grasshoppers, spiders, beetles, caterpillars, crickets, dragonflies, centipedes, snakes, frogs, fish, crawfish, lizards, earthworms, and snails.

DISTRIBUTION. The Red-shouldered Hawk breeds from Minnesota, Ontario, and southern Quebec south to central Mexico and the Florida Keys. It is

NEST OF RED-SHOULDERED HAWK. The Red-shouldered is the most common nesting hawk in Alabama.

C. W. Summerour

resident in California and Lower California. It winters north to Kansas, Illinois, and New York, rarely farther.

ABUNDANCE IN ALABAMA (*most seen in a day*). *Mountain Region*: 13, September 20, 1952 (Mulga Fire Tower, T. A. Imhof). *Gulf Coast*: 22, October 19, 1957 (Fall Count, Mobile Bay Area).

TIME OF BREEDING. Data on 37 nestings: Building, February 3 to April; eggs, March 8 to April 29; young in nest, April 7 to May 18; young just out of nest, May 1 to June 23.

BANDING. A bird shot at Oak Hill, Wilcox Co., December 27, 1936 was banded as a nestling, June 14, 1931 at Huntington, Massachusetts. See Map 35.

Broad-winged Hawk
Buteo platypterus (Vieillot) [343] (Plate 13, facing page 176)

The adult Broad-winged Hawk is dark brown above and whitish below, heavily barred with reddish-brown. When this bird is at rest, its plumage differs from that of the larger, slimmer Red-shouldered Hawk by the *broad, white bars* on the *short tail* and by the *absence* of *red shoulders*. Since young Red-shouldered Hawks also lack the reddish-brown shoulder and the reddish-brown under parts, young birds are best distinguished by shape, especially by the shortness of the tail. In flight, the Broad-winged Hawk is small and chunky, and the under side of the short wings is white with a dark border. This hawk's call is penetrating

NEST OF BROAD-WINGED HAWK.   This migratory hawk is locally common in summer.

C. W. Summerour

and rather like the call of the Wood Pewee, but recognizable as that of a hawk by its volume.

In Alabama, the Broad-winged Hawk is a locally common, summer resident, and as a transient it is fairly common in spring and common to abundant in fall. In winter it is rare on the Gulf Coast, occasional in the Coastal Plain, and has been recorded as far north as Birmingham. (See Map 39.) It migrates in fairly large flocks usually along ridges but sometimes along the shores of the Gulf. In summer it nests in wooded areas, especially in the northern half of the state. Blue Jays, crows, Mockingbirds, kingbirds, and others often harass this inoffensive bird excessively.

NESTING. This hawk prefers to place its nest in a crotch of a hardwood ten to eighty feet up, but sometimes it selects a pine. It is made of twigs and bits of bark, lined with bark strips, moss, and sometimes leafy green twigs. The two to four pale greenish or grayish-white eggs are heavily marked with brown spots.

FOOD. This very beneficial bird lives on snakes and other reptiles, large insects, and rodents. So wholly dependent is it on insects and reptiles that when these animals are dormant in winter, it must migrate to the tropics.

DISTRIBUTION. The Broad-winged Hawk breeds from central Alberta and New Brunswick, mainly east of the Mississippi River, south to central Texas and the Lesser Antilles. It migrates in large flocks through the United States and Central America to winter from southern Mexico and northern Florida, rarely farther north, south to Peru and Brazil.

OCCURRENCE IN ALABAMA. (Normal: March 17 to November 18; Out-of-season: December, January, and February) *Tennessee Valley*: March 27 (1948, Russellville, E. O. Willis) to October 25 (1957, specimen in Auburn Wildlife collection, Decatur, Maurice Baker), most seen, 87, September 23, 1960 (Brownsboro, Madison Co., J. C. and Margaret Robinson). *Mountain Region*: March 17 (1956, Palmerdale, Jefferson Co., Adele West) to November 3 (1952, Gadsden, Edith Clark); also December 26, 1960 and January 6, 1961 (an adult, Birmingham, R. S. Weston); most seen, 442, September 17, 1959 (Fairfield, T. A. Imhof). *Piedmont*: March 23 (1957, Coosa Co., Harriett Wright) to September 25 (1957, 5000 birds, Rockford, Coosa Co., R. W. Thrasher). *Upper Coastal Plain*: March 31 (1951, Bear Swamp, Autauga Co., C. W. Summerour) to November 18 (1958, Montgomery, R. W. Skinner); also February 16, 1914 (specimen in Dept. of Archives and History, Autaugaville, L. S. Golsan). *Lower Coastal Plain*. April 2 (1958, Beatrice, Monroe Co., R. W. Skinner) to October 12 (1956, Jackson, W. U. Harris); most seen, 400+, September 16, 1959 (Castleberry, Mr. and Mrs. T. C. Swindell). *Gulf Coast*: March 25 (1960, Spring Hill, J. L. Dorn) to November 8 (1959, 31+ birds, Dauphin Island, T. A. Imhof and many others); also December 30, 1960 (Dauphin Island, Blanche Chapman and others and Bayou La Batre, T. A. Imhof); also January 2, 1960 (Dauphin Island, Ava Tabor and D. C. Holliman) and Hurricane, Baldwin Co., 2 birds present throughout January and February 1960, 1 of which was netted and banded on February 25 (D. D. Stamm); most seen, 150, September 25, 1957 (Fort Morgan, J. E. Keeler).

TIME OF BREEDING. Data on 10 nestings: Building, April 8; eggs, April 28 to May 30; young in nest, June 2 to July 16.

BANDING. A bird banded as a nestling at Willowdale, Ontario, July 10, 1944 was recovered at Frankville, Washington Co., May 8, 1945. See Map 35.

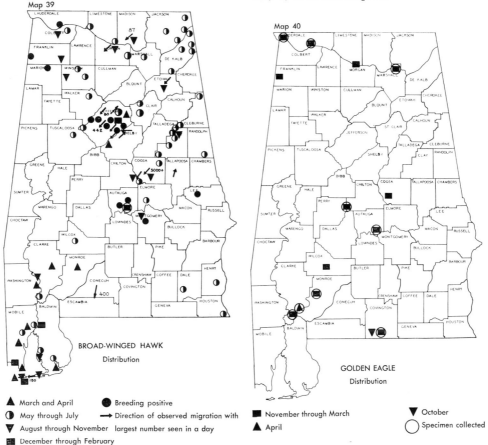

BROAD-WINGED HAWK
Distribution

GOLDEN EAGLE
Distribution

▲ March and April   ● Breeding positive
◐ May through July   → Direction of observed migration with
▼ August through November   largest number seen in a day
▦ December through February

■ November through March
▲ April

▼ October
○ Specimen collected

[Swainson's Hawk]
Buteo swainsoni Bonaparte [342] (Plate 13, facing page 176)

This hawk is slightly larger than the Red-tailed Hawk and has a similar shape. The *adult* Swainson's Hawk is dark brown above, has a white throat, a *dark brown chest,* a light-colored belly and a grayish, finely-barred tail. The immature and melanistic (blackish) birds do not adhere to these characteristics and can best be identified in flight. When seen from below, the *primaries* and *secondaries* are *dusky,* and the *wing coverts* are *whitish.*

[184]

This western hawk is accidental in fall in Alabama and is not known to breed here. It prefers open country, especially prairies and farms. In habits, flocking, temperament, and winter range it greatly resembles the Broad-winged Hawk.

NESTING AND FOOD. The nest, generally in an isolated patch of trees, is built of twigs, weeds, grasses, inner bark, and green leaves. The female lays two to four pale greenish or bluish eggs marked with brown. This hawk feeds almost exclusively on injurious rodents and insects, particularly meadow mice, gophers, and grasshoppers. Occasionally it eats lizards and frogs.

DISTRIBUTION. Swainson's Hawk breeds from Alaska, Great Slave Lake, and Manitoba south to central Mexico and east to Iowa and Oklahoma, and rarely Illinois and Missouri. It has wandered to most states east of the Mississippi River in fall and migrates in large flocks through Central America to winter in Argentina.

OCCURRENCE IN ALABAMA. *Upper Coastal Plain only*: A bird banded as a nestling by Stuart Houston at Rousay Lake, Yorkton, Saskatchewan in July 1946 was shot on a farm near Selma about November 10, 1946. See Map 35.

[Rough-legged Hawk]
Buteo lagopus (Pontoppidan) [347] (Plate 13, facing page 176)

This large soaring hawk has a *broad black tip* on its usually *white tail*. Blackish birds are numerous in this species, but in any plumage the Rough-legged Hawk usually shows white at the base of the tail and the base of the primaries, while black appears on the lower belly, tip of tail and outermost wing coverts. When the plumage is puzzling, this hawk is best identified by shape, for it is larger, has longer wings, and a longer tail than any other eastern *Buteo*. The Rough-legged Hawk hovers habitually in flight, while other *Buteos* hover only occasionally. The like-patterned Marsh Hawk hovers over meadows and also has a white rump, but it is a slim bird and its wings are held upward at an angle when in flight. In Alabama the Rough-legged Hawk should be identified with extreme care and only by those who have thorough knowledge of our common soaring hawks.

This hawk is casual in winter in the state. It has been recorded twice on the Gulf Coast, once within sight of the Gulf itself. All birds so far recorded from Alabama have been light-phased individuals. This is a bird of the open country, and like the Marsh Hawk it often quarters low over meadows and pastures. It prefers perching on stumps, bare trees, or even on the ground rather than using exposed branches of live trees. It is not known to breed in this state.

[185]

NESTING AND FOOD Placed on a high ledge of a cliff or in a tall tree, the nest is made of sticks, grasses, and weeds. It usually contains three to five pale greenish-white, brown-blotched eggs. A very efficient mouser, this hawk lives almost entirely on meadow mice, lemmings, and other ground rodents. Occasionally it eats insects, especially grasshoppers, and sometimes it eats carrion. More than any other hawk, it hunts in twilight, an adaptation to the short arctic winter days.

DISTRIBUTION. The Rough-legged Hawk breeds in the New World from northwestern Alaska, Baffin Island, and Labrador south to northern Alberta and Newfoundland. It winters from southern British Columbia and Quebec south to southern California and Virginia, rarely to the Gulf states.

OCCURRENCE IN ALABAMA. (November 2 to February 2.) *Tennessee Valley*: Present for over a week in January 1940 (Wheeler Refuge, T. Z. Atkeson, Jr.) and January 28 to February 3, 1951 (D. C. Hulse). *Mountain Region*: No record. *Piedmont*: No record. *Upper Coastal Plain*: January 9 to February 1956 (Macon Co., J. E. Keeler and R. W. Thrasher) and November 2, 1960 (Montgomery, R. W. Skinner). *Lower Coastal Plain*: No record. *Gulf Coast*: January or February 1956 (Mobile, C. S. Robbins) and December 30, 1960 (Dauphin Island, Clustie McTyeire and Larry Rosen).

Golden Eagle
Aquila chrysaetos (Linnaeus)   [349]   (Plate 12, facing page 168)

The *adult* Golden Eagle is a *dark* bird which, when seen from below, shows a *small amount* of *light color* at the *base of* the *primaries* and at the *base* of the *tail* feathers. In the immature bird these areas are whiter and more extensive. The immature Bald Eagle has white on the wing coverts, but the Bald Eagle holds its wings perfectly flat, while the Golden Eagle curves the ends of its primaries upwards in typical *Buteo* fashion. At very close range, the golden color of the hindneck and the feathering clear to the toes is evident. In flight it greatly resembles a big soaring hawk, but the large size, long wings, and big bill mark it an eagle.

The Golden Eagle is rare in winter in Alabama, and although it apparently occurs annually, it does not breed here. (See Map 40.) It is a bird of the wild country and occurs particularly in mountains and deserts. In winter occasional birds occur in more settled areas where livestock is raised or where waterfowl concentrate. This bird is a powerful flyer and is most to be admired when gracefully maneuvering over wild country. Mated pairs appear to spend the winter together.

NESTING AND FOOD. The aerie is a bulky platform to which additions are made each year. It is built of large sticks and lined with smaller sticks and grass, and is usually on an inaccessible cliff, or sometimes in a tall tree. The two eggs are white with bold and handsome markings of chestnut, sienna, and purple. In wilder regions this eagle eats large rodents, especially rabbits, woodchucks, squirrels, gophers, and prairie dogs, and also includes on its menu fawns and large birds such as grouse, waterfowl, and wild turkeys. In more settled regions, particularly in winter, it adds poultry and the young of domestic animals including sheep, goats, and pigs.

DISTRIBUTION. The Golden Eagle breeds in mountainous country from northern Alaska and northern Quebec south to northern Lower California, central Mexico, western Texas, New York, and Maine, and possibly farther south in the Appalachian Mountains. It winters over most of this range and less commonly south to the Gulf states.

OCCURRENCE IN ALABAMA. (October 17 to April 15.) *Tennessee Valley*: Specimen at Wheeler Refuge, 1934 (Waterloo, *fide* D. C. Hulse); January 8, 1956 (2 birds, Red Bay, E. C. Mahan); March 1911 (specimen, near Florence, Delos H. Bacon); December 19 and 26, 1959 (Decatur, *fide* T. Z. Atkeson, Jr.); November 1921 (specimen, Preston, Marshall Co., Mrs. Bessie R. Samuel). *Mountain Region*: No record. *Piedmont*: January 27, 1956 (2 birds, Hatchett Creek, Coosa Co., M. F. Prather) and 1 seen at the same place in winters of 1958-59 and 1959-60 (M. F. Prather and M. H. Perry). *Upper Coastal Plain*: December 1, 1923 (immature male specimen in the Dept. of Archives and History, near Prattville, J. E. Churchill, *fide* E. G. Holt, *Auk* 41:601-602); near Planters-ville, Dallas Co., 2 birds watched through December 1955 and an adult female mounted specimen now in Rush General Store, Planters-ville, trapped while eating young goats on January 1, 1956. *Lower Coastal Plain*: Florala, October 17, 1959 (H. M. Stevenson) and January 17, 1908, specimen in U. S. National Museum (2 birds present for some time and reported to have killed some sheep, specimen trapped by sheep owner and identi-fied by G. Clyde Fisher, *Wilson* Bull. 20:55); Finchburg, Monroe Co., March 1953, an adult shot and taken captive (*fide* W. F. Colin); Choctaw Bluff, Clarke Co., February 14, 1957, immature specimen in the Dept. of Conserva-tion, caught in steel trap set beside freshly-killed 18 pound turkey (*fide* R. W. Skinner); April 15, 1956, an adult shot while capturing a wild turkey (M. W. Gaillard); Camden, Wil-cox Co., December 9, 1958 (Lovett Williams). *Gulf Coast*: No record.

Bald Eagle
Haliaeetus leucocephalus (Linnaeus)   [352]   (Plate 12, facing page 168)

The Bald Eagle is the national bird of the United States. The adult is *black* with a *white head* and *tail*, a yellow bill, and yellow legs. The immature bird lacks the white head and tail and usually shows much *white* in the *under wing linings*. It can be recognized as an eagle by its large size, dark color, and long rounded wings. The Bald Eagle has a big bill and head and in flight soars with its wings held flat.

This bird is a locally common, breeding, winter resident on the Gulf Coast, in the Tennessee Valley, and possibly in one or two intervening places. It is

FALCONIFORMES: ACCIPITRIDAE: BALD EAGLE

uncommon to rare in winter in the remainder of the state. (See Map 41.) It occurs near rivers and lakes, where it spends much of its time soaring high over the water or perched in the top of a dead tree along the shore. Shortly after the winter-visiting eagles return north to breed, the Alabama eagles finish nesting and also move northward. Thus, few Bald Eagles remain in June and July.

NESTING. The Bald Eagle uses sticks to build a huge nest at the top of a tall tree close to water. This nest is occupied each year, added to each year, and often contains trinkets. The two, rarely three, eggs are dull-white, granular, and very small for so large a bird.

FOOD. Fish, especially catfish, is the main item of food. It obtains its food from other fish-eaters, and eats it dead or alive. Perhaps its most frequent victim is the Osprey, which it worries until it drops its fish; whereupon the eagle swoops down and snatches the fish in mid-air. It also eats carrion, small animals such as rodents, opossums, raccoons, snakes, and small water animals. Occasionally it includes wounded waterfowl and shorebirds in its diet.

DISTRIBUTION. The Bald Eagle is resident from northwestern Alaska, northern Mackenzie, and Labrador south to southern Lower California, northern Mexico, and Florida. It breeds locally throughout this range in favorable locali-

NEST OF BALD EAGLE. This species builds an immense structure of sticks and adds to it year after year.

C. W. Summerour

YOUNG BALD EAGLE. This nestling was five weeks old when photographed.

ties such as coastal Alaska, the upper Mississippi Valley, the Great Lakes, Chesapeake Bay, and the Gulf coasts of Florida and Alabama, but it is absent from arid regions. Most northern birds retire southward in winter, and southern-breeding birds migrate north after the winter breeding season. This migration pattern has been amply demonstrated by the banding activities of the late Charles L. Broley.

OCCURRENCE IN ALABAMA. (Throughout the year.) *Tennessee Valley*: August 19 (1946, Wheeler Refuge, Paul Bryan) to May 7 (1912, Florence, A. H. Howell); also July 2, 1957 (Wheeler Refuge, H. H. Grammer) and July 8, 1956 (near Florence, D. C. Hulse); most seen, 27, February 25, 1955 and 50, January 1960 (Waterloo, Ralph Allen). *Mountain Region*: September 24 (1936, St. Clair Co., H. M. Stevenson) to April 26 (1953, Cheaha, Ala. Orn. Soc.). *Piedmont*: May 4, 1937 (Auburn, D. H. McIntosh). *Upper Coastal Plain*: October (Waxahatchee Creek, Chilton Co., W. W. Owen) to at least March 26 (1955, Marion, T. A. Imhof and others). *Lower Coastal Plain*: Early August (1956, Jackson, W. U. Harris) to June 2 (1956, Choctaw Bluff, M. W. Gaillard). *Gulf Coast*: Late August (1955, Dauphin Island, R. L. Chermock) to May 1

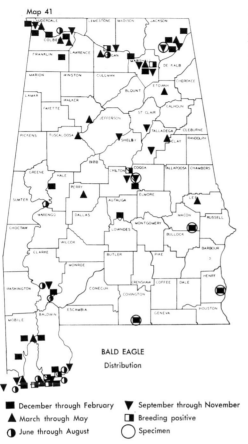

Map 41

BALD EAGLE
Distribution

■ December through February ▼ September through November
▲ March through May ◨ Breeding positive
◐ June through August ○ Specimen

(1954, Alabama Point, T. A. Imhof); also June 2 and 10, 1940 (Bon Secour and Perdido bays, H. M. Stevenson) and June 17, 1956 (an immature bird, Lillian, B. L. Monroe, Jr.); most seen, 6, October 22, 1949 (Fort Morgan Peninsula, T. A. Imhof and others).

TIME OF BREEDING. Data on 4 to 6 Tennessee Valley nestings: Building, late December to January; eggs, January to early March; dependent young, April to at least May 6. Data on 4 to 10 Gulf Coast nestings: Eggs, February; young in nest, March 17.

BANDING. A bird banded as a nestling at Portland, Ontario, June 24, 1945 by C. L. Broley was killed on the Coosa River, 50 miles below Birmingham, November 19, 1945. See Map 35.

SUBFAMILY CIRCINAE: HARRIERS

Marsh Hawk
Circus cyaneus (Linnaeus) [331] (Plate 13, facing page 176)
OTHER NAMES: Rabbit Hawk, Harrier

The Marsh Hawk is a small-bodied, *slender* bird, streaked brown with lighter-colored under parts and a *white rump*. It has a long tail and long, narrow, rounded wings, which it holds in a V when gliding low over meadows. The adult male is silvery gray with black wing tips.

This bird is common on migration and in winter throughout the state. It is sometimes abundant, as on the Gulf Coast during migration and in the

Tennessee Valley and the Black Belt in winter. Although it summers occasionally, even in pairs, no evidence of breeding has as yet been found in Alabama. The Marsh Hawk occurs almost everywhere, and is especially common on meadows, marshes, and other open country where it quarters low, rarely flying above the treetops. Habitually absent from extensive woodland, it may be seen flying high over these places on migration. The silvery adult male becomes rarer southward but has been noted even on the coast.

NESTING AND FOOD. This bird builds a neat nest of fine grasses, placing it on the ground in the tall grass of a marsh or meadow. The eggs are dull bluish-white or greenish-white and are usually four to six in number. The Marsh Hawk prefers to eat the many kinds of rodents found in the grass, particularly rats and rabbits. It also takes grasshoppers, other insects, water birds, small grass-dwelling birds, frogs, lizards, and snakes.

DISTRIBUTION. In the Western Hemisphere, the Marsh Hawk breeds from northwestern Alaska and Labrador south to northern Lower California, southern New Mexico, the Ohio Valley, and southeastern Virginia, and rarely in the southeastern United States. It winters from British Columbia, Saskatchewan, and the southern parts of our northernmost states south to Colombia, Cuba, Florida, and the Bahamas.

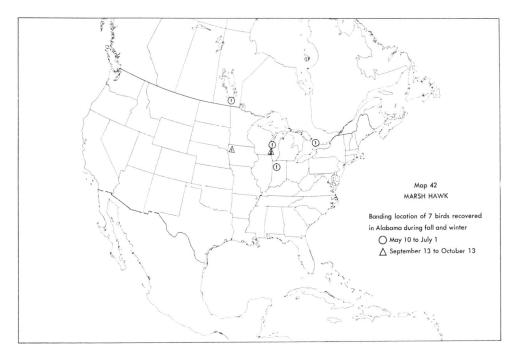

Map 42
MARSH HAWK

Banding location of 7 birds recovered
in Alabama during fall and winter
◯ May 10 to July 1
△ September 13 to October 13

E. P. Haddon

NEST OF OSPREY. This bird is often mistaken
for the adult Bald Eagle; their nests are also
similar.

Map 43

OSPREY
Distribution

◑ June and July   ● Breeding positive
■ December and January

OCCURRENCE IN ALABAMA. (August 11 to May 5; occasional in summer.) *Tennessee Valley*: August 11 (Wheeler Refuge, J. H. Steenis) to May 5 (1949, Wheeler Refuge, W. T. Meadows); abundant, October to March, gray males, November to March; pairs recorded at Wheeler Refuge several times in summer, e.g. July 1 and 2, 1947 (L. S. Givens and J. H. Heflin); most seen, 30, roosting on the ground, January 1957 (Wheeler Refuge, Leo Martin). *Mountain Region*: August 29 (1936, Birmingham, H. M. Stevenson) to first week in May (1957, Gadsden, Edith Clark); most seen, 7, September 20, 1952 (Birmingham, T. A. Imhof). *Piedmont*: September 26 (1952, Auburn, F. W. Fitch) to April 24 (1953, Auburn, H. G. Good). *Upper Coastal Plain*: August 11

(1960, an adult male, Autauga Co., Ralph Allen) to April 18 (1956, Marion, Lois McCollough); most seen, 29, November 25, 1958 (Montgomery, R. W. Skinner). *Lower Coastal Plain*: September 15 (1958, Camden, D. W. Speake) to April 1 (Columbia, the T. Z. Atkesons). *Gulf Coast*: August 27 (1946, Fort Morgan, T. A. Imhof) to May 1 (1954, Fort Morgan, T. A. Imhof); most seen, 203, October 19, 1957 (Fall Count, Mobile Bay Area).

BANDING. Of 7 banded Marsh Hawks reported from Alabama, 4 were recovered on the Gulf Coast, and 1 each from Madison, Dallas, and Sumter counties, all during the period, October 21 to February 9. For place of banding, see Map 42.

FAMILY PANDIONIDAE: OSPREYS

Osprey
Pandion haliaetus (Linnaeus)   [364]   (Plate 12, facing page 168)
OTHER NAME: Fish Hawk

In wing spread and total length, the Osprey is almost as large as an eagle, but its body is much smaller. This bird has a *black back*, a *white head* with a *black mask*, a white belly, and *black wrist marks* on the bend of the wing. It has a rather long tail and its long *wings* have a *noticeable crook* in them so that in flight the Osprey closely resembles a gull. This crook makes each wing appear like a very shallow inverted V. The wrist joint is carried forward of the place where the leading edge of the wing joins the body.

Throughout Alabama this bird is common on migration in spring and uncommon in fall. On the Gulf Coast, in the Tennessee Valley, and possibly in the intervening area, it is locally a fairly common, breeding, summer resident which rarely winters. (See Map 43.) It frequents the vicinity of water, either rivers, ponds, lakes, bays, or the Gulf.

NESTING. The nest of the Osprey is a large, bulky affair usually built in the top of a tall tree near water. Sticks, twigs, grasses, moss, and debris are the building materials, and the nest is used year after year, often with additions each year. It looks very much like the nest of the Bald Eagle, but the Osprey more often chooses dead trees. At least one Osprey nest in Alabama was known to be also occupied earlier in the season for several years by the

[193]

FALCONIFORMES: PANDIONIDAE: OSPREY

Great Horned Owl. The two to four yellowish or pinkish dull white eggs are handsomely marked with coppery red and various shades of brown.

FOOD. The Osprey feeds exclusively on fish, often so large that the bird has difficulty landing them and runs a real danger of being pulled under water. They include catfish, menhaden, herring, goldfish, sunfish, trout, shad, and perch. When this bird spies a fish, it hovers over the water, makes a spectacular plunge, sometimes from several hundred feet, that would kill a lesser bird. Coming up from the water, it carries its prey head-forward to a favorite perch to eat at leisure.

DISTRIBUTION. The Osprey occurs near water in nearly all temperate and tropic parts of the world. In North America it breeds as far north as there are trees, south to Lower California, western Mexico, the Gulf states, and the Florida Keys, and including all the intervening area. It winters from Lower California and the Gulf states south to Peru and Brazil, and occasionally farther.

OCCURRENCE IN ALABAMA. (February 21 to November 6; sometimes winters.) *Tennessee Valley*: March 24 (1951, Scottsboro, Adele West) to October 15 (1949, Wheeler Refuge, T. A. Imhof and J. A. Doubles); also November 20, 1950 (Wheeler Refuge, D. C. Hulse) and December 23 and 25, 1942 (Wheeler Refuge, Paul Bryan and J. H. Steenis). *Mountain Region*: March 27 (1949, Birmingham, T. A. Imhof) to May 26 (1946, Birmingham, T. A. Imhof) and September 13 (1937, Birmingham, H. M. Stevenson) to October 2 (1939, Birmingham, H. M. Stevenson). *Piedmont*: March 28 (1952, Au-

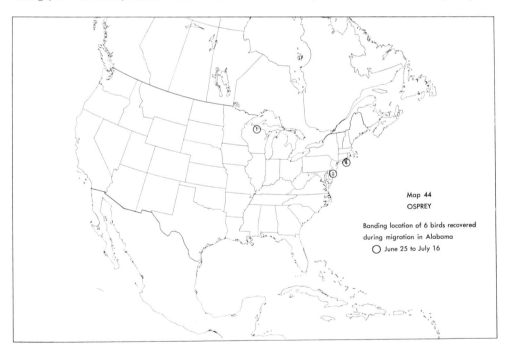

Map 44
OSPREY

Banding location of 6 birds recovered during migration in Alabama
○ June 25 to July 16

burn, H. G. Good) to May 16 (1953, Auburn, W. F. Helms) and September 28, 1953 (Auburn, W. F. Helms). *Upper Coastal Plain*: March 6 (1956, 2 birds, Marion, Lois McCollough) to May 7 (1929, Prattville, L. S. Golsan) and early September (Montgomery, R. W. Skinner) to October 23 (1954, Marion, Lois McCollough); also June 21, 1911, and June and July 1912 (Autaugaville, L. S. Golsan); July 21 and 29, 1959 (Manack, Lowndes Co., R. W. Skinner). *Lower Coastal Plain*: Mid-March (1957, specimen in the Dept. of Conservation collection, Florala, Don Thomas) to May 9 (1958, Lake Tholloco, T. A. Imhof) and October 1 (1958, Camden, Lovett Williams) to October 13 (1949, Andalusia, W. R. Middleton). *Gulf Coast*: February 21 (1931, Fairhope, Helen Edwards) to November 6 (1948, Gulf Shores,

F. M. Weston); also December 27, 1958 and December 30, 1960 (Dauphin Island, Blanche Chapman and others); January 24, 1912 (Orange Beach, A. H. Howell); and January 25, 1931 (Gulf Shores, Helen Edwards); most seen, 11, May 1, 1954 (Fort Morgan, Ala. Orn. Soc.).

TIME OF BREEDING. Data on 35 nestings: Building, March 11 to June 12; eggs, April 15 to May 24; dependent young, May to July 9.

BANDING. Six Ospreys, banded elsewhere as nestlings, have been recovered in Alabama during the period May 5 to 8 and August 30 to October 15, 2 in Jefferson Co., 2 in Montgomery Co., 1 at Eufaula, and 1 near Talladega. For place of banding, see Map 44.

FAMILY FALCONIDAE: CARACARAS AND FALCONS

SUBFAMILY FALCONINAE: FALCONS

These birds have a streamlined shape, long, pointed wings, a long tail, and are built for speed. Their bills and feet are powerful and the upper mandible is notched near the tip. Nobility of the Middle Ages kept falcons as pets and trained them to hunt, which is probably the reason they are called noble hawks.

Peregrine Falcon

Falco peregrinus Tunstall   [356]   (Plate 13, facing page 176)
OTHER NAME: Duck Hawk

This *crow-sized* falcon is very dark above, lighter-colored below, and has a *black mustache mark* running down from the eye. The Peregrine Falcon is capable of speeds in excess of an incredible hundred miles per hour.

In Alabama this falcon is rare and local in winter and on migration. On the Gulf Coast and in the Tennessee Valley, particularly in fall, it is fairly common. It breeds locally in the Tennessee Valley and possibly also on Lookout Mountain. (See Map 45.) It prefers a tall cliff near water, but it may occur in a wide variety of places that have water in the vicinity. It is even apt to winter in a large city, where it can find water near tall buildings, which make a good substitute for cliffs.

[195]

FALCONIFORMES: FALCONIDAE: PEREGRINE FALCON

NESTING. The three or four dull white eggs are heavily spotted with reddish or dark brown. The female lays them on a bare ledge or crevice on an inaccessible cliff or rarely in a tall tree near water. Both parents vigorously defend the nest, even attacking humans if the young are handled.

FOOD. The Peregrine Falcon feeds chiefly on birds, especially waterfowl, shorebirds, and other water birds. In winter around cities it preys on domestic pigeons and outdistances the fastest racer. The Chimney Swift is about the only bird fast enough to have immunity from its attacks.

DISTRIBUTION. In the Western Hemisphere, the Peregrine Falcon breeds locally from Alaska, northern Baffin Island, and Greenland south to Lower California, central Mexico, Texas, and the Gulf states. It winters from Vancouver Island, Colorado, Nebraska, southern Ontario, and New Brunswick south to Chile and Argentina.

Map 45

PEREGRINE FALCON

Distribution in Summer

◑ May through August   ● Breeding positive

OCCURRENCE IN ALABAMA. (Throughout the year.) *Tennessee Valley*: Migrants, August 26 (1950, Wheeler Refuge, D. C. Hulse) to April 27 (1950, Wheeler Refuge, D. C. Hulse); has bred near the mouth of Elk River from 1892 (F. W. McCormack) to at least 1948 (Paul Bryan) and near the mouth of the Paint Rock River from 1901 (H. E. Wheeler) to at least 1954 (E. C. Mahan). *Mountain Region*: September 18 (1954, Birmingham, T. A. Imhof) to April 12 (1954, Gadsden, Edith Clark); also June 11, 1943 (Mentone, DeKalb Co., H. M. Stevenson). *Piedmont*: No record. *Upper Coastal Plain*: September 10 (1886, Greensboro, W. C. Avery) to at least January 1 (1957, Marion, Lois McCollough). *Lower Coastal Plain*: No record. *Gulf Coast*: September 11 (1958, Dauphin Island, H. A. J. and Cora Evans) to May 1 (1954, Fort Morgan, T. A. Imhof); most seen, 9, October 19, 1957 (Fall Count, Mobile Bay Area).

TIME OF BREEDING. Data on 4 Tennessee Valley nestings: Young in nest, April 19 to early June.

Pigeon Hawk

Falco columbarius Linnaeus   [357]   (Plate 13, facing page 176)
OTHER NAME: Merlin

The Pigeon Hawk is about the *size* of a *Sparrow Hawk*. The male is dark blue above; the female and the immature bird are dark brown. All are heavily streaked below, and the tail has light and dark stripes. Unlike our other two falcons, this bird has *no black markings* on the *face*. Its flight is more dashing and it sails less than does the Sparrow Hawk. Although the Sharp-shinned Hawk is about the same size and has a blue back, the Pigeon Hawk's long, pointed wings and falcon flight will immediately distinguish the two species.

In Alabama on fall migration this hawk is common on the Gulf Coast and uncommon elsewhere in the state. In spring it is uncommon throughout. It is uncommon in winter north to the Mountain Region (Birmingham and Anniston) and rare in the Tennessee Valley. It is not known to nest in Alabama. It occurs most frequently over open areas, especially beaches and meadows, but on migration it moves rapidly over wooded, hilly country. Because it lives most of the summer in the far north, it is not very suspicious of man.

NESTING AND FOOD. The Pigeon Hawk builds a twig nest in an evergreen, in a tree hole, on the ground, or on a cliff ledge, and lays four or five eggs which resemble those of a Peregrine Falcon. This hawk feeds mostly on small birds up to the size of pigeons, flickers, and grackles. It can outdistance most birds, for it even catches swifts and swallows occasionally, but alert birds can escape by skillful dodging or a dash to cover. This hawk varies its diet with small mammals and large insects.

DISTRIBUTION. In America the Pigeon Hawk breeds from as far north as trees grow in northwestern Alaska, Labrador, and Newfoundland south to California and the northern parts of our northern states. It winters from British Columbia, Wyoming, and the Gulf states, rarely north to Ontario and Quebec, south to Peru, Venezuela, and the West Indies.

OCCURRENCE IN ALABAMA. (Normal: September 11 to May 16; Out-of-season: July 27.) *Tennessee Valley*: September 12 (1951, Wheeler Refuge, D. C. Hulse) to October 16 (1953, Wheeler Refuge, D. C. Hulse) and April 1 (1952, Wheeler Refuge, D. C. Hulse) to May 6 (Wheeler Refuge, *fide* T. Z. Atkeson, Jr.) and wintered in 1949-50 at Wheeler Refuge (*fide* T. Z. Atkeson, Jr.); February 15, 1959 (Huntsville, J. C. and Margaret Robinson); also July 27, 1951, a probable cripple (Decatur, D. C. Hulse). *Mountain Region*: September 11 (1937, Birmingham, H. M. Stevenson) to May 2 (1954, Gadsden, Edith Clark). *Piedmont*: No record. *Upper Coastal Plain*: September 22 (1955, Marion, Lois McCollough) to at least December 22 (1893, specimen in the Avery collection, Greensboro, W. C. Avery). *Lower Coastal Plain*: September 22 (1958, Camden, Lovett Williams) to April 14 (1957, Jackson, W. U. Harris). *Gulf Coast*: September 13 (1959, Dauphin Island, H. A. J. and Cora Evans) to May 16 (1958, Sand Island, T. A. Imhof, M. W. Gaillard, and J. C. Gray); most seen in migration, 15, October 19, 1957 (Fall Count, Mobile Bay Area), winter, 7 birds netted and banded from November 17,

1959 to February 21, 1960 (Hurricane, D. D. Stamm).

BANDING. A bird banded at Cedar Grove, Wisconsin by Helmut Mueller, September 30, 1953 was recovered at Huntsville, October 31, 1953, and another from Cedar Grove, banded September 26, 1954, was found near Albertville sometime before October 10, 1954. One bird covered this 650 mile (straight-line) distance in 31 days and the other in less than 14 days! See Map 35.

Sparrow Hawk

Falco sparverius Linnaeus   [360]   (Plate 13, facing page 176)
OTHER NAMES: Killy Hawk, Kestrel

This is our smallest, most common, and most handsome falcon. It is largely reddish-brown, barred on the back and lighter below. The crown is reddish, but the rest of the *head* is *white* with *blue lines*. The *male* has *blue wings*, while the *female's* are *brown*. The dark-tipped, reddish-brown tail is a good identification mark. This small falcon's flight is not as dashing as that of the other falcons, and it often hovers. Its distinctive shrill call is said to be the origin of one of its common names.

The Sparrow Hawk is a common but somewhat local permanent resident in Alabama. It is much more abundant from September to March when its numbers are more than tripled by birds from farther north. In summer it nests commonly in north Alabama in the wilder, hilly, wooded areas, particularly near cliffs or tall, dead trees. Farther south it becomes more thinly scattered and is found in open areas all the way to the coast. In flat country a telephone pole near a field is its favorite perch. North of this state, where the shrike is less common, the Sparrow Hawk is much more abundant.

NESTING. This bird nests in natural cavities, abandoned woodpecker holes, or sometimes in holes near the roof of a building. It rarely uses any nesting material for the four or five eggs, which are often heavily marked with reddish-brown.

FOOD. The Sparrow Hawk is almost entirely an insect-eater, with a marked preference for grasshoppers and crickets. When these items are scarce, it eats beetles, spiders, shrews, mice, small snakes, lizards, and, rarely, small birds.

DISTRIBUTION. The Sparrow Hawk breeds from Alaska, northern Ontario, and Nova Scotia south through Central America and the West Indies to

Patagonia. It winters north to southern British Columbia, Iowa, southern Ontario, and Nova Scotia.

ABUNDANCE IN ALABAMA (*most seen in a day*). Huntsville, 9, December 6, 1958 (J. C. and Margaret Robinson); Birmingham, 9, December 28, 1957 (Christmas Count); Auburn, 6, January 2, 1954 (Christmas Count); Marion, 7, February 27, 1954 (T. A. Imhof); Covington Co., and Conecuh Co., 10, October 19, 1956 (T. A. Imhof and L. C. Crawford); Mobile Bay Area, 131, October 19, 1957 (Fall Count).

TIME OF BREEDING. Data on 14 nestings: Building, March 22; eggs, April 11 to May 12; dependent young, April to June 22.

ORDER GALLIFORMES: MEGAPODES, CURASSOWS, PHEASANTS, AND HOATZINS

These stocky birds have short, stubby bills and short, rounded wings which allow them to make sudden but short flights, often in dense cover. Their feet are strong and well adapted for scratching. The after-shafts of their body feathers provide considerable insulation in cold weather. Warm body plumage, high calory seed diet, and poor ability for sustained flight result in few migratory species in this group.

FAMILY TETRAONIDAE: GROUSE AND PTARMIGAN

[Ruffed Grouse]
Bonasa umbellus (Linnaeus)   [300]   (Plate 14, facing page 208)
OTHER NAMES: Pheasant, Partridge

The Ruffed Grouse is a large, chicken-like bird, grayish-brown in color and somewhat resembling a short-tailed female pheasant. The *tail* of this grouse is *fan-shaped* and may be either gray or red with a *black band near the end* and a *white tip*. The nostrils and lower legs are feathered. The drumming of the male sounds like the starting of a car or an outboard motor in the distance.

Formerly this bird was a permanent resident in the hilly country of northeastern Alabama. An undated record of a brood of young in the summer of 1913 (Howell, 1928:119) indicates that it nested here. This was the last positive record. Some birds, however, may still persist in small numbers in DeKalb or Jackson counties. This grouse lives in the wilder, brushy, hilly woodlands, on mountain sides, ridge tops, and in gulches; it often frequents dense laurel thickets. It is rarely seen on the ground, but will explode into the air when it is almost underfoot.

NESTING. Placed on the ground, the nest is well hidden in dense brush near a log or under a fallen tree. It is made of old leaves, the stems and roots of weeds and grasses, and usually holds ten or twelve whitish to pale brown, rarely spotted, eggs.

[200]

FOOD. The Ruffed Grouse has a varied diet which includes woodland items that are readily available Thus in summer it feeds mostly on insects, while in fall and winter it takes fruits, nuts, leaves, buds, and grain.

DISTRIBUTION. The Ruffed Grouse is resident below the tree limit from Alaska, Mackenzie, and Labrador south to northern California, northern Colorado, Tennessee, northern Georgia, and formerly northern Alabama.

OCCURRENCE IN ALABAMA. *Mountain Region only*: Formerly resident on Sand Mountain, Lookout Mountain, and the Talladega Mountains, the last authentic record is that of a female with a brood near Carpenter on Sand Mountain, Jackson Co., in the summer of 1913 (A. H. Howell, 1924:119).

INTRODUCTION. In the fall of 1958, 65 Ohio birds were released in the William B. Bankhead National Forest by the Alabama Dept. of Conservation in an attempt to re-establish the Ruffed Grouse in Alabama.

FAMILY PHASIANIDAE: QUAILS, PHEASANTS, AND PEACOCKS

SUBFAMILY ODONTOPHORINAE: AMERICAN QUAILS

Bobwhite
Colinus virginianus (Linnaeus) [289] (Plate 14, facing page 208)
OTHER NAMES: Partridge, Quail, Bird

The Bobwhite is a small, streaked reddish-brown bird somewhat like a chicken. It has a short dark tail, and the male has black and white head stripes, while the female's stripes are dark and light brown. The clear whistle of three syllables, only two of which can be heard at a distance, indicates the presence of this bird from April to September.

Throughout Alabama this species is a widespread, common to abundant, breeding, permanent resident. It is particularly common in farming areas, weedy, brushy fields, and shrubby woodlands, but less common in wild, hilly country and areas near salt water. Clean farming methods which eliminate hedgerows and excess grain and seeds, or the raising of livestock, which keep cover at a minimum and may trample nests, leave little available habitat for these birds in some farming areas.

NESTING. The well-hidden nest is on the ground under thick cover, often at the base of a tree or stump. It is arched and made of dry grasses, weeds, and leaves. The clutch ranges from eleven to twenty-two pure white eggs which are pear shaped and fit close together in compact layers.

FOOD. More than half of the food the Bobwhite takes consists of weed seeds, with various legumes favorites. Beetles, grasshoppers, bugs, other injurious insects, grain, and fruit give variety to its diet. The fruit, which includes berries, sumac, and wild rose hips, is eaten chiefly in fall and winter while the insects are taken mainly by the young in summer.

DISTRIBUTION. The Bobwhite is resident from Wyoming, southern Minnesota, southern Ontario, and southwestern Maine south to Sonora, Oaxaca, Guatemala, and Cuba. It has been introduced in most western states, Hawaii, New Zealand, the West Indies, and Bermuda.

TIME OF BREEDING. Data on over 45 nestings: Building, April 1; eggs, May 22 to September 19 (November 16, 1955, 3 infertile eggs about 1½ weeks old, Clayton, J. E. Keeler); downy young, May 22 to September 24; young flying by late June.

BANDING. Although generally the Bobwhite rarely moves more than a mile or two, the record of a banded bird from Fairhope recovered in Atmore, 40 miles away, is the second longest distance it has been known to travel.

FAMILY MELEAGRIDIDAE: TURKEYS

Turkey
Meleagris gallopavo Linnaeus   [310]   (Frontispiece, facing page v)

The Turkey, an iridescent black bird similar to a chicken, is very large, with a long neck and tail and powerful legs. The bare skin of the head and neck is bright red in males and bluish in females. The Tom has a bright red wattle hanging down over the bill and a coarse beard jutting out from the breast. Wild Turkeys have chestnut tips on their tail feathers while domestic birds have white tips. Frequent cross-breeding often makes this color distinction unreliable.

This bird was a common and widespread, breeding, permanent resident in Alabama, and apparently maintained itself fairly well until about 1880. From then until about 1945 it was locally common in scattered places, notably in southwestern Alabama, its center of abundance, and in Winston County. With re-introduction and good management, it has virtually re-occupied the parts of the state having its required habitat, and it is now undoubtedly more numerous than it ever was. It is a woodland bird and seems to thrive best on well-watered forests that are half hardwood, with a good proportion of oaks, and broken by well-dispersed clearings of native grasses, legumes, and succulent fruits (R. J. Wheeler, Jr., 1948:20-21).

NESTING. The nest is placed on the ground and is well concealed under weeds, often near the base of a tree. The eight to sixteen eggs are yellowish-white, dotted all over with reddish-brown. One gobbler will service three to five hens, but he takes no part in incubation or rearing the young.

FOOD. The main foods of the Turkey, in order of importance and with the principal times of the year when they are consumed, are: grasses (leaves, mid-spring to mid-fall; seeds, mid-August to mid-October); insects, chiefly grasshoppers, beetles and bugs (early spring through early winter); mast, especially of oaks, beech, dogwood, black gum, and hackberry (late fall to early spring); succulent fruits, mainly berries, grapes, persimmons, and haws (summer and fall) (R. J. Wheeler, Jr., 1948:22-26).

DISTRIBUTION. The Turkey is resident, often locally, from Arizona, southern Colorado, Kentucky, and New York (formerly north to South Dakota, southern Ontario, and Maine), south to central Mexico and southern Florida.

TIME OF BREEDING. Data on over 25 nestings: Eggs, second week in February to August 10; dependent young, April 10 to October 29.

NOTE. Past and present attempts to introduce other members of the Order *Galliformes* in Alabama cannot as yet be evaluated, for only time will determine their success. So far, however, no species has as yet become established. Prominent among those involved are the Chukar (*Alectoris graeca*), the Quail (*Coturnix coturnix*), and several members of the Pheasant family (*Phasianidae*).

TURKEY NEST. An exceptionally large clutch, 22 eggs, was photographed in Monroe County, April 9, 1954.

W. F. Colin

ORDER GRUIFORMES: CRANES, RAILS, AND ALLIES

These marsh dwellers have short tails, rounded wings, generally long legs, and perforate nostrils. Although usually shy and retiring, they have loud calls and are quite active at dawn or dusk or in cloudy weather. The young are downy when hatched.

FAMILY GRUIDAE: CRANES

SUBFAMILY GRUINAE: CRANES

These birds resemble herons except that cranes have short bills, bare red skin on the face, long back feathers which curl down over the tail, and blaring, bugle-like calls. They fly with neck extended and with sharp upstrokes of the wings.

[Whooping Crane]
Grus americana (Linnaeus) [204]

This is a big bird, larger than the Great Blue Heron. The Whooping Crane is white except for a little red on the face, dark bill, black legs, and black primaries. From a distance it may be confused with the White Pelican, Wood Ibis, or Snow Goose, but the Whooping Crane can be identified by the long extended neck and the sharp upstroke of the wings.

About 35 Whooping Cranes remain in existence. Formerly the species was uncommon in winter and on migration in Alabama. It has not been recorded in the state during this century and was never known to nest here. It lives in wild, uninhabited, open regions, such as barren grounds, extensive coastal marshes, and shallow bays.

NESTING AND FOOD. The nest is well built of grasses and reeds and placed on the ground in marshes. The two eggs are olive or buffy, blotched with irregular brown spots. This crane feeds on frogs, fish, small mammals, corn, other grains, and the succulent roots of water plants.

DISTRIBUTION. The Whooping Crane bred formerly from Mackenzie and the Hudson Bay south to Nebraska and Iowa. It was noted on migration on the Atlantic Coast from Massachusetts to Georgia, and wintered from the Gulf states to Mexico. At present, the pitiful remnant breeds in northern Saskatchewan and southern Mackenzie and migrates through Nebraska to the Texas Coast where the whole population winters on Aransas National Wildlife Refuge. An occasional bird is seen on migration as far east as Illinois and in winter on the Louisiana Coast.

OCCURRENCE IN ALABAMA. (Winter, no dates available.) *Tennessee Valley*: No record. *Mountain Region*: No record. *Piedmont*: No record. *Upper Coastal Plain*: W. C. Avery says that it was seen many years prior to 1890 in the Cypress Slough of the Warrior River, Millwood, Hale Co. L. S. Golsan and E. G. Holt record a flock of 5 or 6 birds seen near Prattville late in November or early December 1899, the last record for Alabama. *Lower Coastal Plain*: No record. *Gulf Coast*: Capt. W. M. Sprinkle, an Audubon Society warden, told Arthur Howell that this bird was formerly common in winter on Dauphin Island.

[Sandhill Crane]

Grus canadensis Linnaeus   [206]   (Plate 6, facing page 96)
OTHER NAME: Crane

This *large, long-legged gray* bird has a bare red crown and *long back feathers* that *curl down over the tail*. About the size of the Great Blue Heron, this crane is heavier bodied, has a thinner bill about as long as its head, and flies with its neck extended. During the breeding season and while migrating it is sometimes noisy and gives a loud bugle-like call; in winter, however, it gives a raucous shriek much like the sound made by drawing chalk over a blackboard.

The Sandhill Crane is rare and local in winter in Baldwin County where summer records indicate that a pair or two may still breed. Inland it is a casual transient. It frequents the open pine flats, especially boggy openings with small ponds and marshes. Although it is very shy and avoids man as much as possible, it sometimes forages in cornfields. Although most people in Alabama apply the word crane to herons, many residents of Baldwin County give the name only to the Sandhill Crane.

NESTING. The nest of grasses and reeds is found on the ground in a marsh, generally on a slight rise. It usually contains two pale olive to buffy-brown eggs, marked all over with reddish-brown spots.

FOOD. This crane subsists mainly on roots, bulbs, and grains, particularly corn. This diet is varied with grasshoppers, beetle grubs, other large insects, spiders, frogs, lizards, snakes, and mice.

DISTRIBUTION. The Sandhill Crane breeds from northeastern Siberia, Alaska, and Baffin Island south locally to California, Colorado, South Dakota, and Michigan, and also from coastal Mississippi and southern Georgia to southern Florida. It winters from California, Texas, and the northern Gulf Coast south to central Mexico and southern Florida.

OCCURRENCE IN ALABAMA. (Throughout the year.) *Tennessee Valley*: No record. *Mountain Region*: No record. *Piedmont*: No record. *Upper Coastal Plain*: September 24, 1932 (6 birds migrating, Prattville, L. S. Golsan). *Lower Coastal Plain*: No record. *Gulf Coast*: Non-residents, November 30 (1947, 14 birds, Elberta, F. M. Weston) to March 20 (1958, Elberta, F. C. Seibert); recent in summer, June 18, 1958 (Romar Beach, Durwood Rider); June 23, 1960 (Orange Beach, *fide* J. L. Dorn) and August 16, 1960 (southern Baldwin Co., *fide* J. E. Keeler); most seen, 29, winter, 1959-60 (*fide* J. L. Dorn and J. E. Keeler) and 25, winter, 1954-55 (F. C. Seibert, R. W. Skinner and others).

TIME OF BREEDING. Near mouth of Perdido Bay, young bird captured with adult, August 1911 (A. H. Howell, 1924:85).

FAMILY RALLIDAE: RAILS, GALLINULES, AND COOTS

These chicken-like marsh birds (often called Mudhens, Marshhens, or Meadowhens) are capable of swimming, although none of them has webbed feet and only the coots have lobes on their toes. They are classed as game birds, but are very secretive; the American Coot, which occurs on open water with ducks in winter, is the only one regularly hunted in Alabama.

SUBFAMILY RALLINAE: RAILS

Retiring and reluctant to flush, rails are seldom seen. Even people living near marshes or meadows are often unaware of their presence. Yet they are noisy and active in still, cloudy weather and at dawn and dusk. If their calls are known and the proper habitat is visited during these hours, they will be easily found, for they are much more common than supposed.

Occasionally a rail flushes close at hand in a marsh. It gets aloft with labored flight and dangling legs and soon drops back into the grass. Nevertheless, these heavy-bodied and short-winged birds migrate considerable distances. Because Alabama marshes rarely freeze, the rails that breed here in summer are usually present throughout the year, and rails from farther north spend the winter here.

Rails can compress their bodies enough to walk through the grass without shaking the stems and betraying their presence. Their ability to do so gave rise to the expression "thin as a rail."

King Rail
Rallus elegans Audubon   [208]   (Plate 15, facing page 216)
OTHER NAMES: Marsh Hen, Freshwater Marsh Hen

This large rail, long-billed and reddish-brown, is the fresh-water counterpart of the salt-water Clapper Rail. The Clapper Rail of coastal Alabama is almost as reddish as the King Rail, which is slightly larger, less gray (especially on the back and cheeks), and more prominently barred on the flanks. Habitat is a useful guide in identification. Some calls of the King Rail are similar to those of the Clapper Rail, but generally the King Rail gives a deeper call in a longer series.

The King Rail is a locally common permanent resident in the Coastal Plain of Alabama, especially near the coast. North of the Fall Line it is less common in summer and has been recorded once in winter. It is known to nest in most places where it has been recorded in summer. This rail lives in fresh or brackish marshes and rarely visits salt marshes, which the Clapper Rail frequents. Often, when ideal habitat is scarce, the King Rail lives in wet, grassy areas that could hardly be called marshes.

NESTING. The nest is on the ground or slightly above it, or low in a buttonbush, in marshes or wet grassy places. It is made of the surrounding grasses and arched over to conceal six to twelve dull white or pale buff eggs spotted lightly with lilac and reddish-brown.

FOOD. This bird eats frogs, tadpoles, crawfish, snails, small fish, spiders, insects, and the seeds of a variety of marsh grasses. The insects include beetles, grasshoppers, aquatic bugs, and the nymphs of dragonflies.

DISTRIBUTION. The King Rail breeds from Nebraska, southern Minnesota, New York, and Massachusetts south to central Mexico and Cuba. It winters in the southern part of its breeding range north to the Gulf states and New Jersey, and occasionally in most of our northeastern states.

OCCURRENCE IN ALABAMA. (Throughout the year.) *Tennessee Valley*: April (1911, Leighton, F. W. McCormack) to November 21 (Wheeler Refuge, J. H. Steenis). *Mountain Region*: April 19 (1955, Fairfield, T. A. Imhof) to October 6 (1955, Fairfield, T. A. Imhof); also January 6, 1961 (Fairfield, T. A. Imhof). *Piedmont*: No dates available. *Upper Coastal Plain*: Permanent resident. *Lower Coastal Plain*: Permanent resident. *Gulf Coast*: Permanent resident; most seen, 12, October 6, 1956 (Fall Count, Mobile Bay Area).

TIME OF BREEDING. Data on 14 nestings: Eggs, March 24 to June 1; dependent young, May 30 to July 13.

[208]

Richard A. Parks

Clapper Rail

Rallus longirostris Boddaert   [211]   (Plate 15, facing page 216)

OTHER NAME: Saltwater Marsh Hen

Resembling a small chicken in size and habits, this rail is *large* and *grayish* with a *long, slightly down-curved bill* and black and white barred flanks. The Clapper Rail that occurs in Alabama is more *reddish* and closely resembles the slightly larger King Rail, but the Clapper Rail has grayer cheeks, a grayer back, and less prominent barring on the flanks. Its call, usually in a long series and not as deep as the King Rail's is the best means of establishing the presence of this bird. It calls most frequently at dawn or dusk, during the night, or upon hearing any loud noise such as a gunshot, a passing jet aircraft, or a clap of thunder.

The Clapper Rail is strictly confined to salt marshes, where it is common to abundant all year and nests in summer. It is this bird's habit to keep well hidden in the grass, flushing rather easily if disturbed. But it often ventures out onto the muddy shores of ditches and bayous, especially at dawn, at dusk, or at low tide.

NESTING. The nest of the Clapper Rail is slightly elevated, placed near water, and built of the surrounding grasses. It is usually arched over for better concealment. Five to fifteen, most commonly seven or eight, pale lavender eggs spotted with brown are a normal clutch. High tides destroy many Clapper Rail nests.

FOOD. The fiddler crab is the principal food of this rail, but it also eats other small crabs, snails, shrimp, shellfish, minnows, clamworms, aquatic insects, and even the young of the diamond-backed terrapin. It takes a small amount of seeds of marsh grasses, mostly in winter.

DISTRIBUTION. The Clapper Rail breeds in salt marshes from California to Peru, from New England to the West Indies and Brazil, in the lower Colorado River Valley, and in the Valley of Mexico. It winters sparingly almost as far north as it breeds and migrates usually along the coast so that it is casual in the interior.

OCCURRENCE IN ALABAMA. *Gulf Coast only:* Permanent resident; most seen, 44, December 21, 1957 and December 27, 1958 (Christmas Counts, Dauphin Island).

TIME OF BREEDING. Data on 37 nestings: Eggs, April 10 to July 5; downy young, May 19 to August 24; young flying by June 15.

[209]

Virginia Rail

Rallus limicola Vieillot   [212]   (Plate 15, facing page 216)

This *reddish-brown, long-billed* rail is about *half the size* of the King Rail. The Virginia Rail has *gray cheeks* which are almost black in immature birds. The Sora is just as small, but it has a stubby bill. The call of the Virginia Rail is a long series of notes like those of the Clapper and King Rails, but on a much higher pitch and sometimes double-noted. Other notes somewhat resemble the squealing of hungry pigs.

The Virginia Rail frequents fresh-water marshes, but on migration it may occur in any wet, grassy place, such as a ditch in a field or even a salt-water marsh. In the Tennessee Valley of Alabama, this species is uncommon on migration, but it has bred here at least once. This is the only positive breeding record for the state although two birds once lingered into June at Birmingham. In the remainder of the state it is uncommon on migration and in winter, but it is common on the Gulf Coast.

NESTING. This bird builds a rather compact nest of rushes and reeds and usually places it in a tuft of marsh grass. It lays six to twelve creamy to yellowish-white eggs spotted with reddish-brown or lavender.

FOOD. The Virginia Rail feeds mainly on water animals, including worms, snails, spiders, crustaceans, insects, and small fish. Insects it eats commonly are beetles, bugs, ants, wasps, grasshoppers, crickets, and the larvae of damsel-flies, dragonflies, and true flies. The diet is varied, especially in winter, with the seeds of marsh grasses, rushes, and sedges.

DISTRIBUTION. The Virginia Rail breeds from British Columbia and Nova Scotia south to Lower California, Oklahoma, the Ohio Valley, and coastal North Carolina, rarely farther south. It winters from British Columbia, Texas, northern Alabama, and North Carolina, rarely farther north, south to Guatemala and Florida.

OCCURRENCE IN ALABAMA. (August 11 to June 5; bred once.) *Tennessee Valley*: August 18 (1946, Wheeler Refuge, L. S. Givens and J. C. Salyer, II) to November 5 (1947, Wheeler Refuge, H. H. Grammer) and April (Wheeler Refuge, *fide* T. Z. Atkeson, Jr.) to May 11 (1941, Florence, H. M. Stevenson); bred in 1945. *Mountain Region*: August 13 (1950, Birmingham, T. A. Imhof) to May 4 (1953, Birmingham, T. A. Imhof); 2 birds to June 5, 1949 (Birmingham, T. A. Imhof); most seen, 5, December 24, 1949 (Birmingham, T. A. Imhof). *Piedmont*: No record. *Upper Coastal Plain*: August 11 (1938, Tuscaloosa, H. M. Stevenson) to April 1 (1957, Livingston, Jenkins Jackson). *Lower Coastal Plain*: April 14, 1958 (Camden, G. Matschke). *Gulf Coast*: August 25 (1939, Gulf Shores, H. M. Stevenson) to May 2 (1959, Cedar Point, T. A. Imhof); most seen, 8, December 29, 1956 and January 2,

1960 (Christmas Counts, Dauphin Island).
TIME OF BREEDING. Data on

1 nesting: Decatur, downy young, June 1945
(L. S. Givens).

Sora
Porzana carolina (Linnaeus)   [214]   (Plate 15, facing page 216)

Almost the same size as the Virginia Rail, this bird can be readily distinguished by its *short, yellow bill*. The Sora, like the Virginia Rail, is brownish on the back and has barred flanks, but the *adult* Sora has a *black face* and *crown* and slaty-blue cheeks, neck, and breast. The *immature* bird is *largely yellowish* on the head, neck, and breast, and it lacks the black markings. The Sora has three common calls: a high-pitched whinny, a two-noted whistle, and a sharp, high-pitched note. The last is the response of this highly nervous bird to a nearby disturbance. Throwing a stone into the marsh is a highly effective method of locating this bird in winter or on migration, when it is usually silent.

This is another fresh-water rail, although on migration it is likely to occur throughout the state in any wet, grassy locality, including salt marshes. It is common throughout Alabama on migration, and common in winter south of the Tennessee Valley. Although no nesting has been recorded in the state, the bird has been noted several times in summer. Sometimes it is abundant on the coast on migration, and almost always in Alabama it is at least twice as numerous as the Virginia Rail.

NESTING AND FOOD. The nest is rather loosely built of marsh grasses, and is slightly raised above the water. Sometimes it has a canopy. There are between seven and thirteen drab-colored eggs thoroughly spotted with chestnut and lavender. Because of its short bill, this bird cannot probe in the marsh mud for animals as do the long-billed rails. Especially in winter it eats chiefly plant life which, in the southeastern states, consists of the seeds of paspalum, wild rice, duckweeds, algae, cordgrass, smartweeds, and other water plants. It also feeds on beetles, other insects, snails, spiders, and crustaceans.

DISTRIBUTION. The Sora breeds from British Columbia, southern Mackenzie, and Nova Scotia south to Lower California, southern New Mexico, the Ohio Valley, and Maryland. It winters from California, Texas, northern Alabama, and South Carolina, occasionally farther north on the Atlantic Coast, south through Central America and the West Indies to Peru and Trinidad.

OCCURRENCE IN ALABAMA.
(Normal: August 20 to May 19; Out-of-season: June 1 and July 25.) *Tennessee Valley*:

August 28 (1940, Florence, H. M. Stevenson) to October 15 (1949, Wheeler Refuge, T. A. Imhof and others) and April 4 (1890, speci-

[211]

men not preserved, Leighton, F. W. McCormack) to May 19 (Leighton, F. W. McCormack). *Mountain Region*: August 29 (1936, Birmingham, H. M. Stevenson) to May 12 (1955, Fairfield, T. A. Imhof); most seen, migration, 6, April 9, 1956 (Fairfield, T. A. Imhof) and winter, 5, February 15, 1955 (Fairfield, T. A. Imhof). *Piedmont*: July 25, 1925 (an injured bird, Auburn, J. M. Robertson). *Upper Coastal Plain*: September 20 (1955, Marion, Lois McCollough) to May 11 (1956, Marion, T. A. Imhof); also June 1,

1912 (Autaugaville, L. S. Golsan); most seen, 30+, September 22, 1956 (Marion, Lois McCollough). *Lower Coastal Plain*; March 22, 1957 (Florala, T. A. Imhof). *Gulf Coast*: August 20 (1953, Gulf Shores, F. M. Weston) to May 3 (1959, Cedar Point, T. A. Imhof and others); also June 1, 1930 (an injured bird, Fairhope, Helen Edwards); most seen, migration, 73, April 26, 1958 (Spring Count, Mobile Bay Area), winter, 15, January 2, 1960 (Cedar Point, T. A. Imhof).

Yellow Rail
Coturnicops noveboracensis (Gmelin)   [215]   (Plate 15, facing page 216)

This small, elusive rail is buffy-yellow except for a darker crown, light brown stripes on the back, lightly-barred flanks, and *white wing patches* which show in flight. The close resemblance of its back pattern to that of the *Coturnix* quail is the reason for the scientific name of this rail. The immature Sora also shows much yellow, but the Yellow Rail is smaller, lighter on the back, and more difficult to flush. Normally the Yellow Rail can be flushed only with a bird dog or by dragging a rope through the grass. Peterson (1947) described the call as a long series of ticking notes in groups of two and three.

This bird inhabits short-grass marshes and fields such as pastures and hay meadows, preferably where broomsedge grows. In Alabama it is locally common in winter in the Black Belt, rare on the Gulf Coast, and is not known to breed here. The species is so secretive and so seldom encountered in normal field work that it very likely may be more common than our data indicate.

NESTING AND FOOD. The Yellow Rail builds a nest on the ground in meadows, using dry grasses. The female lays six to ten creamy-buff eggs finely spotted with reddish-brown. For its food this bird prefers the seeds of sedges, smartweeds, nutrush, bristlegrass, and other plants. It also takes fresh-water snails, beetles, grasshoppers, ants, wasps, fly larvae, bugs, and various crustaceans. It probably feeds on seeds as does the Sora, especially in winter.

DISTRIBUTION. The Yellow Rail breeds from Mackenzie, Quebec, and New Brunswick south to Alberta, Wisconsin, and Massachusetts, and also in California. It winters in California and in the Gulf states from western Louisiana to southern Florida.

OCCURRENCE IN ALABAMA. (November 21 to February 22.) *Tennessee* *Valley*: No record. *Mountain Region*: No record. *Piedmont*: No record. *Upper Coastal*

Plain: November 21 (1912, specimen, Barachias, E. G. Holt) to February 22 (1957, specimen in Dept. of Conservation collection, Maytag Plantation, Bullock Co., W. L. Holland); other specimens, Univ. of Wisconsin collection (Montgomery, 1876, L. Kumlien), Avery collection (Greensboro, December 17, 1891, W. C. Avery), Dept. of Archives and History collection (Barachias, December 11, 1911, E. G. Holt). *Lower Coastal Plain*: No record. *Gulf Coast*: February 19, 1917 (specimen in U. S. National Museum, Bayou La Batre, W. L. Bryant).

Purple Gallinule
Porphyrula martinica (Linnaeus)   [218]   (Plate 15, facing page 216)

This beautiful, brightly-colored rail has a *bluish-purple neck and under parts* and a bronzy-green back. Its yellow-tipped *bill is red,* the *frontal shield is light blue,* and the under tail coverts are white. In flight this rail dangles its *yellow legs,* a good identification mark. It makes various cackling notes, but none of them serve to identify the bird except to one of long experience with both gallinules.

The Purple Gallinule is rare and local in summer in the Coastal Plain of Alabama. It is known to breed only south of the Black Belt, and is widespread and reasonably common only on the Gulf Coast. In spring it is rare north of the Fall Line. It lives in fresh-water marshes and in the reedy borders of lakes and ponds, especially where waterlilies grow. Apparently it prefers deeper water than that frequented by other fresh-water rails. It often walks across lily pads or swims in nearby open water.

NESTING. The nest is built over water, sometimes several feet above it. Constructed of marsh grasses and arched over for concealment, it contains six to ten creamy eggs thinly spotted with lavender.

FOOD. This bird feeds mainly on the seeds, fruits, and other parts of wild rice, windmill grass, paspalum, duckweed, wild millet, signal grass, spikerush, and other aquatic plants. It also takes, chiefly in spring, aquatic beetles and bugs, other aquatic insects, mollusks, and other small water animals.

DISTRIBUTION. The Purple Gallinule breeds in lowlands from western Tennessee, central Alabama, and South Carolina south through Central America and the West Indies to Peru and northern Argentina. It winters north to Louisiana and Florida, and on migration occurs rarely in almost all the northeastern United States and southeastern Canadian provinces.

OCCURRENCE IN ALABAMA. (April 11 to November 9.) *Tennessee Valley*: May 5, 1953 (identified in the hand, Guntersville, Edith Clark and others). *Mountain Region*: April 28, 1955 and May 12, 1955 (Fairfield, T. A. Imhof). *Piedmont*: May 12, 1952, May 16, 1951, and June 4, 1935 (Auburn, H. G. Good). *Upper Coastal Plain*: June or July 1885 (Bear Swamp, Autauga Co., L. S. Golsan); June 11, 1956 (specimen in Dept. of Conservation collection, Demopolis Lake, W. W. Beshears) and June 25, 1955 (Marion, T. A. Imhof). *Lower Coastal Plain*: Reported by the T. Z. Atkesons as nesting regularly near Columbia, Houston Co. *Gulf Coast*: April 11 (1937, specimen in Auburn collection, Gulf Shores, H. J. Good) to Nov. 9 (1957, Dauphin Is., Ava Tabor and others).

TIME OF BREEDING. Data on 3 Gulf Coast nestings: Eggs, April 19 (J. C. Gray); nest of unknown contents, May; downy young, July 4 (C. W. Summerour).

Common Gallinule

Gallinula chloropus (Linnaeus) [219] (Plate 15, facing page 216)

OTHER NAMES: Florida Gallinule, Mudhen

This rail is not so highly-colored as the Purple Gallinule. It is slaty-gray, browner on the back, and its *frontal shield* and yellow-tipped *bill* are *red*. A long stripe on each flank is white, and the under tail coverts are mostly black. The Common Gallinule makes a variety of harsh, loud, complaining, chicken-like sounds, but these calls, like those of the Purple Gallinule, will be of little help to the novice in identification. They are of use only to observers who pay frequent dawn and dusk visits to marshes to listen to rail calls and who combine listening with patient sight identification of the callers.

The Common Gallinule is an uncommon and local summer resident in suitable habitat, mostly in the Coastal Plain. Breeding data are few, but it probably breeds throughout the Coastal Plain wherever it is found in summer. On the Gulf Coast, notably at the head of Mobile Bay, it is common in summer and on migration and uncommon in winter. It has also been noted once in winter in the Black Belt. It lives in the same type of marshes as the Purple Gallinule but ranges farther north.

NESTING. The nest is a platform of dry marsh grasses, often buoyant, and sometimes placed a foot or two above water. On rare occasions it is on dry land near the marsh. The six to twelve buffy-white, sparsely brown-spotted eggs are incubated as soon as laid so that the young hatch out one at a time.

FOOD. This bird feeds on grasses, seeds, water insects, worms, and snails.

DISTRIBUTION. In the Western Hemisphere the Common Gallinule breeds, often locally, from California, Nebraska, southern Ontario, and southern Quebec south through Central America and the West Indies to Chile and Argentina. It winters from southern California, Texas, and South Carolina southward, and in fall occurs casually north and east of the breeding range.

OCCURRENCE IN ALABAMA. (Throughout the year.) *Tennessee Valley*: 2 killed prior to 1912 (Leighton, *fide* F. W. McCormack); August 26, 1950 (Wheeler Refuge, D. C. Hulse) and 2 present, August 7 to 16, 1955 (D. C. Hulse and others). *Mountain Region*: March 19 (1956, Fairfield, T. A. Imhof) to October 26 (1955, Fairfield,

T. A. Imhof). *Piedmont*: Lee Co., summer of 1934 (Lake Wilmore, *fide* H. G. Good) and summer of 1954 (Whatley's Lake, W. F. Helms and others). *Upper Coastal Plain*: April 12 (1957, Marion, Lois McCollough) to November 13 (1956, Marion, Lois McCollough); also February 7, 1959 (2 birds, Gainesville, Jenkins Jackson, R. W. Skinner, and others). *Lower Coastal Plain*: March 20 (1957, Andalusia, L. C. Crawford) to October 20 (1956, Coffee County Lake, T. A. Imhof and L. C. Crawford). *Gulf Coast*: Common,

March to November, specimen in U. S. National Museum, Nigger Lake, November 30, 1915 (A. H. Howell); most seen, summer, 11, June 21, 1958 (Mobile Delta, T. A. Imhof and J. R. Davis), fall, 12, November 1, 1958 (Mobile Delta, Lois McCollough and others).

TIME OF BREEDING. Data on 3 nestings: Eggs, 6, June 10, 1954 (Whatley's Lake, Lee Co., W. F. Helms); full-grown young, June 20, 1958 (Nigger Lake, Baldwin Co., T. A. Imhof and J. R. Davis) and September 3, 1960 (Cochrane Causeway, J. L. Dorn).

SUBFAMILY FULICINAE: COOTS

American Coot

Fulica americana Gmelin   [221]   (Plate 15, facing page 216)
OTHER NAMES: Poule d'Eau, Foolhen, Water Guinea

This bird is closely related to the gallinules, but it occurs more often on open water, and so is frequently thought to be a duck. The American Coot, however, has a small head which it pumps back and forth like a chicken, and it has a small *whitish bill* and *frontal shield*. It is a *slate-gray* bird, darker on the head and neck, with white under tail coverts and a small white border on the inner edge of the wing. Its feet are green and lobed. This bird dives expertly and when taking wing patters across the water.

Throughout Alabama the American Coot is abundant in winter and on migration, and uncommon, rarely breeding, in summer. (See Map 46.) In winter this not-too-wary bird occurs on practically all bodies of fresh water in the state and often forms dense rafts on open water, sometimes with ducks. In summer it usually occurs singly or in small groups on small, marshy ponds where it probably breeds more often than noted. Many nesting attempts probably go unnoticed because summering pairs remain in seclusion and very likely their young fall prey to turtles, bass, water snakes, or other predators. Some summering birds are undoubtedly hunting season casualties, but many go through antics remarkably similar to courtship.

NESTING. The nest, sometimes found floating, is a rather large platform of grasses and dead or decaying marsh vegetation. This coot lays seven to sixteen creamy eggs finely and evenly spotted with dark brown and black.

FOOD. In the southeastern states, most of the food of this species consists of the leaves and seeds of water plants, such as duckweeds, widgeon

PLATE 15

CLAPPER RAIL
Adult, Sexes Alike
Page 209

KING RAIL
Adult, Sexes Alike
Page 207

SORA
Adult, Sexes Alike
Page 211

YELLOW RAIL
Adult, Sexes Alike
Page 212

VIRGINIA RAIL
Adult, Sexes Alike
Page 210

COMMON GALLINULE
Adult, Sexes Alike
Page 214

PURPLE GALLINULE
Adult, Sexes Alike
Page 213

LEAST BITTERN
Adult, Sexes Alike
Page 100

AMERICAN COOT
Adult, Sexes Alike
Page 215

AMERICAN BITTERN
Adult, Sexes Alike
Page 101

[216]

Richard Parks

grass, pondweeds, muskgrass, naiad, spikerush, and the like. This is varied, especially in summer, with fish, snails, aquatic insects, other small mollusks, crustaceans, worms, and spiders.

DISTRIBUTION. The American Coot breeds from British Columbia, southern Mackenzie, and New Brunswick south locally to central Mexico, Tennessee, and New Jersey, and sporadically to Nicaragua and the Greater Antilles. It winters from British Columbia, New Mexico, Texas, the Ohio Valley, and Maryland, and occasionally farther northeast, south to Panama and the Lesser Antilles.

OCCURRENCE IN ALABAMA. (Throughout the year.) *Tennessee Valley*: Common, September 12 (1958, Wheeler Refuge, J. B. Sullivan and others) to May 21 (1954, Wannville, J. H. Heflin), summer, see Map 46; most seen, 25,000, April 7, 1936 (Wheeler Reservoir, A. R. Cahn); recent, 1500, November 5, 1951 (Wheeler Refuge, J. H. Sutherlin and others). *Mountain Region*: Common, October 6 (1935, Birmingham, H. M. Stevenson) to May 12 (1955, Fairfield, T. A. Imhof); most seen, winter, 15,000, December 27, 1942 (Lake Purdy, M. F. Prather), summer, 15 in 1915 (Oxford Lake near Anniston, R. H. Dean). *Piedmont*: Common, October 1 (1952, Lake Martin, W. T. Meadows and J. R. Bean) to May 7 (1959, Auburn, Lovett Williams). *Upper Coastal Plain*: Common, September 21 (1955, Marion, Lois McCollough) to May 28 (1959, Livingston, Jenkins Jackson); most seen, winter, 800, March 7, 1952 (Marion, T. A. Imhof), summer, 16, June 1, 1956 (Marion, Lois McCollough). *Lower Coastal Plain*: Common, October 1 (1952, Coffee Co., Geneva Co., and Barbour Co., W. H. McDuffie, Gramble, and J. H. Crook) to May 26 (1956, Jackson, T. A. Imhof); most seen, 5000, January 13, 1954 (Florala, T. C. Hattaway). *Gulf Coast*: Common, September 17 (1957, Cochrane Causeway, W. F. Colin) to May 11 (1938, Cochrane Causeway, F. M. Weston); most seen, winter, 26,000, November 17, 1952 (Mobile Delta, W. F. Colin), summer, 60+, June and July 1960 (Cochrane Causeway, J. L. Dorn).

TIME OF BREEDING. Data on 3 nestings: Young, June 3, 1952 and August 16, 1951 (Swan Creek, Limestone Co., J. H. Heflin) and July 30 to mid-August, 1960 (Gulf Shores, M. W. Gaillard).

Map 46

AMERICAN COOT.
Distribution in Summer

◑ May 15 to August 15   ● Breeding positive

BANDING. See Map 47. Of the 12 Illinois-banded birds, 1 made the trip to Alabama in 10 days, another in 26, and 2 in 28 days! Of 41 recoveries in Alabama, 3 are from Madison Co., and 1 each from Altoona, Etowah Co., Montevallo, Hayneville, Selma, Prattville, and Gantt, and 32 from the Gulf Coast.

[217]

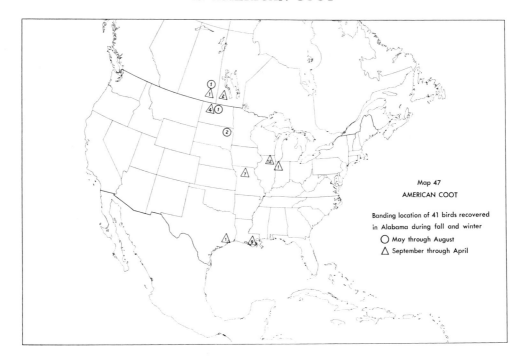

Map 47

AMERICAN COOT

Banding location of 41 birds recovered
in Alabama during fall and winter
○ May through August
△ September through April

ORDER CHARADRIIFORMES: SHOREBIRDS, GULLS, AUKS, AND ALLIES

Birds of this rather large order have the same general shape, including long pointed wings. The birds frequent the sea and its borders, occur in large dense flocks, and breed mostly in the far north, where they hatch downy, well-developed young. Although exceptions are frequent, many of them have dense plumage, webbed feet, short tails, short bills, and legs set in the center of the body.

SUBORDER CHARADRII: JACANAS AND SHOREBIRDS

Shorebirds and jaçanas have long, slender, soft bills and short tails. The shorebirds (superfamily *Charadrioidea*) have long pointed wings with very long innermost wing feathers, and they are usually strong long-distance fliers. In all probability they are the champion migrants of the bird world, for many of them breed in the Arctic and winter south of the Equator. Usually their legs are long and the hind toe either small or absent. They live in or near the margins of almost all bodies of water. Their calls are distinctive, pleasing, and melodious. For their size, they have large eggs, and the young are downy and are hatched well developed.

FAMILY HAEMATOPODIDAE: OYSTERCATCHERS

American Oystercatcher
Haematopus palliatus Temminck   [286]   (Plate 18, facing page 256)
OTHER NAME: Redbill Snipe

This oystercatcher, almost our longest and certainly our heaviest shorebird, is about the size of an average duck. It has a *black head* and *neck* and a large, *bright red bill* adapted to opening the shells of mollusks. Its back is dark bronzy-brown; its belly, white; and its legs, flesh-colored. In the immature bird the bill is a duller color. In flight the American Oystercatcher shows a prominent white wing stripe. Its call is a rapidly repeated, penetrating whistle.

This big shorebird frequents sand flats and beaches, especially those near oyster reefs. Its distribution along the coast is spotty, apparently determined by the location of these reefs. In Alabama, this oystercatcher is an uncommon, breeding, permanent resident in coastal Mobile County.

NESTING. This bird lays two or three creamy-white eggs speckled with brown, black, or lavender in a slight depression in the sand of a deserted beach, often a small sandbar in a shallow bay.

FOOD. Oysters, clams, mussels, and other shellfish are the main food of this bird. Occasionally it eats sea-worms and insects.

DISTRIBUTION. The American Oystercatcher is resident and local on the Atlantic and Gulf coasts from New Jersey to the West Indies, Texas, and Argentina, but it is rarer in winter north of North Carolina. On the Pacific Coast it is resident from Lower California to Chile.

OCCURRENCE IN ALABAMA. *Gulf Coast only*: Permanent resident; most seen, 12 or 15, April 6, 1926 (Bayou La Batre, W. L. Bryant), recent, 7, October 6, 1956 (Cedar Point and Bayou La Batre, T. A. Imhof, H. C. Loesch, and Lois McCollough); specimen, in U. S. National Museum, November 30, 1915 (Coffee Island, A. H. Howell); specimen in Dept. of Conservation collection, August 17, 1961 (Dauphin Island, R. W. Skinner).

TIME OF BREEDING. Data on 3 nestings: Copulation, April 25; dependent young, April 19 to May 2.

FAMILY CHARADRIIDAE: PLOVERS, TURNSTONES, AND SURFBIRDS

These birds are heavier in build than the sandpipers and snipes. They also differ in having shorter, thicker bills, larger eyes, bolder head and neck patterns, and more melodious calls.

SUBFAMILY CHARADRIINAE: PLOVERS

The family characteristics are well developed in the birds of this subfamily.

Semipalmated Plover
Charadrius semipalmatus Bonaparte   [274]   (Plate 16, facing page 224)
OTHER NAMES: Ring-necked Plover, Ringed Plover

This plover closely *resembles* the *Killdeer*, even to the color of the back, but it is about half the size of a Killdeer and has *but one breast band*. Furthermore, it has yellow legs and a yellow bill with a black tip, but the bill is usually all dark in winter and in immature birds. The call is a distinctive high-pitched, two-syllabled whistle.

On the Alabama Coast this bird is common in winter and on migration and uncommon to rare in summer. Inland it is uncommon to common in favored places on migration. It is not known to breed in this state. This plover frequents mudflats where it associates with the small sandpipers usually found there. Occasionally it can be found on sand areas, and inland it usually occurs on exposed flats of large rivers or ponds.

NESTING AND FOOD. The nest is a grass-lined hollow near water. It usually holds four buffy to olive-buff eggs marked with dark brown or black. Much of the food eaten by this bird consists of low-flying insects—grasshoppers, locusts, mosquitoes, and others. In addition it takes small crustaceans, mollusks, and the eggs of marine animals.

DISTRIBUTION. The Semipalmated Plover breeds in the Arctic from the Bering Sea to southern Baffin Island and Greenland south to British Columbia, southern James Bay, the north shore of the Gulf of St. Lawrence, and southern Nova Scotia. Non-breeding birds summer south to Panama. It winters on the Pacific Coast from California to Chile and on the Atlantic, Gulf, and Caribbean coasts from South Carolina to Patagonia.

OCCURRENCE IN ALABAMA. (Throughout the year.) *Tennessee Valley*: April 24 (1950, Wheeler Refuge, T. A. Imhof) to May 22 (1960, Swan Creek, 40 birds, J. C. and Margaret Robinson) and August 5 (1952, Wheeler Refuge, Eugene Cypert) to September 18 (1954, Decatur, D. C. Hulse). *Mountain Region*: May 12 (1937, Birmingham, H. M. Stevenson and 1946, T. A. Imhof, S. R. and Isabel Tipton) to May 28 (1960, Hammondville, DeKalb Co., Adele and Eugene West) and August 12 (1936, Birmingham, H. M. Stevenson) to September 18 (1937, Birmingham, H. M. Stevenson). *Piedmont*: April 14 and 28, 1953 (Auburn, H. G. Good). *Upper Coastal Plain*: April 30 (1954, Marion, T. A. Imhof) to May 24 (1956, Marion, T. A. Imhof) and August 17 (1939, Tuscaloosa, H. M. Stevenson) to October 3 (1954, Marion, Lois McCollough). *Lower Coastal Plain*: May 9, 1958 (Headland, T. A. Imhof). *Gulf Coast*: Common, July 29 (1955, Fort Morgan, H. M. Stevenson) to June 5 (1914, Dauphin Island, J. L. Peters and 1940, Gulf Shores, H. M. Stevenson); most seen, spring, 69, May 2, 1959 (Spring Count, Mobile Bay Area), summer, 15+, June 15 and 16, 1956 (Dauphin Island, T. A. Imhof and others), fall, 82, October 6, 1956 (Fall Count, Mobile Bay Area) and winter, 100, December 29, 1956 (Dauphin Island, J. L. Dorn).

Piping Plover

Charadrius melodus Ord [277] (Plate 16, facing page 224)

OTHER NAME: Beach Plover

This small plover has a white belly and a very pale back, the color of the dry sand that it frequents. It has a *short, black-tipped yellow bill* which in *winter* is all *black*. A black bar runs across the forehead and a black band across the breast. In winter, the breast band becomes incomplete. On its *white-bordered tail* is a *large black patch* and in flight it shows a broad, white wing stripe. Its *legs* are an *orange-yellow* color and its call is a distinctive, rather low-pitched, two-syllabled whistle.

This plover is common in winter and on migration on Gulf Coast beaches. Inland it is rare in fall, and it is not known to breed in Alabama. It is its habit to run rapidly across a sand flat where it blends so perfectly that, when it stops, it seems to disappear.

NESTING AND FOOD. This bird chooses the ridge of a stable sand dune or a sandbar in midstream for its nest, which is a hollow lined with shell or pebbles. The four creamy-white eggs are uniformly marked with large and small dark brown spots. The species depends on marine worms, fly larvae, beetles, and other small animals found on sandy beaches for its food.

DISTRIBUTION. The Piping Plover breeds locally from Alberta, Quebec, and Newfoundland south to central Nebraska, the south shores of Lake Michigan and Lake Erie, and down the Atlantic Coast to Virginia. It winters on the Atlantic and Gulf coasts from South Carolina to southern Texas, and more rarely in the Bahamas and the Greater Antilles.

OCCURRENCE IN ALABAMA. (July 23 to May 3.) *Tennessee Valley*: September 9, 1955 (5 birds, Decatur, D. C. Hulse). *Mountain Region*: September 13, 1937 (Birmingham, Lake Purdy, H. M. Stevenson). *Piedmont*: No record. *Upper Coastal Plain*: August 3, 1938 (Tuscaloosa, H. M. Stevenson). *Lower Coastal Plain*: No record. *Gulf Coast*: July 23 (1955, Dauphin Island, R. L. Chermock) to May 3 (1959, Dauphin Island, T. A. Imhof and D. C. Holliman); most seen, fall, 250, November 24, 1956 (Dauphin Island, Lois McCollough) winter, 117, December 21, 1957 (Dauphin Island, E. O. Willis).

Snowy Plover
Charadrius alexandrinus Linnaeus   [278]   (Plate 16, facing page 224)
OTHER NAME: Beach Plover

This plover is slightly smaller and slightly paler than the Piping Plover. It also differs in having a bigger head, a thinner, longer, *black bill, bluish legs*, a *black ear patch*, and a black bar on each side of the breast. In winter, when the Piping Plover also has a black bill and the head markings of the two species are not very prominent, the Snowy Plover can always be distinguished by its bluish legs.

The Snowy Plover is a thinly-scattered, local but regular permanent resident only on the outer beaches and sandbars in Baldwin and Mobile counties. It breeds commonly on the more deserted sand islands and uncommonly near settled areas.

NESTING. The two or three pale buffy eggs are marked with dark brown and black. They are laid in a depression in the sand on a deserted beach close to the Gulf.

FOOD. In Alabama the Snowy Plover eats small crustaceans, mollusks, marine worms, aquatic insects, and seeds.

DISTRIBUTION. In North America this bird breeds inland in river valleys from Washington, Utah, Oklahoma, and Kansas south to southern Lower California and northern Texas; on the northern Gulf Coast from Texas to Florida; and in the Bahamas and the Greater Antilles. It winters on the Pacific Coast from Oregon to Mexico, and on the Atlantic Coast from Louisiana and Florida south to Venezuela, the Bahamas, and the Greater Antilles.

OCCURRENCE IN ALABAMA. *Gulf Coast only*: Permanent resident; most seen, 5, March 11, 1955 (Fort Morgan Peninsula, T. A. Imhof).

TIME OF BREEDING. Data on 10 nestings: Eggs, April 9 to June 24; downy young, June 24.

Wilson's Plover
Charadrius wilsonia Ord   [280]   (Plate 16, facing page 224)
OTHER NAME: Thick-billed Plover

Wilson's Plover somewhat resembles the Semipalmated Plover but it can be distinguished by its larger size, thick black breast band, *large black bill, white line over* the *eye*, and flesh-colored legs. The female has a brown breast band. The call of the Wilson's Plover is a whistle a little like that of the Great Crested Flycatcher, but it is shorter and less explosive.

This plover is a common, breeding, summer resident on the immediate coast in Alabama. Its occurrence in the state is almost confined to this one area, but it has been recorded inland once in fall. Wilson's Plover normally occurs on the sandy shores, beaches, and mudflats of islands.

NESTING. This plover prefers to nest on a coastal island. The nest is a depression in the sand containing a few pieces of broken shell, and it is extremely difficult to locate. The three eggs are pale olive or greenish-gray, splashed and spotted with blackish-brown.

FOOD. This bird eats crabs, shrimp, some mollusks, and flies.

DISTRIBUTION. Wilson's Plover is resident on the Pacific Coast from Lower California to Peru and breeds along the Atlantic and Gulf coasts from Virginia and the Bahamas, and rarely southern New Jersey, south to Texas

PLATE 16

RUDDY TURNSTONE
Adult Male, Summer, Sexes Similar
Page 230

PIPING PLOVER
Adult Male, Sexes Similar
Page 221

SNOWY PLOVER
Adult Male, Sexes Similar
Page 222

WILSON'S PLOVER
Adult Male, Summer, Sexes Similar
Page 223

SEMIPALMATED PLOVER
Adult, Sexes Alike
Page 220

KILLDEER
Adult, Sexes Alike
Page 225

AMERICAN GOLDEN PLOVER
Adult, Summer, Sexes Alike
Page 227

BLACK-BELLIED PLOVER
Summer, Sexes Alike
Page 229

BLACK-BELLIED PLOVER
Winter, Sexes Alike
Page 229

[224]

Richard Parks

NEST OF WILSON'S PLOVER. This species lays its three eggs in a depression in the sand.

and Venezuela. It winters from Texas and Florida south to the West Indies and Brazil.

OCCURRENCE IN ALABAMA. (March 11 to November 6.) *Tennessee Valley*: No record. *Mountain Region*: October 18, 1959 (Gadsden, Edith Clark). *Piedmont*: No record. *Upper Coastal Plain*: No record. *Lower Coastal Plain*: No record. *Gulf Coast*: March 11 (1955, Fort Morgan, T. A. Imhof) to November 6 (1948, Fort Morgan, F. M. Weston); most seen, 47, August 24, 1956 (Dauphin Island, T. A. Imhof and others).

TIME OF BREEDING. Data on 5 nestings: Eggs, June 20 and 25; downy young, June 12; flying by June 12.

Killdeer

Charadrius vociferus Linnaeus   [273]   (Plate 16, facing page 224)
OTHER NAMES: Killdee, Upland Plover, Killdeer Plover

The Killdeer is a large plover with a dark brown back, white belly, *two black bands* across the *chest*, and a rather long, reddish-brown tail. A very noisy bird, its most common note is a distinctive whistle of two syllables which its common name imitates.

CHARADRIIFORMES: CHARADRIIDAE: KILLDEER

A plover of the uplands, it is especially common around farms, in pastures, in short-grass fields, and on pond and lake margins. In winter it is abundant and occupies the whole state. As a breeder in summer, it is common north of the Fall Line but becomes less common and more widely scattered southward in the Coastal Plain. Nevertheless it does occur during the breeding season within a few miles of the Gulf, but only rarely.

NESTING. Generally this bird nests on the bare ground, especially in gravelly places, within fifty yards of the water. The three to four eggs are dull buffy and are thickly spotted and blotched with black and with dark brown.

FOOD. The Killdeer subsists almost entirely on insects and crustaceans. These include weevils, boll weevils, grasshoppers, crickets, mosquitoes, many kinds of beetles, flies, crane flies, ticks, worms, crawfish, and various marine worms.

DISTRIBUTION. This species breeds from northern British Columbia, southern Mackenzie, northern Ontario, and southern Quebec south to southern Lower California, central Mexico, and the Greater Antilles. It also breeds in Peru and Chile. It winters from southern British Columbia, Colorado, southern Illinois, western New York, and Long Island south to Venezuela and the West Indies.

KILLDEER AND EGGS. Like most plovers, the Killdeer makes no attempt at nest construction.

R. C. Erickson

FOUR NEWLY HATCHED KILLDEER. Protective coloration makes the young of this species very difficult to see.

OCCURRENCE IN ALABAMA. (Throughout the year.) *Tennessee Valley*: Permanent resident; most seen, 150, November 14, 1953 (Wheeler Refuge, T. A. Imhof and others). *Mountain Region*: Permanent resident; most seen, 341, December 20, 1958 (Christmas Count, Birmingham). *Piedmont*: Permanent resident. *Upper Coastal Plain*: Permanent resident; most seen, winter, 365, December 27, 1957 (Christmas Count, Marion), summer, 140, July 13, 1957 (Sumter Co., and Greene Co., T. A. Imhof and others). *Lower Coastal Plain*: Permanent resident. *Gulf Coast*: Common, August 20 (1953, Foley, F. M. Weston) to May 17 (1958, Cochrane Causeway, T. A. Imhof and M. W.

Gaillard); bred at Spring Hill in 1940 (J. L. Dorn); most seen, 245, December 28, 1956 (Christmas Count, Mobile).

TIME OF BREEDING. Data on 30 nestings: Eggs, March 16 to June 12; downy young, April 1 to July 14; young on the wing by May 27.

BANDING. A Killdeer banded on Cochrane Causeway by C. S. Robbins on January 9, 1954 was recaptured by him at the same place on January 18, 1956. Another banded at Key West, Fla., February 21, 1939, was found dead at Oneonta on February 21, 1940. A third Killdeer was banded at Blackriver, Michigan, July 6, 1935 as a chick, and found at Tuscumbia, October 20, 1935.

American Golden Plover
Pluvialis dominica Müller [272] (Plate 16, facing page 224)

About the size of the Killdeer, this plover is a more streamlined and thinner bird. In winter plumage (as it is usually seen in the United States), it has a light belly, and the crown and back look like a finely-woven basket, for they are brown with fine yellowish-brown spots. The bird is then best identified in flight by the *even brownish color* of the *back, wings,* and *tail* and by its distinctive call. In summer plumage the back is brighter and the *belly is black clear to* the *tail.* A broad white stripe runs from the bill over the eye and down the side of the neck.

The famous, far-flying Golden Plover is uncommon in spring and rare in fall on the Gulf Coast. Elsewhere in Alabama it is rare in spring and fall. It is not known to breed here. Usually it occurs on short-grass fields, bare flats, or beaches, and occasionally on mudflats. Essentially it is an open-country bird and has been noticed to have a particular fondness for burnt-over fields.

NESTING AND FOOD. The nest, a slight depression on the tundra, generally holds four creamy-white to buffy-brown eggs which are boldly spotted with brown and black. The bird's main foods are grasshoppers, other insects, and crustaceans.

DISTRIBUTION. The American Golden Plover breeds on Arctic coasts and islands from eastern Siberia and Baffin Island south to Churchill, Manitoba. It winters in southeast Asia, Polynesia, Hawaii, Brazil, Bolivia, Paraguay, Uruguay, and Argentina, and casually on the northern Gulf Coast of the United States, and in Peru and Chile. In spring it migrates through the Mississippi Valley, and in fall usually from Nova Scotia to Trinidad non-stop around the eastern side of the Bermuda High. However, in fall many birds occur on the Atlantic and Pacific coasts and a few even in the Mississippi Valley. The endurance and mysterious navigational ability of a bird that annually flies at least 20,000 miles cannot help but arouse admiration and wonder.

OCCURRENCE IN ALABAMA. (March 17 to April 12 and October 7 to November 15.) *Tennessee Valley*: November 14 and 15, 1935 (26 birds, Wheeler Refuge and Decatur, T. A. Imhof, A. F. Ganier, B. B. Coffey, and others). *Mountain Region*: March 22, 1947, flock of 39 (Birmingham, T. A. Imhof and M. H. Perry); April 12, 1961 (Birmingham, T. A. Imhof); October 7, 1960 (3 birds, Birmingham, T. A. Imhof, Idalene Snead, and Emmy Brownlie); and early October 1943 (Camp Sibert, Etowah Co., T. A. Imhof). *Piedmont*: November 9, 1959 (a female specimen, Auburn Univ. collection, Auburn, J. L. Dusi). *Upper Coastal Plain*: April 5, 1960 (85 birds, 1 a specimen in the Dept. of Conservation collection, Montgomery, R. W. Skinner). *Lower Coastal Plain*: No record. *Gulf Coast*: March 17 (1960, 6 birds, Theodore, J. L. Dorn) to April 12 (1957, 5 birds, Theodore, J. L. Dorn); also November 1, 1958 (21 birds, Cochrane Causeway, B. L. Monroe, Jr. and F. M. Weston) and November 2, 1958 (1 bird, Cochrane Causeway, R. W. Skinner and Lovett Williams); specimen in U. S. National Museum, March 26, 1933 (Foley, Homer Flagg and Kenneth Edwards).

Black-bellied Plover

Squatarola squatarola (Linnaeus)　[270]　(Plate 16, facing page 224)
OTHER NAMES: Beetlehead, Blacksnipe

The Black-bellied Plover, the largest and stockiest of its family in Alabama, has a gray crown and back and white under parts in its winter plumage. In summer it acquires a black belly and resembles the Golden Plover, although its back is gray with no trace of yellow, and the under tail coverts are white. In any plumage it can be distinguished from the Golden Plover by its *white wing patches, white tail,* and *black axillars.* The call of the Black-bellied Plover is a distinctive, loud, high-pitched whistle.

Mudflats are the favorite habitat of this bird. On the coast of Alabama, it is common to abundant on migration, common in winter, and uncommon in summer. Inland it is uncommon in fall at Wheeler Refuge, and rare on migration elsewhere. The Black-bellied Plover is not known to breed in the state.

NESTING AND FOOD. This plover's nest is a depression on the tundra which it lines with grass and leaves. In it the female lays four olive-buff, heavily black-spotted eggs. The bird eats marine insects, small mollusks, crustaceans, worms, grasshoppers, and sometimes berries.

DISTRIBUTION. This species occurs nearly throughout the world. In the Western Hemisphere it breeds on Arctic coasts and islands from northern Alaska to western Baffin Island. It winters on the coast from southern British Columbia and New Jersey, rarely Massachusetts, south to northern Chile and Brazil. Non-breeders summer on the Atlantic and Gulf coasts of the United States and in Ecuador and Panama.

OCCURRENCE IN ALABAMA. (Throughout the year.) *Tennessee Valley*: May 11, 1952 (4 birds, Guntersville, Blanche Chapman and others), May 15, 1952 (Wheeler Refuge, H. H. Grammer and J. H. Sutherlin) and August 21 (1953, Wheeler Refuge, D. C. Hulse) to November 22 (1952, Wheeler Refuge, T. A. Imhof); most seen, 22, October 15, 1949 (Wheeler Refuge, T. A. Imhof and others). *Mountain Region*: November 27, 1958 (Lake Purdy, Harriett Wright). *Piedmont*: No record. *Upper Coastal Plain*: Several specimens prior to 1890 (Greensboro, W. C. Avery); October 3 (1954, Marion, Lois McCollough) to November 8 (1957, Marion, Lois McCollough and T. A. Imhof); most seen, 4, October 25, 1957 (Marion, Lois McCollough). *Lower Coastal Plain*: No record. *Gulf Coast*: Common, early August to late May; most seen spring, 100, May 2, 1959 (Spring Count, Mobile Bay Area), summer, 4, June 16, 1956 (Dauphin Island, T. A. Imhof and others), fall, 235, September 23, 1955 (Dauphin Island, T. A. Imhof and W. W. Beshears), winter, 194, December 21, 1957 (Dauphin Island, E. O. Willis and T. A. Imhof).

Ruddy Turnstone

Arenaria interpres (Linnaeus)   [283]   (Plate 16, facing page 224)
OTHER NAME: Calicoback

The Ruddy Turnstone, a little larger than the Spotted Sandpiper, has *orange legs* and is variously marked with brown, reddish-brown, black, and white. In *spring* plumage the back is *reddish-brown,* the belly and most of the *face* are *white,* and a *large black patch* marks the *foreneck* and chest with *black streaks* running from it onto the *face.* In *fall,* the back, face, *foreneck,* and *chest* become *dark brown,* the legs grow duller, but the bird still retains its distinctive appearance. In *flight,* at any season, it shows a *variegated pattern* of black, white, and brown; the most prominent of these markings are the wide black band on the white tail, two white wing stripes, and the *large white diamond* on the *lower back.* This bird's three-syllabled call is low, rapid, and distinctive.

In Alabama the Ruddy Turnstone is fairly common on migration and in winter on the coast, where a few birds are apt to linger through the summer. Inland it is rare in fall and occurs mostly in the Tennessee Valley. It is not known to breed anywhere in the state. This bird is fond of pebbly, gravelly beaches and flats. Occurring along the shore, particularly where there are shells, stones, or rocks, it is especially abundant on the oyster flats of southern Mobile County.

NESTING AND FOOD. The Ruddy Turnstone nests near water by lining a hollow on the tundra with grass and seaweed. There are usually four greenish-gray eggs marked with yellowish and brown. This bird eats grasshoppers, maggots, other insects, worms, crustaceans, the spawn of the horseshoe crab, and other small marine life found on the beach. It feeds by turning over stones, pebbles, shells, and other beach debris to capture the small animals hiding beneath.

DISTRIBUTION. In the Western Hemisphere, the Ruddy Turnstone breeds along the coasts of the Arctic Ocean from Alaska to Greenland. It winters on the Pacific Coast from central California to Chile and on the Atlantic Coast from South Carolina, occasionally Massachusetts, south to Brazil. It occurs on migration over the greatest part of North America, and small numbers summer far south of the breeding range.

OCCURRENCE IN ALABAMA. (Throughout the year.) *Tennessee Valley*: August 30 (1952, 3 birds, Decatur, D. C. Hulse) to September 19 (1958, Decatur, D. C. Hulse); specimen in U. S. National Museum, September 16, 1950 (Decatur, D. C. Hulse). *Mountain Region*: No record. *Piedmont*: No record. *Upper Coastal Plain*: No record. *Lower Coastal Plain*: October 11, 1949 (River Falls, Covington Co., W. R. Middleton). *Gulf Coast*: Common, July 26 (1960, Dauphin Island, D. C. Holliman) to May 25 (1957, Little Dauphin Island, T. A. Imhof and others); most seen, spring, 150, April 19, 1958 (Dauphin Island, S. A. Gauthreaux and others), summer, 4, July 5, 1913 (Dauphin Island, A. H. Howell), fall, 45, November 6, 1959 (Dauphin Island, T. A. Imhof), winter, 122, December 21, 1957 (Dauphin Island, E. O. Willis and others).

FAMILY SCOLOPACIDAE: WOODCOCK, SNIPE, AND SANDPIPERS

A larger and more complex group than the plovers, this family contains birds that are generally more plainly colored, although quite a few are brightly reddish in summer. Their legs are longer and their bills are longer, thinner, and softer because they often feed with much probing in the mud or sand, while plovers rarely if ever probe. Except for the Sanderling, birds of this family have four toes.

SUBFAMILY SCOLOPACINAE: WOODCOCK AND SNIPE

These shorebirds have long bills, striped heads, and plump bodies. They occur mostly in upland swamps and marshes. In the order *Charadriiformes*, these are the only game birds.

American Woodcock

Philohela minor (Gmelin) [228] (Plate 14, facing page 208)
OTHER NAMES: Hill Partridge, Swamp Partridge, Bécasse, Timber Doodle

Chunky and almost neckless, the American Woodcock is a brownish bird slightly larger than the Bobwhite. This shorebird has a *long bill, rounded wings,* and *crosswise barring* on the *head.* It usually flushes from swampy thickets like a helicopter, with a whistling sound of the wings that is typical of this bird. The same sound issues from the stiffened wings during courtship flights. The American Woodcock's call is a short, explosive, nasal, belching noise, somewhat like that of the Common Nighthawk.

This game bird is an uncommon and local permanent resident in most of Alabama, but it is rare in the Tennessee Valley in winter and on the Gulf

Coast in summer. It is most commonly recorded from November to March when northern birds are present and local breeders are more noticeable because of courtship. (See Map 48.) A rather mysterious bird, it occurs most often in low, wet woods, especially swampy thickets, and feeds extensively on nearby open, damp, grassy areas at night. It is usually active at early dawn, late dusk, or on moonlit nights and cloudy days. Thus, in many places it may go unrecorded. A diligent search often proves it to be a resident where its presence was entirely unsuspected.

NESTING. The American Woodcock nests in a depression in dead leaves, often using pine needles for a lining. It may select wet woods near water or open, dry woods a little distance from its foraging haunts. There are three or four eggs, buffy to grayish-white, and usually thickly spotted with reddish-brown.

FOOD. This bird feeds almost entirely on underground worms, especially earthworms and the worm-like larvae of insects. Because it obtains them by probing with its long, flexible-tipped bill, it cannot feed well in dry or frozen ground. Occasionally, however, it eats beetles, locusts, grasshoppers, crane flies, other insects, and sometimes small seeds.

DISTRIBUTION. The American Woodcock breeds from southern Manitoba, southern Quebec, and Nova Scotia south to southern Louisiana and northern

NEST OF AMERICAN WOODCOCK. This bird nests in brushy areas or in open woods usually not far from water.

C. W. Summerour

Florida. It winters from southern Missouri, the Ohio Valley, and southern New Jersey, and occasionally farther north, south to Texas and central Florida.

OCCURRENCE IN ALABAMA. (Throughout the year.) *Tennessee Valley*: Permanent resident; most seen, 15, May 15, 1947 (Wheeler Refuge, J. H. Heflin). *Mountain Region*: Permanent resident. *Piedmont*: Permanent resident. *Upper Coastal Plain*: Permanent resident; most seen, 20, January 12, 1913 (Montgomery, L. S. Golsan and E. G. Holt). *Lower Coastal Plain*: Permanent resident. *Gulf Coast*: More common, October 8 (1933, Fairhope, F. M. Weston) to February 1 (1958, Bon Secour, T. A. Imhof and others); most seen, 30, January 23, 1953 (Foley, George Allen).

TIME OF BREEDING. Data on 18 nestings: Eggs, February 20 to March 31, April 30, 1938, 12 eggs!, "could have been the product of three females" (Wheeler Refuge, Paul Bryan, in Lincoln, 1951, *Auk* 65:376); downy young, February 25 to April 13; older, dependent young to July.

BANDING. Data on 4 recoveries follow: *Banded*, Louisiana, near Baton Rouge, December 19, 1953; *recovered*, Gordo, Pickens Co., January 23, 1954; *banded*, Louisiana, near Baton Rouge, December 22, 1952; *recovered*, Mantua, Greene Co., December 15, 1953; *banded*, Louisiana, near Baton Rouge, December 29, 1952; *recovered*, Waugh, Montgomery Co., December 12, 1955; *banded*, Michigan, near Lansing, adult male, May 14, 1955; *recovered*, Brooklyn, Conecuh Co., February 28, 1956.

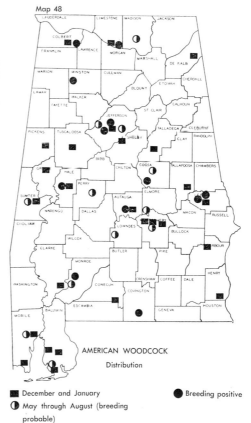

Map 48

AMERICAN WOODCOCK
Distribution

■ December and January
◐ May through August (breeding probable)
● Breeding positive

[European Woodcock]
Scolopax rusticola Linnaeus [227]

The European Woodcock differs from the American Woodcock in being *much larger* and in having *under parts thickly barred* with *fine black lines*.

Accidental in Alabama, this bird occurs in the same wet, brushy places as does the American Woodcock. It is not known to breed here.

NESTING AND FOOD. These habits differ little from those of the American Woodcock.

DISTRIBUTION. This species breeds in northern Eurasia and winters as far north as the ground remains unfrozen. It is accidental in North America with at least six records for the United States.

OCCURRENCE IN ALABAMA. *Upper Coastal Plain only*: Bear Swamp, Autauga Co., March 2, 1889, specimen not preserved (L. S. Golsan, *Auk* 56:482-483).

Common Snipe

Capella gallinago (Linnaeus)   [230]   (Plate 14, facing page 208)
OTHER NAMES: Wilson's Snipe, Squatting Snipe, Jack Snipe

This long-billed, quail-sized shorebird resembles the much chunkier American Woodcock. The snipe, however, has *lengthwise stripes* on the *head* and *pointed wings* which make no whistling sound as do the woodcock's. When flushed, the Common Snipe utters a rasping call and goes off on a *zig-zag course*.

While the American Woodcock prefers swamps, this species occurs in fresh marshes, other wet, grassy areas, and occasionally on mudflats. In Alabama, this snipe is common to abundant in fall and winter, and abundant in spring in those areas which provide its natural habitat. This means, of course, that it is rare or absent in large areas in the state which lack suitable cover. It is not known to breed here.

NESTING AND FOOD. The nest is a grass-lined depression in marshy ground. It usually holds three or four grayish-olive eggs which are marked with reddish-brown and black. The main portion of this bird's diet consists of insects—grasshoppers, locusts, cutworms, diving beetles, crane flies, and the like. It also eats crawfish, leeches, earthworms, and the seeds and roots of a few plants such as smartweed.

DISTRIBUTION. In the Western Hemisphere the Common Snipe breeds from western Alaska, northern Mackenzie, northern Quebec, and Labrador south to southern California, Colorado, Iowa, and northern New Jersey. It winters from southern British Columbia, central Colorado, and Virginia, and casually farther north, south through Central America and the West Indies to Colombia and southern Brazil.

OCCURRENCE IN ALABAMA. (August 6 to May 23.) *Tennessee Valley*: August 6 (1954, Wheeler Refuge, D. C. Hulse) to May 23 (Wheeler Refuge, *fide* T. Z. Atkeson, Jr.); most seen, 100, April 1955 (Wheeler Refuge, Leo Martin). *Mountain Region*: September 2 (1934, Birmingham, H. M. Stevenson) to May 11 (1927, 1 banded at Anniston, R. H. Dean); most seen, winter, 94, December 20, 1958 (Christmas Count, Birmingham), spring, 74, February 27, 1956 (Birmingham, T. A. Imhof). *Piedmont*: November 9 (1959, Auburn, J. L. Dusi) to April 23 (1959, Auburn, Lovett Williams). *Upper Coastal Plain*: September 2 (1938, Tuscaloosa, H. M. Stevenson) to April 30 (1955, Marion, Lois McCollough); most seen, fall, 275, November 18, 1956 (Marion, Lois McCollough), winter, 200+, January 24, 1947 (Marion, T. A. Imhof). *Lower Coastal Plain*: September 20 (1957, Andalusia, T. A. Imhof and Lovett Williams) to April 18 (1958,

Jackson, T. A. Imhof, W. U. Harris, and J. R. Davis). *Gulf Coast*: September 29 (1957, Dauphin Island, E. O. Willis and others) to May 2 (1959, Gulf Shores, F. M. Weston, Lovett Williams, and L. E. Goodnight); most seen, 321, January 19, 1953 (Cochrane Causeway, F. X. Lueth).

BANDING. Three snipe banded by C. S. Robbins along Cochrane Causeway, have been retaken by him at the same place as follows: February 14, 1953 to January 10, 1954; January 10, 1954 to January 17, 1956; and January 17, 1954 to January 18, 1956. A fourth snipe, banded at Birmingham, April 17, 1960, was recaptured at the same place, November 20, 1960.

SUBFAMILY TRINGINAE: CURLEWS, YELLOWLEGS, AND ALLIES

These shorebirds are generally large, long-billed, and loud-voiced. As a rule they are grayish in color and have dark wings.

[Long-billed Curlew]

Numenius americanus Bechstein   [264]   (Plate 18, facing page 256)
OTHER NAME: Sicklebill

About the size of an average duck, the Long-billed Curlew is one of our largest shorebirds. Its coloring is *even buffy* throughout with *hardly noticeable head stripes,* and its *long, down-curved bill* is six inches in length. In flight the under surface of the wings shows bright cinnamon. Its calls are two mellow notes and a rapidly-whistled triplet.

This bird was formerly more common and probably abundant, but at present it is an uncommon migrant on the Gulf Coast of Alabama. It was never known to breed in the state. The Long-billed Curlew occurs around shallow coastal lagoons and in the nearby mudflats and grassy areas.

NESTING AND FOOD. This bird chooses short grass on the open prairie for its nest, a grass-lined depression, which contains three or four eggs pale buffy to grayish-buff spotted with dark brown and lavender. The Long-billed Curlew eats grasshoppers, locusts, and other large grass insects. On the coast it has been observed feeding on fiddler crabs.

DISTRIBUTION. This shorebird breeds on the Great Plains from British Columbia and Manitoba south to Utah, New Mexico, and Texas. It formerly bred over a much wider area. It winters from central California, southern Arizona, New Mexico, coastal Texas, and Louisiana, and rarely farther east, south to Guatemala.

OCCURRENCE IN ALABAMA. *Gulf Coast only*: March 22 (1912, Dauphin Island, A. H. Howell) to May 13 (1960, Dauphin Island, J. L. Dorn) and August 6 (1960, Fort Morgan, J. L. Dorn) to October 6 (1956, Bayou La Batre, T. A. Imhof and Lois McCollough); most seen, 5, on many occasions, spring and fall. No preserved specimen for Alabama is known.

Whimbrel

Numenius phaeopus (Linnaeus)　[265]　(Plate 18, facing page 256)
OTHER NAMES: Hudsonian Curlew, Jack Curlew, Hookbill Snipe

This curlew is a large, brown shorebird with a long, down-curved bill. In contrast to the Long-billed Curlew, the Whimbrel's *head stripes are prominent*, and the bird is smaller in size and has a shorter bill. Many spring Whimbrels appear almost as buffy as the Long-billed Curlew, but this species is rarely uniformly buffy below, nor does it have the cinnamon wing linings. The call of the Whimbrel is a rather plaintive, pleasing whistle, and its alarm is a rapidly-whistled phrase.

On the coast of Alabama the Whimbrel is a migrant, common in spring and uncommon in fall. Inland it is rare on migration, and strangely enough, it has been noted inland earlier in spring and later in fall than on the coast. This bird is not known to breed in the state. It frequents mudflats and sandbars, but it often feeds in short grass or on plowed fields.

NESTING AND FOOD. This curlew nests in a grass-lined depression on the tundra. The female lays four creamy to pale olive-gray eggs which are boldly marked with dark brown. The bird feeds on fiddler crabs, sand spiders, June bugs, other beetles, grasshoppers, worms, and other small animals that frequent the shore.

DISTRIBUTION. In America the Whimbrel breeds on Arctic coasts from the mouth of the Yukon in Alaska, along the north shore of Mackenzie, and down the Hudson Bay to James Bay, and non-breeders remain all summer in many coastal areas of the United States and south to Ecuador. It migrates mainly along the Atlantic and Pacific coasts, but a few birds occur in the Mississippi Valley, especially in spring. It winters from Lower California to Chile, and from Texas and South Carolina to the mouth of the Amazon River.

OCCURRENCE IN ALABAMA. (Normal: April 4 to May 30 and July 16 to August 31; Out-of-season: February 6 to March 5 and October 11.) *Tennessee Valley*: Wheeler Refuge, February 6 and 7, 1960 (D. C. Hulse and others); February 13 to March 5, 1959 (D. C. Hulse and others) and small flocks, August 18, 1947 (L. S. Givens) and August 26, 1940 (J. H. Steenis). *Mountain Region*: October 11, 1960 (Birmingham, W. A. Baker). *Piedmont*: No record. *Upper Coastal Plain*: No record. *Lower Coastal Plain*: May 1930 (1 bird shot and examined in the hand, Columbia, T. Z. Atkeson, Jr.). *Gulf Coast*: April 4 (1959, Dauphin Island, Ava Tabor and others) to May 30 (1956, Gulf Shores, B. L. Monroe, Jr.) and July 16 (1960, Dauphin Island, D. C. Holliman) to August 31 (1958, Dauphin Island, S. A. Gauthreaux and others); most seen, 35, April 21, 1956 (Dauphin Island, J. L. Dorn and others); specimen in U. S. National Museum, July 27, 1913 (Dauphin Island, E. G. Holt).

Upland Plover

Bartramia longicauda (Bechstein)   [261]   (Plate 17, facing page 240)
OTHER NAMES: Upland Sandpiper, Field Plover, Papabotte, Bartramian Sandpiper

Slightly larger than a Killdeer, this plain, brown-streaked bird is best identified by shape. The comparatively *short bill, long,* thin *neck, small head,* and white eye ring cause it to resemble a dove. Its white-tipped *tail* is very *long* for a shorebird. On short flights it appears to move only the tips of its wings. It has a weird, whistling flight call and a pleasing alarm call which its Creole name, Papabotte, imitates.

The Upland Plover is fairly common on migration in Alabama, especially in spring. It is most common in the Black Belt and rare on the coast. Although birds are often noted in June and July, this species is not known to breed here. The Upland Plover frequents short-grass fields such as airports, hay meadows, pastures, and golf courses. An observer who knows the call can distinguish an occasional bird flying overhead at night. Formerly very common, this species has been so decimated by hunting and destruction of its habitat that 25 years ago it was thought to be headed for extinction. The hunting of it has now practically ceased, but the destruction of its habitat has not.

NESTING AND FOOD. This bird breeds on prairies and other short-grass areas. It builds a nest of dried grasses on the ground, conceals it well, and in it lays four pale creamy to buffy eggs, spotted with lavender and dark brown. The Upland Plover subsists almost entirely on large grass-dwelling insects. These include grasshoppers, locusts, boll weevils, other weevils, beetles, crickets, cutworms, other grubs, and a host of others. It is also known to eat crawfish.

DISTRIBUTION. The Upland Plover breeds from southern Alaska, southern Mackenzie, Manitoba, southern Ontario, southern Quebec, and Maine south to Oregon, northeastern Utah, southern Oklahoma, Missouri, the Ohio Valley, and central Virginia. It winters on the pampas of South America from Uruguay and southern Brazil to Argentina and Chile.

OCCURRENCE IN ALABAMA. (March 7 to May 9 and July 12 to October 26, also June 18 and summered once.) *Tennessee Valley*: March 15 (1948, Wheeler Refuge, L. S. Givens) to May 4 (1959, Mooresville, Margaret Robinson) and August 15 (1951, Wheeler Refuge, D. C. Hulse and Paul Bryan) to August 21 (1957, Wheeler Refuge, T. A. Imhof, T. Z. Atkeson, Jr., and W. M. Depreast); also June 18, 1960 (4 birds, Swan Creek, J. C. and Margaret Robinson). *Mountain Region*: March 23 (1937 and 1940, Birmingham, H. M. Stevenson) to May 9 (1955, Birmingham, T. A. Imhof) and July 14 (1936, Birmingham, H. M. Stevenson) to October 6 (1954, Birmingham, T. A. Imhof and F. B. Daniel); most seen, 25, March 30, 1940 (Birmingham, H. M. Stevenson). *Piedmont*: September 7, 1943 (Auburn, H. M. Stevenson). *Upper Coastal Plain*: March 7

(1913, Barachias, B. H. Holt) to April 28 (1939, Tuscaloosa, H. M. Stevenson) and July 12 (1912, Barachias, E. G. Holt and 1938, Tuscaloosa, H. M. Stevenson) to October 26 (1916, Barachias, E. G. Holt); also summered once prior to 1914 (Barachias, B. H. Holt). *Lower Coastal Plain*: May 9, 1958, specimen in Auburn Wildlife collection (Wilcox Co., S. G. Clawson) and October 4, 1956 (Houston Co., J. E. Keeler). *Gulf Coast*: March 20 (1945, Spring Hill, J. L. Dorn) to April 30 (1955, Fort Morgan, H. M. Stevenson) and July 29 (1955, Fort Morgan, H. M. Stevenson) to October 6 (1956, Dauphin Island, T. A. Imhof).

Spotted Sandpiper

Actitis macularia (Linnaeus)   [263]   (Plate 17, facing page 240)
OTHER NAME: Teeter Snipe

The Spotted Sandpiper is a small bird, olive-brown above and white below. The spring adult has rather large, *dark spots* on the *under parts* and a white line over the eye. In fall and immature plumages this bird lacks the spots but has a white mark at the shoulder. The *constant teetering* (dipping the rear of the body) and the *arched wing stroke* with *frequent short sails* mark this species as different from other shorebirds. Observers who learn to identify the spring adult first will find that the teetering and the wing strokes of the fall bird make it easy to recognize. The call of this bird is a two-noted whistle, neither as high pitched nor as penetrating as that of the Solitary Sandpiper.

On migration this sandpiper is common throughout the state, especially in spring. It winters rarely on the Gulf Coast and was noted once in winter in the Piedmont. Although it has been reported quite often in summer, especially in the Tennessee Valley, no definite breeding evidence has as yet been obtained in Alabama. This bird occurs on exposed lake, pond, and stream borders, and rarely on tidal flats. Except for the Killdeer, and possibly the Common Snipe, it is more widely distributed in Alabama than any other shorebird. Although it frequently occurs on the coast, it is essentially an inland bird.

NESTING. The nest is a well-built cup of grass, leaves, and weed stems in a depression in the ground. It is usually well hidden in short grass near water. The four eggs are creamy, buffy, or grayish, with either large or small dark spots.

FOOD. The Spotted Sandpiper is primarily an insect-eater, feeding on grasshoppers, beetles, May flies, cutworms, and many kinds of aquatic insects. It sometimes varies this diet with crawfish.

DISTRIBUTION. This bird breeds from along the tree limit in northwestern Alaska, northern Manitoba, and northern Labrador south to southern California, central Texas, western North Carolina, and Virginia. It winters from British

Columbia, southern Arizona, the northern Gulf Coast from Louisiana to Florida, and South Carolina to Chile and Argentina.

OCCURRENCE IN ALABAMA. (March 21 to January 17.) *Tennessee Valley*: April 24 (1950, Wheeler Refuge, T. A. Imhof) to May 25 (1941, Florence, H. M. Stevenson) and July 15 (1911, Stevenson, *fide* A. H. Howell) to October 14 (Wheeler Refuge, *fide* T. Z. Atkeson, Jr.); also June 7, 1957 (mouth of Paint Rock River, T. A. Imhof) and summered at Wheeler Refuge in 1952 (D. C. Hulse and T. A. Imhof); most seen, 53, May 4, 1957 (Wheeler Refuge, Ala. Orn. Soc.). *Mountain Region*: April 8 (1946, Birmingham, T. A. Imhof) to June 6 (1959, Birmingham, T. A. Imhof) and July 15 (1935, Birmingham, H. M. Stevenson) to October 27 (1956, Hammondville, Ala. Orn. Soc.); most seen, 12, May 4, 1940 (Birmingham, H. M. Stevenson). *Piedmont*: March 21 (1952, Auburn, H. G. Good) to May 15 (1936, Auburn, H. S. Peters) and August 10 (1952, Stroud, H. M. Stevenson) to September 10 (1958, Auburn, Lovett Williams); also December 26, 1959 (Auburn, J. L. Dusi); most seen, 7, April 30, 1955 (Auburn, T. A. Imhof and H. G. Good). *Upper Coastal Plain*: March 21 (1884, Greensboro, W. C. Avery) to June 1 (1960, Livingston, Jenkins Jackson) and July 20 (1959, Livingston, Jenkins Jackson) to October 27 (1956, Marion, Lois McCollough); also November 17 to December 4, 1938 (Tuscaloosa, H. M. Stevenson). *Lower Coastal Plain*: April 15 (1957, Jackson, W. U. Harris) to May 25 (1956, McIntosh, T. A. Imhof and W. F. Colin) and September 14 (1956, Jackson, T. A. Imhof and W. U. Harris) to October 26 (1957, Jackson, W. U. Harris). *Gulf Coast*: March 29 (1952, Bear Point, H. M. Stevenson) to June 1 (1914, Petit Bois Island, A. H. Howell) and July 14 (1960, Dauphin Island, D. C. Holliman) to November 29 (1958, Dauphin Island, J. Verner and others); also December 21, 1957 (2 birds, Cedar Point and Coden Bayou, E. O. Willis and T. A. Imhof); December 30, 1932 (Fairhope, Homer Flagg); January 12, 1951 (Cochrane Causeway, C. S. Robbins) and January 17, 1933 (Fairhope, Homer Flagg); most seen, 15, May 14, 1950 (southern Baldwin Co., H. M. Stevenson).

Solitary Sandpiper
Tringa solitaria Wilson   [256]   (Plate 17, facing page 240)

The Solitary Sandpiper is *dark* on the *head, back,* and *wings,* and it has a white belly, a *white eye ring,* and *black bars* on the *white outer tail feathers.* It is a little larger than the Spotted Sandpiper and somewhat resembles a small yellowlegs, but it has green legs and lacks the white rump. It does not teeter, but nods, and it flies much like a swallow. The Solitary Sandpiper's call is more drawn out, more penetrating, and higher pitched than the Spotted Sandpiper's.

In Alabama this species is common on migration, especially inland, but it is not known to breed here. It likes woodland pools, but also frequents the same pond and stream borders that attract the Spotted Sandpiper. Contrary to its name, this bird frequently occurs in small flocks in this state.

NESTING AND FOOD. This bird is variously reported as nesting on high mountains, on the ground, in hollow trees and other strange places, and even as using the abandoned tree nests of other birds, but actually little is known of its nesting habits. The eggs differ little in color, size, or number from those

PLATE 17

SOLITARY SANDPIPER
Sexes Alike
Page 239

LEAST SANDPIPER
Fall, Sexes Alike
Page 249

WHITE-RUMPED SANDPIPER
Fall, Sexes Alike
Page 247

SEMIPALMATED SANDPIPER
Fall, Sexes Alike
Page 254

WESTERN SANDPIPER
Fall, Sexes Alike
Page 255

SPOTTED SANDPIPER
Spring, Sexes Alike
Page 238

SANDERLING
Fall, Sexes Alike
Page 259

BUFF-BREASTED SANDPIPER
Sexes Alike
Page 258

PECTORAL SANDPIPER
Sexes Alike
Page 246

DUNLIN
Fall, Sexes Alike
Page 250

KNOT
Fall, Sexes Alike
Page 245

UPLAND PLOVER
Sexes Alike
Page 237

SHORT-BILLED DOWITCHER
Fall, Sexes Alike
Page 251

[240]

Richard A. Parks

of other shorebirds. The Solitary Sandpiper feeds on insects especially those that live in water. It eats grasshoppers, moths, beetles, caterpillers, worms, spiders, small crustaceans, and the like and also small frogs and small mollusks.

DISTRIBUTION. This species breeds from central Alaska, northern Mackenzie, central Quebec, and Labrador south to southern Canada (British Columbia to Quebec) and summers in the northern United States. It winters from southeastern Texas and southern Georgia, and rarely Lower California and the West Indies, south to Argentina.

OCCURRENCE IN ALABAMA. (February 27 to May 28 and July 3 to November 15.) *Tennessee Valley*: April 6 (1954, Wheeler Refuge, Eugene Cypert) to May 28 (Wheeler Refuge, *fide* T. Z. Atkeson, Jr.) and July 15 (1911, Stevenson, A. H. Howell) to November 15 (1953, Wheeler Refuge, B. B. Coffey); most seen, 6, August 29, 1949 (Wheeler Refuge, T. A. Imhof). *Mountain Region*: March 16 (1937, Birmingham, H. M. Stevenson) to May 19 (1948, Birmingham, T. A. Imhof) and July 3 (1936, Birmingham, H. M. Stevenson) to October 22 (1935, Birmingham, H. M. Stevenson); most seen, 20, April 22, 1961 (Hammondville, DeKalb Co., T. A. Imhof and others). *Piedmont*: April 2 (1953, Auburn, H. G. Good) to May 4 (1955, Auburn, H. G. Good) and July 19 (1936, Auburn, N. H. Giles) to at least August 18 (1958, Auburn, Lovett Williams); most seen, 15, April 30, 1959 (Auburn, Lovett Williams). *Upper Coastal Plain*: February 27 (1955, Marion, Lois McCollough) to May 24 (1956, Marion, T. A. Imhof) and August 1 (1960, Livingston, Jenkins Jackson) to November 13 (1955, Marion, Lois McCollough). *Lower Coastal Plain*: March 22 (1957, Geneva, T. A. Imhof) to May 11 (1956, Choctaw Bluff, T. A. Imhof, M. W. Gaillard, and G. A. Carleton) and September 20, 1957 (Andalusia, T. A. Imhof and Lovett Williams); most seen, 6, May 9, 1958 (Geneva, T. A. Imhof). *Gulf Coast*: March 17 (1960, Dauphin Island, J. L. Dorn) to May 20 (1911, Bayou La Batre, A. H. Howell) and August 1 (1959, Gulf Shores, H. M. Stevenson) to October 6 (1956, Fort Morgan, F. M. Weston and L. E. Goodnight); most seen, 47, April 13, 1957 (Spring Count, Mobile Bay Area).

Willet

Catoptrophorus semipalmatus (Gmelin) [258] (Plate 18, facing page 256)

Larger than the Greater Yellowlegs, this long-billed shorebird has a pale gray head and back, a much paler belly, and blue legs. In summer plumage the head and breast are spotted. A very plain looking bird until it flies, it then reveals a *large white wing stripe, black primaries,* and a white tail. The usual calls of this very noisy bird are loud and distinctive. Thus, at rest the Willet may be difficult to identify, but flying or calling it is unmistakable.

On the Gulf Coast of Alabama, this bird is a common resident in summer and uncommon in winter. Inland it is uncommon to rare on migration and occurs most often in spring in the Tennessee Valley. It is known to breed only on the coast. It prefers beaches, mudflats, and salt marshes and occurs inland on exposed margins of lakes, rivers, and ponds.

NESTING. For its nest the Willet finds a hollow in the sand close to the marsh and lines it rather carelessly with grass and reeds, concealing it well. There are usually four eggs, greenish-white to dark brownish-olive with bold markings of brown and lavender.

FOOD. This bird subsists on worms, aquatic insects, mollusks, shrimp, and crabs, especially fiddler crabs. It probes for its food in the mud, and sometimes it turns over stones and other beach debris.

DISTRIBUTION. The Willet breeds from eastern Oregon, central Alberta, and southern Manitoba south to northeastern California, Colorado, and rarely Nebraska and South Dakota. It also breeds coastally in Nova Scotia, from New Jersey to Texas, and in the Bahamas and Greater Antilles. It summers south to Ecuador, and it winters from northern California, coastal Texas, Virginia, and the Bahamas south to the Galapagos Islands, Peru, and Brazil. It occurs on migration in the Mississippi Valley and Ontario.

OCCURRENCE IN ALABAMA. (Throughout the year.) *Tennessee Valley*: April 2 (1889, Leighton, F. W. McCormack) to May 8 (1946, 9 birds, Wheeler Refuge, Clarence Cottam and J. H. Steenis) and June 27 (1951, Wheeler Refuge, D. C. Hulse) to September 30 (1887, Leighton, F. W. McCormack); most seen, 20, May 5, 1950 (Wheeler Refuge, H. H. Grammer and J. H. Sutherlin). *Mountain Region*: April 24, 1959 (Lake Mac, Talladega, J. L. Dusi and others) and August 19 and 29, 1936 (Lake Purdy, H. M. Stevenson). *Piedmont*: No record. *Upper Coastal Plain*: April 29, 1945 (Autaugaville, L. S. Golsan); April 30, 1955 (19 birds photographed, Marion, Lois McCol-lough) and May 12, 1912 (4 birds, Autaugaville, L. S. Golsan). *Lower Coastal Plain*: May 8, 1957 (Columbia, Henry Co., the T. Z. Atkesons). *Gulf Coast*: Common, late February to November; most seen, spring, 120, April 21, 1956 and April 13, 1957 (Spring Counts, Mobile Bay Area), summer, 50 pairs breeding on Dauphin Island, June 14-16, 1956 (T. A. Imhof and others), winter, 39, December 30, 1960 (Christmas Count, Dauphin Island).

TIME OF BREEDING. Data on 55 nestings: Eggs, late April to June 17; dependent young, June 15 to July 30; flying by June 15.

Greater Yellowlegs

Totanus melanoleucus (Gmelin)   [254]   (Plate 18, facing page 256)
OTHER NAMES: Tattletale Snipe, Yellowlegs Snipe

This rather large, dark gray sandpiper has *long, bright yellow legs, dark* unpatterned *wings,* and a *white rump* and *tail.* Its long, thin bill is very slightly upturned. Its *loud whistle,* given in *three or four syllables,* usually sounds the alarm to all birds in the vicinity.

On the Gulf Coast, the Greater Yellowlegs is a common transient which regularly winters and summers in small numbers. Inland it is uncommon on migration but is sometimes common, as in the Tennessee Valley where it often winters. This bird is not known to breed anywhere in the state. It prefers mudflats and pond borders, but also often occurs on beaches and sandbars. Its elevated position and loud voice make it an ideal lookout and alarm-giver for other shorebirds with which it customarily flocks.

NESTING AND FOOD. In a depression in the ground, usually unlined, the Greater Yellowlegs lays four grayish or deep buff eggs spotted with lavender and dark brown. It lives on small fish, aquatic insects, mollusks—especially snails—worms, and crustaceans.

DISTRIBUTION. The Greater Yellowlegs breeds from Alaska, central Alberta, and northern Quebec south to central British Columbia, southern Quebec, and Newfoundland. Non-breeders summer in coastal United States and south to the West Indies and South America. It winters from Oregon, central New Mexico, Texas, northern Alabama, and South Carolina, and often farther north on the Pacific and Atlantic coasts and in the Mississippi Valley, south to southern South America.

OCCURRENCE IN ALABAMA. (Throughout the year.) *Tennessee Valley*: July 23 (Leighton, F. W. McCormack) to June 3 (Wheeler Refuge, *fide* T. Z. Atkeson, Jr.); most seen, migration, 40, May 4, 1957 (Wheeler Refuge, Ala. Orn. Soc.), winter, 12, January 12, 1957 (Wheeler Refuge, T. A. Imhof and others). *Mountain Region*: March 8 (1958, Birmingham, T. A. Imhof) to April 24 (1937, Birmingham, H. M. Stevenson) and August 4 (1936, Birmingham, H. M. Stevenson) to November 22 (1947, Birmingham, T. A. Imhof). *Piedmont*: Probably regular transient, the only dated record, November 9, 1959 (Auburn, J. L. Dusi). *Upper Coastal Plain*: March 1 (1958, 3 birds, Marion, Lois McCollough) to May 17 (1956, Marion, Lois McCollough) and July 21 (1959, 15 birds, Alabama River, Lowndes Co., R. W. Skinner) to December 15 (1959, Livingston, Jenkins Jackson); most seen, 26, October 25, 1957 (Marion, Lois McCollough). *Lower Coastal Plain*: March 22 (1957, 10 birds, Brundidge, T. A. Imhof) to May 1 (1952, Point A Lake, Andalusia, W. R. Middleton) and October 13, 1949 (Andalusia, W. R. Middleton). *Gulf Coast*: Common, March to May and August to November; most seen, spring, 100, April 12, 1959 (Cochrane Causeway, Lovett Williams), fall, 27, October 19, 1957 (Fall Count, Mobile Bay Area).

Lesser Yellowlegs
Totanus flavipes (Gmelin)   [255]

This bird is about one-third smaller than the Greater Yellowlegs, has a smaller, straighter bill, but otherwise closely resembles it. Relative size is often misleading, and unless the two species are seen together, they are best identified by call. The Lesser Yellowlegs gives a shorter, sharper, *two-syllabled call* instead of the louder, more penetrating sound in three or four syllables given by the larger bird.

On migration, the Lesser Yellowlegs is fairly common to common in Alabama. It is rare in summer and winter on the coast, and it is not known to breed in the state. More numerous and widespread than the Greater Yellowlegs, it occurs in the same habitat, either mixed with other shorebirds or in large pure flocks. Apparently it is more abundant inland, especially in the Tennessee Valley.

NESTING AND FOOD. The nest is a depression in the ground usually sheltered by a tuft of grass. In it are laid four creamy, buffy, or clay-colored eggs boldly marked or finely spotted with blackish or lavender. Insects, including ants, bugs, flies, and grasshoppers, are the principal food. The bird varies this diet with worms, snails, small fish, and small crustaceans.

DISTRIBUTION. The Lesser Yellowlegs breeds from Alaska, northern Mackenzie, northern Manitoba, and northern Quebec south to British Columbia, southern Manitoba, and west-central Quebec. Non-breeders remain as far south as Argentina. Most of the species migrate through the Mississippi Valley to winter in Argentina and Chile, but smaller numbers remain north to Mexico, the Gulf Coast of the United States, and the Atlantic Coast to South Carolina, casually to Massachusetts.

OCCURRENCE IN ALABAMA. (Throughout the year.) *Tennessee Valley*: March 15 (1950, Wheeler Refuge, D. C. Hulse) to June 10 (1951, Wheeler Refuge, D. C. Hulse) and July 18 (1947, Wheeler Refuge, L. S. Givens) to November 9 (1948, Wheeler Refuge, T. A. Imhof); also November 25, 1956 (Wheeler Refuge, Adele West and Harriett Wright); most seen, 105, August 29, 1949 (Wheeler Refuge, T. A. Imhof) and 100, September 6, 1892 (Leighton, F. W. McCormack). *Mountain Region*: March 30 (1940, Birmingham, H. M. Stevenson) to April 27 (1954, Birmingham, T. A. Imhof and others) and August 8 (1936, Birmingham, H. M. Stevenson) to October 2 (1946, Birmingham, T. A. Imhof and 1956, Gadsden, Edith Clark). *Piedmont*: March 24 (1955, Kellyton, Coosa Co., Blanche Dean) to April 30 (1955, Auburn, H. G. Good and T. A. Imhof); no fall dates. *Upper Coastal Plain*: March 1 (1958, 2 birds, Marion, Lois McCollough) to May 24 (1956, 6 birds, Marion, T. A. Imhof and Lois McCollough) and August 29 (1938, Tuscaloosa, H. M. Stevenson) to November 8 (1957, Marion, Lois McCollough); most seen, 18, May 5, 1956 (Marion, Lois McCollough). *Lower Coastal Plain*: March 22 (1957, Geneva, T. A. Imhof) to May 13 (1951, Pike Co., C. W. Summerour) and September 20 (1957, Andalusia, T. A. Imhof and Lovett Williams) to October 3 (1958, Camden, Lovett Williams). *Gulf Coast*: Common, February to late May and late June to November; most seen, 100, April 12, 1959 (Cochrane Causeway, Lovett Williams).

SUBFAMILY CALIDRIDIINAE: SANDPIPERS, GODWITS, AND ALLIES

Generally small, these birds have white wing stripes and bills about as long as their heads. In the spring they are often reddish or buffy in color, and they range from sparrow size to robin size. Their calls are single-noted and their voices squeaky. Members of this subfamily are often called "peeps" by bird students, who want a name for these birds that are usually difficult to identify until they fly or call.

Knot

Calidris canutus (Linnaeus)   [234]   (Plate 17, facing page 240)

OTHER NAME: Robin Snipe

Medium-sized but larger than the Spotted Sandpiper, the Knot is a rather chunky shorebird. It has a *whitish tail* and a rather *short bill.* In the spring, when it has a robin-red face and under parts, it is like no other American shorebird except the dowitchers, but these have longer bills and white areas extending far up the back. In the fall, the Knot's back is gray and the under parts are white. In this plumage the larger size, straight bill, and whitish tail will distinguish it from the quite similar Dunlin.

On the Alabama Coast the Knot is an uncommon transient which rarely winters. Inland, it has been noted so far only in the Tennessee Valley in fall. The bird is not known to breed anywhere in the state. Usually it occurs in compact flocks on sandbars, beaches, or mudflats.

NESTING AND FOOD. The Knot nests on the tundra by lining a depression in the ground with grass. It lays four light pea-green, brown-speckled eggs. Small mollusks, grasshoppers, diving beetles, fly larvae, cutworms, other insects, marine worms, crustaceans, and crawfish comprise its diet. In the fall it eats a considerable amount of aquatic plants, especially widgeon grass.

DISTRIBUTION. In the Western Hemisphere this species breeds on Arctic islands and coasts from Alaska to northern Greenland. It summers in small numbers on the south Atlantic and northern Gulf coasts of the United States, and it winters coastally from California, Texas, the northern Gulf Coast, and Virginia, and rarely Massachusetts, south to Patagonia.

OCCURRENCE IN ALABAMA. (Normal: March 11 to June 3 and July 5 to November 3; Out-of-season: December 27 and January 2.) *Tennessee Valley*: August 26, 1950 (4 birds, Wheeler Refuge, T. A. Imhof); August 29, 1949 (3 birds, T. A. Imhof); and November 3 (Clarence Cottam). *Mountain Region*: No record. *Piedmont*: No record. *Upper Coastal Plain*: No record. *Lower Coastal Plain*: No record. *Gulf Coast*: March 11 (1955, 25 birds, Alabama Point, T. A. Imhof) to June 3 (1914, 30 birds, 2 specimens in U. S. National Museum, Dauphin Island, J. L. Peters) and July 5 (1913, specimen, U. S. National Museum, Dauphin Island, A. H. Howell) to October 31 (1958, 25 birds, Dauphin Island, T. A. Imhof and Lois McCollough); also December 27, 1958 (Little Dauphin Island, T. A. Imhof) and January 2, 1960 (6 birds, Little Dauphin Island, T. A. Imhof).

Pectoral Sandpiper

Erolia melanotos (Vieillot)   [239]   (Plate 17, facing page 240)
OTHER NAMES: Cherook, Krieker, Grass Snipe

The Pectoral Sandpiper is normally a little larger than the Spotted Sandpiper, but some individuals are as big as a snipe and others the size of a Semipalmated Sandpiper. This bird's *chest streakings* are *brownish* and *end abruptly,* and it has *greenish legs* and a very faint white wing stripe. It walks with its head and long neck erect, and it is like a small, short-billed snipe in its color, actions, and the places it frequents. When it is flushed, the Pectoral Sandpiper utters a distinctive creaking call.

In Alabama, this bird is common on migration and has been recorded in winter once inland and once on the coast. It is not known to breed here. It is more numerous inland, especially in the Tennessee Valley. Usually it occurs in wet, grassy areas such as the margins of inland lakes and ponds, all kinds of marshes, and prairie pools, and frequently it associates with the Common Snipe and the Least Sandpiper.

In the breeding season, the male is able to inflate the streaked part of his chest until it almost equals his whole body in size. Inflating and deflating this chest pouch plays an important role in courtship antics, which include additionally a flight song with weird notes and unusual posturing and strutting before the female.

NESTING AND FOOD. The nest of the Pectoral Sandpiper is a sparsely-lined hollow in the ground. The bird lays four eggs which are greenish-drab marked with brown. Crickets, grasshoppers, insect larvae, earthworms, snails, shellfish, and other small animals of wet, grassy areas form the major part of its food. Sometimes it adds a bit of aquatic plants such as smartweeds and pondweeds.

DISTRIBUTION. The Pectoral Sandpiper breeds on Arctic coasts from northeastern Siberia to northeastern Mackenzie and Southampton Island and south in Alaska to the mouth of the Yukon River. It migrates rarely on the Pacific Coast, commonly through the Mississippi Valley, and commonly on the Atlantic Coast, especially in fall, and it winters from Peru and Bolivia to central Patagonia, and rarely north to the United States.

OCCURRENCE IN ALABAMA. (Normal: February 27 to May 20 and July 23 to November 29; Out-of-season: January 2 and 24.) *Tennessee Valley*: March 20 (1960, Decatur, J. C. and Margaret Robinson) to May 16 (1952, Wheeler Refuge, D. C. Hulse) and July 29 (1952, Wheeler Refuge, D. C. Hulse) to October 27 (1945, Guntersville, H. M. Stevenson); most seen, spring, 50, May 10, 1951 (Wheeler Refuge, D. C. Hulse), fall, 40, September 12, 1958 (Wheeler Refuge, T. A. Imhof and others). *Mountain Region*: March 8 (1958, 17 birds, Birmingham, T. A. Imhof) to May 9 (1935, Birmingham, H. M. Stevenson) and July 24 (1935, Birmingham, H. M. Stevenson) to November 16 (1946, Birmingham, T. A. Imhof and others); most seen, 32, March 22, 1947 (Birmingham, T. A. Imhof and M. H. Perry). *Piedmont*: April 18, 1953 (Auburn, H. G. Good). *Upper Coastal Plain*: February 27 (1954, Marion, T. A. Imhof) to May 20 (1956, Marion, Lois McCollough) and July 25 (1938, 12 birds, Tuscaloosa, H. M. Stevenson) to November 13 (1955, Marion, Lois

McCollough); also January 24, 1947 (Marion, T. A. Imhof); most seen, spring, 50, March 1, 1958 (Marion, Lois McCollough), fall, 30, September 29, 1956 (Marion, Lois McCollough). *Lower Coastal Plain*: March 22 (1957, Geneva, T. A. Imhof) to May 9 (1958, Headland, T. A. Imhof); also September 20, 1957 (Andalusia, T. A. Imhof and Lovett Williams). *Gulf Coast*: March 17 (1960, Theodore, J. L. Dorn) to May 13 (1960, Dauphin Island, J. L. Dorn) and July 23 (1955, specimen in Univ. of Ala. collection, Dauphin Island, Ottilie Chermock) to November 29 (1958, Dauphin Island, J. Verner and others); also January 2, 1960 (Dauphin Island, Ava Tabor and others).

White-rumped Sandpiper
Erolia fuscicollis (Vieillot)　[240]　(Plate 17, facing page 240)

This medium-sized peep is best identified by the *white rump*, which is usually noticeable only in flight. The bird's upper parts are reddish-brown in spring and grayish-brown in fall. The brown streaks on the breast extend down onto the flanks in a manner quite different from the sharp, straight-line ending of the breast streaks on the Pectoral Sandpiper. Over its *eye* the White-rumped Sandpiper has a *prominent white line* which is more conspicuous in spring. This bird has a very thin call somewhat resembling that of the Water Pipit and also resembling that of the Western Sandpiper, but it is thinner and weaker and the pitch is higher.

In Alabama the White-rumped Sandpiper is uncommon to rare on migration, particularly in spring and in the Coastal Plain. Oddly it is unrecorded in fall in the Tennessee Valley and on the Gulf Coast. Although spring migration lasts well into mid-June, this species is not known to breed here. It usually frequents grassy places but also occurs often on mudflats.

NESTING AND FOOD. The nest is a depression in the ground lined with leaves. It contains four light-olive to olive-brown eggs, boldly marked with dark brown. This sandpiper eats a variety of insects of which grasshoppers form a large proportion. Other foods include marine worms, bloodworms, snails, other mollusks, crustaceans, and the seeds of aquatic plants such as widgeon grass and sedges.

DISTRIBUTION. The White-rumped Sandpiper breeds on Arctic coasts from northern Alaska to Baffin Island. It migrates chiefly through the Mississippi

[247]

Valley, but is uncommon in Alberta and on the Atlantic Coast, and it winters from Paraguay to southern Patagonia and the Falkland Islands.

OCCURRENCE IN ALABAMA. (April 24 to June 18 and August 26 to October 23.) *Tennessee Valley*: April 24 (1942, Wheeler Refuge, J. H. Steenis) to June 18 (1960, 14 birds, Swan Creek Refuge, J. C. and Margaret Robinson). *Mountain Region*: June 14, 1952 (Attalla, T. A. Imhof and M. H. Perry); August 29, 1936 (Birmingham, H. M. Stevenson); and September 14, 1956 (Gadsden, Edith Clark). *Piedmont*: No record. *Upper Coastal Plain*: May 11 (1957, 2 birds, Marion, Lois McCollough) to May 30 (1891, 4 specimens in the Avery collection, Greensboro, W. C. Avery) and August 26 (1946, Marion, T. A. Imhof) to October 23 (1954, 9 birds, Marion, Lois McCollough). *Lower Coastal Plain*: May 9, 1958 (4 birds, Headland, T. A. Imhof). *Gulf Coast*: May 1 (1954, Fort Morgan, T. A. Imhof and others) to June 16 (1956, Dauphin Island, B. L. Monroe, Jr., T. A. Imhof, and others); most seen, 75, May 11, 1960 (Little Dauphin Island, J. L. Dorn).

Baird's Sandpiper
Erolia bairdii (Coues)   [241]

Because of its close resemblance to the White-rumped Sandpiper, this medium-sized peep is difficult to identify. Both birds have a white line over the eye and are about the same size. But Baird's Sandpiper can always be identified by its *scaly* appearing *back, buffy breast, dark legs,* and *lack of white rump.* This bird's crown is often paler than those of other peeps. Thorough familiarity with other peeps and clear observation of all four distinguishing field marks are necessary before attempting to identify Baird's Sandpiper.

This species is casual in September on the Gulf Coast of Alabama. Because it is difficult to spot in large flocks of peeps it may be more numerous than supposed. It is not known to breed in this state. This species occurs on prairie ponds, grassy sloughs, and sandy areas, generally with other peeps.

NESTING AND FOOD. The female lays four eggs, buffy with chestnut-brown spots, in a depression lined with grass and leaves and sheltered by a tuft of grass. The principal food of this bird is insects, including ground beetles, weevils, grasshoppers, and the larvae of mosquitoes and crane flies. It also eats algae and amphipods.

DISTRIBUTION. Baird's Sandpiper breeds on Arctic coasts from northeastern Siberia and northern Greenland south to Mackenzie. It winters from Ecuador and Bolivia south to Chile and Argentina, and more rarely north to El Salvador. It migrates mainly between the Mississippi River and the Rocky Mountains and through Central America, but it also occurs locally on Atlantic, Pacific, and Gulf coasts.

OCCURRENCE IN ALABAMA. *Gulf Coast only*: September 8, 1936 (male specimen in Auburn Univ. collection, Gulf Shores, Don Eyles) and September 15, 1956 (female specimen in Auburn Univ. collection, J. L. Dusi).

Least Sandpiper
Erolia minutilla (Vieillot)　[242]　(Plate 17, facing page 240)

About the size of our smallest sparrow, the Least Sandpiper is the smallest American peep. It is reddish-brown on the back, brighter in the spring, with a small, dull reddish patch on the chest. Its bill is thin and rather long for its size, and its *legs* are *greenish* or *yellowish-green*. In common with almost all peeps, it has a thin white wing stripe and white sides to its small tail. This bird's call is a high, thin sound so distinctive that the species is often easier to identify by sound than by sight. Habitat is another useful clue in identification, as are the size and the leg color.

The Least Sandpiper is abundant on migration and in winter in the state, and is often more abundant inland than on the coast, even in winter. (See Map 49.) It is not known to breed in Alabama. This bird frequents the areas of marshes where the grass is sparse, the muddier areas, and mudflats and pond and lake borders. Sometimes it occurs on the beach itself. It flocks alone or with any of the other peeps.

NESTING AND FOOD. The three or four creamy-buff to light drab eggs, heavily spotted with chestnut and lavender, are laid in a grass- and leaf-lined depression in the ground near water. The Least Sandpiper's diet consists in the main of the larvae and adults of small aquatic insects such as mosquitoes, midges, and other small flies. It also eats grasshoppers, diving beetles, and other insects.

DISTRIBUTION. The Least Sandpiper breeds from northwestern Alaska and northern Labrador south to southern Alaska, James Bay, Newfoundland, and Nova Scotia, and summers regularly south to the Gulf Coast of the United States. It winters from Oregon, southern Utah, central Texas, northern Alabama, and North Carolina south to central Peru and central Brazil and occurs on migration throughout the United States and west to northeastern Siberia and east to Greenland.

OCCURRENCE IN ALABAMA. (Normal: July 11 to May 29; Out-of-season: June 15 and 16.) *Tennessee Valley*: July 18 (1947, Wheeler Refuge, L. S. Givens) to May 26 (1949, Wheeler Refuge, L. S. Givens); most seen, 43, December 26, 1949 (Wheeler Refuge, T. A. Imhof). *Mountain Region*: May 4 (1953, Birmingham, T. A. Imhof) to May 16 (1936, Birmingham, H. M. Stevenson and 1946, Birmingham, T. A.

Map 49

LEAST SANDPIPER

Distribution in Winter

■ December through February

Imhof) and July 11 (1935, Birmingham, H. M. Stevenson) to December 22 (1956, 22 birds, Birmingham, T. A. Imhof); most seen, fall, 18, September 10, 1955 (Birmingham, T. A. Imhof). *Piedmont*: April 30, 1957 (11 birds, Auburn, Lovett Williams) and May 9, 1959 (Auburn, Lovett Williams); November 9, 1959 (Auburn, J. L. Dusi); and December 26, 1960 (3 birds, Christmas Count, Auburn). *Upper Coastal Plain*: July 25 (1938, Tuscaloosa, H. M. Stevenson) to May 29 (1958, Marion, Lois McCollough); most seen, 145, December 27, 1957 (Christmas Count, Marion). *Lower Coastal Plain*: May 9, 1958 (26 birds, Headland, T. A. Imhof); May 10, 1958 (3 birds, Columbia, T. A. Imhof and T. Z. Atkeson, Sr.); and September 20, 1957 (10 birds, Dothan, T. A. Imhof and Lovett Williams). *Gulf Coast*: July 29 (1955, Gulf Shores, H. M. Stevenson) to May 17 (1958, Cochrane Causeway, T. A. Imhof and M. W. Gaillard); also June 15 and 16, 1956 (Dauphin Island, O. L. Austin and others); most seen, spring, 44, May 2, 1959 (Spring Count, Mobile Bay Area), fall, 77, October 6, 1956 (Fall Count, Mobile Bay Area), winter or early spring, 52, March 3, 1949 (Cochrane Causeway, T. A. Imhof).

Dunlin

Erolia alpina (Linnaeus)   [243]   (Plate 17, facing page 240)
OTHER NAMES: Red-backed Sandpiper, Redback (Spring), Leadback (Fall)

A fairly large peep, the Dunlin has a *long bill curved downward* at the *tip*. In late spring it is easily recognized because of its bright, *reddish-brown* crown and *back* and the *large, square, black patch* on its *belly*. In the fall its back is a fairly even lead gray. In this plumage it resembles several other peeps, including the Knot, but the Dunlin's dull grayish head and chest make it distinct. Other gray-backed sandpipers (Semipalmated and Western Sandpipers, Knot, and Sanderling) in fall plumage are whitish on the sides of the head, throat, and chest. The White-rumped Sandpiper is gray-backed in fall with a darkish chest, but it has a white rump and a straight bill. The Dunlin's call is a nasal, somewhat drawn-out note.

[250]

The Dunlin is common to abundant on migration and in winter on the Alabama coast. It is rare inland in the fall, especially in the Tennessee Valley, and is not known to breed in this state. This species occurs most commonly on coastal mudflats and sandbars, either in pure flocks or mixed with other common peeps.

NESTING AND FOOD. This bird nests in a hollow in the ground near salt marshes or fresh-water lakes and ponds. It lays four pale greenish to brownish-buff eggs which are spotted with brown. The Dunlin eats small mollusks, crustaceans, marine worms, fly larvae, and aquatic beetles. It occasionally varies this diet with the seeds of water plants.

DISTRIBUTION. The Dunlin breeds on Arctic coasts from north-central Siberia to Alaska and down the Hudson Bay to Churchill, Manitoba. It also breeds from Greenland and Iceland east to Russia and south to the British Isles. It winters coastally from southeastern Alaska to Lower California, from Massachusetts to Texas, and in the Eastern Hemisphere. In America it migrates mainly through the Great Lakes region.

OCCURRENCE IN ALABAMA. (Normal: October 4 to May 26; Out-of-season: September 10.) *Tennessee Valley*: October 15, 1949 (10 birds, Wheeler Refuge, T. A. Imhof and J. A. Doubles); October 28, 1955 (10 birds, Wheeler Refuge, T. A. Imhof and W. M. Depreast); and November 15, 1953 (8 birds, Decatur, B. B. Coffey and many others). *Mountain Region*: No record. *Piedmont*: No record. *Upper Coastal Plain*: November 5, 1959 (Marion, T. A. Imhof and F. B. and Laurie Daniel). *Lower Coastal Plain*: October 13, 1949 (2 birds, River Falls, Covington Co., W. R. Middleton). *Gulf Coast*: October 4 (1956, Cedar Point, T. A. Imhof and Lois McCollough) to May 26 (1940, specimen in U. S. National Museum, Fort Morgan, T. D. Burleigh); also September 10, 1957 (Dauphin Island, H. A. J. and Cora Evans); most seen, spring, 330, April 21, 1956 (Spring Count, Mobile Bay Area), fall, 340, November 1, 1958 (Fall Count, Mobile Bay Area), winter, 650, December 29, 1956 (Christmas Count, Dauphin Island).

Short-billed Dowitcher
Limnodromus griseus (Gmelin) [231] (Plate 17, facing page 240)
OTHER NAMES: Red-breasted Snipe, Dormeur

The Short-billed Dowitcher closely resembles the Common Snipe, but it has an even longer bill and can be identified in any plumage by the *white areas* extending from the *tail* and *rump* to a *point far up the back*. In spring this bird's entire under parts are light robin-red, and the dark gray feathers of its back are edged with buff. In fall it is dark gray above and whitish below with a white line over the eye. The call of this dowitcher is very rapid and metallic.

The Short-billed Dowitcher prefers coastal mudflats or occasionally beaches, while the Long-billed Dowitcher most frequently occurs in grassy areas and on inland mudflats. In Alabama the Short-billed Dowitcher is common in

[251]

winter and on migration on the Gulf Coast. Its status inland is unknown and it is not known to breed here.

The Alabama coastal status of these two species of dowitchers is rather well known, but few of the inland records are verified as one species or the other. All the Alabama inland records, instead of being eliminated because they are indefinite as to species, are listed under the long-billed species.

NESTING AND FOOD. The Short-billed Dowitcher builds a loose nest of grasses and leaves in a depression near marshy lakes and ponds. The four eggs are greenish-olive to light clay-colored, spotted with dark brown. The Short-billed Dowitcher feeds on marine worms, grasshoppers, aquatic bugs and beetles, flies, mollusks, and leeches. Occasionally it eats the seeds and sometimes the roots of aquatic plants such as pondweeds, bogbeans, and bulrushes. It probes rapidly and repeatedly in the mud with its bill to obtain its principal foods.

DISTRIBUTION. The Short-billed Dowitcher breeds from southern Alaska and southern Mackenzie south to central Alberta and northern Manitoba, and possibly farther east. It often summers on the Atlantic and Gulf coasts of the United States. It winters, chiefly coastally, from California, southern New Mexico, the northern Gulf Coast, North Carolina, and the West Indies south to Peru and central Brazil.

OCCURRENCE IN ALABAMA. *Gulf Coast only (status inland unknown)*: June 30 (1958, Alabama Point, T. A. Imhof) to May 25 (1957, Little Dauphin Island, T. A. Imhof and others); also June 15 and 16, 1956 (21 birds, Dauphin Island, T. A. Imhof and others); most seen, spring, 120, April 13, 1957 (Spring Count, Mobile Bay Area), fall, 60, October 31, 1958 (Dauphin Island, T. A. Imhof and others), winter, 85, December 27, 1958 (Christmas Count, Dauphin Island).

Long-billed Dowitcher
Limnodromus scolopaceus (Say) [232]

This dowitcher is larger, richer in color, and longer billed than its close relative, the Short-billed Dowitcher. Until recently both dowitchers were thought to be the same species, but it is now known that the birds nest close together without signs of interbreeding. In spring the Long-billed Dowitcher shows the reddish color of the belly extending onto the under tail coverts, and its flanks are distinctly barred. But the differences between these two birds are differences of degree only. In the case of the bill lengths, the female Short-billed Dowitcher is often longer billed than the male Long-billed. The call is perhaps a good method of distinguishing between the two dowitchers, since shorebirds are noted for their distinctive calls. The Long-billed Dowitcher's note is sweet, less metallic, and only at times trebled, while the Short-billed Dowitcher almost invariably trebles its call.

The Long-billed Dowitcher frequents grassy areas or inland mudflats, most often in pure flocks, although it sometimes joins other dowitchers out on the mudflats. In Alabama this species is an uncommon transient on the coast, and its status inland is uncertain. In this book, all inland dowitcher records are arbitrarily listed below. The bird is not known to breed in the state.

NESTING AND FOOD. Little difference between the nesting and feeding habits of the two dowitchers has so far been noted. The preference of the present species for grassier and more inland areas should be reflected in its diet.

DISTRIBUTION. The Long-billed Dowitcher breeds from northeastern Siberia to northwestern Mackenzie, and summers south to Ecuador. It winters from central California, southern Arizona, and the northern Gulf Coast south to Argentina, and more rarely in Cuba and Jamaica.

OCCURRENCE IN ALABAMA. (Only coastal records definitely apply to the present species.) *Tennessee Valley*: April 26 (1957, Wheeler Refuge, L. S. Givens) to May 15 (1891, specimen not preserved, Leighton, F. W. McCormack); also August 29, 1949 (8 birds, Wheeler Refuge, T. A. Imhof). *Mountain Region*: July 3 (1936, Birmingham, H. M. Stevenson) to September 28 (1935, Birmingham, H. M. Stevenson). *Piedmont*: No record. *Upper Coastal Plain*: February 23, 1957 (Marion, Lois McCollough); April 29, 1958 (5 birds, Marion, Lois McCollough); September 14, 1958 (Marion, Lois McCollough); October 14, 1956 (Marion, Lois McCollough); and November 11, 1958 (Livingston, Jenkins Jackson). *Lower Coastal Plain*: No record. *Gulf Coast*: April 6 (1957, Dauphin Island, S. A. Gauthreaux and others) to May 16 (1960, Dauphin Island, J. L. Dorn) and July 5 (1913, 2 specimens in U. S. National Museum, Dauphin Island, A. H. Howell) to November 5 (1955, Dauphin Island, T. A. Imhof and R. L. Chermock); also June 15 and 16, 1956 (25 birds, Dauphin Island, T. A. Imhof and others).

Stilt Sandpiper
Micropalama himantopus (Bonaparte)   [233]
OTHER NAME: Bastard Yellowlegs

The Stilt Sandpiper looks like a cross between a dowitcher and a yellowlegs. It is unmistakable in *spring* plumage—*heavily barred below* and with a *prominent reddish-brown patch* extending from *bill* to *ear*. In *fall* it closely *resembles* the *Lesser Yellowlegs*, especially in flight when its *dark wings* and *white rump* are most noticeable. The Stilt Sandpiper, however, has *green legs,* a more prominent white line over the eye, and a *slight droop* to the *thicker bill*. This bird often feeds like a dowitcher, which also has a white line over the eye and green legs, but the Stilt Sandpiper's legs are longer, and it has no white on its back. The call of this species is like that of the Lesser Yellowlegs but is hoarser.

[253]

In spring the Stilt Sandpiper is uncommon to fairly common on the Gulf Coast. In fall, it is uncommon to rare on the Gulf Coast and in the Tennessee Valley. Elsewhere in Alabama it is rare. This bird is not known to breed in the state. It frequents shallow pond margins, often with the Lesser Yellowlegs, and also associates with dowitchers on mudflats.

NESTING AND FOOD. The nest is a depression in the ground lined with leaves and grass. It usually contains three or four grayish-white or light drab eggs which are boldly marked with reddish-brown or lavender. Inland this species eats mainly insects, especially grasshoppers. On the coast, it usually takes crustaceans, mollusks, clamworms, and fly larvae. It varies both diets with pondweeds, widgeon grass, and other aquatic plants in small proportions.

DISTRIBUTION. The Stilt Sandpiper breeds from northeastern Alaska, northeastern Mackenzie, and northern Ontario south locally to the tree limit. It migrates chiefly through the western Mississippi Valley and Central America to winter in South America south to Argentina.

OCCURRENCE IN ALABAMA. (April 4 to May 20 and August 13 to November 4.) *Tennessee Valley*: August 13 (1947, Wheeler Refuge, L. S. Givens) to October 26 (1955, Wheeler Refuge, D. C. Hulse). *Mountain Region*: November 1 and 4, 1959 (Lake Purdy, Harriett Wright and Marjorie Ayres). *Piedmont*: No record. *Upper Coastal Plain*: November 1, 1957 (Marion, Lois Mc-Collough). *Lower Coastal Plain*: No record. *Gulf Coast*: April 4 (1958, Dauphin Island, Ava Tabor and others) to May 20 (1960, Dauphin Island, C. W. Summerour) and August 26 (1960, Dauphin Island, J. L. Dorn) to September 28 (1940, Cedar Point, J. L. Dorn); most seen, 30+, May 20, 1960 (Dauphin Island, C. W. Summerour).

Semipalmated Sandpiper
Ereunetes pusillus (Linnaeus)   [246]   (Plate 17, facing page 240)

This bird is probably the most common and the plainest of the peeps in Alabama. It is sufficiently nondescript that a few comparisons with other sandpipers seem appropriate. It differs from the Least Sandpiper in being slightly larger, grayer above, whiter on the face and chest, and having a shorter, stouter bill. Moreover, its *legs* are *black* or *greenish-black,* whereas the Least Sandpiper's are green or yellowish-green. Unless the legs are stained with mud, this difference is readily apparent. It is shorter billed than the Western Sandpiper, and it has little or no rust color on its back. Its call lacks the distinctive sound of the Least's and the squeakiness of the Western's, and is much lower in pitch than that of either species.

The Semipalmated Sandpiper is common to abundant on migration on the Gulf Coast of Alabama, where it also winters commonly and summers in small numbers. Inland it is common on migration and is known to winter at least at Marion. Nesting in this state is unknown. This species prefers mudflats or sandy areas but occurs in almost all habitats suitable for shorebirds except the driest. Although it often forms large pure flocks, it is just as likely to occur with any of the other shorebirds.

NESTING AND FOOD. This bird nests in a hollow in the ground which it lines with dry grass. The three or four grayish to olive eggs are boldly marked or finely spotted with brown or reddish-brown. The principal food is insect larvae, especially those of flies, mosquitoes, beetles, caddis flies, and others. It adds ants, wasps, clamworms, crustaceans, mollusks, and the seeds of some aquatic plants, especially bulrushes, to complete its diet.

DISTRIBUTION. The Semipalmated Sandpiper breeds coastally from northern Alaska and Baffin Island south to the mouth of the Yukon River, Churchill, Manitoba, and northern Labrador. Non breeders summer south to Panama. It winters from South Carolina and the northern Gulf Coast south through Central America and the West Indies to Brazil and Chile and migrates mainly east of the Rocky Mountains.

OCCURRENCE IN ALABAMA. (Throughout the year.) *Tennessee Valley*: April 24 (1950, Wheeler Refuge, T. A. Imhof) to May 26 (1948, Wheeler Refuge, L. S. Givens) and July 23 (1889, Leighton, F. W. McCormack) to November 19 (Wheeler Refuge, *fide* T. Z. Atkeson, Jr.); also June 22, 1960 (120 birds, Swan Creek, J. C. and Margaret Robinson); most seen, fall, 75, August 29, 1949 (Wheeler Refuge, T. A. Imhof). *Mountain Region*: May 14 (1948, Birmingham, T. A. Imhof) to May 28 (1949, 35 birds, Birmingham, T. A. Imhof) and August 25 (1955, Birmingham, T. A. Imhof) to September 26 (1936, Birmingham, H. M. Stevenson). *Piedmont*: April 18 and 28, 1953 (Auburn, H. G. Good). *Upper Coastal Plain*: July 25 (1938, Tuscaloosa, H. M. Stevenson) to June 1 (1956, Marion, Lois McCollough); most seen, 130, March 9, 1958 (Marion, Lois McCollough). *Lower Coastal Plain*: No record. *Gulf Coast*: Common, July 22 (1955, specimen in Univ. of Ala. collection, Dauphin Island, R. L. Chermock) to June 5 (1914, Dauphin Island, J. L. Peters and 1940, Gulf Shores, H. M. Stevenson); most seen, spring, 135, May 14, 1950 (Gulf Shores, H. M. Stevenson); summer, 11, June 15 and 16, 1956 (Dauphin Island, T. A. Imhof and others), fall, 1125, November 1, 1958 (Fall Count, Mobile Bay Area), winter, 216, December 30, 1960 (Christmas Count, Dauphin Island).

Western Sandpiper
Ereunetes mauri Cabanis   [247]   (Plate 17, facing page 240)

Similar to the Semipalmated Sandpiper, the Western Sandpiper is rustier on the back, especially in spring, shows more white on the head, and has a *longer bill, thicker* at the *base*, and often with a slight droop at the tip. Since female sandpipers have longer bills than males, bill length is often unreliable

Richard Parks

in field identification, but observers thoroughly familiar with both the Semipalmated and Western Sandpipers are usually able to identify safely as Westerns those birds with bills noticeably longer than the head. The distinctive calls of even the puzzling shorebirds are reliable means of separation to those familiar with these calls. The Western Sandpiper has a thin call which differs from that of the White-rumped Sandpiper in being louder, lower in pitch, and not quite as thin. The Western Sandpiper's call is totally different from that of the Semipalmated Sandpiper.

This peep is common to abundant on migration and in winter on the Alabama Gulf Coast, where it summers rarely. Inland, it is rare, noted most often in the Tennessee Valley in fall. This bird is not known to breed in the state. It may be even more common than the Semipalmated Sandpiper, but difficulty of identification makes its abundance uncertain. The Western Sandpiper occurs in the same habitat as the Semipalmated Sandpiper, but it often feeds in deeper water.

NESTING AND FOOD. The nest, well concealed under curly bunchgrass, is a fragile affair of a few pieces of grass in a small depression in the ground. The four eggs are similar to those of the Semipalmated Sandpiper. The Western Sandpiper feeds on minute fly larvae, aquatic beetles and bugs, small snails, and marine worms.

DISTRIBUTION. This species breeds in northwestern Alaska, and nonbreeders summer as far south as Panama. It winters coastally from California (rarely southeastern Alaska), and North Carolina (rarely New Jersey), south to Venezuela and Peru. It migrates chiefly west of the Rocky Mountains, but occurs uncommonly in the interior and on the Atlantic Coast south of Maine.

OCCURRENCE IN ALABAMA. (Normal: July 5 to May 25; Out-of-season: June 15 and 16.) *Tennessee Valley*: May 4 (1957, Wheeler Refuge, J. L. Dusi) to May 16 (1952, Wheeler Refuge, D. C. Hulse) and August 14 (1951, Wheeler Refuge, D. C. Hulse) to October 28 (1955, Wheeler Refuge, T. A. Imhof); most seen, 20, September 12, 1958 (Wheeler Refuge, T. A. Imhof and others). *Mountain Region*: August 25 (1955, Birmingham, T. A. Imhof) to September 25 (1956, 6 birds, Birmingham, T. A. Imhof). *Piedmont*: No record. *Upper Coastal Plain*: March 28, 1958 (20 birds, Marion, Lois McCollough) and April 4, 1957 (4 birds, Marion, T. A. Imhof). *Lower Coastal Plain*: No record. *Gulf Coast*: July 5 (1913, 2 specimens in U. S. National Museum, Dauphin Island, A. H. Howell) to May 25 (1957, Dauphin Island, T. A. Imhof and others); also June 15 and 16, 1956 (25 birds, Dauphin Island, T. A. Imhof and others); most seen, spring, 156, May 2, 1959 (Spring Count, Mobile Bay Area), fall, 371, October 6, 1956 (Fall Count, Mobile Bay Area), winter, 154, December 21, 1957 (Christmas Count, Dauphin Island).

Buff-breasted Sandpiper
Tryngites subruficollis (Vieillot)   [262]   (Plate 17, facing page 240)

The Buff-breasted Sandpiper is best described as a miniature Upland Plover about the size of a Spotted Sandpiper. In contrast to Baird's Sandpiper, which is buffy only on the breast, the *entire under parts* of the Buff-breasted Sandpiper are *buffy*. This bird is almost devoid of streaking, has a pale *buffy eye ring,* and yellow legs. When in flight the wings show a white under surface shading darker at the tips. The drawn-out call of one syllable is low in volume but high in pitch.

The Buff-breasted Sandpiper is rare on fall migration in Alabama and is not known to breed here. Like the Upland Plover, it occurs in dry, short-grass areas such as airports, pastures, and golf courses. On the coast it frequents dry, sandy areas.

NESTING AND FOOD. Grass and withered leaves line the depression in the ground in which this bird lays four grayish to pale olive-buff eggs marked with brown. Largely an insect-eater, this sandpiper feeds on beetles, the larvae of flies and mosquitoes, crickets, ants, grasshoppers, minute mollusks, and occasionally the seeds of water plants.

DISTRIBUTION. The Buff-breasted Sandpiper breeds along Arctic coasts and islands from northern Alaska to northern Mackenzie. It winters in central Argentina and migrates through the Canadian prairies and the Mississippi Valley, and occasionally east to the Atlantic Coast.

OCCURRENCE IN ALABAMA. (August 10 to September 26.) *Tennessee Valley*: September 14, 1955 (flock of 5 and probably 14 others, 1 now specimen in U. S. National Museum, Wheeler Refuge, E. A. Byford and others); September 23, 1955 (2 birds, E. A. Byford) and September 12, 1958 (3 birds, T. A. Imhof, J. B. Sullivan, T. Z. Atkeson, Jr. and W. M. Depreast). *Mountain Region*: No record. *Piedmont*: August 10, 1952 (Stroud, Chambers Co., H. M. Stevenson). *Upper Coastal Plain*: September 7, 1948 (Tuscaloosa, H. M. Stevenson) and September 24, 1938 (Northport, H. M. Stevenson). *Lower Coastal Plain*: No record. *Gulf Coast*: Gulf Shores, September 8, 1959 (specimen in Auburn Univ. collection, J. L. Dusi) and September 12, 1955 (J. L. Dusi); Spring Hill College Golf Course, September 26, 1941 (J. L. Dorn).

Marbled Godwit
Limosa fedoa (Linnaeus)   [249]   (Plate 18, facing page 256)

The Marbled Godwit is a *very large, rich buffy-brown* shorebird which has a *long, slightly upturned bill.* The all-over buffy-brown color is evenly and finely barred, even on the wings and tail, so that no light or dark areas appear anywhere on the bird. The name Godwit may be echoic of the harsh, two-syllabled call.

On the Gulf Coast of Alabama, this large shorebird is a rare spring and uncommon fall migrant. It is known to have wintered at least once. Inland it is a rare spring transient. Nowhere in the state is it known to nest. In the company of many other shorebirds, it occurs on mudflats and sandbars, but it feeds in deeper water more often than its companions and it sometimes forages in grassy areas.

NESTING AND FOOD. The nest is a grass-lined depression on dry prairie not far from water. The four eggs are creamy-buff to light olive-drab, and are thickly spotted with brown. The Marbled Godwit feeds to a large extent on injurious grass insects, especially grasshoppers. Along the coast it eats mollusks, snails, crustaceans, worms, leeches, and water insects.

DISTRIBUTION. The Marbled Godwit breeds from central Alberta and southern Manitoba south to central Montana and South Dakota. Formerly it also bred in Utah, Nebraska, Iowa, and Wisconsin. Non-breeders summer south to Mexico. It migrates along the Pacific Coast from British Columbia southward, rarely through the Mississippi Valley, and rarely on the Atlantic Coast south to the Lesser Antilles, and it winters from California, the northern Gulf Coast, and South Carolina south to Chile.

OCCURRENCE IN ALABAMA. (August 26 to April 26.) *Tennessee Valley*: March 27, 1960 (Decatur, J. C. and Margaret Robinson) and April 16 and 17, 1950 (Wheeler Refuge, D. C. Hulse and many others). *Mountain Region*: No record. *Piedmont*: No record. *Upper Coastal Plain*: Greensboro, 3 birds seen by W. C. Avery in the spring of 1880, 1 collected but apparently not preserved. *Lower Coastal Plain*: No record. *Gulf Coast*: April 13 (1957, Cochrane Causeway, Karl and Marion Zerbe and H. G. Loftin) to April 26 (1959, Dauphin Island, Lovett Williams) and August 21 (1911, specimen in U. S. National Museum, Dauphin Island, J. S. Gutsell) to October 6 (1956, Dauphin Island, T. A. Imhof and many others); also a flock of 9, 2 of which were collected, November 5 (Univ. of Ala. collection, R. L. Chermock); wintered on Little Dauphin Island in 1955-56, apparently successfully, for 6 were seen April 20, 1956 (Bayou La Batre, T. A. Imhof and H. C. Loesch).

Sanderling
Crocethia alba (Pallas)   [248]   (Plate 17, facing page 240)
OTHER NAMES: Beach Snipe, Sandpiper

The Sanderling is a small, plump, whitish shorebird with a very conspicuous *white wing stripe* and a stout black bill. In spring this bird becomes reddish on the back, head, and breast, but in fall and winter its back is gray and the under parts and much of the head are white. In this plumage it is the whitest of the sandpipers. The Sanderling utters a short, two-syllabled call which is distinctive.

This bird, the characteristic sandpiper of the beaches, is common to abundant on migration and in winter on the coast, where a few birds summer. Inland, it is rare on migration, and it is not known to breed in Alabama. The Sanderling sometimes forsakes its beaches for other sandy areas or mudflats, but none the less it is probably the most common year-round shorebird in coastal Alabama. Anyone who visits the beach must have watched this bird run rapidly out after a receding wave, snatch a food particle from the sand, and retreat rapidly before the advance of the next wave.

NESTING AND FOOD. The Sanderling lines a depression in the ground with leaves or grass and in it lays four light olive-brown eggs speckled and spotted with brown. This bird eats small sea-life—shrimp, other crustaceans, mollusks, marine worms, fly larvae—and a few seeds for variety.

DISTRIBUTION. The Sanderling breeds on Arctic islands from Southampton and northern Greenland through Iceland and Spitzbergen to northern Siberia. Non-breeding birds remain in summer south to Venezuela. Migration is chiefly coastal, but a few birds pass through the Mississippi Valley. It winters on all coasts from southern British Columbia and Massachusetts to Patagonia.

OCCURRENCE IN ALABAMA. (Throughout the year.) *Tennessee Valley*: August 21 (1957, 3 birds, Wheeler Refuge, T. A. Imhof, T. Z. Atkeson, Jr., and W. M. Depreast) to October 15 (1949, 6 birds, Wheeler Refuge, T. A. Imhof and others). *Mountain Region*: May 9 (1936, Birmingham, H. M. Stevenson) to May 12 (1946, Birmingham, S. R. Tipton, Isabel Tipton, and T. A. Imhof) and August 20 (1960, Birmingham, Harriett Wright) to October 3 (1935, Birmingham, H. M. Stevenson). *Piedmont*: No record. *Upper Coastal Plain*: August 18 and 19, 1939 (Tuscaloosa, H. M. Stevenson). *Lower Coastal Plain*: No record. *Gulf Coast*: Common, July 27 (1911, specimens in U. S. National Museum, Petit Bois Island, J. S. Gutsell) to June 3 (1914, 5 birds, Dauphin Island, J. L. Peters); most seen, 180, September 23, 1955 (Dauphin Island, T. A. Imhof and W. W. Beshears).

FAMILY RECURVIROSTRIDAE: AVOCETS AND STILTS

These very noisy birds are boldly patterned in black and white. They have very long legs and very long, thin bills, sometimes curved upward.

SUBFAMILY RECURVIROSTRINAE: AVOCETS AND STILTS

American Avocet
Recurvirostra americana Gmelin   [225]   (Plate 18, facing page 256)

A large, strikingly-colored shorebird, this avocet is white with two broad, black stripes on its back. The outer half of its white wings is black, while the inner half has a broad diagonal black stripe. In spring, the head and neck are tan. This bird has very long blue legs and its *long, thin, black bill is curved sharply upward*. Its loud, sharp call consists of a single, often repeated syllable.

The American Avocet in Alabama is rare in fall in the Tennessee Valley, and rare in spring and fall on the Gulf Coast. It is not known to nest here. The species occurs on prairie marshes and sloughs, around pond margins, and on sandbars. It often forages in deep water.

NESTING AND FOOD. Constructed of grasses and weed stems, the nest is hidden in marshes. It contains three or four pale olive or buffy eggs spotted with brown. This avocet subsists on various insects obtained from the water or the nearby grass. These include diving beetles, grasshoppers, billbugs, and flying insects. It also eats snails and marine worms.

DISTRIBUTION. The American Avocet breeds from eastern Washington, southern Alberta, and southern Manitoba (formerly to Great Slave Lake), south to southern California, southern New Mexico, and southern Texas (formerly Wisconsin, Illinois, and New Jersey). It winters from central California and southern Texas, rarely farther east, south to Guatemala and is occasional on migration east to the Atlantic Coast from New Brunswick to Florida and the West Indies.

OCCURRENCE IN ALABAMA. (September 29 to November 7; Out-of-season: March 17 and April 7.) *Tennessee Valley*: September 29, 1960 (9 birds, Wheeler Refuge, D. C. Hulse and H. H. Grammer); October 15 to 22, 1949 (specimen in U. S. National Museum, T. A. Imhof and E. A. Byford); November 1, 1951 (2 birds, H. H. Grammer, T. Z. Atkeson, Jr., and D. C. Hulse) and November 7, 1950 (10 birds, J. H. Sutherlin and H. H. Grammer). *Mountain Region*: No record. *Piedmont*: No record. *Upper Coastal Plain*: No record. *Lower Coastal Plain*: No record. *Gulf Coast*: March 17, 1956 (Dauphin Island, R. L. Chermock); April 7, 1959 (Cochrane Causeway, F. M. Weston); and October 19, 1957 (Cochrane Causeway, E. O. Willis, G. L. Carter, and H. G. Loftin).

Black-necked Stilt

Himantopus mexicanus (Müller)   [226]   (Plate 18, facing page 256)
OTHER NAME: Longshanks

This shorebird is *black and white* and has *thin red legs* which are extremely *long,* about twelve inches in length. Its *bill* is black, *needle-thin,* and rather *long.* The bird is black above and white below, has a white rump, light gray tail, and is white on the cheeks and crown and over the eye. It is a noisy bird with a sharp, rapidly-repeated call which becomes higher in pitch and increases from two syllables to three as the bird gets more excited.

On the Alabama Gulf Coast, the Black-necked Stilt is a casual fall visitor near ponds and rain pools. Although it breeds in neighboring states, it is not known to breed in Alabama.

NESTING AND FOOD. Small colonies of these birds establish themselves along the coast or about western lakes. The nest may be either a hollow in the sand lined with grass or shells, or a poorly-built affair of grass and small stems hidden in marsh vegetation. The three or four eggs are buffy and spotted with dark brown. The Black-necked Stilt feeds extensively on aquatic beetles, especially the predaceous diving variety. It also eats grasshoppers, fly larvae, billbugs, snails, crustaceans, and other small aquatic life. Despite its long legs, it usually feeds in shallow water.

DISTRIBUTION. This shorebird breeds from Oregon, casually to Saskatchewan, Nebraska, coastal Texas, coastal Louisiana, and South Carolina south through Central America and the West Indies to the Galapagos Islands, Peru, and northern Brazil. It winters from California, Louisiana, and the West Indies southward.

OCCURRENCE IN ALABAMA. *Gulf Coast only*: August 9, 1953 (Romar Beach, H. M. Stevenson); October 6 and 7, 1956 (specimen in Florida State Univ. collection, Dauphin Island, S. M. Russell, E. O. Willis, and Lovett Williams); and October 15, 1960 (Dauphin Island, H. D. Haberyan and many others).

FAMILY PHALAROPODIDAE: PHALAROPES

Phalaropes are sea-going sandpipers which have toes variously lobed for swimming. The most peculiar characteristic of these birds is the fact that the male takes on all domestic duties, including nest-building, incubation, and care of the young. The female, which wears the brighter colors, merely lays the eggs.

Red Phalarope
Phalaropus fulicarius (Linnaeus)   [222]

This bird resembles the Sanderling in size and color, even to the prominent white wing stripe. It is blue-gray on the back, white below, white on most of the head, and it has a *short black stripe through* and *behind the eye*. This stripe is called the phalarope mark. The *bill is short, thick,* and *dark*, with a yellowish base. In *spring*, this bird is dark on the back and on the top of the head, *red* on the entire *under parts* and *white* on the *cheeks*. The male has duller coloring than the female.

The Red Phalarope is regular, sometimes common, in winter in the Gulf of Mexico off the Alabama and Florida coasts. It has been recorded once inland in Alabama. Since it is a bird of the open sea, its presence inland was probably due to storms. It is unknown in the state as a breeder.

NESTING AND FOOD. The nest is a depression in the ground lined with moss or grass, and the female lays three to four dull greenish or yellowish-gray eggs, spotted with brown. On the tundra this bird feeds on insects, crustaceans, and other water animals. On the open sea, it lives on minute marine animals which it usually catches by spinning around like a top and stabbing its bill into the roiled-up water.

DISTRIBUTION. The Red Phalarope breeds from northern Alaska, northern Ellesmere Island, and Greenland south to the Yukon Delta and Hudson Bay and also from Iceland to eastern Siberia. It winters on the open sea from southern California and the northern Gulf of Mexico south to the Falkland and Juan Fernandez islands and New Zealand. It migrates off both coasts of the United States and is casual inland in at least a dozen states.

OCCURRENCE IN ALABAMA. *Tennessee Valley*: No record. *Mountain Region*: No record. *Piedmont*: No record. *Upper Coastal Plain*: Pickett Springs near Montgomery, January 1924, a male specimen in the collection of Kenneth Underwood of Montgomery, shot on a pond by Dan Holt (E. G. Holt, *Auk* 41:601). *Lower Coastal Plain*: No record. *Gulf Coast*: (For the purpose of this list, Alabama is considered as including that part of the Gulf within sight of land. Most of the records below could not be included as Alabama observations; however, they are doubtless of interest to seagoing Alabamians.) According to Francis M. Weston of Pensacola (1953, *Auk* 70:491-492) it is regular, sometimes common in winter from 30 to 50 miles out in the Gulf, rarely as close as 5 miles, noted from October 13 (1951, Frank Bray) to March 21 (1948, W. L. Boyden); most seen, 300, February 29, 1948 (W. L. Boyden and C. C. Gunter); specimens, March 14, 1948 (W. L. Boyden) and December 12, 1950 (C. C. Gunter). All of these records were made from fishing boats out of Pensacola and in positions off the coasts of both Florida and Alabama.

Wilson's Phalarope
Steganopus tricolor Vieillot   [224]

This bird *resembles* a small *yellowlegs*, especially in flight when it shows a *white rump* and *dark wings*. Wilson's Phalarope, however, is pure *white below* and on much of the head. It has the black phalarope mark through the eye, a *long, thin, black bill,* and dark greenish legs. In spring plumage, it has a broad, dark red stripe through the eye and on the side of the neck and another down the back. The coloring of the male is duller than that of the female.

This bird is casual on migration in Alabama and is not known to nest here. It is more coastal and less marine than other phalaropes, and when on land it usually flocks with the Lesser Yellowlegs.

NESTING AND FOOD. The nest is a grass-lined depression, well hidden in moist meadows. It usually holds four creamy, buff, or drab eggs which are thickly spotted with brown. This phalarope feeds largely on aquatic insects found along the shore. Predaceous diving beetles, bugs, the larvae of mosquitoes, crane flies, and other flies make up the bulk of its diet. This is varied with brine shrimp, amphipods, the eggs of water fleas, and the seeds of water plants.

DISTRIBUTION. Wilson's Phalarope breeds from British Columbia, Manitoba, and southern Ontario south to central California, Colorado, and northwestern Indiana. It migrates on all coasts of the United States but is more common west of the Mississippi River, and it winters in Argentina, rarely Chile, and casually in the Falkland Islands and southern Texas.

OCCURRENCE IN ALABAMA. (Normal: August 17 and 30; September 5 and 25; Out-of-season: May 5.) *Tennessee Valley*: August 30, 1946 (Wheeler Refuge, L. S. Givens). *Mountain Region*: No record. *Piedmont*: No record. *Upper Coastal Plain*: No record. *Lower Coastal Plain*: No record. *Gulf Coast*: May 5, 1940 (3 birds, Cochrane Causeway, J. L. Dorn); August 17, 1961 (specimen in Dept. of Conservation collection Dauphin Island, R. W. Skinner); September 5, 1911 (specimen in U. S. National Museum, Bayou La Batre, J. S. Gutsell); September 25, 1943 (Cochrane Causeway, J. L. Dorn).

[Northern Phalarope]
Lobipes lobatus (Linnaeus)   [223]

The Northern Phalarope closely resembles a Sanderling, but is *darker* on the *back* and on the top of the head and has a *needle-like black bill*. It has the usual *phalarope mark*—a thick, *dark line through* and behind the *eye*. In spring plumage, most of the head is dark gray, the throat is white, and the neck is rusty-red. The male's coloring is duller than the female's.

This phalarope is casual in fall in Alabama and is not known to breed here. A bird of the open ocean, it sometimes occurs on migration on small bodies of water, especially coastal bays.

NESTING AND FOOD. The four thickly brown-blotched, greenish or buffy eggs are laid in a grass- or leaf-lined hollow on the tundra. Like other phalaropes, this bird obtains its food by spinning rapidly and stabbing its bill in the roiled-up water. Its diet is similar to that of the Red Phalarope.

DISTRIBUTION. The Northern Phalarope breeds from northern Alaska and Greenland south to the Aleutian Islands, northern Manitoba, southern James Bay, and Labrador and also from Iceland to Siberia. It winters off the coasts of western South America, Africa, Asia, and the East Indies, and in this hemisphere it migrates off both coasts of the United States and to some extent through Canada and the Mississippi Valley.

OCCURRENCE IN ALABAMA. (October 9 and 13.) *Tennessee Valley*: October 13, 1949 (2 birds swimming in the main channel of the Tennessee River at Decatur, D. C. Hulse). *Mountain Region*: No record. *Piedmont*: No record. *Upper Coastal Plain*: October 9, 1954 (1 bird watched spinning and dabbing at Lakeland Farm, Marion, Lois McCollough). *Lower Coastal Plain*: No record. *Gulf Coast*: No record.

SUBORDER LARI: SKUAS, GULLS, TERNS, AND SKIMMERS

These birds have relatively short, stout bills and feet and very long, narrow, pointed wings. In flight they carry their wings with a decided crook so that the bend (wrist) is higher and farther forward than the inner half. This wing shape is called "gull-winged" by aircraft engineers.

FAMILY STERCORARIIDAE: JAEGERS AND SKUAS

These are brown and white sea birds with long, narrow wings, hooked bills, and a small white area at the base of the primaries. They resemble gulls but act like hawks, for they rob other sea birds of their food, often by forcing them to disgorge it. In the field, immature jaegers can seldom be identified as to species.

[Pomarine Jaeger]
Stercorarius pomarinus (Temminck) [36]
OTHER NAME: Robber Gull

The Pomarine Jaeger, largely dark brown in color, is almost as big as a Herring

Gull. The bird's plumage may vary from almost entirely dark brown to white below with a dark cap. In the field, the only sure way to identify the species is to note the blunt, twisted, central tail feathers of the adult. This peculiarity is lacking in immature birds. This jaeger and the Parasitic Jaeger have similar plumage, but the Pomarine Jaeger is larger, heavier-bodied, and generally darker, and it is more heavily barred below and has more white in the wing, the webs of several primaries being white. It is risky to identify immature birds on this basis alone, however.

Preferring the open sea, the Pomarine Jaeger seldom ventures near shore. It winters in the Gulf of Mexico (from October to April) but so far it has been detected only once on the Alabama coast.

NESTING AND FOOD. The nest is a cup of grasses in a dry area on tundra. It usually holds two olive or brown eggs spotted with darker brown. In the far north, this species feeds on small mammals and the eggs and young of nearly all birds. Outside the breeding season, it prefers to rob other sea birds of their food. When victims are unavailable, it feeds on any kind of animal matter, dead or alive.

DISTRIBUTION. In the Western Hemisphere, the Pomarine Jaeger breeds from western Alaska to western Greenland, mainly north of the Arctic Circle. It winters at sea from southern California to Peru, and from North Carolina and the Gulf of Mexico to Mexico and the West Indies.

OCCURRENCE IN ALABAMA. *Gulf Coast only*: October 18 and 19, 1957 (an adult, Dauphin Island, T. A. Imhof and many others).

[Parasitic Jaeger]
Stercorarius parasiticus (Linnaeus) [37]
OTHER NAME: Robber Gull

Slightly smaller than the Ring-billed Gull, this jaeger, like the Pomarine Jaeger, is mostly dark brown, varying from almost total dark brown plumage to white below with a dark cap. Adults can be identified by the *pointed central tail feathers.* Immature birds lack this characteristic and are usually impossible to identify as to species. The Parasitic Jaeger is smaller, thinner, usually lighter in color, and has less white in the wing than the Pomarine Jaeger. The long central tail feathers are also common to the Long-tailed Jaeger, but on this bird they are six to ten inches in length. The Long-tailed Jaeger is also much thinner, usually whiter below, and has less white in the wing, and its flight is more graceful, almost tern-like.

[266]

The Parasitic Jaeger winters in the Gulf of Mexico (from about October to April), and preferring the open sea, rarely comes near land. It has been noted twice in spring on the Alabama Coast.

NESTING AND FOOD. The nest, usually holding two or three brown-spotted, grayish eggs, is a hollow on the tundra sparsely lined with leaves and grass. This jaeger consistently robs other sea birds, usually gulls and terns, of their catch of fish or mollusks. When no victim is in sight, it eats almost any kind of seafood. During the breeding season it often takes small mammals or the eggs and young of other sea birds.

DISTRIBUTION. The Parasitic Jaeger breeds in the Western Hemisphere from northwestern Alaska and northern Greenland south to the Aleutian Islands, southern Mackenzie, Hudson Bay, and northern Labrador. It winters from southern California to the Straits of Magellan and from Maine to Argentina. In the interior of the United States it is casual on migration.

OCCURRENCE IN ALABAMA. *Gulf Coast only*: March 11, 1955 (1 bird in intermediate plumage, Alabama Point, mouth of Perdido Bay, T. A. Imhof) and April 21, 1956 (1 light-phased bird entering Mobile Bay and chasing gulls, Fort Morgan, B. L. Monroe, Jr.).

FAMILY LARIDAE: GULLS AND TERNS

These are largely white, long-winged sea birds which often show some black on the head, tail, or wing tips and have gray on the back and wings. Immature birds usually have much brown in their plumage. These birds are web-footed and their flight is very powerful.

SUBFAMILY LARINAE: GULLS

Generally larger than terns, gulls are more robust and have stouter bills and feet. Of the members of this subfamily occurring in Alabama, the adults have a white tail while immatures have either a very dark tail or one with a dark band near the tip. Gulls often sit on the water like ducks, and, unlike terns, they eat refuse and dead sea animals. Gulls perform a valuable service in keeping harbors and beaches free of decaying animal and vegetable matter.

[Great Black-backed Gull]
Larus marinus Linnaeus   [47]   (Plate 19, facing page 272)

The *adult* Great Black-backed Gull is even larger than the Herring Gull and is easily recognized by its very *dark gray back* and *wings*. The legs are pink, the larger bill yellow with a red spot, and the rest of the bird is white. The *immature* bird is *brown* and its *head and belly* are *whitish*. Thus the plumage of the immature foreshadows the pattern of the adult—dark back and wings and a light-colored body.

In Alabama the Great Black-backed Gull is casual in winter on the Gulf Coast and is not known to breed in the state. This species is increasing steadily on the Atlantic Coast, and it is reasonable to assume that in the future more birds will reach the Gulf. Although the bird associates freely with the Herring Gull, the Great Black-backed Gull rarely occurs inland but is rather partial to the outer beaches.

NESTING AND FOOD. The nest, a bulky affair of debris, is found in the open in an isolated area, usually on an island. This bird nests alone or in small colonies, and it lays three brown-blotched olive eggs. In summer it devours the eggs and young of smaller sea birds. The rest of the year it feeds on dead or live animals that occur along the shore. It dominates other sea birds and forces them to give up their food.

DISTRIBUTION. The Great Black-backed Gull breeds from Greenland and northwestern Russia south to Long Island, rarely New Jersey, and coastal France. It winters from the mouth of the St. Lawrence River south to the Great Lakes, coastal North Carolina, and the Mediterranean and Caspian seas, rarely but increasingly to Florida, and casually to the Gulf of Mexico.

OCCURRENCE IN ALABAMA. *Gulf Coast only*: Single immature birds near Mobile, December 28, 1956 (Blakely Island, T. A. Imhof, Rosemary Gaymer, and Clustie McTyeire) and December 28, 1959 (Cochrane Causeway, J. L. Dorn).

Herring Gull
Larus argentatus Pontoppidan   [51]   (Plate 19, facing page 272)
OTHER NAME: Seagull

The Herring Gull is large and white with *flesh-colored legs* and a *red spot* on its *yellow bill*. Its back and wings are gray, but the *wing tips* are *black with large white spots*. The immature bird is entirely dark brown in its first year, with much white appearing on the head and rump in the second year. Its bill and feet are dusky, but are not reliable for differentiating between this species and the immature Ring-billed Gull.

In Alabama, the Herring Gull is common in winter on the Gulf Coast and on the Tennessee River. It is uncommon to fairly common in the intervening area, especially along river valleys and on lakes during or immediately after rain. This bird occurs in all salt-water areas and often concentrates on beaches or in other areas where it can obtain garbage, offal, or refuse. Although a few immature birds remain through the summer on the coast, this species is not known to breed in the state.

NESTING AND FOOD. This gull breeds in colonies either along the coast or on islands on large inland lakes. The nest is usually in a hollow in the ground, but occasionally it is wedged in a tree. It normally contains three light bluish or dark olive-brown eggs which are marked with dark brown or black. The Herring Gull eats all kinds of dead or live sea animals, especially fish, mollusks, and crustaceans. It also takes garbage and offal. With the other gulls, it follows ships and loiters around docks and beaches to pick up scraps. To facilitate the eating of shellfish, this bird often drops them from a height onto a hard surface to break their shells.

DISTRIBUTION. In the Western Hemisphere, the Herring Gull breeds from Alaska and Greenland south to British Columbia, Montana, the Great Lakes, and Virginia, and non-breeders summer in the Aleutian Islands and south to the Gulf of Mexico. It winters on Atlantic and Pacific coasts from southern Alaska and the Gulf of St. Lawrence south to El Salvador, Mexico, and Cuba, casually to Panama, and also on the Great Lakes and larger rivers in the United States.

OCCURRENCE IN ALABAMA. (Throughout the year.) *Tennessee Valley*: Common, October 26 (1956, North Sauty Refuge, T. A. Imhof and M. W. Gaillard) to May 19 (Wheeler Refuge, *fide* T. Z. Atkeson, Jr.); also recorded at Wheeler Refuge in June, August, and September (*fide* T. Z. Atkeson, Jr.); most seen, 66, December 20, 1948 (Wheeler Refuge, J. H. Steenis and others). *Mountain Region*: November 2 (1947, Birmingham, T. A. Imhof) to March 20 (1955, East Lake, Birmingham, Adele West); most seen, 7, December 20, 1952 (Lake Purdy, T. A. Imhof). *Piedmont*: About November 1 (1947, Mitchell Dam, recovery of banded bird) to at least January 26 (1949, Coosa River near Rockford, recovery of banded bird). *Upper Coastal Plain*: October 20 (1938, Tuscaloosa, H. M. Stevenson) to April 21 (1921, Tallapoosa River, *fide* P. A. Brannon). *Lower Coastal Plain*: Seven banding recoveries dated from about October 10 (1934, Dothan) to about May 27 (1945, Coffee Springs) and about June 10 (1935, Washington Co.,) indicate that the species is regular in this region; most seen, 7, October 20, 1956 (Lake Tholloco, T. A. Imhof and L. C. Crawford). *Gulf Coast*: Common, October to April; most seen, winter, 700, December 28, 1956 (Christmas Count, Mobile), summer, 7, several dates, June, July, and August, 1956 through 1959 (Dauphin Island, T. A. Imhof and many others).

BANDING. Of 95 Herring Gulls, banded mostly as chicks and recovered in Alabama, 27 came from the Great Lakes, mostly Lakes Huron and Michigan, and 68 came from the North Atlantic Coast, Quebec and New Brunswick to Long Island. Atlantic Coast birds comprise 91% of 56 Gulf Coast recoveries, and a regularly smaller proportion as one goes inland, until they make up only 18% of 11 Tennessee Valley recoveries. In other regions, the total recoveries are: Mountain Region, 10; Piedmont, 4; Upper Coastal Plain, 7; and Lower Coastal Plain, 7. Indications are that in Alabama the Great Lakes birds winter primarily inland, mostly on the Tennessee River; Atlantic Coast birds winter on the Gulf Coast, and during winter storms considerable trading back and forth occurs.

Ring-billed Gull

Larus delawarensis Ord   [54]   (Plate 19, facing page 272)

OTHER NAME: Seagull

The Ring-billed Gull looks like a smaller Herring Gull, but it has *yellowish or greenish legs* and a *black ring* on the *smaller bill*. Once the species is learned at close range by frequent observations, then in distance identification the smaller size, more buoyant flight, and darker wing tips are useful. *Immature* birds are dusky, showing more light areas on the head and tail than Herring Gulls of the same age. In these plumages, it is best identified by the *narrow black band near* the *tip* of the *white tail*.

The Ring-billed Gull is common to abundant in winter and rare in summer in the Tennessee Valley and on the Gulf Coast. In other parts of Alabama, it is fairly common to uncommon in winter, especially as a visitor to lakes, ponds, and rivers during or after rain. Although occurring in the same places as the Herring Gull, this species is more common inland. The Ring-billed Gull is not known to nest in Alabama.

NESTING AND FOOD. This gull nests in colonies in marshes. It builds a nest of reeds and grasses and lays two or three bluish-white to dark brown eggs which are marked with brown and lavender. The bird's food is similar to that of the Herring Gull except that it eats less garbage, and inland it eats large insects, especially grasshoppers.

DISTRIBUTION. The Ring-billed Gull breeds on interior lakes from Washington, northern Alberta, and Manitoba south to northern California, southern Colorado, and South Dakota, and also on the Great Lakes and in the Gulf of St. Lawrence. Non-breeders summer over a much wider area south to the northern Gulf of Mexico. It winters from Oregon, Montana, the Great Lakes, and Maine south to southern Mexico and Cuba.

OCCURRENCE IN ALABAMA. (Throughout the year.) *Tennessee Valley*: Common, late July to late May; most seen, 975+, February 5, 1955 (Guntersville, T. A. Imhof and others). *Mountain Region*: September 25 (1952, Birmingham, M. H. Perry) to May 15 (1955, specimen in Univ. of Ala. collection, West Blocton, Bibb Co., Clay Sansing); most seen, 11, March 13, 1956 (Birmingham, T. A. Imhof and Emmy Brownlie). *Piedmont*: October 3 (1958, Lineville, T. A. Imhof and C. T. Hornady) to March 27 (1960, Mitchell Lake, Harriett Wright); most seen, 100, November 22, 1959 (Mitchell Lake, Harriett Wright). *Upper Coastal Plain*: October 12 (1957, Marion, Lois McCollough) to April 13 (1957, 5 birds, Marion, Lois McCollough); also about May 2, 1949 (Hurtsboro, Russell Co., recovery of banded bird); most seen, 9, March 26, 1955 (Marion, T. A. Imhof and others). *Lower Coastal Plain*: September 20 (1957, Lake Tholloco, T. A. Imhof and Lovett Williams) to at least December. *Gulf Coast*: Common, September to May; most seen, 1000, December 29, 1956 (Christmas Count, Dauphin Island), summer, 25+, June 15 and 16, 1956 (Dauphin Island, T. A. Imhof and others).

BANDING. Of 22 banded Ring-billed Gulls found in Alabama, 1 came from North Dakota and 21 from the Great Lakes; Michigan, 18, and Ontario, 3. Fourteen of these 22 were found on the Gulf Coast and the other 8 fairly evenly in other regions of the state but only 1, surprisingly, from the Tennessee Valley.

Laughing Gull
Larus atricillas Linnaeus   [58]   (Plate 19, facing page 272)

The Laughing Gull is small and white with a *black head* and *dark wings* that are even *darker* at the *tips*. Its feet are dark, the bill is bright red, and an incomplete white ring circles the eye. In winter plumage, the head is white with dark streaks. *Immature* birds resemble the winter adult, but the head, neck, *breast,* and end of the tail are *dark,* usually with a *brownish tinge,* while the rump is white and the bill and feet are dark. This gull's cry is like high-pitched laughter.

A common to abundant, non-breeding, permanent resident on the Gulf Coast of Alabama, this small gull is rare inland. On the coast it is especially abundant during times of migration, but in mid-summer and mid-winter its numbers are greatly reduced. Summer birds are probably from colonies sixty or so miles to the southwest on the Chandeleur Islands of Louisiana, or possibly from some nearer breeding colony which is unknown. This gull occurs around harbors, bays, beaches, and the like. It feeds in the same manner as the Herring and Ring-billed Gulls and sometimes flocks with them.

NESTING. The Laughing Gull nests in colonies either on inaccessible sandy islands or in marshes. Sometimes it builds a substantial nest of grasses and seaweed, but more often it settles for a grass-lined hollow in the sand. It lays two to five dull grayish to dark olive eggs heavily marked with brown, reddish-brown, black, and lavender.

FOOD. This bird eats principally marine animals and large insects. Favorite items are small fish—including catfish—crabs, shrimp, water beetles, water bugs, ants, grasshoppers, and spiders. On occasion it waits for the Brown Pelican to surface from its dive, lights on its head, and then helps itself to the food in the enormous pouch.

DISTRIBUTION. The Laughing Gull breeds on Atlantic and Gulf coasts from Nova Scotia to Yucatan, from southern California to Sonora, and also in the Lesser Antilles and Venezuela. It winters coastally from California and North Carolina, and occasionally farther north, to Peru and Brazil.

[272]

Richard A Parks

OCCURRENCE IN ALABAMA.
(Throughout the year.) *Tennessee Valley*:
January 10 through 16, 1952 (Wheeler Refuge,
D. C. Hulse); April 7 and 16, 1941 (Clarence
Cottam and J. H. Steenis) and May 26, 1942
(J. H. Steenis and Clarence Cottam). *Mountain Region*: Gadsden, a bird found at a fish
pond, October 23, 1950, had been banded as
a chick on Cobb's Island, Virginia, July 18,
1950. *Piedmont*: No record. *Upper Coastal
Plain*: No record. *Lower Coastal Plain*: No
record. *Gulf Coast*: Permanent resident; most
seen, migration, 11,000+, October 6, 1956
(Fall Count, Mobile Bay Area), winter, 1631,
December 28, 1959 (Mobile, J. L. Dorn).

BANDING. See Mountain Region
above for the only recovery for Alabama.

[Franklin's Gull]

Larus pipixcan Wagler [59] (Plate 19, facing page 272)

OTHER NAME: Prairie Dove

Although much like the Laughing Gull, Franklin's Gull is slightly smaller and
has a much smaller bill. *Adults* have a *broad white band* which *separates* the
gray of the *wing* from the *black* of the *wing tips*. Immature birds of this species
are whiter on the forehead and under parts than immature Laughing Gulls,
but at one stage the two species look so much alike that they can be distinguished
from each other with certainty only by taking bill measurements.

In Alabama, Franklin's Gull has been recorded once in spring and once in
winter in the Tennessee Valley. It is not known to breed in the state. Immature
birds may occur regularly, especially in fall on the coast or in the Tennessee
Valley, but they cannot usually be distinguished and so it is almost impossible
to determine their relative status. The inland-breeding, plains-loving Franklin's
Gull is more apt to occur over inland waters and marshes.

NESTING AND FOOD. This prairie gull breeds in large colonies among
rushes and reeds, usually on a lake shore. It makes a small cup in a large,
floating mass of vegetation and in it lays three brown-marked, pale buff to
olive-brown eggs. It feeds extensively on insects, especially grasshoppers, and
a variety of those that fly over marshes or other grasslands, or those exposed by
the plow.

DISTRIBUTION. Franklin's Gull breeds from Alberta and Manitoba south
to Oregon and Iowa. It migrates east to Lake Erie and the Mississippi Valley,
rarely farther, to winter mainly along the Pacific Coast from Guatemala and
Louisiana to Chile.

OCCURRENCE IN ALABAMA.
Tennessee Valley only: Decatur, June 1, 1958,
a pair of adults watched for over an hour at
rest and in flight (D. C. Hulse) and January
4, 1960 (an adult, D. C. Hulse).

Bonaparte's Gull
Larus philadelphia (Ord) [60] (Plate 19, facing page 272)

Even smaller than the Laughing Gull, Bonaparte's Gull has a correspondingly lighter, tern-like flight. The wings and back are gray and it wears a *conspicuous white triangle* on the *outer wing*. The head and bill are black, the feet are red, and the rest of the body is white. In *winter,* the head is white with a *black spot* behind the *eye*. The *young* bird is similar to the winter adult, but it has a *narrow black tail band* and the white triangle on its wing is less sharply defined.

This small gull is uncommon to common in winter on the Gulf Coast. Inland, it is rare during migration, occurring mostly in spring in the Tennessee Valley, where it may possibly winter. It is not known to breed in Alabama. In the interior, it often frequents lakes and plowed fields, but on the coast it prefers harbors, bays, or the open sea and feeds with other gulls and terns. Bonaparte's Gull seldom follows ships or loiters around piers, probably because it rarely eats dead food.

NESTING AND FOOD. This gull nests ten to twenty feet up in a spruce or tamarack usually near water and often in a muskeg. The bird builds with sticks, moss, and dead grass and usually lays three olive-gray eggs with brown spots. In summer in the interior, this gull lives chiefly on large insects. On the coast it eats small fish, shrimp, other crustaceans, marine worms, and other small animals of the sea.

DISTRIBUTION. Bonaparte's Gull breeds inland from northwestern Alaska, northern Mackenzie, and Ontario south to central British Columbia and Saskatchewan, and occasionally summers farther south, especially on the Atlantic Coast. It winters on the Great Lakes and coastally from Washington to Mexico, and from Massachusetts to Yucatan. On migration it sometimes occurs far west or east of its normal routes—for example, on Laysan Island, or in Peru, Greenland, or Europe.

OCCURRENCE IN ALABAMA. (October 12 to May 23.) *Tennessee Valley*: November 29 (1952, flock of 10, Decatur, D. C. Hulse) to May 23 (1954, Decatur, D. C. Hulse); most seen, 25, April 1, 1955 (Decatur, D. C. Hulse). *Mountain Region*: November 16, 1946 (Lake Purdy, T. A. Imhof, M. H. Perry, and S. R. Tipton). *Piedmont*: No record. *Upper Coastal Plain*: December 23, 1944 (Tuscaloosa, S. R. Tipton) and January 1, 1957 (Marion, Lois McCollough). *Lower Coastal Plain*: No record. *Gulf Coast*: October 12 (1958, Cochrane Causeway, J. C. and Margaret Robinson) to May 2 (1959, Baldwin Co., H. M. Stevenson, F. M. Weston, and others); most seen, 1200+, January 31, 1958 (Alabama Point, T. A. Imhof and others).

SUBFAMILY STERNINAE: TERNS

Terns, known locally as Strikers or Sea Swallows, are generally smaller than gulls and differ from them in having narrower wings, a forked tail, and weaker legs. The feet, although webbed, are so ill-adapted for swimming that few observers have ever seen a tern sit duck-like on the water. Most species of this subfamily are white with a black cap, and all of them are more graceful in flight than gulls. They usually point their thin, sharp bills downward at an angle, whereas gulls direct their stouter bills forward.

Gull-billed Tern

Gelochelidon nilotica (Gmelin) [63] (Plate 20, facing page 288)

This tern has a *black* cap, *bill,* and feet, the back and wings are gray, and most of the remainder of the body is white. The *bill* of this bird is thick, short, and *gull-like,* and the *tail* is *barely forked.* The tips of the outer primaries show a small amount of black. In winter and in immature plumages, the entire head is white except for some dark markings, especially around and behind the eye. In this plumage, this tern closely resembles a small gull, but its flight and the slight fork to the tail mark it as a tern. One of its usual calls is a rasping laugh similar to a weak call of a katydid.

The Gull-billed Tern is an uncommon summer resident on the Gulf Coast, and it breeds in southern Mobile County. It is common on migration near salt water, and small numbers winter in upper Mobile Bay and in the Mississippi Sound. Although it feeds readily with other terns over salt water, it prefers to forage over marshes and nearby waters.

NESTING. This bird nests usually on an island, where it chooses either the reeds of a marsh or a hollowed-out place in the sand. The nest contains three olive-buff eggs irregularly marked with brown, black, and lavender.

FOOD. Like most terns, this species eats insects and small marine animals. These include beetles, spiders, dragonflies, and crustaceans that occur on sand.

DISTRIBUTION. The Gull-billed Tern breeds locally from Maryland (formerly from New Jersey) to Texas, and also in the Bahamas, Cuba, southern California, and on all other continents, including Australia. It winters locally in this hemisphere from California and Alabama south to Argentina.

OCCURRENCE IN ALABAMA. *Gulf Coast only:* Common, April to early November; most seen, 75+, August 6, 1960 (Fort Morgan, J. L. Dorn), winter, 4, De-

cember 29, 1956 (Dauphin Island, J. L. Dorn and C. M. Valentine).
TIME OF BREEDING. Data on

3 nestings near Cedar Point: Incubating birds attended by mates June 15 and 16, 1956 (T. A. Imhof and others).

Forster's Tern

Sterna forsteri Nuttall [69] (Plate 20, facing page 288)

This tern is white with pale gray wings and back, a black cap, thin bill, and a very long, forked tail. The bill is usually dark, but in summer in most adults it turns orange-red with a black tip. In this species the pale gray back and wings show little contrast with the tail color, and the *outer primaries are silvery.* The Common Tern has dusky primaries, and the wings and back are dark enough to show contrast in good light. In *winter* and *immature* plumages, the *black* of the cap in Forster's Tern is reduced to a *patch over* the *eyes* and *ears;* however, birds changing from the solid cap of summer may show black on the back of the head just as the Common Tern does. In the hand, Forster's Tern can be distinguished from the Common Tern by the white outer webs of the outer tail feathers, for the Common Tern has white inner webs and dusky outer webs. The harsh calls of this tern and the Roseate Tern sound like the ripping of heavy cloth; other notes are shorter than those of the Common Tern, but otherwise similar.

Forster's Tern is probably the most widespread of its genus in Alabama. On the Gulf Coast it is a common permanent resident, becoming abundant and more widespread in winter and on migration. A few pairs nest in Mobile County. Inland, it is rare to uncommon on migration, especially in the Tennessee Valley in fall. This tern is partial to water near marshes, and thus occurs more frequently in marshy bays than does the Common Tern, which is apt to stay just offshore in the Gulf.

NESTING. In the interior, Forster's Tern nests in fresh marshes and on the coast it selects salt marshes. Its nest is usually made of reed stems and other marsh plants lined with finer material, but it may use a shell-lined depression in the sand. The two or three white to pale green or brownish-drab eggs are spotted with brown and lilac.

FOOD. This bird is said to have a more varied diet than other terns. It not only eats all manner of insects, caught both on the wing and on the water, but also numbers of small sea animals, especially fish.

DISTRIBUTION. Forster's Tern breeds in the interior from Washington and southeastern Manitoba south to California, Colorado, Nebraska, and northeastern Illinois, and formerly it bred in southern Ontario. Coastally it breeds from Maryland to Mexico. It winters from central California and Virginia, and often farther north, south to Guatemala.

OCCURRENCE IN ALABAMA. (Throughout the year.) *Tennessee Valley*: April 28 (1951, Wheeler Refuge, D. C. Hulse) to June 10 (1955, 42 birds, Wheeler Reservoir, T. A. Imhof) and July 20 (1955, Wheeler Refuge, D. C. Hulse) to October 3 (1947, Wheeler Refuge, L. S. Givens). *Mountain Region*: April 23, 1961 (5 birds, Hammondville, DeKalb Co., T. A. Imhof and others); May 1, 1960 (Cleveland, Blount Co., T. A. Imhof); and August 31, 1950, about 6 hours after passage of a hurricane (4 birds, Bayview Lake, Birmingham, T. A. Imhof). *Piedmont*: No record. *Upper Coastal Plain*: No record. *Lower Coastal Plain*: May 9, 1958 (Florala, T. A. Imhof) and September 20, 1957 (15 birds, Florala and Lake Tholloco, T. A. Imhof and Lovett Williams). *Gulf Coast*: Permanent resident; most seen, spring, 565, May 16, 1958 (Dauphin Island, T. A. Imhof, M. W. Gaillard, and J. C. Gray), fall, 310, November 1, 1958 (Fall Count, Mobile Bay Area), winter, 300, December 28, 1956 (Cochrane Causeway, T. A. Imhof and others).

TIME OF BREEDING. Data on 2 Mobile Co. nestings: Eggs, June 23 (M. W. Gaillard); young just able to fly, June 27 (T. A. Imhof, H. C. Loesch, and J. C. Gray).

Common Tern
Sterna hirundo Linnaeus [70] (Plate 20, facing page 288)

Closely resembling Forster's Tern, this species can usually be distinguished from it only at very close range in good light by those familiar with both species. *Adult* Common Terns are distinguished by the *dusky primaries* and the *contrast between* the *grayer back* and *whiter rump* and *tail*. Bill color in any plumage is rarely useful. Surprisingly the two species are most easily separated in *winter* and *immature plumages*. At these times the reduced *black cap* of the Common Tern *extends* completely *around* the *back* of the *head*, instead of being confined to the eye and ear as is that of Forster's Tern. At that period of the year when birds are changing to or from the summer cap, distinction may be difficult. The call of the Common Tern is harsh and double-noted, more drawn out than that of Forster's Tern.

The Common Tern is common throughout the year on the Gulf Coast of Alabama. It is most numerous during migration and its numbers decrease in winter. It is not known to breed in the state, but it may do so occasionally on the coast when conditions are favorable. Inland it is uncommon in the Tennessee Valley and rare elsewhere, generally occurring after storms. Because it is so difficult to separate this bird from Forster's Tern, the exact status of the species on the coast is uncertain, but Forster's Tern is unquestionably more numerous. The Common Tern frequents beaches and sandbars and feeds mostly over open salt water. It prefers the Gulf and only on rare occasions forages near marshy areas.

[277]

NESTING. This tern usually nests in colonies on undisturbed islands. It lays three greenish-white to deep brown eggs which are heavily blotched with black, brown, or lavender. The nest is often a mere hollow in the sand, sometimes lined with a few pieces of grass, seaweed, shells, or sticks. But on occasion this bird makes a substantial nest of sticks.

FOOD. The diet of the Common Tern consists mostly of small fish. It also eats shrimp, other small crustaceans, aquatic insects, flying insects, and grasshoppers.

DISTRIBUTION. Nearly cosmopolitan, the Common Tern breeds in the Americas locally from Mackenzie, central Ontario, and the Gulf of St. Lawrence south to Alberta, the Great Lakes, and coastally to Texas, Venezuela, and the Bahamas. It winters from western Mexico, the northern Gulf Coast, and South Carolina south to the Straits of Magellan.

OCCURRENCE IN ALABAMA. (Throughout the year.) *Tennessee Valley*: March 31 (1953, 6 birds, Wheeler Refuge, D. C. Hulse) to May 30 (1954, 30 birds, Wheeler Refuge, D. C. Hulse) and July 2 (1953, Decatur, D. C. Hulse) to September 16 (1950, Decatur, D. C. Hulse); most seen, 125, May 24, 1951 (Wheeler Refuge, D. C. Hulse). *Mountain Region*: April 29, 1937 (Birmingham, H. M. Stevenson) and August 8 (1936, Birmingham, H. M. Stevenson) to September 12 (1958, Hanceville, Cullman Co., T. A. Imhof and J. B. Sullivan); most seen, 10, August 31, 1950, immediately after a hurricane (Birmingham, T. A. Imhof). *Piedmont*: No record. *Upper Coastal Plain*: August 18, 1939, after a hurricane (Tuscaloosa, H. M. Stevenson). *Lower Coastal Plain*: No record. *Gulf Coast*: Permanent resident; most seen, 1100, May 16, 1958 (Sand Island and Dauphin Island, T. A. Imhof, M. W. Gaillard, and J. C. Gray).

[Roseate Tern]
Sterna dougallii Montagu   [72]

Except for the black cap, this graceful tern looks white at a distance, for its back and wings are a very pale gray. It has red feet and its bill may be totally black, but is usually red at the base. At very close range a faint rosy hue is apparent on the breast. In immature and winter plumages, the forehead becomes white, and the head then resembles that of the Common Tern in winter. Like Forster's Tern, this species has a very *long, deeply-forked tail*, but the Roseate Tern's tail *extends beyond* the *folded wing tips* when it is at rest. The bird has two calls, one of which resembles the ripping of heavy cloth and is too similar to a call of Forster's Tern to be very useful in identification. The alternate call, however, which is two-syllabled and similar to calls of the Sandwich Tern and Semipalmated Plover, is often a reliable means of identification.

The Roseate Tern is a rare transient on the Gulf Coast and is not known to breed in Alabama. It occurs in the bays and along the outer strip of land near the Gulf. From the limited number of records here, the bird appears to be strictly confined to salt water in this state.

NESTING AND FOOD. This species nests in colonies, often with other gulls and terns, on rocky or sandy beaches or on islands. The two buffy eggs spotted with reddish-brown are laid in a slight, sometimes sparsely lined, hollow either hidden in grass or in the open. This tern feeds almost entirely on small fish found near the surface of salt water.

DISTRIBUTION. The Roseate Tern breeds locally in the Western Hemisphere along the coast from Nova Scotia to Venezuela. It winters coastally from the West Indies, casually north to North Carolina and south to Brazil.

OCCURRENCE IN ALABAMA. *Gulf Coast only*: March 29 (1952, Gulf Shores, H. M. Stevenson) to May 3 (1961, Dauphin Island, Owen Davies) and August 9 (1953, Gulf Shores, H. M. Stevenson) to August 28 (1946, Gulf Shores, T. A. Imhof); also June 14, 1952 (Gulf Shores, H. M. Stevenson); most seen, 6, April 20, 1956 (Bayou La Batre, T. A. Imhof and H. C. Loesch).

Sooty Tern

Sterna fuscata Linnaeus [75] (Plate 20, facing page 288)
OTHER NAME: Wideawake

The Sooty Tern is about the size of Forster's Tern and is *black above* and *white below*. It has a *white forehead* and white on the sides of the deeply-forked tail. Its bill and feet are black. The immature bird is brown with a lighter belly and has white speckling on its back. This bird's off-repeated call and its round-the-clock activity during the breeding season have earned it the nickname "Wideawake."

This tropical tern is not known to nest in Alabama but visits the state casually at almost any season both on the coast and inland on the Coastal Plain. The Sooty Tern normally remains on the open sea out of sight of land, but it seems to be carried long distances by tropical storms and its visits to Alabama are associated with this type of weather. The bird probably goes aloft at the approach of a storm to ride it out, sometimes in the "eye" itself.

NESTING AND FOOD. This tern nests in colonies, usually on islands beyond the continental shelf. Data indicate that some birds nest every nine months instead of the usual twelve. The one to three creamy-buff eggs, marked with brown and lavender, are laid in a hollow in the sand. Small fish and crustaceans are the principal items of this tern's diet.

[279]

DISTRIBUTION. The Sooty Tern breeds from Yucatan (formerly Texas and Louisiana), Dry Tortugas, and the Bahamas south to Venezuela, and through the West Indies to tropical Atlantic islands. After tropical storms it often occurs far north of this range in many states of the United States and even to Nova Scotia. It winters from the northern Gulf of Mexico to Brazil and the Falkland Islands. It also occurs in the Pacific and Indian oceans.

OCCURRENCE IN ALABAMA. (March, April, June, and September as noted below.) *Tennessee Valley*: No record. *Mountain Region*: No record. *Piedmont*: No record. *Upper Coastal Plain*: Tuscaloosa, a mummified specimen now in the Univ. of Ala. collection, found on the University campus about March 1, 1957 (*fide* R. L. Chermock) and a specimen, not preserved, found by Ben Sergeant about the fall of 1940 (*fide* R. W. Harper). Prattville, see BANDING below. *Lower Coastal Plain*: No record. *Gulf Coast*: Fairhope, April 10, 1938, specimen in the Auburn Univ. collection "after a hard blow from the south" by D. H. McIntosh (F. S. Barkalow, 1939, *Wilson Bull.* 51:121). Dauphin Island, June 15, 1956, a dying bird now specimen in the Univ. of Ala. collection (M. W. Gaillard).

BANDING. A dead bird found in the schoolyard at Prattville, September 19, 1960, had been banded on the Dry Tortugas Islands, July 9, 1960, and was probably carried inland by Hurricane Ethel.

Bridled Tern
Sterna anaethetus Scopoli   [76]   (Plate 20, facing page 288)

Resembling the Sooty Tern in size and shape, the Bridled Tern differs in having a lighter-colored back, whiter tail, and a *white collar* on the *hindneck*. The white of the forehead extends over and behind the eye.

The Bridled Tern has been recorded only once in Alabama. This sighting took place on the coast the day after a hurricane. Normally the bird remains at sea beyond sight of land.

NESTING AND FOOD. The nest is usually in a colony of such other sea birds as its close relative, the Sooty Tern. The single brown-spotted white egg is laid among rocks or in the entrance of a burrow. This tern eats small fish, squids, and other marine animals taken near the surface of the sea.

DISTRIBUTION. The Bridled Tern breeds from British Honduras and the Bahamas through the West Indies to Venezuela and also in the Eastern Hemisphere. Outside the breeding season, it wanders regularly to the east coast of Florida and much less regularly to Nicaragua, Alabama, and South Carolina, probably after tropical storms.

OCCURRENCE IN ALABAMA. *Gulf Coast only*: Gulf Shores, September 2, 1932, the day after passage of a hurricane, 6 birds seen and a specimen, now in the U. S. National Museum, was picked up on the beach (Helen Edwards, 1933, *Auk* 50:105).

Least Tern

Sterna albifrons Pallas   [74]   (Plate 20, facing page 288)

This species is the *smallest* of our *terns,* for it is only slightly more than half the size of Forster's Tern. It has a *black-tipped yellow bill,* yellow feet, and a black cap with a *white forehead.* It is otherwise patterned like the other white-bodied, gray-winged terns. The wingbeat is more rapid than other terns and the notes of its harsh and squealing call are higher pitched.

The Least Tern is a common to abundant summer resident on the Gulf Coast where it nests, usually in large colonies. Inland, it is uncommon to rare on migration, occurring especially in the Tennessee Valley. Although it sometimes remains in the Tennessee Valley all summer, it is not as yet known to breed away from the coast. On the coast, it is most common on beaches and in other sandy areas, particularly new fills. Inland it frequents large rivers, ponds, and lakes, and prefers to be near shallows and sandbars. Inland records of the Least Tern probably include both inland birds on migration and storm-driven coastal birds.

NESTING. The two to four greenish to dull, drab eggs are irregularly marked with brown and lavender. They are laid in shallow depressions, lined with pebbles or shells, in sandy or gravelly places. Pairs of this bird are scattered irregularly over beaches, sandbars, and similar areas. It often breeds close to humans and does not need to retire to the seclusion of isolated islands as do most colonial terns.

FOOD. This little tern subsists mostly on small fish and an occasional small crustacean or flying insect.

DISTRIBUTION. In the Americas, the Least Tern breeds coastally from California to Peru and from Massachusetts to Brazil. Inland it breeds on islands in the Mississippi and Missouri rivers to Nebraska, Kansas, South Dakota, and Iowa. It winters from the Gulf of California and the Gulf of Mexico south to Brazil.

OCCURRENCE IN ALABAMA. (April 4 to October 22.) *Tennessee Valley*: May 26 (1956, Wheeler Refuge, D. C. Hulse) to September 1 (1943, Wheeler Refuge, H. M. Stevenson). *Mountain Region*: June 4, 1954 (1 bird over a small farm pond near Fort Payne, H. M. Stevenson and others); July 31, 1948 (3 birds, Bayview Lake, Birmingham, T. A. Imhof); and October 3, 1960 (Lake Purdy, Birmingham, Harriett Wright).

Piedmont: No record. *Upper Coastal Plain*: August 18 and 19, 1939 (after a hurricane, Tuscaloosa, H. M. Stevenson). Specimen shot on Cocke's Pond before 1890 (Greensboro, W. C. Avery). Autaugaville, 1 shot, August 1, 1939 by R. S. Thompson and identified by L. S. Golsan. Montgomery Co., 2 seen, 1 collected in 1880 or 1881 by "AMR" (AMR 1883, *Forest and Stream* 20:323). *Lower Coastal Plain*: No record. *Gulf Coast*: April 4

(1959, Dauphin Island, Ava Tabor and others) to October 22 (1949, Fort Morgan, T. A. Imhof and others); most seen, breeding, 700+, May 17, 1958 (Cedar Point and Cochrane Causeway, T. A. Imhof and M. W. Gaillard), fall, 3000+, August 31, 1958 (Dauphin Island, S. A. Gauthreaux and others).

TIME OF BREEDING. Data on over 700 nestings in 11 colonies: Eggs, May 12 to July 29; small young, May 12 to July 21; flying but dependent young, June 15-July 21.

Royal Tern

Thalasseus maximus (Boddaert)   [65]   (Plate 20, facing page 288)

OTHER NAME: Redbill

This is a big tern, about the size of a Ring-billed Gull. It is white except for light gray wings, a black cap, an orange-red bill, and black feet. It differs from the slightly larger and heavier Caspian Tern in having a more crested head, a deeper fork to the tail, and white on the under side of its primaries. In *winter and immature plumages*, the *forehead* and *much* of the *top* of the *head* are *unstreaked white*. These parts of the Caspian Tern are always streaked or black. Most Royal Terns, even in breeding plumage, show some white on the forehead, while many Caspian Terns retain the black cap late in the fall.

The Royal Tern is an abundant summer resident on the Gulf Coast, but because it requires undisturbed islands for nesting, it breeds only occasionally in the state. It bred irregularly on Pelican Island near the mouth of Mobile Bay prior to 1893, but this island was washed away by a hurricane. This tern is widespread in all coastal waters and is unknown inland. Large flocks join other gulls and terns, especially the Laughing Gull, to follow fishing boats in quest of scraps.

NESTING. This species nests in large, dense colonies on sandy coastal islands. The nest is a slight hollow in the sand, and the bird lays two or three whitish eggs, blotched with dark brown and lavender. Nests are often so close together that, when the birds are incubating, the sand between them is barely visible. The Royal Tern tolerates only its close relative, the Sandwich Tern, in its nesting colonies.

FOOD. Fish, especially menhaden, yellow perch, and bluefish, with a small amount of crustaceans, make up the food of the Royal Tern. Flocks of these and other terns, feeding on small fish driven to the surface, usually indicate to fishermen that there are larger fish directly below.

DISTRIBUTION. The Royal Tern breeds on the Pacific Coast of Mexico, on Atlantic coasts from Maryland to Mexico, and in the Bahamas, the West Indies, Venezuela, and West Africa. It ranges north to San Francisco Bay and rarely to Massachusetts, especially after hurricanes, and winters coastally from California to Peru, from North Carolina to Argentina, and in West Africa.

OCCURRENCE IN ALABAMA. *Gulf Coast only*: Permanent resident; most seen, spring, 4200+, May 16, 1958 (Dauphin Island, T. A. Imhof, M. W. Gaillard, and J. C. Gray), fall, 2800, October 6, 1956 (Fall Count, Mobile Bay Area), winter, 350, February 8, 1957 (Bon Secour Bay to Alabama Point, T. A. Imhof and others).

TIME OF BREEDING. Data on 50+ nestings on Sand Island: One egg each, about June 10, 1958 (J. C. Gray).

BANDING. One bird, banded at Cape Romain Refuge, South Carolina, July 25, 1947, was found dead at Fish River, November 12, 1947.

Sandwich Tern

Thalasseus sandvicensis (Latham)   [67]   (Plate 20, facing page 288)
OTHER NAME: Cabot's Tern

Perhaps best described as a dark-billed counterpart of the Royal Tern, this species is as small as Forster's Tern. The adult Sandwich Tern has a black cap with a ragged crest, light gray wings, black legs, and a *yellow-tipped black bill*. This yellow tip, which it retains in winter, is often difficult to see in the strong light of the sea coast, so that the bill sometimes appears as short and stubby as that of the Gull-billed Tern. The Sandwich Tern can be distinguished by its *ragged crest*, often with some white on the forehead, by the deeper fork to the tail, by a white collar between the black cap and gray back, and by its general resemblance to the Royal Tern. In winter or immature plumages, the top of the head is white like that of the Royal Tern. In this plumage, especially if the bill cannot be seen well, it may be confused with the Gull-billed Tern, but there are these differences: the Gull-billed Tern has a very white head, little fork to the tail, and some black in the wing tips. The Sandwich Tern, moreover, has a pleasing two-noted call, and the Gull-billed Tern has not.

On the Gulf Coast of Alabama, this tern is an uncommon to fairly common summer resident, rare in winter, and probably breeds here only as often as the Royal Tern. It is usually confined to the outer islands and peninsulas and associates closely with the Royal Tern.

NESTING. It nests on undisturbed coastal islands, often in colonies of the Royal Tern. The slight hollow in the sand which forms the nest holds two or three creamy to buffy eggs marked with black, brown, reddish-brown, or lavender. These eggs often show considerable variation within the clutch. They are rarely left unattended.

FOOD. This species eats small fish, the young of larger fish, small mollusks, and crustaceans. Mullet, garfish, sand launce, shrimp, and squid are typical.

[283]

DISTRIBUTION. In the New World the Sandwich Tern breeds on Atlantic coasts from North Carolina (formerly Virginia), to Yucatan, and also in the Bahamas. It occurs in summer casually north to Massachusetts and south to Panama and winters from southern Mexico, the northern Gulf Coast, and the Bahamas south on both coasts of Central America to Panama and Argentina, and in the West Indies.

OCCURRENCE IN ALABAMA. *Gulf Coast only*: Common, March 19 (1949, Fort Morgan, H. M. Stevenson) to November 29 (1957, Gulf Shores, B. L. Monroe, Jr. and H. M. Stevenson); most seen, 450, May 16, 1958 (Dauphin Island, T. A. Imhof, M. W. Gaillard, and J. C. Gray).

Caspian Tern

Hydroprogne caspia (Pallas)   [64]   (Plate 20, facing page 288)
OTHER NAME: Redbill

Although it resembles the Royal Tern, this species is a bit larger and heavier, has a *heavier, blood-red bill*, less fork to the tail, and is *dusky* on the *under surface* of the *primaries*. The Caspian Tern keeps its black cap later in the fall than does the Royal Tern, and when at length the cap does change, the white crown shows black *streaks*, even on the *forehead*. The Royal Tern, which has a more crested look, shows clear white on the forehead, often even in the breeding season. Although the call of the Caspian Tern is deeper and hoarser than the Royal Tern, this difference is of slight value in identification.

The Caspian Tern is common in winter and uncommon to rare in summer on the Gulf Coast of Alabama. It is not known to breed anywhere in the state. Inland, it is uncommon on migration, occurring especially in the larger river valleys. The Caspian Tern often associates with the Royal Tern in winter; however, it occurs much more often in brackish or fresh-water areas and near marshes. Thus on the coast, it is more common in the Mississippi Sound and at the head of Mobile Bay.

NESTING. This bird breeds in colonies which settle in isolated areas— usually islands. Normally these are on large inland lakes, but from time to time the Caspian Tern will colonize an island along the coast. The two or three pale olive-buff eggs, laid in a slight depression in the ground, are marked with dark brown and lavender.

FOOD. Small fish, secured by diving from the air, form almost the entire diet of this large tern.

DISTRIBUTION. In the Western Hemisphere, the Caspian Tern breeds locally on large interior lakes from Great Slave Lake to Klamath Lake and the Great Lakes, and on the north shore of the Gulf of St. Lawrence and probably even farther north. It also breeds on the Pacific Coast in California and Lower California, and on the Atlantic Coast from Virginia to Texas. It winters on the coast from California to Mexico and from South Carolina (casually North Carolina), to Mexico, Cuba, and Hispaniola. On migration it occurs in the Mississippi Valley and on the Atlantic Coast of the northeastern United States.

OCCURRENCE IN ALABAMA. (Throughout the year.) *Tennessee Valley*: April 25 (1955, Wheeler Reservoir, D. C. Hulse) to June 10 (1955, Wheeler Dam, T. A. Imhof) and July 10 (1957, Decatur, M. F. Baker) to November 11 (1953, Decatur, D. C. Hulse); most seen, 20, September 23, 1952 (Wheeler Refuge, D. C. Hulse). *Mountain Region*: August 31, 1950 (2 seen after a hurricane, Bayview Lake, Birmingham, T. A. Imhof). Gorgas, see BANDING below. *Piedmont*: No record. *Upper Coastal Plain*: Marion, see BANDING below. *Lower Coastal Plain*: No record. *Gulf Coast*: Permanent resident; most seen, summer, 40, June 27, 1958 (Cedar Point, T. A. Imhof), migration, 1000+, October 6, 1956 (Fall Count, Mobile Bay Area), winter, 230, January 18, 1957 (Mississippi Sound, T. A. Imhof and others).

BANDING. All 17 banded Caspian Terns recovered in Alabama were banded as chicks on the Great Lakes, mostly Lakes Michigan and Huron. One of them when recaptured was 17 years old! Of 14 coastal recoveries, 12 were during the period October 14 to January 20, and 1 each in early April and early June. The 3 inland recoveries are for Tuscumbia, September 18, 1934; Warrior River near Gorgas, October 3, 1923; and Marion, September 14, 1935.

Black Tern

Chlidonias niger (Linnaeus)   [77]   (Plate 20, facing page 288)

OTHER NAME: Sea Pigeon

In *breeding, adult plumage,* the Black Tern has a *black head, black under parts,* and *dark gray wings* and *tail.* It is a small tern, only a little larger than the Least Tern. In other plumages, the bird has white under parts, but it can always be recognized by the variously *pied pattern* of *black* and *white* on the head and hindneck, and by the dark gray back, wings, and tail.

In migration on the Alabama coast, this dark-winged tern is common in spring, abundant in fall, often summers in large numbers, and is accidental in winter. Inland it is rare to uncommon in spring and uncommon to common in fall, occurring particularly in the Tennessee Valley. On the coast it occurs along the beaches with resident terns, but inland it prefers the vicinity of marshes and the shallow fresh water. Although the species is often abundant in summer on the coast and the habitat seems ideal, no positive breeding evidence has ever been discovered, despite a diligent search.

NESTING. This tern nests in a hollow barely above water in the marshy edges of interior lakes and sloughs. It lines the nest carelessly with grass, and lays two to four eggs which are brownish-olive, heavily marked with brown.

FOOD. The Black Tern eats insects of any kind it encounters. Those preferred are the large aquatic types and those that fly over water. Included are dragonfly nymphs, water beetles, the cotton-boll worm, army worm, click beetle, weevils, and grasshoppers. It also takes a few fish and some crawfish.

DISTRIBUTION. The Black Tern breeds in the Americas on interior lakes from central British Columbia and northern Ontario south to California, northern Missouri, the Ohio Valley, and New Brunswick, and non-breeders remain south to Panama and the northern Gulf Coast. It winters from Panama to Chile and Surinam and casually on the northern Gulf Coast. The main path of migration is through the interior of the United States, but a secondary one of importance is coastal, on the Atlantic Coast from Nova Scotia to North Carolina, especially in fall.

OCCURRENCE IN ALABAMA. (Normal: April 20 to October 22; Out-of-season: December 31.) *Tennessee Valley*: May 4 (1957, Wheeler Refuge, Ala. Orn. Soc.) to June 10 (1955, Wheeler Refuge, T. A. Imhof and D. C. Hulse) and July 14 (1953, Wheeler Refuge, D. C. Hulse) to October 5 (1951, Wheeler Refuge, D. C. Hulse). *Mountain Region*: May 2, 1935 (Birmingham, H. M. Stevenson) and July 3 (1936, Birmingham, H. M. Stevenson) to September 15 (1960, Birmingham, Harriett Wright); most seen, 110, September 1, 1950 (Bayview Lake, Birmingham, after a hurricane, T. A. Imhof). *Piedmont*: August 10, 1952 (3 birds, Stroud, Chambers Co., H. M. Stevenson) and August 27 through 29, 1960 (33 birds, Mitchell Lake, D. O. and Harriett Wright). *Upper Coastal Plain*: May 11 (1958, Marion, Lois McCollough) to June 1 (1956, 5 birds, Marion, Lois McCollough) and July 22 (1958, 3 birds, Montgomery, Lovett Williams) to September 16 (1956, Marion, Lois McCollough); most seen, 8, August 22, 1960 (Montgomery, R. W. Skinner). *Lower Coastal Plain*: July 13, 1958 (Camden, Lovett Williams) and September 20, 1957 (50 birds, Lake Tholloco and Florala, T. A. Imhof and Lovett Williams). *Gulf Coast*: April 20 (1956, Cedar Point, T. A. Imhof) to October 22 (1949, Cochrane Causeway, T. A. Imhof); also December 31, 1960 (12 birds observed well, Cochrane Causeway, J. L. Dorn and M. W. Gaillard); most seen, summer, 1000+, June 15 through 17, 1956 (Dauphin Island, T. A. Imhof, O. L. Austin, and others), migration, 9000, August 6, 1960 (Fort Morgan, J. L. Dorn).

FAMILY RYNCHOPIDAE: SKIMMERS

Black Skimmer

Rynchops nigra Linnaeus   [80]   (Plate 20, facing page 288)
OTHER NAMES: Shearwater, Razorbill, Scissorbill

The Black Skimmer is closely related to the terns. Its wings, its back, and the center of its tail are black, while the under parts and outer tail feathers are white. There is a wide white stripe between the eye and the bill, and the *black-tipped red bill* is narrow and deep, with the *lower mandible* much *longer than* the *upper*. The immature bird has a smaller bill and is brownish where

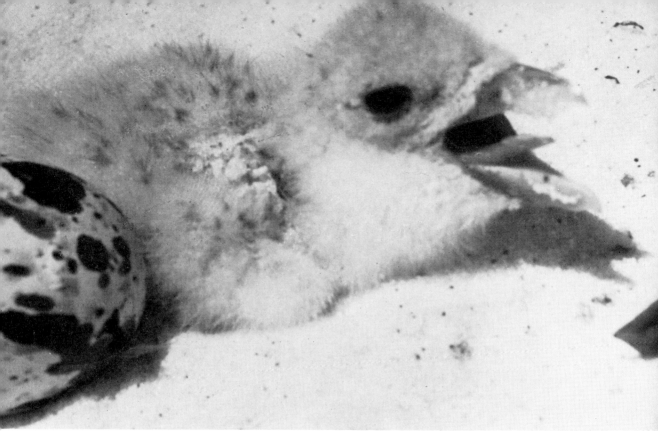

YOUNG BLACK SKIMMER. Recently hatched, this bird rests on sand beside a second egg.

the adult is black, but it is enough like the adult to be easily recognized. The call is a low-pitched, rather nasal bark.

This bird is a locally common and sometimes abundant, breeding, permanent resident on the Alabama Coast, particularly in Mobile County. Inland it is accidental after storms. It usually occurs on the bay side of the outer islands and feeds in shallow water along the beaches or rests in flocks on sandbars. Apparently it does most of its feeding at night. In winter it concentrates in large flocks.

NESTING. The nest is a shallow depression in the sand, usually just above the high water mark. In it the bird lays one to four, usually three and rarely five, pale blue, greenish, or buff eggs, spotted and blotched with dark brown, black, and lavender. The Black Skimmer breeds on sandy islands in colonies which are often pure but frequently include the Least Tern.

FOOD. This bird feeds by flying low with the long, lower mandible in the water, skimming for small marine life. In this fashion it gets small fish, mollusks, small crabs, and other crustaceans.

DISTRIBUTION. The Black Skimmer breeds locally on the Pacific Coast from Mexico to Chile and on the Atlantic Coast from Massachusetts to Argentina.

[287]

PLATE 20

ROYAL TERN
Summer, Adult, Sexes Alike
Page 282

CASPIAN TERN
Summer, Adult, Sexes Alike
Page 284

ROYAL TERN
Winter, Adult, Sexes Alike
Page 282

CASPIAN TERN
Winter, Sexes Alike
Page 284

GULL-BILLED TERN
Winter, Sexes Alike
Page 275

LEAST TERN
Adult, Sexes Alike
Page 281

BLACK TERN
Summer, Adult, Sexes Alike
Page 285

GULL-BILLED TERN
Summer, Adult, Sexes Alike
Page 275

BLACK TERN
Winter, Sexes Alike
Page 285

SOOTY TERN
Adult, Sexes Alike
Page 279

BRIDLED TERN
Adult, Sexes Alike
Page 280

COMMON TERN
Winter, Sexes Alike
Page 277

COMMON TERN
Summer, Sexes Alike
Page 277

SANDWICH TERN
Summer, Sexes Alike
Page 283

FORSTER'S TERN
Summer, Sexes Alike
Page 276

SANDWICH TERN
Winter, Sexes Alike
Page 283

FORSTER'S TERN
Winter, Sexes Alike
Page 276

BLACK SKIMMER
Adult, Sexes Alike
Page 286

[288]

Richard Parks

It winters coastally from Mexico and South Carolina to southern South America. It is casual in the West Indies and accidental inland in the United States.

OCCURRENCE IN ALABAMA. (Throughout the year.) *Tennessee Valley*: No record. *Mountain Region*: No record. *Piedmont*: No record. *Upper Coastal Plain*: August 17 and 18, 1939, after a hurricane (Tuscaloosa, H. M. Stevenson). *Lower Coastal Plain*: No record. *Gulf Coast*: Permanent resident; most seen, summer, 1020, August 25, 1956 (Dauphin Island and vicinity, T. A. Imhof, M. W. Gaillard, and H. C. Loesch), winter, 250, January 19, 1957 (Mississippi Sound, T. A. Imhof and others).

TIME OF BREEDING. Data on 355+ nestings in 11 colonies: Eggs, May 12 to September 14; downy young, June 15 to September 23; dependent flying young, July 27 to October; the greatest nesting activity in August, for nests are frequently destroyed by summer storms.

ORDER COLUMBIFORMES: SAND-GROUSE, PIGEONS, AND DOVES

FAMILY COLUMBIDAE: PIGEONS AND DOVES

SUBFAMILY COLUMBINAE: PIGEONS AND DOVES

For the most part well-known, the small-headed birds of this order have small bills which are soft at the base. Their wings are long and so, usually, are their tails, which are either pointed, square, or rounded. Their flight is strong, rapid, direct, and often audible, producing a noticeable whistle. Special glands in the neck predigest their grain food into a creamy mass known as pigeons' milk, which is fed to the young. There is no more biological basis for distinguishing between pigeons and doves than between sheep and goats or beans and peas.

Rock Dove
Columba livia Gmelin   [313.1]
OTHER NAMES: Wild Pigeon, Park Pigeon

A native of Africa, Europe, and Asia, the Rock Dove has been extensively domesticated in the United States. Many of the domestic birds have escaped and become the common "pigeons" of city streets.

The typical color of this bird is dark slate gray with a white rump and white under the wings. It has red feet, a dark brown bill, and a bronze and green iridescent patch on the side of the neck. There has been so much crossbreeding among the escaped birds in America that numerous variations of plumage occur.

In Europe, the bird breeds on sea cliffs, while in America it uses ledges of tall buildings and other structures. This species may occur in many habitats, but it is best known as a frequenter of city parks where it nests on nearby buildings. It lays two white eggs, and its favorite foods are grains and seeds.

In Alabama the bird, or its hybrids, occurs in many places, usually nesting close to man, where grain is easily obtained—for example, where it is processed as feed for domestic animals. The Rock Dove exists in various stages of wildness from almost complete dependence on man to complete independence.

White-winged Dove

Zenaida asiatica (Linnaeus)　[319]　(Plate 14, facing page 208)

This dove resembles the Mourning Dove, but it is heavier, has a *white band on the rounded tail,* and on its *wing* a *diagonal white patch* noticeable as a long white line on the lower edge when the bird is at rest.

In Alabama, this bird is rare to uncommon in winter on the Gulf Coast and casual farther inland on the Coastal Plain. It is not known to breed in the state. (See Map 50.) Single birds may flock with the Mourning Dove, but more often the White-winged Dove occurs alone or in small pure flocks. It frequents the same places as the Mourning Dove.

NESTING AND FOOD. The two creamy-white eggs are laid in a frail structure of sticks and weeds in low trees and bushes. This dove eats the same kinds of seeds and grains as the Mourning Dove. One Alabama specimen had a stomach crammed with partridge peas. In the west, it eats the seeds of various desert grasses.

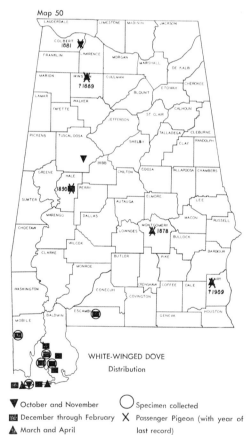

Map 50

DISTRIBUTION. The White-winged Dove is resident from southeastern California and southeastern Texas south to western Panama; the Bahamas to the Greater Antilles; and from Ecuador to Chile. It occurs irregularly northward, especially in fall and winter, to British Columbia, Washington, Colorado, Louisiana, Mississippi, Alabama, Florida, and New York.

WHITE-WINGED DOVE
Distribution

▼ October and November　◯ Specimen collected
▨ December through February　✕ Passenger Pigeon (with year of
▲ March and April　　　　　last record)

OCCURRENCE IN ALABAMA. (First week in October to April 20.) *Tennessee Valley*: No record. *Mountain Region*: No record. *Piedmont*: No record. *Upper Coastal Plain*: First week in October 1956 (Cottondale, Tuscaloosa Co., R. L. and Ottilie Chermock). *Lower Coastal Plain*: December 1949 (1 bird shot, Brewton, *fide* J. E. Keeler). *Gulf Coast*: October 12 (1957, Dauphin Island, S. A. Gauthreaux and others) to April 20 (1942, Daphne, J. L. Dorn); most seen, 7, October

17, 1959 (Dauphin Island, T. A. Imhof and others); several specimens obtained in this region are in the U. S. National Museum and the Dept. of Conservation collection, and birds are noted in game bags almost every year.

Mourning Dove

Zenaidura macroura (Linnaeus)   [316]   (Plate 14, facing page 208)
OTHER NAMES: Turtle Dove, Dove

The Mourning Dove has a small head, a *long, pointed tail,* and is rather thin and streamlined. It is slaty-blue above, reddish-fawn below, and has large white spots on its tail. It has a *black spot behind* its black *eye,* the bill is also black, and the feet are red. This bird's flight is direct and rapid, and the wing beat usually produces a noticeable whistle, especially when the dove is flushed. Its call is a slow mournful cooing which becomes lower in pitch and volume at the end.

This bird is a common and often abundant, widespread, breeding, permanent resident in Alabama. Northern birds substantially increase its ranks in winter. It generally occurs in farming areas, and often uses the woodlots for nesting and the nearby fields for feeding. Frequently it roosts on the ground.

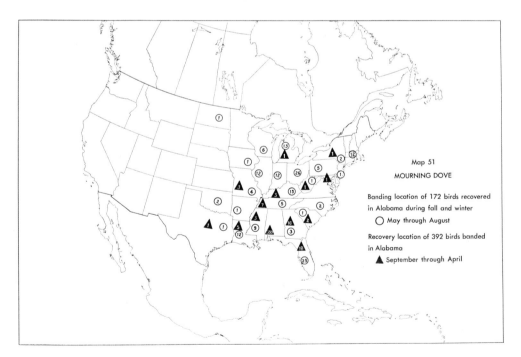

Map 51
MOURNING DOVE

Banding location of 172 birds recovered in Alabama during fall and winter
○ May through August

Recovery location of 392 birds banded in Alabama
▲ September through April

COLUMBIFORMES: COLUMBIDAE: MOURNING DOVE

NESTING. The nest is a very flat, loosely-built platform of twigs, pine needles, and grass in Alabama. It is usually wedged in a pine or cedar about ten to twenty feet above the ground, but is sometimes built on the ground itself. The nest tree is often located in a farmyard or on the edge of a field. The Mourning Dove lays two, or occasionally three, white eggs and may often raise as many as three successful broods per season (Moore and Pearson, 1941:11).

FOOD. Most of the Mourning Dove's food is weed seeds, legumes, and waste grain, but it occasionally takes small fruits and a very small amount of animal matter. This bird consumes a great variety of seeds throughout the year, especially grass and weed seed. Several wild legume seeds are eaten by the Mourning Dove, as well as some cultivated varieties, such as cowpeas, soybeans, and peanuts. The favorite grain is wheat, but frequently it takes waste corn, oats, rye, barley, and buckwheat.

DISTRIBUTION. This species breeds from Alaska, Quebec, and New Brunswick south to Mexico and Cuba, and in western Panama. It is the only game bird that breeds in forty-nine of the fifty states. It winters from British Columbia, Iowa, Michigan, Ontario, New York, and Massachusetts south to Panama.

MOURNING DOVE NEST.   This unusual photograph shows two stages in the life cycle of Mourning Doves in the same nest.

F. S. Barkalow, Jr.

ABUNDANCE IN ALABAMA (*most seen in a day*). Colbert Co. (Leighton), "thousands in old oat patch, over 100 shot," July 16, 1889 (F. W. McCormack); Madison Co., 350, February 7, 1959 (J. C. and Margaret Robinson); Jefferson Co., 335, December 26, 1960 (Christmas Count, Birmingham); Fall Counts, Mobile Bay Area, 535+, October 6, 1956; 517, October 19, 1957; and 400, November 1, 1958; Little Dauphin Island, 190+ in one flock, November 4, 1955 (T. A. Imhof); Random Roadside counts, Alabama, maximum, 32.1 per 100 miles (August 1949); minimum, 3.5 per 100 miles (April 1952); average (September 1948 to September 1952), 11.75 per 100 miles (J. E. Keeler, 1952:10).

TIME OF BREEDING. Data on over 800 nestings: Eggs and young every month of the year, 95% from February to October.

BANDING. For place of banding of 502 doves recovered in Alabama and place of recovery of 392 birds banded in Alabama, see Map 51. Breakdown follows: *Banded* in Alabama, *recovered* in Alabama, 330; *banded* elsewhere, *recovered* in Alabama, 172; *banded* in Alabama, *recovered* elsewhere, 62; total birds involved, 564. An additional interesting recovery is that of a bird banded on Dauphin Island, October 16, 1959, and shot at Jay, Florida, 75 miles *northeast* on December 9, 1959. This is an example of redirected migration, for the bird was probably blown off course against the coast on its way to its wintering grounds.

[Passenger Pigeon]
Ectopistes migratorius (Linnaeus)   [315]
OTHER NAME: Wild Pigeon

Though the Passenger Pigeon once darkened the sky and was numbered by the millions, it is now extinct. In its day it was much larger than the Mourning Dove, had a longer tail and longer wings, and the head was blue-gray without the black spot behind the eye. The bird was swift and silent in flight.

In Alabama, this species was abundant in winter. It began to disappear about 1880 and was last seen in the fall of 1890 at Greensboro by W. C. Avery. (See Map 50.) The last known individual died in the Cincinnati Zoölogical Garden, September 1, 1914. The Passenger Pigeon nested, roosted, and fed in enormous numbers in the forest. Although it was known to nest in Mississippi and Georgia, no Alabama nesting has been reported.

NESTING. The nest was a flimsy affair consisting of a few sticks placed in a crotch of a tree. The birds nested in very large colonies, sometimes as many as fifty in one tree. The female laid one or two pure white eggs.

FOOD. Mast, especially that of oak, chestnut, beech, pine, and hemlock, was the principal food of this pigeon. It also consumed a great variety of seeds, grains, and wild berries. It varied this assortment with caterpillars, grasshoppers, other insects, worms, snails, and occasionally tender green shoots.

DISTRIBUTION. The Passenger Pigeon bred formerly from Montana, southern Quebec, and Nova Scotia south to Kansas, Oklahoma, Mississippi, and Georgia. It wintered mainly from Arkansas, Tennessee, and North Carolina to the northern Gulf Coast. It was accidental or casual north to Baffin Bay, west to British Columbia, south to southern Mexico and Cuba, and east to Bermuda, and was recorded at least once each in Scotland, Ireland, and France.

OCCURRENCE IN ALABAMA. (Probably winter resident throughout, the only dated records being in late October and early November; see below.) *Colbert County*, McCormack says that the last great flight there was in "immense flocks of thousands and millions. Since that year (1881) I have not seen a pigeon." (Leighton News, Vol. 2, No. 10, May 15, 1891). A large flock was reported to McCormack by Robert Karsner at Bush Pond on October 27, 1889. *Greens-boro*, a single bird was shot in the winter of 1887, and Dr. Avery saw a flock of about 200 the first week in November 1890. *Upper Choctawhatchee River*, Henry Co., B. O. Peterson of Abbeville claims to have seen a small flock there in the fall of 1909. This record is not accepted generally, but Arthur Howell seems to accept it (A. H. Howell, 1924:123). I have no way of judging it, but list it in the hope that someday supporting evidence may be produced.

Ground Dove
Columbigallina passerina (Linnaeus) [320] (Plate 22, facing page 320)
OTHER NAME: Mourning Dove

This *sparrow-sized,* grayish dove has much *reddish-brown* in its rounded wings and a *stubby black tail.* It walks with this tail upright, bobbing its head as it steps. The legs are red and the reddish bill is tipped with black. Its moaning,

NEST OF GROUND DOVE IN PINE TREE. This small dove also nests on the ground.

F. S. Barkalow, Jr.

oft-repeated call has earned it the name of "Mourning Dove" in much of the Alabama Coastal Plain area.

The Ground Dove is a common, but irregular and local, breeding, permanent resident on the Coastal Plain. Farther north in Alabama it is rare. (See Map 52.) It frequents sandy areas such as roadsides, farms, dooryards, and even sheltered beaches. This bird spends a great deal of its time on the ground, and is trustful, flushes closely, and is rarely molested by man.

NESTING. The nest is a frail, loose structure of weeds and some sticks usually built low in a tree or on the ground in low cover. Occasionally this dove will choose to build on top of an old nest abandoned by a bird of another species. Accumulated droppings in the flimsy nest give it added strength as the young mature. Two white or creamy-white eggs make a clutch.

FOOD. The Ground Dove feeds on berries and the seeds of weeds and grasses. Two birds collected in Alabama contained seeds of privet and wood sorrel.

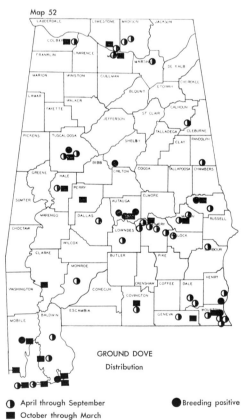

Map 52

GROUND DOVE
Distribution

◑ April through September   ● Breeding positive
■ October through March

DISTRIBUTION. This species is resident from southeastern California, southern Arizona, Texas, Alabama, and South Carolina south to Ecuador and Brazil. It occasionally ranges north in the Mississippi Valley to Iowa and on the Atlantic Coast to New York.

OCCURRENCE IN ALABAMA. (Throughout the year.) *Tennessee Valley*: May 5, 1953 (Wheeler Refuge, L. S. Givens) and September 23 (1950, trapped and banded, D. C. Hulse) to January 17 (1951, 2 birds, D. C. Hulse); specimen in the Wheeler Refuge collection, October 22, 1954 (Priceville, D. C. Hulse). Leighton, 2 specimens by F. W. McCormack, February 24, 1921 and May 4, 1889. Marshall Co., mid-May 1955 (Redstone Arsenal, E. C. Mahan) and first week in June 1955 (Grant, E. C. Mahan). *Mountain Region*: June 5, 1954 (Choccolocco, Calhoun Co., 3 birds, T. A. Imhof and H. M. Stevenson), and said by Joe Cobb of Choccolocco and Birmingham to have been present for three years. Wilton, Shelby Co., very close to the Fall Line, July 20, specimen, and August 17, 1936 (W. A. Rosene and H. S. Peters). *Piedmont*: June 24, 1939 (Roanoke, Randolph Co., H. M. Stevenson). Lee Co., uncommon permanent resident (H. G. Good, F.

W. Fitch, H. S. Peters, and others). *Upper Coastal Plain*: Permanent resident; most seen, 6, November 12, 1923 (Booth, Autauga Co., L. S. Golsan). *Lower Coastal Plain*: Permanent resident. *Gulf Coast*: Permanent resident; most seen, 25, November 1, 1958 (Fall Count, Mobile Bay Area); a flight through this area, mostly in October and November, indicates that part of the population, probably young of the year, is migratory.

TIME OF BREEDING. Data on 10 nestings: Well-developed eggs in ovary, July 20 and September 23; eggs, May 1 to September 22; dependent young, June 8 to at least July.

ORDER PSITTACIFORMES: LORIES, PARROTS, PARAKEETS, AND MACAWS

FAMILY PSITTACIDAE: LORIES, PARROTS, AND MACAWS

SUBFAMILY PSITTACINAE: PARROTS AND MACAWS

[Carolina Parakeet]
Conuropsis carolinensis (Linnaeus)   [382]
OTHER NAMES: Carolina Paroquet, Carolina Parrot, Parrot

The Carolina Parakeet is undoubtedly extinct, but it was formerly plentiful. This bird resembled a Mourning Dove in shape and size, even to the long tail. It was bright green with a yellow head which deepened to orange at the base of the bill, and it had a small patch of yellow on its wing.

A few birds of this species have been reported from Florida since 1900, but hope has dimmed as the reports turn out to be escaped exotic parakeets. At one time this species was a permanent resident on the Coastal Plain of Alabama. It was probably common to abundant and undoubtedly bred in the state.

NESTING. No competent ornithologist is known to have examined a nest of the Carolina Parakeet. Some reports say the bird nested in hollow trees, while others contend it built a nest similar to the Mourning Dove in colonies on cypress trees in swamps. The two or three deeply-pitted eggs were white with a faint hint of yellow.

FOOD. The feeding habits of this bird were very destructive, for, though it ate a great variety of wild fruits and seeds, it also ate all kinds of cultivated fruits and grains. Annoyingly, it ate fruit before it was ripe or tore fruit apart to get at the seeds.

Its destructiveness and its habit of keeping in dense flocks contributed in large measure to its downfall. The birds were shot for food, sport, plumage, as game, and as pests. A flock sometimes continued to hover over a fallen comrade until there was opportunity to kill every last bird. Though it is easy to see why this bird disappeared, it is still deplorable that one of our few tropical birds should be so exterminated.

PSITTACIFORMES: PSITTACIDAE: CAROLINA PARAKEET

DISTRIBUTION. The Carolina Parakeet ranged from North Dakota, Iowa, Ohio, and central New York south to central Texas and southern Florida.

OCCURRENCE IN ALABAMA. "Probably disappeared from Alabama prior to 1880," (A. H. Howell, 1924:155). Earlier records are: Several hundred near the Alabama River below Cahaba, January 6, 1826 (Saxe-Weimar); numbers near the Alabama River below Claiborne, January 8, 1826 (Saxe-Weimar); 80 or 100 near Selma about De-cember 20, 1858 (P. H. Gosse). N. C. Brown states that at Coosada in 1878 it was "well known to most of the older local sportsmen and is said once to have been common, though none had been seen for many years." At Greensboro in 1890, W. C. Avery records the bird as "formerly common but not seen for many years."

ORDER CUCULIFORMES: CUCKOOS AND PLANTAIN-EATERS

FAMILY CUCULIDAE: CUCKOOS, ROADRUNNERS, AND ANIS

SUBFAMILY PHAENICOPHAEINAE: NONPARASITIC CUCKOOS

These long-tailed birds have two toes directed forward and two directed to the rear. Unlike their relatives in the Eastern Hemisphere, they build their own nests. The eggs are laid at rather long intervals, so that eggs and young of various ages may be found in one nest at the same time.

Yellow-billed Cuckoo

Coccyzus americanus (Linnaeus)   [387]   (Plate 22, facing page 320)
OTHER NAME: Rain Crow

This cuckoo is a long slender, furtive bird about the size of a Mourning Dove. It is immaculately white below and dark brown above, with *reddish-brown in the wings*. There are *large white spots* on the *under side* of its *very long tail*, and the *lower mandible* is *yellow* while the upper is black. The song is a rapid series of about fifteen notes which gradually slows at the end, and the call is a single deep, prolonged note. It and the Black-billed Cuckoo are said to call more often just before it rains; hence, they are commonly called "Rain Crows."

The Yellow-billed Cuckoo is a common, breeding, summer resident and a common transient throughout Alabama. It frequents hardwoods, preferring the leafier middle stories, and often occurs in the shade trees of towns. It is generally motionless when perched, so that it may be undetected unless it calls or flies.

NESTING. The nest is a very flat, loosely-built platform of twigs, grass, leaves, and sometimes *Usnea* moss. It is usually placed less than twenty feet from the ground on a horizontal limb in a thick part of a hardwood, often a hawthorn. On rare occasions the bird nests in a pine. It lays two to four pale greenish-blue eggs.

FOOD. A great destroyer of caterpillars, this bird eats even the hairy kind disdained by most other birds. The stomach becomes so felted with caterpillar hairs that the bird often sheds the lining and grows a new one. It also eats large quantities of beetles, bugs, locusts, grasshoppers, ants, wasps, flies, dragonflies, crickets, and even small treefrogs. Occasionally it eats the eggs of other birds, and often it eats small fruits such as raspberries, blackberries, mulberries, and wild grapes.

DISTRIBUTION. The Yellow-billed Cuckoo breeds from British Columbia and Quebec south to Mexico, the Greater Antilles, and the Virgin Islands. It migrates through Central America to winter in northern South America and south to Argentina. It is accidental in many places in western Europe.

OCCURRENCE IN ALABAMA. (March 28 to November 8.) *Tennessee Valley*: May 3 (1957, Wheeler Refuge, T. A. Imhof) to October 18 (1959, Huntsville, J. C. and Margaret Robinson); most seen, 12, May 22, 1959 (Decatur, D. C. Hulse and others). *Mountain Region*: April 9 (1947, Birmingham, T. A. Imhof) to October 19 (1954, Birmingham, Idalene Snead and Emmy Brownlie); most seen, spring, 28, May 30, 1949 (Warrior River, Tuscaloosa Co., T. A. Imhof and others), fall, 25+, August 23, 1948 (Fairfield, T. A. Imhof). *Piedmont*: April 12 (1926, Auburn, W. A. Ruffin) to September 30 (1936, specimen, Auburn, F. S. Barkalow). *Upper Coastal Plain*: April 13 (1960, Montgomery, R. W. Skinner) to October 22 (1959, Livingston, Jenkins Jackson); most seen, 17, July 13, 1957 (Greene Co., and Sumter Co., T. A. Imhof and others). *Lower Coastal Plain*: April 15 (1957, Jackson, W. U. Harris) to November 1 (1957, Jackson, T. A. Imhof and W. U. Harris); most seen, 30, April 18, 1958 (Jackson, T. A. Imhof, W. U. Harris, and J. R. Davis). *Gulf Coast*: March 28 (1942, Spring Hill, J. L. Dorn) to November 8 (1959, Dauphin Island, T. A. Imhof and F. B. Daniel); most seen, spring, 38, April 26, 1958 (Spring Count, Mobile Bay Area), fall, 28, October 19, 1957 (Fall Count, Mobile Bay Area) and 12, November 1, 1958 (Fall Count, Mobile Bay Area).

TIME OF BREEDING. Data on 23 nestings: Eggs, May 2 to August 14; dependent young, May 16 to at least July 13.

Black-billed Cuckoo

Coccyzus erythropthalmus (Wilson)   [388]   (Plate 22, facing page 320)
OTHER NAME: Rain Crow

Although its resemblance to the Yellow-billed Cuckoo is close, this bird may be distinguished, in good light, by its *black lower mandible*, *lack* of *rufous* on the *wings*, the *narrow white bars* on the *under side* of the *tail*, and its red eye ring. Its song is rhythmic, with the notes grouped in threes, fours, or fives, and not slowing toward the end, but otherwise it is like that of the Yellow-billed Cuckoo.

In Alabama, this cuckoo is uncommon on migration and usually occurs a little later in the season than the Yellow-billed Cuckoo. It bred one year in Jefferson County, and possibly it breeds rarely elsewhere in the Mountain Region. It frequents the same places, and is probably even more often overlooked because it is customarily silent.

NESTING. The nest differs from that of the Yellow-billed Cuckoo only in that it is a more substantial structure and is usually placed lower in the tree. The eggs appear to be the same in color and size.

FOOD. This cuckoo eats substantially the same food as the Yellow-billed Cuckoo. Any slight difference is caused by the bird's more northern range.

DISTRIBUTION. The Black-billed Cuckoo breeds from southern Saskatchewan, southern Quebec, and Nova Scotia south to Wyoming, northwestern Arkansas, Tennessee, northern Alabama, and northern South Carolina, and possibly in Alberta, Idaho, and Colorado. It winters from Colombia to Peru, is casual on migration in the West Indies, and is accidental in several countries of western Europe.

OCCURRENCE IN ALABAMA. (Normal: April 18 to June 7 and August 2 to November 2; Out-of-season: November 17.) *Tennessee Valley*: April 18 (1914, specimen in the U. S. National Museum, Scottsboro, *fide* A. H. Howell) to May 24 (1951, Wheeler Refuge, D. C. Hulse) and August 2 (1951, Wheeler Refuge, D. C. Hulse) to October 24 (1935, Wheeler Dam, J. Bamberg). *Mountain Region*: April 26 (1953, Cheaha, H. G. Good) to June 7 (1957, Higdon, Jackson Co., T. A. Imhof and 1959, Dismals, Winston Co., Blanche Chapman) and August 31 (1932, Birmingham, H. M. Stevenson) to October 10 (1953, Birmingham, T. A. Imhof). *Piedmont*: April 27, 1940 (Auburn, H. G. Good); May 2, 1923 (Auburn, J. M. Robertson); and September 15, 1936 (specimen, Auburn, H. G. Good). *Upper Coastal Plain*: April 20 (1927, Autaugaville, L. S. Golsan) to May 25 (1939, Tuscaloosa, H. M. Stevenson) and September 17 (1938, Tuscaloosa, H. M. Stevenson) to October 25 (1894, specimen, Autaugaville, L. S. Golsan); most seen, 4, May 15, 1955 (Marion, Lois McCollough). *Lower Coastal Plain*: No record. *Gulf Coast*: April 20 (1942, Spring Hill, J. L. Dorn) to May 15 (1960, Delchamps, J. L. Dorn) and September 13 (1959, Dauphin Island, H. A. J. and Cora Evans) to November 2 (1958, specimen in the Dept. of Conservation collection, Dauphin Island, R. W. Skinner and Lovett Williams); also November 17, 1959 (1 netted and banded, Hurricane, D. D. Stamm).

TIME OF BREEDING. Data on 2 Jefferson Co. 1961 nestings: Building, May 8 to 23; eggs, May 23 (C. W. Summerour).

ORDER STRIGIFORMES: OWLS

Well-marked and easily-recognized, these nocturnal birds of prey have eyes that are directed forward and enclosed in a facial disk. Their flight is noiseless because of a fringe of flexible barbs on the trailing edge of the flight feathers. Their bills are strongly hooked, and the feet and often the toes are feathered, the claws, sharp, and the fourth toe is reversible. These birds usually nest very early and are apt to use the nests of other animals. In flight, owls look like big-headed giant moths.

FAMILY TYTONIDAE: BARN OWLS

SUBFAMILY TYTONINAE: BARN OWLS

Barn Owl

Tyto alba (Scopoli) [365] (Plate 21, facing page 304)
OTHER NAMES: Monkey-faced Owl, White Owl, Hoot Owl

This easily-recognized owl has a *heart-shaped face, white* or *buffy under parts,* and reddish-brown to buffy upper parts. It is finely but thinly spotted above and below with dark brown. On its middle toe this owl has a comb-like process. This bird has long legs and usually sits upright. Its calls, often heard while it hunts at night, consist of a variety of hissing, snoring, and screaming notes, of which the drawn-out hiss seems to be most helpful in identification.

The Barn Owl is an uncommon to fairly common, breeding, permanent resident throughout most of Alabama. In winter it often becomes common, particularly in the Black Belt and on the Gulf Coast. Many times after a diligent search, this species is discovered where its presence has been entirely unsuspected. It is strictly nocturnal, and commonly passes the day in the top of a deserted structure—a barn, cupola, church steeple, or perhaps in a hollow tree. At night, it hunts over open areas such as meadows, farmlands, city dumps, or wherever rodents are abundant.

NESTING. This owl usually lays its three to seven or more chalky-white eggs at irregular intervals so that eggs and young of various ages may be in one nest simultaneously. The nest is almost always in some sort of cavity, often in a building or a hollow tree. The owl seldom brings in nesting material,

[303]

[304]

Richard A. Parks

YOUNG BARN OWLS. These owls nest in a variety of places, including man-made structures.

but disgorges pellets to form a bed for the eggs. Nest boxes are best placed twelve to eighteen feet high on a barn and should be at least ten by eighteen inches and eighteen inches high. The entrance hole should be six inches in diameter four inches above the floor. Larger boxes also attract this owl.

FOOD. The highly beneficial Barn Owl is a prodigious eater of rodents, and is known to eat its weight in injurious mice and rats in one night. Gophers, shrews, ground squirrels, and other small animals are included in its diet, and occasionally it takes a grass-dwelling bird, a large insect, or even a frog. It is not known to prey on poultry, and it lives amicably close to domestic pigeons. Like most owls, it swallows its food whole or in large chunks, and the indigestible bones and hair are disgorged in the form of round pellets. An examination of these bones gives us an accurate picture of the food habits of this bird, for nearly all mammals can be identified by their skulls alone. A study of 190 such skulls taken from Barn Owl pellets at Auburn revealed a high proportion of cotton rats and least shrews. (Dusi, 1957, *Alabama Birdlife* 5:7-8).

DISTRIBUTION. This owl occupies nearly all the tropical and temperate parts of the world. In North America, it is resident from British Columbia, the

[305]

southern parts of our most northern states, and southern New England (casually farther north), south to southern Argentina. Some northern birds, probably mostly immatures, retire southward in winter. (See Banding, below.)

TIME OF BREEDING. Data on 5+ nestings: Eggs, April 1; dependent young, January 8 to May 13.

BANDING. Six birds banded in summer in the north (see Map 53) have been recovered in Alabama during the period November 20 to February 27, at Hamilton, Sylacauga, Columbiana, Opp, Theodore, and Foley. A seventh, banded in December at Montgomery, was recovered nearby in April.

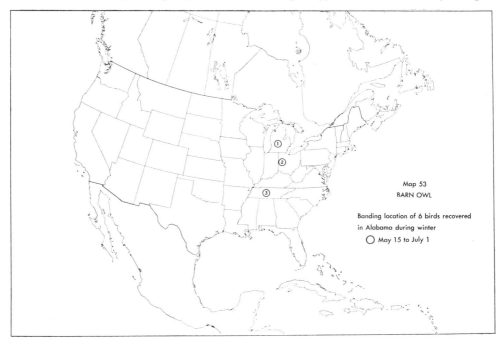

Map 53
BARN OWL

Banding location of 6 birds recovered in Alabama during winter
◯ May 15 to July 1

FAMILY STRIGIDAE: TYPICAL OWLS

Most of these owls have eartufts, short legs, and streaked plumage. They otherwise closely resemble the Barn Owls, but the middle toenail lacks the comb-like process of the Barn Owls.

Screech Owl
Otus asio (Linnaeus) [373] (Plate 21, facing page 304)
OTHER NAMES: Squinch Owl, Death Owl, Red Owl, Kitty Owl

The Screech Owl is a *small, chunky* owl with *eartufts*. This species, streaked above and below, normally has two color phases. One phase is gray, and the other a bright reddish-brown, the latter being by far the more common in Alabama. The call of the Screech Owl is a quivering, mourning whistle that can be easily imitated.

This bird is a common and widespread, breeding, permanent resident in Alabama. It often occurs around houses and farms, particularly in orchards and more open hardwoods. Although strictly nocturnal, the bird is occasionally seen during the day sitting in a nest box or tree hole, or perched on a limb closely pressed to the trunk with its eartufts raised so that it resembles a part of the tree.

NESTING. The nest is in a tree cavity, often a gnarled old tree, or in a nest box. For this owl the nest box should be eight by eight by fifteen inches high, and should have an entrance three inches in diameter about a foot above the floor. It is best placed ten to thirty feet above ground in an orchard or clump of trees. The Screech Owl rarely uses nest material for the three to seven pure white eggs.

FOOD. This owl has a diet that includes mice, rats, shrews, chipmunks, squirrels, bats, large beetles, grasshoppers, crickets, locusts, moths, caterpillars, and other insects. It also obtains an astonishing variety of birds including those bigger than itself, and a variety of reptiles, amphibians, crawfish, spiders, snails, and fish. Insects, mice, and birds, in that order, form the bulk of its diet.

DISTRIBUTION. The Screech Owl is resident from southeastern Alaska, British Columbia, southern Manitoba, and southern Quebec south to Lower California, central Mexico, and Florida.

TIME OF BREEDING. Data on 15 nestings: Eggs, March 28 to May 31; dependent young, April 24 to October 15.

BANDING. A single tame young Screech Owl, banded at Fairhope, was seen and band examined frequently from July 1930 to July 1931.

Great Horned Owl
Bubo virginianus (Gmelin)   [375]   (Plate 21, facing page 304)

The Great Horned Owl, *larger* and *heavier* than a *Red-tailed Hawk,* has *prominent eartufts* and a *white collar.* It is brown above, and below it is heavily streaked crosswise with dark brown. It has a deep hooting voice and usually doubles or trebles its notes.

This big owl is widespread in woodlands throughout the year in Alabama. It often occupies the top of a clump of tall pines, usually in the wilder, more rugged wooded areas of the state, and in Alabama the Great Horned Owl nests very early.

NESTING. This bird ordinarily appropriates the stick nest of some other large bird, especially the Red-tailed or Red-shouldered Hawk. It sometimes remodels or cleans out some of the debris before it lays its one or two white eggs. The typical Alabama nest is found fairly high in a pine or some other evergreen. One nest in the state was known to be used later in the season by an Osprey.

FOOD. This owl feeds chiefly on medium-sized mammals. Rabbits are the most frequent meal, but it also eats mice, rats, skunks, opossums, and others, and has even been known to attack porcupines and domestic cats and dogs. It has an extensive appetite for birds, including domestic poultry, game birds, and even hawks and other owls. Besides all of these, it manages to eat snakes, frogs, fish, and large insects. Wherever domestic or game birds are readily available, this owl does considerable damage, but it eats whatever is easiest to obtain, and this is most often rodents.

DISTRIBUTION. The Great Horned Owl breeds from near the tree limit in Alaska and Labrador south to the southern tip of South America. Northern birds move a bit southward in winter.

TIME OF BREEDING. Data on 15 nestings: Eggs, January 18 to March 7; young in nest, January 23 to April 15; young out of nest by March 7.

Burrowing Owl
Speotyto cunicularia (Molina)   [378]   (Plate 21, facing page 304)

The Burrowing Owl and the Screech Owl are about the same size—both small. This species is easy to recognize because it *lacks eartufts,* and has *long legs* and a *short tail.* It is a grayish-brown above, barred crosswise below, and has a pale facial disk. Its call resembles the whistle of a small locomotive.

The Burrowing Owl is a ground owl which frequents prairies, deserts, and other open areas and is falsely reputed to live in harmony with rattlesnakes and prairie dogs. It is active in the daytime, and in Alabama is apt to occur on beaches and other open or sandy areas around piles of driftwood and other debris. It is rare in fall and winter on the coast and is not known to nest in this state.

NESTING AND FOOD. This owl appropriates a hole deserted by some other animal—a prairie dog, badger, armadillo, or fox, for example—and enlarges it if necessary to suit its nesting needs. A variety of dead or decaying materials, often cow or horse dung, is used for the lining and the nest chamber. The six to eleven white eggs are usually heavily stained. This bird feeds on large numbers of injurious insects and rodents, and will eat its full weight in one day if that much food is obtainable. It takes an occasional snake, lizard, frog, fish, small bird, scorpion, or crawfish.

DISTRIBUTION. The Burrowing Owl breeds from British Columbia, Manitoba, and Minnesota east to Iowa and Louisiana and south locally to the southern tip of South America. It also breeds in the Bahamas, Florida, and the West Indies. It winters north to California, Arizona, and central Texas, and eastward along the northern Gulf Coast to Florida.

OCCURRENCE IN ALABAMA. *Gulf Coast only*: October 19 (1957, Dauphin Island, S. A. Gauthreaux) to February 24 (1956, Fort Morgan, J. L. Dorn and others); most seen, 2, November 5 to December 31, 1959 (Dauphin Island, T. A. Imhof and many others); specimen, in U. S. National Museum, February 3, 1912 (Blakely Island, A. H. Howell).

Barred Owl

Strix varia Barton   [368]   (Plate 21, facing page 304)
OTHER NAMES: Hoot Owl, Swamp Owl

This large grayish owl *lacks eartufts* and is *barred crosswise* on the *head* and *neck* and *lengthwise* on the *belly*. This and the Barn Owl are the only owls in Alabama that have *brown eyes.* All others have yellow eyes. The Barred Owl hoots frequently, and in groups as large as four or more they gather in the bottomlands and hoot back and forth as if they were holding a conference. The hooting then becomes quite varied and very expressive. The usual call is eight hoots given in couplets.

Perhaps our most common owl, this is a common and widespread, breeding, permanent resident throughout Alabama. Its favorite haunts are swamps, bottomlands, hammocks, and lake borders, but it occurs as well in most wooded areas in the state. It is not as nocturnal as the Screech Owl, for it often hoots or flies about in the late afternoon or on cloudy days.

NESTING. Most of the time the Barred Owl nests in a natural tree cavity, often appropriating an old hawk or squirrel nest, and in Alabama rarely if ever building its own. It usually lays one or two white eggs which are sometimes destroyed by flooding from heavy rains when the bird has selected an open-topped cavity.

FOOD. The Barred Owl depends on what is locally available for its food. It usually eats a large variety of mammals, especially ground-dwelling

[309]

EGGS OF BARRED OWL IN OPEN-TOP TREE CAVITY.

YOUNG BARRED OWLS.

rodents. It also takes large insects, small birds, rarely domestic poultry, occasionally other owls, frogs, snakes, crawfish, and other cold-blooded animals.

DISTRIBUTION. The Barred Owl is resident east of the Rocky Mountains from British Columbia, Quebec, and Nova Scotia south to Texas and southern Florida and in mountains to Honduras.

TIME OF BREEDING. Data on 14 nestings: Eggs, February 14 to March 27; dependent young, March 25 to May 30.

BANDING. A Barred Owl banded by C. N. Hinderer at Montgomery, October 21, 1932 was killed by a train near the same place, December 17, 1938.

Long-eared Owl
Asio otus (Linnaeus)   [366]   (Plate 21, facing page 304)

This *crow-sized owl* looks like a miniature Great Horned Owl. It differs only because it lacks the white collar, has proportionately *longer eartufts* set *closer together,* is striped lengthwise on the belly, and is smaller. This bird is quite slender and is frequently difficult to detect when it stretches itself out close to a tree trunk. It has a variety of calls of which the most useful in identification are probably a hoot, which is drawn-out and quavering like the Screech Owl's, and several cat-like mewing notes.

The Long-eared Owl is rare and irregular in winter in the northern half of Alabama. It has been recorded only twice on the coast and it does not nest anywhere in the state. In winter it usually flocks in dense cover, preferably pines and other evergreens. In regions with snow and few evergreens, the species is easily spotted by searching for pellets on the snow in evergreen thickets. But in Alabama, where there is little or no snow and the pine thickets are innumerable, this owl is difficult to find, and actual records of its occurrence are few.

NESTING AND FOOD. Occasionally this owl builds its own nest, but usually it appropriates a nest abandoned by a hawk, crow, magpie, or squirrel. It sometimes occupies a tree cavity or even builds on the ground, but most often the nest is found in an evergreen. There are three to eight white eggs. A very large proportion of this owl's food consists of injurious mammals, particularly mice and shrews. Besides other mammals, the remainder of its diet includes small birds (taken mainly when the owl is feeding young), large insects (especially beetles), frogs, and snakes.

DISTRIBUTION. In North America, the Long-eared Owl breeds from British Columbia, Mackenzie, southern Quebec, and Nova Scotia south to Lower

California, Oklahoma, Arkansas, and Virginia. It winters from British Columbia and southern Ontario south to northern Mexico, the Gulf states, and Florida.

OCCURRENCE IN ALABAMA. (November 1 to March 3.) *Tennessee Valley*: February 4, 1891 (specimen, Leighton, F. W. McCormack). *Mountain Region*: No record, *Piedmont*: No record. *Upper Coastal Plain*: Greensboro, 5 birds shot between December 27 (1893) and March 3 (1894), 1 specimen in the Avery collection (December 27, 1893, W. C. Avery); most seen, 8 or 10 in an Osage-orange hedge, December 27, 1893; De-cember 12, 1909 and January 4, 1911 (Bear Swamp, Autauga Co., L. S. Golsan); December 27, 1957 (Marion, Lois McCollough and Clustie McTyeire). *Lower Coastal Plain*: No record. *Gulf Coast*: November 1, 1958 (specimen in La. State Univ. collection, Little Dauphin Island, S. M. Russell and others) and December 30, 1960 (Dauphin Island, Clustie McTyeire and Larry Rosen).

Short-eared Owl
Asio flammeus (Pontoppidan)   [367]   (Plate 21, facing page 304)

This owl is slightly larger than the Long-eared Owl, and is a *buffy-brown* color, rather *heavily streaked* on the *chest*. Its eartufts are so small that they are seldom seen. In flight, as seen from below, the bird shows a *long, rounded, buffy wing*, with a *large dark spot* on the *bend*. The Short-eared Owl, like the Barn Owl, hunts over meadows at night, but the wing markings and streaked under parts readily distinguish this species. Occasionally this owl calls like a barking dog.

The Short-eared Owl frequents marshes and meadows and is often abroad in daylight. Generally it flushes from the ground, especially from tall grass, and with an erratic, moth-like flight it moves to another part of the marsh or meadow. At dawn and dusk it quarters over open areas, taking up during the dark hours the patrolling duties the Marsh Hawk practices during daylight. In Alabama, this owl is uncommon in winter in the Tennessee Valley and Black Belt, and is rare and irregular in winter in the remainder of the state. It often occurs in flocks, but it does not breed here.

NESTING AND FOOD. This owl builds a platform of dried grasses and sometimes feathers on the ground in marshes or meadows, particularly in tall grass. The female usually lays five to seven white eggs. The Short-eared Owl subsists chiefly on harmful rodents such as meadow mice, house mice, and cotton rats. When rodent fare is scarce, it eats small grass-dwelling birds and injurious insects, particularly grasshoppers, May beetles, and cutworms.

DISTRIBUTION. In North America, the Short-eared Owl breeds irregularly and locally from northern Alaska and Baffin Island south to southern California, Colorado, southern Illinois, and coastal Virginia. It winters from southern

British Columbia, Minnesota, southern Ontario, and Massachusetts south to Lower California, central Mexico, and Florida, and casually to Guatemala and Cuba.

OCCURRENCE IN ALABAMA. (September 20 to May 15.) *Tennessee Valley*: September 26 (1950, Wheeler Refuge, T. A. Imhof) to May 15 (Wheeler Refuge, *fide* T. Z. Atkeson, Jr.); specimen, November 19, 1891 (Leighton, F. W. McCormack). *Mountain Region*: January 10, 1958 (West Blocton, Bibb Co., Lois McCollough); April 1, 1953 (Gadsden, Edith Clark); and specimen shot in winter, date and year unknown (Birmingham, C. L. Christy). *Piedmont*: No record. *Upper Coastal Plain*: September 20 (1960, Autauga Co., J. E. Keeler) to at least February 14 (1937, specimen in Auburn Wildlife collection, Selma, E. F. Kennamer); most seen, 8, January 15, 1960 (Montgomery, R. W. Skinner and J. E. Keeler). *Lower Coastal Plain*: December 1939 (1 shot, Columbia, Henry Co., T. Z. Atkeson, Jr.). *Gulf Coast*: November 19, 1941 (Cedar Point, J. L. Dorn).

Saw-Whet Owl

Aegolius acadicus (Gmelin)   [372]

This, the smallest owl occurring in Alabama, can be readily distinguished by its *size* and its *lack of ear tufts*. The adult is brown above, white below, with broad brown stripes, and it has prominent whitish marks above and below the eyes. The immature bird is an even chocolate brown above and below, and it has prominent wide white stripes above the eyes. The distinctive call notes are said to sound like the filing of a saw; hence the name.

Strictly nocturnal, the Saw-whet Owl frequents dense woodlands, especially low, damp woods with evergreen thickets; in settled areas it seems to be partial to Japanese honeysuckle. It spends the day roosting in dense thickets or in cavities, and thus it often goes unnoticed; however, when it is discovered it is so ridiculously tame that it allows close approach and sometimes capture. In Alabama it has been recorded but once—in November.

Nesting and food. This little northern owl nests in natural cavities, particularly abandoned woodpecker holes, where it lays 5 or 6 white eggs. It subsists on small mammals, chiefly mice.

Distribution. The Saw-whet Owle breeds from southern Alaska, northern Ontario, and Nova Scotia south to southern California, Oklahoma, and Maryland, and in mountains to central Mexico and Tennessee. It winters as far north as it breeds, but at lower elevations in the west, and south, sporadically, to Louisiana and Florida.

OCCURRENCE IN ALABAMA. *Tennessee Valley only*: Brownsboro, Madison Co., November 10, 1961, an adult netted, banded, and photographed in color (J. C. and Margaret Robinson).

ORDER CAPRIMULGIFORMES: GOATSUCKERS, OILBIRDS, AND ALLIES

FAMILY CAPRIMULGIDAE: GOATSUCKERS

These grayish or brownish nocturnal birds have large eyes, a very large mouth, and long wings. Their bills and feet are weak. They often feed over pastures at dusk, and it was once thought that they drank goat's milk.

SUBFAMILY CAPRIMULGINAE: GOATSUCKERS

These brownish woodland birds are more strictly nocturnal.

Chuck-will's-widow
Caprimulgus carolinensis Gmelin   [416]   (Plate 22, facing page 320)
OTHER NAMES: Whip-poor-will, Dutch Whip-poor-will, Chuck

The Chuck-will's-widow is a fairly *large*, reddish-brown bird streaked with black. It is the largest of our three goatsuckers, nearly twice the size of the Whip-poor-will. The male has white on the inner webs of the outer tail feathers and a narrow white line below the *buffy throat*. The female shows pale buff where the male is white. When flushed from the ground in the woods, this bird can usually be identified as the Chuck-will's-widow by its large size and, if a front view is obtained, by its buffy throat. But the species can best be recognized by its voice. The song is a loud, slow, vigorous whistle, which sounds like its name. For calls it utters a low, emphatic, chucking and various growling, often frog-like notes.

This goatsucker is common in woodlands in summer and breeds throughout the state, even in the breeding range of the Whip-poor-will. It seems to prefer woodlands that contain both oaks and pines, and in hilly country occurs along branches in bottoms and thickets. It spends the day on the ground, on a fence post, or perched lengthwise on a limb.

NESTING. The two mottled, rich creamy to pale creamy eggs are laid on dead leaves on the ground in partially-shaded woods, usually in an opening or near an old road. The sitting parent is well camouflaged, but when flushed it often acts as if injured in order to lure the enemy from the nest.

FOOD. Feeding almost entirely on night-flying insects, this goatsucker takes May beetles, scarabs, other beetles, moths, dragonflies, grasshoppers, mosquitoes, flying ants, bugs, and the like. On rare occasions it swallows, apparently by accident, a small bird, usually a hummingbird or warbler.

DISTRIBUTION. The Chuck-will's-widow breeds from Kansas, the Ohio Valley, and southern New Jersey south to central Texas and southern Florida, and occurs casually north to southeastern Canada. It winters from Guatemala and the Bahamas and occasionally the northern Gulf Coast, south to Colombia.

OCCURRENCE IN ALABAMA. (Normal: March 27 to October 7; Out-of-season: December 27 and January 2.) *Tennessee Valley*: April 9 (1947, Russellville, E. O. Willis) to August 28 (1948, Russellville, E. O. Willis). *Mountain Region*: April 6 (1955, Birmingham, Mims Williamson) to September 3 (1955, Birmingham, Harriett Wright). *Piedmont*: March 27 (1955, Auburn, H. G. Good) to at least June (several observers). *Upper Coastal Plain*: March 31 (1935, Booth, Autauga Co., L. S. Golsan) to September 3 (1879, specimen in Avery collection, Greensboro, W. C. Avery). *Lower Coastal Plain*: April 3 (1960, Old Texas, Monroe Co., R. W. Skinner) to at least June. *Gulf Coast*: March 27 (1960, Spring Hill, J. L. Dorn) to October 7 (1956, specimen in Fla. State Univ. collection, Dauphin Island, Lovett Williams); also December 27, 1958 (Little Dauphin Island, T. A. Imhof) and January 2, 1960 (Dauphin Island, Ava Tabor and D. C. Holliman).

TIME OF BREEDING. Data on 17 nestings: Eggs, April 13 to June 19; dependent young, June 17 to 26.

EGGS OF CHUCK-WILL'S-WIDOW. The species lays its eggs on a carpet of leaves on the ground.

C. W. Summerour

Whip-poor-will
Caprimulgus vociferus Wilson   [417]   (Plate 22, facing page 320)

The Whip-poor-will is a smaller, more northern goatsucker about the size of the Common Nighthawk. The white on the male Whip-poor-will is more prominent than that found on the Chuck-will's-widow, for this species has white outer tail feathers and a wider white band below its *throat*, which is *black*. The white of the male is replaced by a buff color in the female. At rest, the wings of this species fall far short of the tail, whereas the Common Nighthawk's wings extend to the tip of the tail or even slightly beyond. Voice is the best means of distinguishing this bird. Its song, which is imitated by its name, is loud, emphatic, and rapidly-repeated, often in such a long series that one wonders if the bird will give out of breath. The call sounds like that of a Hermit Thrush but is much more powerful.

In Alabama, this bird occurs, like the Chuck-will's-widow, in woodlands of oak and pine, and along branches in the bottoms and thickets of hilly country. It is common in summer in the northern mountains of Alabama, generally above 1,000 feet but sometimes in nearby valleys down to 600 feet. Although only two definite breeding records are known from the state, the species undoubtedly breeds in June wherever it occurs. (See Map 54.) It is common to fairly common in winter in sandy areas on the Gulf Coast and rare to uncommon on migration in the rest of the state. In Alabama, the closest approach of the winter range to the summer range is only 220 miles.

NESTING. The two white eggs, marked and spotted with gray and brown, are laid on dead leaves on the ground in fairly open, unevenly-shaded places in the woods.

FOOD. This goatsucker feeds almost entirely on insects, of which it takes a great variety. Common fare are moths, mosquitoes, caddis flies, and other flying insects; it also eats grasshoppers, locusts, crickets, ants, and beetles obtained from the ground or under decaying bark.

DISTRIBUTION. The Whip-poor-will breeds from Saskatchewan, southern Quebec, and Nova Scotia south to central Mexico, Texas, the northern parts of the Gulf states, and coastal Virginia. It winters from northern Mexico, Texas, the southern parts of the Gulf states, and coastal South Carolina, rarely coastal North Carolina, south to El Salvador and Honduras, casually Costa Rica and Cuba.

OCCURRENCE IN ALABAMA. (Throughout the year.) *Tennessee Valley:* April 11 (1948, Russellville, E. O. Willis) to September 8 (1960, Brownsboro, Madison Co., J. C. and Margaret Robinson); most heard, 24, night of May 16-17, 1959 (Franklin Co., B. B. Coffey). *Mountain Region:* March 22 (1911, Sand Mountain, Jackson Co., E. W. Graves) to September 30 (1933, Birmingham, H. M. Stevenson); most heard, 13, June 5, 1960 (Fort McClellan, T. A. Imhof and John Beck). *Piedmont:* March 27 (1936, Auburn, H. S. Peters) to April 23 (1940, Auburn, H. G. Good); no fall dates. *Upper Coastal Plain:* March 29 (1909 and 1914, Barachias, E. G. Holt) to May 5 (1913, Autauga Co., L. S. Golsan) and August 25 (1934, Booth, L. S. Golsan and 1950, Montgomery, C. W. Summerour) to October 30 (1925, Autauga Co., L. S. Golsan). *Lower Coastal Plain:* March 27 (1959, Coffeeville, Clarke Co., J. E. Keeler) to April 16 (1952, Grove Hill, Julia Helms); no fall dates. *Gulf Coast:* September 8 (1932, Fairhope, Homer Flagg) to April 23 (1960, Delchamps, J. L. Dorn); most seen, winter, 3, December 21, 1957 and January 2, 1960 (West Fowl River, T. A. Imhof, J. L. Dorn, and M. W. Gaillard); banded at Hurricane, Baldwin Co., February 3 and 22, 1960 (D. D. Stamm); for other winter records, see Map 54.

TIME OF BREEDING. Data on 2 nestings: Young in nest, June 10, 1943 (Mentone, H. M. Stevenson); female speci-

men with enlarged gonads, June 19, 1959 (Arley, Winston Co., T. A. Imhof).

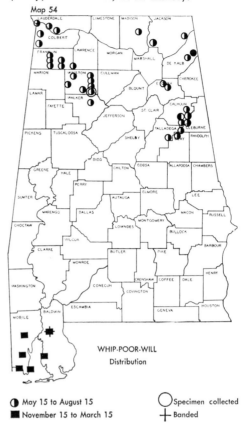

Map 54

WHIP-POOR-WILL

Distribution

◗ May 15 to August 15
■ November 15 to March 15

◯ Specimen collected
✛ Banded

SUBFAMILY CHORDEILINAE: NIGHTHAWKS

Common Nighthawk

Chordeiles minor (Forster)   [420]   (Plate 22, facing page 320)

OTHER NAME: Bullbat

The male Common Nighthawk, a gray goatsucker, has a white throat band, a white bar across the tail, and a *white bar across* the *wings.* The buffier female lacks the white tail bar, shows less white in the wings, and has a buffy throat band. At rest, this bird's *long wings* extend just beyond the tip of the *tail,* which is *forked,* whereas the other two goatsuckers found in Alabama have rounded tails, and their wings fall far short of the tip. In flight, the Common Nighthawk

COMMON NIGHTHAWK INCUBATING. Gravel roofs are frequently selected as nest sites by this species.

frequently utters a nasal sound. During courtship, the male makes a spectacular dive, and as he pulls out of it his wing feathers make a booming sound.

This bird is a common, breeding, summer resident throughout Alabama. In fall it is often abundant on migration. It frequents bare, open areas, particularly those that are gravelly, sandy, or paved. It hunts mostly at night or in the dawn or dusk hours, even flying among the taller buildings in the center of our cities. Although it sometimes hunts in broad daylight, it normally passes the day perched on a gravelly roof or another bare area, or perched lengthwise on the limb of a tree.

NESTING. The one or two pale buff or creamy eggs are heavily marked with brown, black, and gray, and laid in almost any bare area. Frequently this is a flat, gravelly roof or some such ground spot as a sand dune or a recently plowed field.

FOOD. This nighthawk lives almost entirely on injurious insects caught on the wing. These include winged ants (especially carpenter ants), beetles of all kinds, grasshoppers, locusts, mosquitoes, flies, moths, sweat bees, plant lice, leaf chafers, boll weevils, and stoneflies.

[318]

CAPRIMULGIFORMES: CAPRIMULGIDAE: COMMON NIGHTHAWK

DISTRIBUTION. The Common Nighthawk breeds from southern Yukon and central Quebec south to central Mexico, Jamaica, and Puerto Rico. It winters in South America from Colombia and Venezuela south to central Argentina.

OCCURRENCE IN ALABAMA. (April 6 to November 8.) *Tennessee Valley*: April 7 (1960, Huntsville, J. C. and Margaret Robinson) to October 8 (1891, Leighton, F. W. McCormack); most seen, 220, September 6, 1948 (Florence, H. M. Stevenson). *Mountain Region*: April 6 (1955, Birmingham, T. A. Imhof) to November 8 (1958, Gadsden, Edith Clark); most seen, 94, September 13, 1947 (Birmingham, T. A. Imhof). *Piedmont*: April 17 (1960, Mitchell Lake, Harriett Wright) to October 9 (1957, Auburn, J. E. Keeler). *Upper Coastal Plain*: April 17 (1912, Autaugaville, L. S. Golsan) to October 27 (1954, Marion, Lois McCollough); most seen, spring, 200, May 12, 1926 (Autauga Co., L. S. Golsan), fall, 100 almost daily between August 31 and September 20, 1913 (Autauga Co., L. S. Golsan). *Lower Coastal Plain*: April 30 (1951, Andalusia, W. R. Middleton) to September 27 (1958, Camden, Lovett Williams); most seen, 350, September 21, 1957 (Dale Co., and Henry Co., T. A. Imhof and Lovett Williams). *Gulf Coast*: April 6 (1912, Spring Hill, A. H. Howell) to October 22 (1949, Foley, T. A. Imhof); most seen, spring, 100, May 8, 1960 (Dauphin Island, J. L. Dorn), fall, 260, September 24, 1959 (Spring Hill, J. L. Dorn).

TIME OF BREEDING. Data on over 28 nestings: Eggs, April 24 to July 14; dependent young, June 2 to July 17; flying by June 17.

[319]

PLATE 22

RUFOUS HUMMINGBIRD
Adult Male
Page 325

RUBY-THROATED HUMMINGBIRD
Adult Male
Page 323

YELLOW-BILLED CUCKOO
Sexes Alike
Page 300

CHIMNEY SWIFT
Sexes Alike
Page 321

BLACK-BILLED CUCKOO
Sexes Alike
Page 301

GROUND DOVE
Sexes Alike
Page 295

COMMON NIGHTHAWK
Male, Sexes Similar
Page 317

WHIP-POOR-WILL
Male, Sexes Similar
Page 316

CHUCK-WILL'S-WIDOW
Sexes Similar
Page 314

Richard A. Parks

ORDER APODIFORMES: SWIFTS AND HUMMINGBIRDS

These are small birds with weak feet and long, blade-like wings. They spend most of their waking hours on the wing.

FAMILY APODIDAE: SWIFTS

SUBFAMILY CHAETURINAE: SPINE-TAILED SWIFTS

Chimney Swift

Chaetura pelagica (Linnaeus)   [423]   (Plate 22, facing page 320)
OTHER NAMES: Chimney Sweep, Chimney Swallow

Contrary to popular opinion, this bird is not a swallow, even though in flight it closely resembles one. Like the goatsuckers, the Chimney Swift has a big mouth, small, weak bill, and weak feet. In flight it appears tailless, and in a glide the position of its wings and body give it a shape like a bow and arrow. Its flight gives the impression that the wings are beaten alternately, but slow-motion pictures have proved this is not so. This bird and the Peregrine Falcon share the distinction of being the fastest flying North American birds. The Chimney Swift is a plain, dark gray bird, somewhat lighter below. Its call is a distinctive, rapid twitter.

In Alabama, the Chimney Swift is a common, breeding, summer resident, abundant as a migrant, especially in fall. It is common around towns but seems to be equally numerous coursing over bodies of fresh water and over mountainous terrain. In September and October, it gathers in flocks of several thousand, and each flock roosts in a favorite chimney.

NESTING. Before this country was settled, the Chimney Swift nested in hollow trees, but now it nests almost exclusively in chimneys. It sometimes builds in other parts of buildings, and still occasionally nests in hollow trees (Tuskegee, May 1953, C. W. Summerour). The nest is a saucer-shaped hammock of dead twigs broken off in flight with the feet or bill and glued to the side of the chimney with the bird's specially-adapted saliva. In the Far East, one

[321]

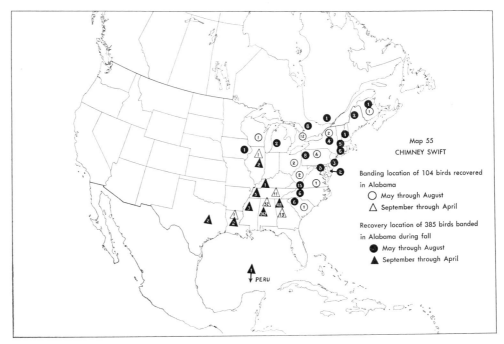

Map 55
CHIMNEY SWIFT

Banding location of 104 birds recovered
in Alabama
○ May through August
△ September through April

Recovery location of 385 birds banded
in Alabama during fall
● May through August
▲ September through April

↓ PERU

swift builds its nest entirely of saliva, and this nest is used to make bird's nest soup, an Oriental delicacy. The Chimney Swift lays three to five pure white eggs.

FOOD. This swift feeds almost entirely on flying insects captured on the wing. Items known to be taken in large numbers are caddis flies, May flies, crane flies, beetles of many kinds, true flies, mosquitoes, flying ants, wasps, bugs, and grasshoppers.

DISTRIBUTION. The Chimney Swift breeds from southeastern Saskatchewan, southern Quebec, and Nova Scotia south to southeastern Texas and central Florida. It migrates through Central America, has been recorded also in Hispaniola, and winters in the Upper Amazon Basin in Peru. Its distribution south of the United States is imperfectly known because many swifts occur in Central and South America which look like the Chimney Swift in the air. Usually the Chimney Swift is rather silent outside the breeding range, and swifts are difficult to collect. The above information on the winter range comes from the recovery of fourteen banded Chimney Swifts in Peru. One of these was banded at Opelika on October 3, 1936, by Harold S. Peters.

OCCURRENCE IN ALABAMA. (March 12 to November 9.) *Tennessee Valley*: March 30 (1948, Russellville, E. O. Willis and 1953, Scottsboro, Mrs. S. G. Worley and 1960, Huntsville, J. C. and Margaret Robinson) to October 13 (Leighton, F. W. McCormack). *Mountain Region*: March 22 (1953 and 1954, Gadsden, Edith Clark) to October 21 (1935, Birmingham, H. M. Stevenson); most seen, 4000+, roosting every year in late September in Birmingham (many observers). *Piedmont*: March 13 (1940, Auburn, R. J. Wheeler, Jr.) to October 16 (1957, Auburn, Lovett Williams). *Upper Coastal Plain*: March 12 (1955, Marion, Lois McCollough) to October 31 (1931, Montgomery, E. G. Holt); most seen, 5000, September 2, 1939 (Tuscaloosa, H. M. Stevenson). *Lower Coastal Plain*: March 22 (1957, Lake Tholloco, T. A. Imhof) to November 9 (1939, Andalusia, Rosa Belle Ard). *Gulf Coast*: March 21 (1932, Fairhope, D. H. McIntosh) to November 4 (1932, Fairhope, D. H. McIntosh); most seen, 1010, September 23, 1955 (Mobile, T. A. Imhof and W. W. Beshears).

TIME OF BREEDING. Data on 16 nestings: Building, April 25; eggs, May 18 to June 20; young in nest, June 6 to July 30.

BANDING. Many thousands of Chimney Swifts have been banded in Alabama at their fall roosting chimneys; 242 of these have been recovered in Alabama and 142 outside the state. Also, 52 swifts recovered in Alabama have been banded elsewhere. See Map 55. Among 25 Chimney Swifts retrapped at the same chimney in Birmingham, 2 birds were at least 8 years old; 1 was 7 years old; 2, 6 years old; 6, 5 years old; 10, 4 years old; and 4, 3 years old.

FAMILY TROCHILIDAE: HUMMINGBIRDS

Hummingbirds as a group are smaller than any other birds. Like swifts they have narrow, stiff, blade-like wings and weak feet. But they have a small mouth, a long, thin bill adapted to sipping nectar from flowers, and highly iridescent plumage. Hummingbird wings beat at about 1,000 strokes per minute; thus these birds can hover, dart, fly backwards, or fly straight up. For their size they consume enormous amounts of energy, and their body temperature is probably higher and their heartbeat faster than those of any other birds.

Ruby-throated Hummingbird

Archilochus colubris (Linnaeus)   [428]   (Plate 22, facing page 320)
OTHER NAME: Hummingbird

The tiny Ruby-throated Hummingbird is the only one of its family that breeds east of the Mississippi River. It is green above and whitish below, and the male has an iridescent, ruby-red throat.

This bird is a common, breeding, summer resident throughout Alabama. It is a woodland bird that frequently visits gardens. In fall migration (mid-August to mid-October) it is sometimes abundant, especially in gardens or along mountain ridges, where it flies along the steep western edges. On the coast, this bird migrates eastward along the outer strip in fall, and crosses water and marshland without a moment's hesitation.

NESTING. The nest is a tiny, lichen-covered cup, barely an inch across. It is lined with soft plant down and saddled on a thin, horizontal or down-sloping limb, often over water. The female lays two tiny, creamy-colored eggs.

[323]

NEST OF RUBY-THROATED HUMMINGBIRD. This tiny nest, about the size of a green walnut, is one of the most beautiful of all bird nests.

FOOD. The Ruby-throated Hummingbird is especially attracted to red flowers. Favorites in Alabama are red buckeye in early spring; cardinal flower and jewelweed in woods in summer; and salvia and hibiscus in fall. Other favorites are mimosa, gladiolus, petunia, butterflybush (*Buddleia*), iris, fuchsia, morning glory, honeysuckle (*Lonicera*), lantana, trumpet vine, and beebalm (*Monarda*). Besides the nectar of these and many other flowers, it eats many spiders, and small insects such as ants, bees, leafhoppers, flies, beetles, and gnats.

DISTRIBUTION. The Ruby-throated Hummingbird breeds east of the Rocky Mountains from central Alberta and southern Quebec south to southern Louisiana and southern Florida. It winters from northern Mexico to Costa Rica and casually or rarely to western Panama and along the Gulf Coast to northeastern Florida.

OCCURRENCE IN ALABAMA. (Normal: March 9 to November 16; Out-of-season: January 1 and 6.) *Tennessee Valley*: April 7 (1958, Wheeler Refuge, T. Z. Atkeson, Jr. and W. M. Depreast) to October 28 (1957, Decatur, Robert Helle). *Mountain Region*: March 31 (1953, Gadsden, Naomi Banks) to November 16 (1955, Gadsden, Edith Clark). *Piedmont*: March 18 (1953, Auburn, H. G. Good) to October 3 (1957, Auburn, Lovett Williams). *Upper Coastal Plain*: March 18 (1934, Booth, Autauga Co., L. S. Golsan) to October 14 (1938, Tuscaloosa, H. M. Stevenson). *Lower Coastal Plain*: March 9 (1958,

Jackson, W. U. Harris) to November 2 (1939, Andalusia, Rosa Belle Ard). *Gulf Coast*: March 12 (1960, Daphne, J. L. Dorn) to November 8 (1959, Dauphin Island, Idalene Snead and others); also January 1 and 6, 1933 (Fairhope, Miss Anna Braun and Mrs. Braun); most seen, spring, 69, April 13, 1957 (Spring Count, Mobile Bay Area), fall, 20, October 6, 1956 (Fall Count, Mobile Bay Area).

TIME OF BREEDING. Data on 21 nestings: Building, April 28 and May 25; eggs, April 23 to August 5; dependent young, July 14 and 20.

[Rufous Hummingbird]
Selasphorus rufus (Gmelin)   [433]   (Plate 22, facing page 320)

The *male* Rufous Hummingbird is *cinnamon-red* on the head, back, tail, and flanks; bright green on the wings and forehead; flame-red on the throat; and white on the chest and belly. The *female* and *immature* birds are *green above* like the Ruby-throated Hummingbird, but they show traces of *rufous* on the *lower back,* especially the *tail,* and have rufous-red flanks, whereas the Ruby-throated has brownish flanks.

The Rufous Hummingbird is accidental, possibly casual, in winter on the Gulf Coast of Alabama. On the coast it frequents gardens that have red flowers, notably salvia, in bloom during the winter.

NESTING AND FOOD. The small moss-and-lichen-covered cup usually holds two white eggs. Normally this bird chooses the low limb of a conifer for nesting and builds near others of its kind. It feeds on nectar, particularly that of red flowers, and it also eats small insects found near these flowers.

DISTRIBUTION. The Rufous Hummingbird breeds from southeastern Alaska and southern Alberta south to central California and southern Idaho. It migrates through the Rocky Mountains to winter in Mexico and occasionally along the northern Gulf Coast to northwestern Florida.

OCCURRENCE IN ALABAMA.
Gulf Coast only: December 26, 1956 (Fairhope, Rosemary Gaymer).

ORDER CORACIIFORMES: KINGFISHERS, MOTMOTS, ROLLERS, BEE-EATERS, AND HORNBILLS

FAMILY ALCEDINIDAE: KINGFISHERS

SUBFAMILY CERYLINAE: TYPICAL KINGFISHERS

Belted Kingfisher
Megaceryle alcyon (Linnaeus)   [390]   (Plate 24, facing page 336)

The Belted Kingfisher is big-headed and big-billed and has a ragged crest. It is mostly bright blue but is white below with a blue breast band, and the female has an extra band that is reddish. The call is a loud, rather high-pitched, distinctive rattle. The striking Belted Kingfisher is seldom confused with any other bird.

This species is a common, breeding, permanent resident near water in most of Alabama. In summer it is uncommon near the coast. In very severe winters, when water freezes over for a week or more, it may temporarily withdraw from the more northern parts of the state. It frequents most watercourses but avoids the narrow, heavily-shaded branches and the open salt water. Except for the breeding season, each bird generally remains alone and jealously guards a stretch of water and its favorite perches.

NESTING. With its big bill and shovel-like claws, this kingfisher digs a three-to-six-foot burrow near the top of an exposed bank. It lays five to eight pure white eggs on the bare soil at one end of the burrow. Occasionally it collects bits of clean fish bones, leaves, scales, and skeletons of large insects to form a small nest.

FOOD. This bird lives almost entirely on small fish, usually not over four inches in length and usually, contrary to popular opinion, not of the game varieties. Game fish are harder to catch, and so the bird weeds out the trash fish and leaves the game fish free of competition for food. Around hatcheries, however, the temptation is too great for the kingfisher, and it sometimes becomes a nuisance. When fish are difficult to obtain, the bird eats crabs, crawfish, mussels, lizards, salamanders, toads, frogs, small snakes, turtles, large insects, berries, clams, and oysters.

CORACIIFORMES: ALCEDINIDAE: BELTED KINGFISHER

DISTRIBUTION. The Belted Kingfisher breeds from northwestern Alaska, southern Yukon, central Quebec, and central Labrador south to southern California, southern Texas, and southern Florida. It winters from southeastern Alaska, the northernmost United States, and southern Ontario south through Central America and the West Indies to Panama and Trinidad.

ABUNDANCE IN ALABAMA (*most seen in a day*). Marshall Co., and Jackson Co., 12, February 5, 1955 (T. A. Imhof and others); Birmingham, 16, December 28, 1957 (Christmas Count); Marion, 12, September 20, 1955 (Lois McCollough); Mobile Bay Area, 53, October 6, 1956 (Fall Count); Dauphin Island, 42, January 2, 1960 (Christmas Count).

TIME OF BREEDING. Data on 11 nestings: Building, February 25 to March 17; eggs, April 6 to 18; dependent young, May 1 to 22.

Richard Parks

ORDER PICIFORMES: WOODPECKERS, JACAMARS, TOUCANS, AND BARBETS

FAMILY PICIDAE: WOODPECKERS AND WRYNECKS

SUBFAMILY PICINAE: WOODPECKERS

These far-ranging woodland birds are called Peckerwoods and Sapsuckers in the South. They have large, powerful, chisel-like bills adapted to hammering and drilling on wood and stiff tail feathers which aid them in climbing trees. Two of their toes point forward and two point to the rear. Their plumage is predominantly black and white with distinctive wing patterns and generally some red on the head, particularly in males. The flight is often undulating, and they are less active on cloudy and rainy days and at dusk. These birds roost and nest in tree holes they dig themselves, and they lay pure white eggs. Their main foods are wood-boring insects, ants, and fruit.

Yellow-shafted Flicker

Colaptes auratus (Linnaeus)   [412]   (Plate 23, facing page 328)
OTHER NAMES: Yellowhammer, Flicker

The Yellow-shafted Flicker is a brownish woodpecker with *golden yellow* on the entire *under side* of the *wings*. It has a white rump, a black chest band, and a crescent of red on the back of the head. Males have a black mustache mark. The name flicker comes from one of its common calls.

In all parts of Alabama, the Yellow-shafted Flicker is a common to abundant, breeding, permanent resident whose numbers are substantially increased in winter by migrants from the north. The species is adaptable to nearly all upland habitats, but it is partial to open woodlands, especially hardwoods. Probably more than any other woodpecker, it feeds on the ground, particularly on lawns.

Many people in this state are aware of the tale concerning the Alabama regiment whose men identified themselves during the War Between the States by wearing yellowhammer feathers in their hats. This story and the widespread abundance of the species led to its being chosen as the state bird of Alabama.

[329]

NESTING. This flicker nests in self-dug holes from one to 100 feet from the ground, preferably in dead trees, either pine, palm, or hardwood. Sometimes it uses natural cavities, and more often than other woodpeckers, a nest box. Such a box should have a seven by seven inch floor, be sixteen to eighteen inches deep, have an entrance two and one half inches in diameter two inches from the top, and be placed six to twenty feet from the ground. For all woodpeckers, the bottom of the box should be filled with wood chips. Otherwise the bird will destroy the nest box making its own chips for the eggs.

FOOD. The Yellow-shafted Flicker eats more ants than any other North American bird. It also takes a large variety of other insects, especially beetles, grasshoppers, crickets, cockroaches, caterpillars, bugs, and flying insects. Its vegetable food consists of berries, other fruits, nuts, and seeds, prominently those of poison-ivy.

DISTRIBUTION. This species breeds from the limit of trees in central Alaska and Quebec south to southern Texas and southern Florida. A few winter almost as far north as the bird breeds, but most winter from southern Canada south.

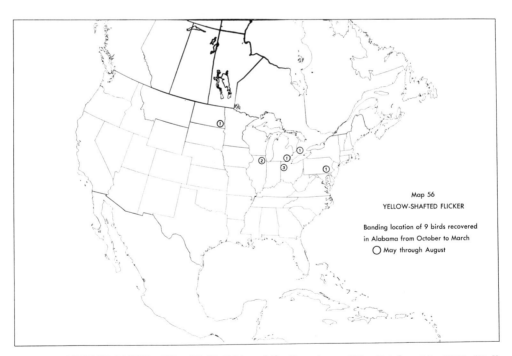

Map 56
YELLOW-SHAFTED FLICKER

Banding location of 9 birds recovered
in Alabama from October to March
◯ May through August

ABUNDANCE IN ALABAMA. (*most seen in a day*). Birmingham, 82, December 26, 1955 (Christmas Count); Mobile Bay Area, 121, October 19, 1957 (Fall Count).

TIME OF BREEDING. Data on 25 nestings: Building, March 15 to April 26; eggs, April 6 to June 20; young in nest, May 8 to June 20; dependent young out of nest, June 1 to July.

BANDING. For place of banding of 9 flickers recovered in Alabama, see Map 56. These birds were recovered during the period October 9 to March 21, in the following Alabama counties: Colbert, Morgan, Marion, Walker, Coosa, Autauga, Montgomery, Geneva, and Mobile.

Pileated Woodpecker

Dryocopus pileatus (Linnaeus)   [405]   (Plate 24, facing page 336)
OTHER NAMES: Logcock, Black Woodcock, Indian Hen, Lord-God, Woodchuck

This *black woodpecker* is the *size* of a *crow* and looks like a crow in flight. But the woodpecker has a red crest and white on the forepart of the wings and the side of the neck. The Pileated Woodpecker's flight is generally quite level, but on short jaunts it shows the up-and-down swing of the smaller members of its family. This big woodpecker's call is similar to that of the Yellow-shafted Flicker, but much louder, more ringing, and more prolonged.

The Pileated Woodpecker is a common, breeding, permanent resident in all wooded parts of Alabama, but it is not as widespread as most of the state's other year-round woodpeckers. Formerly, it lived almost entirely in virgin hardwood bottomland forests, as did the Ivory-billed Woodpecker. As these tracts declined, so did the Pileated Woodpecker, but in recent years it has adapted itself to second-growth timberlands. It now occurs frequently near houses, and even occasionally in backyards and at feeding stations. In most areas it is no longer considered the game bird it was fifty odd years ago. Few sizable patches of woodland in Alabama now lack a pair of these birds.

NESTING. Every year this woodpecker excavates a fresh nest hole, 20 to 85 feet up in a hardwood or pine and preferably in dead wood. In this cavity it lays three to five, usually four, glossy white eggs.

FOOD. Ants form the largest share of this woodpecker's food, with beetles, especially wood-borers, a close second. Besides other insects, it eats small amounts of fruits, especially wild berries and nuts. It feeds within the forest, and makes great excavations in trees in search of carpenter ants and boring beetles. The chips it knocks from the tree are large, often four to six inches long, and many times large oval holes in the trees indicate to the bird student that this species is present.

DISTRIBUTION. The Pileated Woodpecker is resident in timbered regions from southern Mackenzie and central Quebec south to central Texas and southern Florida, and also from British Columbia to California.

ABUNDANCE IN ALABAMA (*most seen in a day*). Birmingham, 26, December 26, 1959; 25, December 26, 1960 (Christmas Counts); southern Clarke Co., 11, January 11, 1958 (T. A. Imhof and others).

TIME OF BREEDING. Data on at least 8 nestings: Eggs, April 8 to 14; dependent young, May 23 to July.

Red-bellied Woodpecker

Centurus carolinus (Linnaeus) [409] (Plate 24, facing page 336)
OTHER NAMES: Zebra Woodpecker, Guinea Sapsucker, Red-headed Woodpecker

This species was named by someone who did not realize that the reddish belly, usually hidden against a tree trunk, is not the bird's most prominent feature. The Red-bellied Woodpecker is grayish with a *zebra-like back,* striped horizontally in black and white. The *male* has a bright *red crown* and *nape,* while only the *nape* of the *female* is *red.* Young birds are brown-headed but still readily recognizable. This bird is noisy and one of its calls, a three-syllabled phrase, is a good clue to its identity. Other calls are chucking and churring notes like those the Red-headed Woodpecker makes, but lower in pitch and volume.

Throughout Alabama, the Red-bellied Woodpecker is a common to abundant permanent resident. It lives and breeds commonly in all types of woodlands, even around houses.

NESTING. This woodpecker drills its hole in almost any kind of tree from five to eighty feet from the ground. On a bed of wood chips in this hole it lays three to five white eggs.

FOOD. Unlike most woodpeckers, this bird eats more fruit than insects, especially in winter. Its fruit diet is quite varied and consists mostly of wild berries. It also eats much mast, especially acorns and occasionally it drinks sap. Its insect food includes beetles, grasshoppers, and flies. Frequently it stores insects and nuts in cracks in wood.

DISTRIBUTION. The Red-bellied Woodpecker is resident from southeastern Minnesota, southern Ontario, western New York, and Delaware south to southern Texas and southern Florida. Near the northern limits it is local and usually absent in winter.

ABUNDANCE IN ALABAMA (*most seen in a day*). Birmingham, 68, December 26, 1960 (Christmas Count); Auburn, 31, January 2, 1954 (Christmas Count); Marion, 44, December 27, 1957 (Christmas Count); southern Clarke Co., 36, January 11, 1958 (T. A. Imhof and others); Mobile Bay Area, 54, October 19, 1957 (Fall Count).

TIME OF BREEDING. Data on 34 nestings: Building, February to April 30; eggs, March 10 to July 21; young in nest, April 23 to July 27; young just out of nest, July 1 to September 20.

Red-headed Woodpecker

Melanerpes erythrocephalus (Linnaeus)   [406]   (Plate 24, facing page 336)
OTHER NAME: Shirt-tail

The Red-headed Woodpecker is *strikingly patterned* in *red, white,* and *dark blue,* the dark blue appearing black except at very close range. The belly, rump, and large *wing patch* are *white;* the *head and neck* are *bright red* in adults and dark brown in immatures; and the rest of the body is dark blue. This bird's flight is more level than that of other woodpeckers. Various churring notes of the Red-headed Woodpecker differ from those of the Red-bellied Woodpecker mainly by being higher in pitch.

In most of Alabama, the Red-headed Woodpecker is a locally common, breeding, permanent resident; yet it is sometimes absent from apparently suitable places. In winter it often moves to swamps or migrates southward. Most movement of this bird seems to take place in April and September. Migration dates are not recorded here because little geographic regularity is apparent, and only part of the population is involved. The species frequents places where dead trees and dead treetops abound. Around towns it chooses telephone poles for foraging and nesting. In 1960 it became common on north Alabama mountaintops in the many dead treetops which resulted from severe ice storms during the previous winter.

NESTING. This woodpecker drills a nest hole from three to eighty feet above the ground in dead wood which may be a telephone pole or a fence post. Starlings frequently evict the woodpecker after the hole is complete. The woodpecker lays three to seven white eggs on a bed of wood chips in the hole. Unless Starlings delay it too long or some other interference uses up too much of the season, a Red-headed Woodpecker may raise two broods.

FOOD. Insects make up about half of the food of this species, especially ants, beetles (including weevils), grasshoppers, caterpillars, bugs, and other flying insects. The remainder of its diet includes chiefly berries, other small fruits, nuts (especially acorns), and a few seeds and grains. It has the habit of storing food for future consumption in cracks and crannies.

DISTRIBUTION. The Red-headed Woodpecker is mainly resident from southern Saskatchewan, southern Ontario, and New York, rare and local farther east, south to northern New Mexico, central Texas, and southern Florida. It retires southward in winter, irregularly but generally from the northern half of the range.

ABUNDANCE IN ALABAMA (*most seen in a day*). Birmingham, 31, December 26, 1953 and January 1, 1951 (Christmas Counts); Demopolis Lake, 31, March 9, 1956 (T. A. Imhof and W. W. Beshears); Dale Co., and Henry Co., 20, September 21, 1957 (T. A. Imhof and Lovett Williams); Monroe Co., 35, February 10, 1956 (T. A. Imhof and W. F. Colin); Mobile Bay Area, 26, April 26, 1958 (Spring Count).

TIME OF BREEDING. Data on over 40 nestings: Building, February 5 to May 11; eggs, April 5 to July 15; young in nest, April 5 to July; dependent young out of nest, May to July 22.

BANDING. A bird caught at Speigner, Elmore Co., December 2, 1940, had been banded at Raleigh, North Carolina, June 23, 1939.

Yellow-bellied Sapsucker

Sphyrapicus varius (Linnaeus)   [402]   (Plate 24, facing page 336)

OTHER NAME: Sapsucker

This black and white woodpecker is much like the Hairy Woodpecker in size and color. The *adult* Yellow-bellied Sapsucker has a *red crown,* and the *male* also has a *red throat,* but the female has a white throat. Immatures have a brownish head and all birds of this species have a yellowish wash on the belly at all ages. In *all plumages,* a *long, white area* extends *lengthwise* on the *closed wing,* a good mark for identifying the species. This bird calls with a distinctive mewing note which is not typical of the calls of woodpeckers.

This is the only woodpecker listed here that does not breed in the state. It is common in winter in all parts of Alabama in nearly all types of woodland. Usually a quiet, solitary bird, it is often overlooked because it spends much of its time clinging quietly to a tree trunk.

NESTING AND FOOD. This sapsucker lays five or six white eggs in a freshly dug hole eight to forty feet above ground in a hardwood. It prefers birch, poplar, elm, or butternut, near water. Its food is primarily the sap of trees which bear nuts and fruit, including pine and cypress. It also eats the cambium layer, which is like a soft inner bark and carries the sap. Additionally it takes ants, flies caught on the wing, some beetles, caterpillars, katydid eggs, spiders, centipedes, many wild fruits, and rarely wood-borers. Its dependence on sap probably explains why it is one of the few woodpeckers that are known to migrate.

Rows of holes drilled around the trunk readily mark those trees attacked by this bird. Little harm is done if it moves on, but in the South where it remains all winter, the tree may be ruined for lumbering purposes or even killed.

DISTRIBUTION. The Yellow-bellied Sapsucker breeds from southeastern Alaska, southern Mackenzie, and southern Labrador south to southern California,

Missouri, northern Ohio, and New England. It also breeds in mountains to northern Georgia. It winters in the southern part of its breeding range and at lower elevations south to Panama and the northern Lesser Antilles.

OCCURRENCE IN ALABAMA. (September 21 to May 13.) *Tennessee Valley*: September 26 (1949, Wheeler Refuge, L. S. Givens) to April 30 (1960, Huntsville, T. A. Imhof). *Mountain Region*: September 21 (1936, Easonville, St. Clair Co., H. M. Stevenson) to April 29 (1954, Hueytown, Clustie McTyeire); most seen, 23, December 26, 1959 (Christmas Count, Birmingham). *Piedmont*: November 2 (1957, Auburn, Lovett Williams) to April 19 (1958, Auburn, Ala. Orn. Soc.). *Upper Coastal Plain*: September 28 (1889, specimen in the Avery collection, Greensboro, W. C. Avery) to April 10 (1951, Montgomery, C. W. Summerour and 1959, Livingston, Jenkins Jackson). *Lower Coastal Plain*: October 7 (1958, Camden, Lovett Williams) to April 8 (1958, Coffeeville, Clarke Co., J. E. Keeler); most seen, 20, January 11, 1958 (Hal's Lake, T. A. Imhof and others). *Gulf Coast*: October 6 (1956, Dauphin Island, S. M. Russell and E. O. Willis) to May 13 (1960, Dauphin Island, J. L. Dorn); most seen, 53, October 19, 1957 (Fall Count, Mobile Bay Area).

Hairy Woodpecker

Dendrocopos villosus (Linnaeus) [393] (Plate 24, facing page 336)

This black and white woodpecker has a white back and several rows of white spots on the closed wing. Males show a small red patch on the back of the head. This species differs from the Downy Woodpecker in being much larger and having a *bill about as long as its head*. Only at close range is it apparent that the Hairy Woodpecker does not have crossbars on its white outer tail feathers. This bird is best identified by its call, which differs from that of the Downy Woodpecker in being louder and higher in pitch.

In Alabama, this woodpecker nests in the wilder and deeper woodlands, either pine or hardwood, and is fairly common throughout the year. It generally occurs alone or in pairs, but occasionally associates with roving bands of titmice and other small woodland birds in winter. Although it is a retiring bird, it sometimes visits feeding stations in winter, since it wanders at that season over a larger territory than it does in summer.

NESTING. This bird's nest hole is dug from nine to sixty feet above the ground usually in a hardwood. There are three to six, usually four, white eggs in a clutch.

FOOD. The main food items are insects, especially the wood-boring larvae of beetles, ants, caterpillars, weevils, aphids, and also spiders and millipedes. This diet is varied, especially in winter, with small amounts of fruits, grains, seeds, and nuts.

[335]

[336]

Richard A. Parks

DISTRIBUTION. The Hairy Woodpecker is resident from central Alaska, Quebec, and Newfoundland south to Mexico, southern Florida, and the Bahamas, and in mountains to Panama. In winter, birds in the far north retire a bit southward, and those in the mountains go to lower elevations.

ABUNDANCE IN ALABAMA (*most seen in a day*). Birmingham, 12, December 31, 1944 and December 29, 1945 (Christmas Counts); Foley, 7, December 27, 1947 (Christmas Count).

TIME OF BREEDING. Data on at least 10 nestings: Eggs, March 26 to 31; dependent young, April 8 to July 12.

Downy Woodpecker

Dendrocopos pubescens (Linnaeus)   [394]   (Plate 24, facing page 336)
OTHER NAMES: Little Peckerwood, Downy, Little Sapsucker

This black and white woodpecker, the smallest of its family, has a white back and several rows of white spots on the closed wing. The male has a spot of red on the back of the head. The *bill* of this bird is shorter than the head, *much smaller* than that of the Hairy Woodpecker, which is a larger bird. The Downy Woodpecker has black bars on its white outer tail feathers. The call is the best differentiation between these two species. The Downy Woodpecker's call is *lower* in *pitch* and *volume* than that of the Hairy Woodpecker.

Throughout Alabama, the Downy Woodpecker is a common and widespread, breeding, permanent resident, for it occurs wherever there are trees. It is the state's most trustful woodpecker, often coming to feeding stations, where in colder weather it is particularly attracted by suet. It usually occurs in groups no larger than a family, and in winter it commonly associates with titmice and other insect-eating woodland birds.

NESTING. The nest hole is dug in a hardwood from eight to fifty feet above the ground. In the Coastal Plain of Alabama, cottonwood and willow trees are frequent sites. This bird sometimes uses a nest box. The three to five eggs are white.

FOOD. Beetles, ants, caterpillars, and moths, in that order, make up the main food supply. This is supplemented with some wild fruits, especially berries of poison-ivy and dogwood. Frequently this woodpecker forages on the smaller twigs of trees and shrubs and even on tall weeds.

DISTRIBUTION. The Downy Woodpecker is resident from Alaska, Quebec, and Newfoundland south to southern California and southern Florida. In winter mountain birds descend into valleys, but otherwise the species seldom moves any distance.

ABUNDANCE IN ALABAMA (*most seen in a day*). Birmingham, 34, December 20, 1952 (Christmas Count); Mobile Bay Area, 13, October 6, 1956 (Fall Count).

TIME OF BREEDING. Data on over 14 nestings: Building, April 13; eggs, April 2 to 22; dependent young, April 20 to June 12.

Red-cockaded Woodpecker
Dendrocopos borealis (Vieillot)   [395]   (Plate 24, facing page 336)

This black and white woodpecker, about the same size as the Hairy Woodpecker, has a *zebra-like back,* a black crown and hindneck, a small red spot near the ear, and a *large white cheek patch.* Its nasal and querulous call note is given so frequently that the call is considered the best way to locate and identify the species.

The Red-cockaded Woodpecker is a local, permanent resident in piney woods in most of Alabama south of the Tennessee River. It usually lives and nests in woods in which about one-quarter or more of the trees are pines. Thus, in the northern part of the state it is uncommon, but as pines increase in number southward in Alabama, it sometimes becomes fairly common to common locally. The bird calls often, and although small, thinly-scattered flocks roam over a large tract of piney woods, the Red-cockaded Woodpecker is usually not difficult to detect.

NESTING. This species nests about thirty feet from the ground, almost invariably in a living pine that has a dead heart. The birds take advantage of the dead heart, but do not cause it. The outside of its nest hole is smeared with pitch, and on a bed of wood chips inside it lays two to six glossy white eggs. Often several pairs nest close together, and if they are not disturbed will use the same trees year after year.

FOOD. Pine mast and the larvae of wood-boring insects form the greater part of this woodpecker's food. Besides these it eats adult beetles, ants, grasshoppers, crickets, wild berries, and seeds. From time to time it feeds near cultivated areas, often on corn worms.

DISTRIBUTION. The Red-cockaded Woodpecker is resident in southern pine forests from eastern Oklahoma, Kentucky, and southern Maryland south to eastern Texas and southern Florida.

ABUNDANCE IN ALABAMA (*most seen in a day*). Birmingham, 12, December 26, 1953 (Christmas Count); Foley, 7, December 27, 1947 (M. H. Perry).

TIME OF BREEDING. Data on 11 nestings: Eggs, April 22 to June 4; young in nest, May 6 to 17; dependent young just out of nest, May 17.

[Ivory-billed Woodpecker]

Campephilus principalis (Linnaeus)   [392]   (Plate 24, facing page 336)
OTHER NAME: Kent

This woodpecker is even larger than the Pileated Woodpecker, which it closely resembles. But the Ivory-billed Woodpecker has a *pale yellow bill* and *large white wing patches, much like* those of the *Red-headed Woodpecker*, and these make it appear narrow-winged in flight. Both sexes are crested; the male has red on the rear half of the head and the neck, but the female shows no red at all. This woodpecker has a long tail, and its flight is direct, with little of the bounding of other woodpeckers. The call is clear and shrill, somewhat like that of a nuthatch, and is quite weak for so large a bird.

The Ivory-billed Woodpecker may now be extinct. It lived in virgin bottom-land hardwood forests and as these woodlands were exploited, the bird, apparently unable to adapt itself, steadily retreated. It was last reported in Alabama in 1907, in Louisiana in 1943, and in Florida in 1950. It may still survive in some remote areas. The last authentic report from Florida was scarcely forty miles from the Alabama line. The birds wander a great deal and there is still hope that the species exists in the state. A century ago it was probably an uncommon, permanent resident in the Coastal Plain and Indian relics indicate that it formerly may have been common and widespread. Although only one positive nesting record is known, it probably bred at all places mentioned below where it at one time occurred.

NESTING. Nest holes have been noted in ash, hackberry, oak, elm, royal palm, cypress, pine, and maple trees, usually in live wood from 25 to 70 feet above the ground. What few nesting data exist show the signs of dying species, probably the result of inbreeding in a small population. The bird lays three to five eggs in March and April, but three or less is usual and very often some of them are infertile. Frequently only one young is reared. The only nest reported from Alabama was seventy feet up in a dead pine (Lamar County, Spring 1886, G. V. Young).

FOOD. The food differs little from that of other woodpeckers. It eats wood-boring beetles, ants, and termites, and such nuts and fruits as pecans, hickory nuts, acorns, hackberries, persimmons, grapes, cherries, magnolia seeds, and poison-ivy seeds.

DISTRIBUTION. The Ivory-billed Woodpecker was formerly resident from southeastern Oklahoma, southern Indiana, and southeastern North Carolina south

PICIFORMES: PICIDAE: IVORY-BILLED WOODPECKER

to southern Texas and southern Florida. The last authentic record was for northwestern Florida, March 3, 1950.

Map 57

IVORY-BILLED WOODPECKER

Distribution

○ Observations (with year of last record)

OCCURRENCE IN ALABAMA. Records listed in Howell (1928:159-160) are 50 or more years old and are from the wild river-bottom swamps in the middle of the Coastal Plain. See Map 57. *Dallas County*: 1859 (P. H. Gosse); *Marengo County*: West side of the Tombigbee River, 1865 (E. M. Hasbrouck); *Hale County*: Ten miles west of Greensboro in a cypress slough of the Warrior River, 1866 (W. C. Avery); *Lamar County*: Crump Springs on the Buttahatchie, spring 1886 (G. V. Young); *Wilcox County*: Fall 1889 (G. V. Young); *Pike County*: North of Troy on the Conecuh River, one bird shot about 1907 (C. W. Howe).

ORDER PASSERIFORMES: PERCHING BIRDS

This, the twenty-eighth order of the Class *Aves*, contains about half the species and they are the most highly developed. Twenty-seven of its sixty-nine families occur in North America (A.O.U. Check-list, 5th ed., 1957), and twenty-one of them are represented on the Alabama list. These songbirds are generally small and have a small, variable bill with a horny covering. Their feet are adapted for perching: the hind toe is the same length as the middle toe and on the same level with the three toes which point forward. Nest-building is well developed, the eggs are proportionately small, the incubation period, short, and the young are hatched naked and helpless. The usual wing has ten primaries but some have only nine, and the tail has twelve long feathers. The majority of these birds live in trees and maintain a nesting territory. The greater number have pleasing, high-pitched songs.

FAMILY TYRANNIDAE: TYRANT FLYCATCHERS

Flycatchers are the least melodious of any of the perching birds; their harsh, explosive calls often sound irritable. Woodland birds, they perch upright in the open and wait for an insect to fly by, whereupon they sally forth and devour it with a loud snap of the bill. Generally these birds have big heads, with bills broad at the base and with prominent bristles at the corners of the mouth.

Eastern Kingbird
Tyrannus tyrannus (Linnaeus)   [444]   (Plate 25, facing page 344)
OTHER NAME: Bee Martin

This robin-sized flycatcher is black above, including the face, and silky-white below, and *has a white band on the tip of the black tail*. The call is an excitable, rasping, one-syllabled note, often followed by a rapid repetition of the same note.

This kingbird, usually the only one in eastern North America, is a common, breeding, summer resident in Alabama and is often abundant on migration. It frequents open areas, especially those around farms, and commonly perches on fences or isolated trees. On the nesting territory it drives away many larger birds, particularly crows.

NESTING. The nest is a rather bulky cup of twigs, rootlets, and finer material placed well out from the trunk on a limb ten to thirty feet from the ground. Isolated trees such as shade trees or those in orchards are favorite sites, but from time to time it even builds in a hole in a hollow tree. The usual clutch is three to five creamy-white eggs marked boldly with various shades of brown, black, and lavender.

FOOD. This kingbird eats primarily injurious insects, and varies this menu with wild fruits. It does eat bees, as its common name implies, but not so extensively as to be of much harm. Insect food includes boll weevils, other beetles, grasshoppers, butterflies, wasps, ants, flies, bugs, mosquitoes, and caterpillars. Almost all wild berries, especially wild cherries, sassafras, red cedar, dogwood, and magnolia berries, are included in its fruit diet.

DISTRIBUTION. The Eastern Kingbird breeds from northern British Columbia, northern Ontario, and southern Quebec south to northeastern California, central Texas, and southern Florida. It winters from Peru to Bolivia.

OCCURRENCE IN ALABAMA. (Normal: March 18 to October 23; Out-of-season: November 7.) *Tennessee Valley*: April 7 (1890, Leighton, F. W. McCormack) to September 22 (1941, Wheeler Refuge, J. H. Steenis and T. Z. Atkeson, Jr.); also October 12, 1941 (Cherokee, Colbert Co., B. B. and Lula Coffey); most seen, spring, 145+, May 4, 1957 (Wheeler Refuge, Ala. Orn. Soc.), fall, 60 in one flock, August 29, 1949 (Decatur, T. A. Imhof). *Mountain Region*: April 1 (1949, Talladega, C. T. Hornady) to September 22 (1953, Birmingham, T. A. Imhof); most seen, 38, May 4, 1953 (Birmingham, T. A. Imhof). *Piedmont*: March 30 (1955, Auburn, H. G. Good) to at least August 10 (1952, Stroud, H. M. Stevenson and 1959, Roanoke, H. M. Stevenson). *Upper Coastal Plain*: March 22 (1913, Barachias, E. G. Holt) to September 22 (1956, Marion, Lois McCollough); also October 23, 1954 (Valley Creek State Park, O. L. Austin, Jr.); most seen, spring, 300, May 4, 1921 (Booth, Autauga Co., L. S. Golsan), fall, 75+, September 6, 1956 (Autauga Co., J. E. Keeler). *Lower Coastal Plain*: March 28 (1959, Camden, Lovett Williams) to September 26 (1958, Camden, Lovett Williams). *Gulf Coast*: March 18 (1919, Spring Hill, E. W. Graves and 1940 and 1943, Spring Hill, J. L. Dorn) to October 7 (1956, Dauphin Island, S. A. Gauthreaux and others); also November 7, 1959 (Dauphin Island, J. C. and Margaret Robinson); most seen, spring, "thousands," May 2, 1960 (Dauphin Island, J. L. Dorn), fall, 200+, September 10, 1959 (Dauphin Island, T. A. Imhof and J. B. Sullivan).

TIME OF BREEDING. Data on 28 nestings: Building, April 26 to June 21; eggs, May 9 to July 25; dependent young, May 4 to July 15.

Gray Kingbird
Tyrannus dominicensis (Gmelin)   [445]   (Plate 25, facing page 344)

Slightly larger than the Eastern Kingbird, this flycatcher is dark gray above and white below, and has a *large black bill* and a *dark mask* through the eye.

The *notched tail is all dark,* without the white tip of the Eastern Kingbird or the white outer feathers of the Western Kingbird. The Gray Kingbird strikingly resembles the Loggerhead Shrike in pattern, and it chooses the same type of perch. Closer observation, however, reveals many flycatcher features: the bigger bill and head, heavier build, shorter tail, more erect posture, and a rather explosive, shrill call. This call, which has three syllables, is sometimes imitated by local Mockingbirds.

The Gray Kingbird lives usually within sight of salt water, preferring the outer islands and peninsulas. It breeds in the state, and has been noted in summer at Fort Morgan since 1950 and Dauphin Island since 1956. In Alabama it frequents the sand dunes close to the Gulf.

NESTING. This flycatcher builds a nest of coarse twigs lined with grasses, and usually selects a spot in red mangroves or oaks no higher than ten or twelve feet. The three or four eggs are pinkish, spotted and blotched with shades of brown and lavender.

FOOD. Primarily an insect-eater, it also consumes lizards and fruits, especially those of palms. Insects include weevils, other beetles, wild bees, wasps, earwigs, moths, caterpillars, dragonflies, cotton worms, crickets, bugs, and cicadas.

DISTRIBUTION. The Gray Kingbird breeds from coastal Alabama, coastal South Carolina, and the Bahamas south through the West Indies to Venezuela. In winter it withdraws from the Bahamas and the United States, and occurs on migration from Honduras to Panama.

OCCURRENCE IN ALABAMA. *Gulf Coast only*: April 23 (1960, Dauphin Island, T. A. Imhof and others and Cedar Point, R. W. Skinner) to September 25 (1957, Fort Morgan, J. E. Keeler); specimen in Univ. of Ala. collection, August 24, 1956 (Dauphin Island, H. M. Stevenson); most seen, spring, 6, May 2, 1959 (Dauphin Island, T. A. Imhof and others), fall, 25+, August 31, 1958 (Dauphin Island, S. A. Gauthreaux and others).

TIME OF BREEDING. Data on 4 nestings: Building (in a live oak), May 14; dependent young, late June to July 4.

Western Kingbird

Tyrannus verticalis Say [447] (Plate 25, facing page 344)
OTHER NAME: Arkansas Kingbird

Like the Eastern Kingbird, the Western Kingbird is robin-sized. It is *largely* a *gray* and *yellow* bird, with its head and neck lighter gray than its back. It has a dark mask through the eye and a yellow belly, and it has *white* on the outer half of the *two outer feathers* of its *black tail.* Although the Great

[343]

[344]

Richard A. Parks

Crested Flycatcher has a similar pattern, it has a rufous-red tail and a darker head.

In Alabama in fall the Western Kingbird is uncommon on the Gulf Coast, where it may winter, and rare inland in the Coastal Plain. In spring it has been recorded once on the coast and once far inland. (See Map 58.) It occurs in open areas, often on beaches. The species is not known to nest in the state.

NESTING AND FOOD. Fairly adaptable, where the situation permits, this kingbird builds a nest of twigs and grasses in a rather open spot usually midway up in a deciduous tree or cedar. The three to five whitish eggs are quite heavily marked with browns and lavender. Bees, wasps, beetles, and grasshoppers form the bulk of its diet, but it also eats bugs, flies, spiders, millipedes, treefrogs, and various berries, especially those of elder and hawthorns.

DISTRIBUTION. The Western Kingbird breeds from southern British Columbia, western Minnesota, southern Ontario, and northwestern Ohio south to northern Mexico and central Texas. It is fairly frequent in fall in the East, especially on the immediate coast from Nova Scotia to Texas, and it winters from Mexico to Nicaragua and in small numbers from Florida north to South Carolina.

OCCURRENCE IN ALABAMA. (Normal: August 29 to December 21; Out-of-season: April 26, May 3, and May 8.) *Tennessee Valley*: No record. *Mountain Region*: May 8, 1960 (Sulphur Springs, DeKalb Co., Margaret and J. C. Robinson and T. A. Imhof). *Piedmont*: No record. *Upper Coastal Plain*: October 13, 1940 (Autaugaville, L. S. Golsan). *Lower Coastal Plain*: September 21, 1957 (Clayhatchee, Dale Co., T. A. Imhof and Lovett Williams); October 8, 1959 (Clayhatchee, J. E. Keeler); October 19, 1958 (Camden, Lovett Williams) and November 2, 1956 (specimen in Florida State Univ. collection, Columbia, Houston Co., H. M. Stevenson). *Gulf Coast*: August 29 (1958, Fort Morgan, B. L. Monroe, Jr., F. M. Weston, and H. M. Stevenson) to at least December 21 (1957, Dauphin Island, Ava Tabor and Electa Levi); also April 26, 1958 (Gulf Shores, B. L. Monroe, Jr. and F. M. Weston) and May 3, 1961 (Dauphin Island, Owen Davies); most seen, 17, November 1, 1958 (Fall Count, Mobile Bay Area).

Scissor-tailed Flycatcher

Muscivora forficata (Gmelin)   [443]   (Plate 25, facing page 344)

This spectacular bird has a *pearly-gray body* and two *black* and *pink tail feathers* which are *nine inches long*, although the bird does not equal the Eastern Kingbird in bulk. The Scissor-tailed Flycatcher's wings, bill, and feet are black, and its sides and wing linings are brilliant pink. Immature birds show less pink and have shorter tails.

In fall this flycatcher is rare to uncommon on the Gulf Coast of Alabama, where it may winter. In spring it is rare both on the coast and inland. (See Map

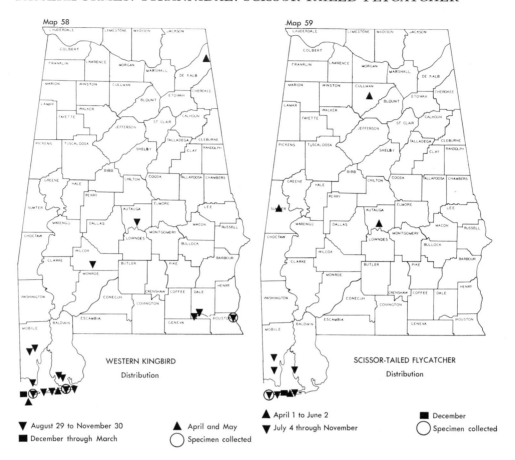

Map 58

Map 59

WESTERN KINGBIRD
Distribution

SCISSOR-TAILED FLYCATCHER
Distribution

▼ August 29 to November 30   ▲ April and May
■ December through March   ◯ Specimen collected

▲ April 1 to June 2   ■ December
▼ July 4 through November ◯ Specimen collected

59.) Nowhere in the state is it known to nest. It frequents open areas and chooses exposed perches, favoring telephone wires, and it acts much like a kingbird.

NESTING AND FOOD. In its bulky, poorly-made nest, usually at medium height on a horizontal limb, it lays four to six brown-spotted, creamy-white eggs. Like all flycatchers, which are primarily insect-eaters, it eats large numbers of beetles, bees, wasps, flies, grasshoppers, locusts, cotton worms, butterflies, bugs, and lacewings. Occasionally it eats small fruits, berries, and seeds.

DISTRIBUTION. The Scissor-tailed Flycatcher breeds from eastern New Mexico and southeastern Kansas east to western Arkansas and western Louisiana and south to southern Texas. It is casual on migration west to California, north to Manitoba and New Brunswick, and east to the Atlantic Coast. It winters from southeastern Texas to Panama and occasionally along the northern Gulf Coast and in Florida.

[346]

OCCURRENCE IN ALABAMA. (Normal: October 5 to November 1 and April 21 to May; Out-of-season: June 2, July 4, and December 27.) *Tennessee Valley*: No record. *Mountain Region*: June 2, 1957 (Cullman, David Brown). *Piedmont*: No record. *Upper Coastal Plain*: April 24, 1953 (Livingston, Amy Mason) and May 1889 or 1890 (specimen not preserved, Autaugaville, L. S. Golsan). *Lower Coastal Plain*: No record. *Gulf Coast*: October 5 (1956, specimen in Univ. of Ala. collection, Dauphin Island, T. A. Imhof and Lois McCollough) to November 1 (1958, 4 birds, Theodore, Bellingrath Gardens, and Fort Morgan, T. A. Imhof, B. L. Monroe, Jr., and F. M. Weston); also April 21, 1956 (Fort Morgan, B. L. Monroe, Jr. and F. M. Weston); April 26, 1960 (Dauphin Island, J. L. Dorn); July 4, 1958 (Dauphin Island, C. W. Summerour) and December 27, 1954 (Fort Morgan, O. L. Austin, Jr.).

Great Crested Flycatcher

Myiarchus crinitus (Linnaeus) [452] (Plate 25, facing page 344)
OTHER NAMES: Crested Flycatcher, Yellow Kingbird

The size of a robin, this flycatcher is olive-green above and has two yellowish wing bars, a *gray throat* and *chest, yellow belly*, and a *reddish-brown tail*. Its long head feathers are often raised in a crest. Its common call is one-syllabled and loud, rising in pitch and increasing in volume at the end.

The Great Crested Flycatcher and the Eastern Wood Pewee are the most common woodland flycatchers of Alabama. The Great Crested is a summer resident which nests throughout the state and is equally common in pines or hardwoods, in wilder woodlands or around farms, and in wooded suburbs. It is easy to find, for it calls often and uses exposed perches.

NESTING. The Great Crested Flycatcher nests in holes, using natural cavities, abandoned woodpecker holes, nest boxes near houses or in rather open woods, and (rarely) even mail boxes. The nest box should be rustic, placed eight to twenty feet above the ground, and built with the following dimensions: six inches square, eight to ten inches high, and with an entrance two inches in diameter, two inches from the top. The bird uses dead leaves to fill up a large cavity and provide a foundation, and then builds the nest proper, using a great variety of materials, but almost always including a snake skin or feathers. The four to six creamy to buffy eggs are handsomely marked with various shades of brown and lavender.

FOOD. This species lives almost entirely on insects. It eats large numbers of beetles (including weevils), moths, caterpillars, grasshoppers, katydids, crickets, sawflies, cicadas, bugs, flies, bees, and wasps. In much smaller amounts it takes dragonflies, spiders, a few lizards, and wild fruit, especially that of sassafras, mulberry, and Virginia creeper. At feeding stations in Alabama it eats peanuts.

DISTRIBUTION. The Great Crested Flycatcher breeds from Saskatchewan and southern Quebec south to central Texas and southern Florida. It winters from southern Texas and southern Florida south through Central America to Colombia.

OCCURRENCE IN ALABAMA. (March 21 to October 12.) *Tennessee Valley*: April 14 (1890, Leighton, F. W. McCormack and 1948, Russellville, E. O. Willis) to September 12 (1958, Wheeler Refuge, T. A. Imhof and others). *Mountain Region*: March 25 (1952, Fairfield, T. A. Imhof) to September 24 (1936, Easonville, St. Clair Co., H. M. Stevenson); most seen, 26, June 14, 1952 (Calhoun Co., T. A. Imhof and others). *Piedmont*: March 28 (1936, Auburn, H. S. Peters and 1954, Auburn, F. W. Fitch and John Pond) to September 11 (1958, Auburn, Lovett Williams). *Upper Coastal Plain*: March 27 (1939, Tuscaloosa, H. M. Stevenson) to September 17 (1951, Montgomery, C. W. Summerour); most seen, 20, May 17, 1952 (Lowndes Co., Ala. Orn. Soc.). *Lower Coastal Plain*: March 23 (1957, Choctaw Bluff, M. W. Gaillard) to September 20 (1957, Andalusia, T. A. Imhof and Lovett Williams). *Gulf Coast*: March 21 (1933, Fairhope, Helen Edwards) to October 12 (1958, Fort Morgan, J. C. and Margaret Robinson); most seen, 110, April 26, 1958 (Spring Count, Mobile Bay Area).

TIME OF BREEDING. Data on 30 nestings: Building, April 24 to May 8; eggs, May 14 to June 9; young in nest, June 4 to July 15; young just out of nest, July 1.

Ash-throated Flycatcher

Myiarchus cinerascens (Lawrence)   [454]   (Plate 25, facing page 344)

This flycatcher is a *small, pale,* western counterpart of the *Great Crested Flycatcher.* The ash-throated bird has a paler brown back, very pale yellow under parts, and a *white throat.* Its bill is *entirely black,* in contrast to the bill of the Great Crested Flycatcher, which has a yellowish lower mandible.

In Alabama, the Ash-throated Flycatcher is accidental on the coast in late fall. It lives in woods but also frequents open, dry areas.

NESTING AND FOOD. This bird lays its four or five brown-streaked whitish eggs in natural cavities of a wide variety, especially liking abandoned woodpecker holes. It seldom uses a snake skin; otherwise its choice of nesting materials is much like that of the Great Crested Flycatcher. It feeds on various flying and crawling insects, of which bugs, caterpillars, bees, wasps, flies, beetles, grasshoppers, plant lice, leafhoppers, and cicadas form the bulk. The small amount of fruit it eats includes chiefly elderberries and mistletoe berries.

DISTRIBUTION. The Ash-throated Flycatcher breeds from eastern Washington and western Colorado south to central Mexico. It winters from the southwestern United States south to El Salvador, and occurs rarely on migration eastward on the Gulf Coast to Pensacola.

OCCURRENCE IN ALABAMA. *Gulf Coast only*: November 3, 1958 (specimen in Louisiana State Univ. collection, Dauphin Island, Lovett Williams and R. W. Skinner, *Auk*, 76:528).

Eastern Phoebe

Sayornis phoebe (Latham) [456] (Plate 25, facing page 344)
OTHER NAMES: Bridge Pewee, Tick Bird

This phoebe is dark gray above and white to very pale yellow below, and it has a *very dark head,* black bill, and dusky flanks. It lacks the eye ring of the smaller *Empidonax* flycatchers and the wing bars and yellow lower mandible of the Eastern Wood Pewee. The Eastern Phoebe can always be recognized by its *tail-wagging habit* and its *voice.* The song, which the name phoebe suggests, is a rather nasal one of two syllables with the second syllable alternately higher, then lower, than the first. The usual call is a *chip* which closely resembles that of the Swamp Sparrow but is nevertheless useful in locating and identifying this species in winter.

The Eastern Phoebe inhabits rather open woods, woods borders, clearings, roadsides, and the vicinity of farms and other homes, especially when they are near water. In Alabama it is a common and widely-distributed permanent resident north of the Coastal Plain and common on migration and in winter in the rest of the state. It breeds almost everywhere that it occurs in summer north of the Fall Line. (See Map 60.) In colder winters it may be absent from the mountain tops. Except on the Gulf Coast or in very rare cases inland, the Eastern Phoebe is our only winter flycatcher, and therefore the identification of any other flycatcher in Alabama in winter should be thoroughly substantiated.

NESTING. This phoebe builds its nest with grass and other plant fibers held together with mud and covered on the outside with moss. Usually the nest is heavily infested with lice. The bird always places its nest out of the weather—for example, under a bridge, culvert, dam, overhanging cliff, road-bank, or near the entrance of a cave or mine. Sometimes it nests in an abandoned or little-used building or on a porch. The three to five white eggs are often dotted faintly around the larger end with black or dark brown.

FOOD. The species eats large quantities of ants, wasps, bees, sawflies, beetles (including boll weevils), leafhoppers, bugs, flies, and mosquitoes. In lesser amounts it takes grasshoppers, crickets, moths, caterpillars, dragonflies, spiders, ticks, and millipedes, and a great variety of wild fruits, especially sumac.

[349]

DISTRIBUTION. The Eastern Phoebe breeds from central Mackenzie and southern Quebec south to New Mexico, Arkansas, central Alabama, and coastal North Carolina. It winters from northern Mexico, Texas, Tennessee, and coastal Maryland, occasionally north to southern Ontario and New England, south to southern Mexico.

OCCURRENCE IN ALABAMA. (Throughout the year.) *Tennessee Valley*: Permanent resident; most seen, 15, June 13, 1953 (Marshall Co., T. A. Imhof and others).

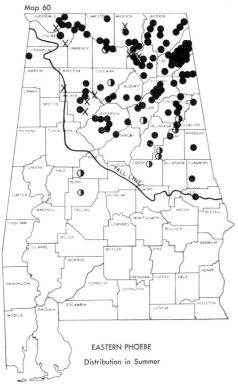

Map 60

EASTERN PHOEBE

Distribution in Summer

◐ May through August   ✗ Records prior to 1930
● Breeding positive

Mountain Region: Permanent resident; birds noted in Birmingham, away from breeding stations, September 11 (1954, T. A. Imhof) to May 2 (1940, H. M. Stevenson); most seen, 11, April 18, 1955 (Gadsden, T. A. Imhof and Edith Clark). *Piedmont*: Permanent resident; birds seen away from breeding stations, October 3 (1958, Lineville and Wedowee, T. A. Imhof and C. T. Hornady) to April 13 (1937, Auburn, *fide* H. G. Good). *Upper Coastal Plain*: September 29 (1934, Tuscaloosa, H. M. Stevenson and 1958, Marion, Lois McCollough) to April 13 (1957, Marion, Lois McCollough); also early May 1952 (Payne Lake, Hale Co., M. H. Perry) and May 14, 1955 (Marion, Lois McCollough); most seen, 15, December 27, 1957 (Christmas Count, Marion). *Lower Coastal Plain*: September 19 (1956, Barbour Co., J. E. Keeler) to April 18 (1958, Jackson, W. U. Harris). *Gulf Coast*: September 17 (1958, Dauphin Island, R. W. Skinner) to April 18 (1957, Dauphin Island, S. A. Gauthreaux and others); most seen, fall, 83, October 19, 1957 (Fall Count, Mobile Bay Area), winter, 68, December 29, 1956 (Christmas Count, Dauphin Island).

TIME OF BREEDING. Data on over 51 nestings: Building, March 6 to May 16; eggs, April 6 to July 12; young in nest, April 16 to July 2; young just out of nest, May 17 to at least June 12.

BANDING. A phoebe caught at Headland, November 1, 1949 was banded as a nestling in New Hampshire, June 21, 1949. Another found at Goshen, Pike Co., in January 1940 was banded as a nestling in Ohio, June 25, 1938.

Say's Phoebe

Sayornis saya (Bonaparte)   [457]   (Plate 25, facing page 344)

Say's Phoebe is slightly larger than the Eastern Phoebe, and it is paler above and darker below. Say's Phoebe has a gray breast, *rusty belly* and *under tail coverts,* and *black tail.* In color pattern it resembles a robin and in actions, a kingbird, but its *tail-twitching habit* and the dark head mark it as certainly a phoebe.

In Alabama this phoebe is accidental on the coast. It frequents dry, open areas and often feeds within a few feet of the ground.

NESTING AND FOOD. Like the Eastern Phoebe, this species chooses sheltered places out of the weather for its flat nest of grass, wool, and hair. The usual clutch is four or five white eggs. The bird feeds on insects and during cold weather varies this diet with fruit. The Alabama specimen (see below) contained a grasshopper, a cricket, and a scarab.

DISTRIBUTION. Say's Phoebe breeds from central Alaska and Manitoba south to central Mexico and east to the central Dakotas, western Kansas, and western Oklahoma. It winters from California and southern Texas to southern Mexico, and occurs casually, particularly in fall, to the Pacific, Atlantic, and Gulf coasts.

OCCURRENCE IN ALABAMA. specimen in Univ. of Ala. collection, Fort *Gulf Coast only*: September 19, 1958 (male Morgan, T. A. Imhof and F. M. Weston).

genus EMPIDONAX

These flycatchers are grayish above and whitish below and have a white eye ring and two white wing bars. Immature birds have buffy wing bars. With the exception of the Yellow-bellied Flycatcher in spring plumage, the four Alabama representatives of this genus are so similar that voice and habitat are the sole means of identifying them in the field. On migration, the task is even more difficult, for they are usually silent and, of course, not confined to their peculiar habitats. They usually occur then in shrubby, wooded areas within twelve feet of the ground. Recent mist-netting activities in the state have given bird students an opportunity to identify these birds in the hand, and have thus greatly increased our knowledge of the season of their occurrence in Alabama.

Except for the Acadian Flycatcher, which breeds commonly in Alabama, birds of this genus are, as a group, common migrants throughout the state. Thus, the status of these three species may be more common than listed. An indication of the season of occurrence of these birds may be obtained from the records of unidentified *Empidonax* flycatchers from the following key localities: *Wheeler Refuge*: April 10 to May 8 and September 12 to October 23 (*fide* T. Z. Atkeson, Jr.); *Birmingham*: April 30 (H. M. Stevenson) to May 24 (1940, H. M. Stevenson) and August 14 (1946, T. A. Imhof) to October 26 (1954, T. A. Imhof, Idalene Snead, and Emmy Brownlie); *Dauphin Island*: March 29 (1958, S. A. Gauthreaux) to May 16 (1960, J. L. Dorn) and August 24 (1956, T. A. Imhof and others) to November 7 (1959, T. A. Imhof and F. B. Daniel).

Yellow-bellied Flycatcher
Empidonax flaviventris (Baird and Baird) [463]

In spring, the Yellow-bellied Flycatcher is distinct because its under parts from throat to belly, are bright yellow, but in fall it cannot be safely distinguished from others of its genus, especially the Acadian Flycatcher, which often shows much yellow on the under parts. The Yellow-bellied Flycatcher breeds in swampy or boggy northern evergreens. Its call is a weak two-syllabled phrase much like the calls of the Eastern Wood Pewee and Semipalmated Plover.

Insofar as is known, this bird is a rare spring and fall migrant in Alabama. It frequents low, shrubby growth on migration. The species is not known to breed in the state.

NESTING AND FOOD. This flycatcher lays three or four white eggs, finely dotted or blotched with brown, in a large nest of small roots and grasses on or near the ground. This bird probably eats more ants than any other flycatcher. It also eats wasps, bees, bugs, flies, moths, caterpillars, spiders, and some berries and seeds, especially those of poison-ivy and mountain ash.

DISTRIBUTION. The Yellow-bellied Flycatcher breeds from northern British Columbia, southern Mackenzie, and central Quebec south to northern North Dakota and northern Pennsylvania. It winters from central Mexico to Panama.

OCCURRENCE IN ALABAMA. (April 16 to May 25 and September 5 to October 17.) *Tennessee Valley*: May 5, 1890 (specimen, not preserved, Leighton, F. W. McCormack) and May 10, 1941 (1 bird singing, Florence, H. M. Stevenson); September 5 and 19, 1960 (netted, Brownsboro, Madison Co., J. C. and Margaret Robinson). *Mountain Region*: April 16, 1955 (Gadsden, Idalene Snead and Edith Clark); Birmingham, May 12, 1937 (H. M. Stevenson); May 24, 1940 (H. M. Stevenson) and September 9 and 12, 1959 (netted, J. B. Sullivan). *Piedmont*: No record. *Upper Coastal Plain*: September 20 and 23, 1890 (2 specimens in the Avery collection, Greensboro, W. C. Avery). *Lower Coastal Plain*: No record. *Gulf Coast*: May 8, 1960 (Dauphin Island, G. H. and Jean Lowery) and May 25, 1957 (specimen in the Univ. of Ala. collection, Dauphin Island, T. A. Imhof and others) and September 9 (1959, netted, Dauphin Island, T. A. Imhof and J. B. Sullivan) to October 17 (1959, netted, Dauphin Island, T. A. Imhof); most seen, 5, netted September 19 and 20, 1958 (Fort Morgan, T. A. Imhof and F. M. Weston).

Acadian Flycatcher
Empidonax virescens (Vieillot) [465]   (Plate 25, facing page 344)

The Acadian Flycatcher wears more green than the other eastern members of its genus. It is grayish-olive on the back, shows some yellow on the belly,

[352]

and has the white eye ring typical of the *Empidonax* flycatchers. This bird lives in moist, southern, deciduous woods, and its distinctive call is a harsh explosive *spit-chee*. But when the bird moves from perch to perch on its breeding territory, it makes a sound like the twittering of chicks nestling under a hen. This second call has been compared to that of the Downy Woodpecker in the distance, and to the voice of a Mourning Dove in flight.

The Acadian Flycatcher is a common, breeding, summer resident in Alabama. It occurs in deep, shady, deciduous woods, especially along streams or in swamps, and it has a special liking for beeches and hornbeams. It occupies the lower limbs and branches, generally not more than twenty feet from the ground.

NESTING. The nest is a rather flimsy, shallow basket strung by its rim from thin, horizontal, parallel twigs of a hardwood, preferably over water, and about eight to twenty-five feet up. When possible the Acadian Flycatcher selects ironwood, hornbeam, elm, or beech, and upon rare occasions a pine, for nesting. In the South, including the Coastal Plain of Alabama, the nest is often composed entirely of Spanish moss. The two to four creamy white to buffy-white eggs are marked with minute brown dots around the larger end, and can usually be seen from below through the nest.

FOOD. The cankerworm is probably this bird's main item of food. It also eats wasps, bees, ants, caterpillars, moths, beetles, flies, crickets, grasshoppers, other insects, spiders, millipedes, and small amounts of wild fruit.

DISTRIBUTION. The Acadian Flycatcher breeds from South Dakota, southern Ontario, and central New England south to southern Texas and central Florida. It winters from Costa Rica to Ecuador and Venezuela.

OCCURRENCE IN ALABAMA. (April 8 to October 17.) *Tennessee Valley*: April 20 (1892, Leighton, F. W. McCormack) to October 7 (1960, netted, Brownsboro, J. C. and Margaret Robinson). *Mountain Region*: April 16 (1955, Gadsden, Edith Clark) to September 19 (1956, Gadsden, Edith Clark); most seen, 11, May 29, 1950 (Short Creek, Jefferson Co., T. A. Imhof) and May 30, 1949 (Warrior River near Lock 14, Tuscaloosa Co., T. A. Imhof and others). *Piedmont*: April 9 (1926, Auburn, H. G. Good) to September 22 (1957, Auburn, Lovett Williams). *Upper Coastal Plain*: April 15 (1913, Autaugaville, L. S. Golsan) to October 9 (1957, Livingston, Jenkins Jackson); most seen, 10, May 29, 1949 (Tuscaloosa, T. A. Imhof and others). *Lower Coastal Plain*: April 18 (1958, Jackson, T. A. Imhof, W. U. Harris, and J. R. Davis) to October 10 (1908, Castleberry, Conecuh Co., A. H. Howell). *Gulf Coast*: April 8 (1959, Bellingrath Gardens, Owen Davies) to October 17 (1959, netted, Dauphin Island, T. A. Imhof and others); most seen, 22, May 26, 1956 (Mount Vernon, T. A. Imhof and W. F. Colin).

TIME OF BREEDING. Data on over 20 nestings: Building, May 8 to June 2; eggs, May 14 to July 17; young in nest, May to June 25.

Traill's Flycatcher
Empidonax traillii (Audubon)   [466]
OTHER NAME: Alder Flycatcher

Traill's Flycatcher is dark grayish above and whitish below with a prominent whitish eye ring and two whitish wing bars. It is the brownest eastern member of its genus. It inhabits hedgerows, orchards, and alder and willow thickets, particularly those near streams. The sharp, explosive call may be either a sneezing *fits-bew'* or a hoarse *wee-beé-o*.

This bird is a rare fall migrant on the Gulf Coast of Alabama, where it has also been recorded once in spring. Inland in the Tennessee Valley and Mountain Region it has been recorded once in spring and several times in fall. Nowhere in the state is it known to nest. On migration it seems to prefer low, shrubby areas, often near water.

NESTING AND FOOD. Traill's Flycatcher builds a deep, thick, grassy cup in a crotch of a bush or low tree, and lays three to four creamy eggs, blotched and dotted with brown. Wasps, bees, ants, various flies, caterpillars, moths, bugs, and grasshoppers form the bulk of its food. It also eats dragonflies, May flies, ticks, spiders, millipedes, and elderberries and other small fruits.

DISTRIBUTION. Traill's Flycatcher breeds from central Alaska and central Quebec south to southern California, western Texas, Arkansas, western Maryland, and northern New Jersey, and in mountains to North Carolina. It winters from southern Mexico to Argentina.

OCCURRENCE IN ALABAMA. (Normal: August 29 to October 17; Out-of-season: April 10 and May 7.) *Tennessee Valley*: May 7, 1912 (1 bird in song, Florence, A. H. Howell) and September 5 and 26, 1960 (netted, Brownsboro, J. C. and Margaret Robinson). *Mountain Region*: September 11, 1959 (2 birds netted, Birmingham, J. B. Sullivan). *Piedmont*: No record. *Upper Coastal Plain*: No record. *Lower Coastal Plain*: No record. *Gulf Coast*: August 29 (1958, specimen in Florida State Univ. collection, Fort Morgan, B. L. Monroe, Jr., F. M. Weston, and H. M. Stevenson) to October 17 (1960, 1 netted, Dauphin Island, Margaret Robinson); also April 10, 1959 (1 netted, Dauphin Island, T. A. Imhof and others).

Least Flycatcher
Empidonax minimus (Baird and Baird)   [467]

This, the grayest eastern member of its genus, is dark grayish above and whitish below with a prominent whitish eye ring and two whitish wing bars. It inhabits rural areas, hedgerows, woods borders, and orchards. The call is a very sharp, easily-recognized, explosive *che-béc*, strongly accented on the second syllable.

In Alabama the Least Flycatcher is uncommon to rare on migration, recorded most often in fall and on the coast. The species is not known thus far to breed in Alabama, although it does in nearby states. Possible breeders would be likely to occur in June in northern Alabama in orchards or near houses in farming areas. On migration this species frequents low, shrubby places, especially those near water.

NESTING AND FOOD. The compact, well-made nest is firmly attached to an upright crotch or group of twigs, and the usual clutch is three or four creamy-white eggs. Ants, wasps, bees, beetles, bugs, flies, moths, caterpillars, and grasshoppers are the principal foods. Occasionally this bird also eats May flies, dragonflies, spiders, and wild berries such as blackberries and elderberries.

DISTRIBUTION. The Least Flycatcher breeds from southwestern Yukon and central Quebec south to British Columbia, Kansas, the Ohio Valley, and in mountains to northern Georgia. It winters from southern Mexico to Panama.

OCCURRENCE IN ALABAMA. (April 24 to May 8 and August 28 to November 7.) *Tennessee Valley*: April 24, 1914 (specimen in U. S. National Museum, Muscle Shoals, A. H. Howell) and September 12 and 29, 1960 (netted, Brownsboro, J. C. and Margaret Robinson). *Mountain Region*: April 30 (1936, Birmingham, H. M. Stevenson) to May 8 (1948, Birmingham, T. A. Imhof) and September 9 (1953, Fairfield, T. A. Imhof) to October 8 (1954, ceilometer casualty, now specimen in Univ. of Cincinnati collection, Birmingham, T. A. Imhof and F. B. Daniel). *Piedmont*: No record. *Upper Coastal Plain*: No record. *Lower Coastal Plain*: No record. *Gulf Coast*: August 28 (1958, Elberta, H. M. Stevenson) to November 7 (1959, Dauphin Island, H. M. Stevenson and others); includes several specimens and netted birds.

Eastern Wood Pewee

Contopus virens (Linnaeus)   [461]   (Plate 25, facing page 344)
OTHER NAME: Tick Bird

This wood pewee is a plain flycatcher, the size of a sparrow, with a dark gray back, a lighter belly, and dark flanks, and it has *no eye ring*. Although it closely resembles the Eastern Phoebe, the Eastern Wood Pewee has *two white wing bars* and a *yellow lower mandible*, and it does not wag its tail. This bird's call, which suggests its name, is a plaintive whistle, repeated endlessly and heard when most birds are silent—for example, at noon in midsummer.

The Eastern Wood Pewee is a common, breeding, summer resident which shares with the Great Crested Flycatcher almost every patch of woods in Alabama. It may be a little more partial to deciduous woods, but it is versatile enough to adapt itself to pines, even the almost pure forests of longleaf and slash pine.

NESTING. The nest is small and dainty, shaped like a shallow cup, and well camouflaged and lichen-covered. Usually it rests in the level fork of a small limb well out from the trunk of a large tree. The bird lays two or three whitish or cream-colored eggs, marked with various shades of brown and lavender.

FOOD. This flycatcher feeds mainly on flies, but it also takes wasps, bees, ants, beetles, caterpillars, moths, grasshoppers, and bugs. Occasionally it eats spiders, millipedes, and wild berries.

DISTRIBUTION. The Eastern Wood Pewee breeds from southern Manitoba and southern Quebec south to southern Texas and central Florida. It winters from Costa Rica to Peru.

OCCURRENCE IN ALABAMA. (April 3 to November 8.) *Tennessee Valley*: April 18 (1891, Leighton, F. W. McCormack) to October 22 (1935, Wheeler Dam, J. Bamberg). *Mountain Region*: April 7 (1960, Gadsden, Edith Clark) to November 5 (1958, Gadsden, Edith Clark); most seen, 40, September 14, 1946 (Birmingham, T. A. Imhof). *Piedmont*: April 3 (1936, Auburn, H. S. Peters) to October 21 (1939, specimen in Auburn Univ. collection, Auburn, D. H. McIntosh). *Upper Coastal Plain*: April 4 (1914, Autaugaville, L. S. Golsan) to October 24 (1890, Greensboro, W. C. Avery); most seen, 12, April 23, 1955 (Autauga Co., E. G. Holt and T. A. Imhof). *Lower Coastal Plain*: April 5 (1957, Jackson, W. U. Harris and T. A. Imhof) to October 23 (1957, Jackson, W. U. Harris); most seen, 40, September 17, 1958 (Camden, Lovett Williams). *Gulf Coast*: April 8 (1933, Fairhope, Helen Edwards) to November 8 (1959, Dauphin Island, Idalene Snead and others); most seen, 65, September 16, 1960, after Hurricane Ethel (Dauphin Island, J. L. Dorn).

TIME OF BREEDING. Data on 17 nestings: Building, May 9 to 24; eggs, May 6 to July 5; young in nest, May 26 to July 14; young just out of nest, June 1 to August 10.

Olive-sided Flycatcher

Nuttallornis borealis (Swainson)   [459]   (Plate 25, facing page 344)

Although it resembles the somewhat smaller Eastern Wood Pewee in color, the Olive-sided Flycatcher is chunky and has a big head, a large bill, and a short tail. The *white* of the throat extends downward in a *narrow line separating* the *dark* of the two *sides,* and a *tuft* of *white feathers,* usually visible, *sticks out* from *behind* the *wings* near the base of the tail. This bird's call is a three-syllabled whistle.

In Alabama, the Olive-sided Flycatcher is a rare spring transient and an uncommon fall transient which occurs mostly inland. It is not known to nest in the state. Even on migration it usually occupies an exposed perch, selecting the edge of an opening in the woods near water when it is available.

NESTING AND FOOD. The nest is a rather large cup made of twigs and lined with *Usnea* moss and other fine materials. It is well hidden, far out from the trunk, usually on the lowest branch of a northern conifer near a swamp or bog. The three eggs are beautiful, creamy-white to pale-salmon marked with small blotches or spots of light brown. For food, this species takes flying insects, seldom varying its diet with crawling insects or fruit as do other flycatchers. Apparently more than any other bird, it lives on one order of insects, *Hymenoptera,* or bees, ants, and wasps, especially honeybees and flying ants. It also eats beetles, moths, bugs, dragonflies, grasshoppers, and flies.

DISTRIBUTION. The Olive-sided Flycatcher breeds from northern Alaska and central Quebec south to Lower California, central Arizona, northern Wisconsin, and southern New England, and in mountains to Tennessee and North Carolina. It winters from Colombia and Venezuela to Peru.

OCCURRENCE IN ALABAMA. (April 20 to May 15 and August 30 to October 22.) *Tennessee Valley*: No record. *Mountain Region*: Early May (1946, Birmingham, Isabel Tipton and Blanche Dean) to May 15 (1949, Birmingham, T. A. Imhof and others) and September 16 (1954, Birmingham, T. A. Imhof) to October 20 (1935, Birmingham, H. M. Stevenson). *Piedmont*: May 9, 1908 (Woodbine, A. A. Saunders). *Upper Coastal Plain*: October 3 (1934, 2 birds, Autauga Co., L. S. Golsan) to October 22 (1919, 2 birds, Autauga Co., L. S. Golsan); also April 20, 1957 (Marion, Lois McCollough); male specimen, not preserved, October 17, 1915 (Bear Swamp, L. S. Golsan). *Lower Coastal Plain*: No record. *Gulf Coast*: August 30, 1959 (Dauphin Island, H. A. J. and Cora Evans); September 10, 1959 (Dauphin Island, T. A. Imhof and J. B. Sullivan); October 7, 1956 (Dauphin Island, S. M. Russell and E. O. Willis); and October 15, 1939 (Spring Hill College, J. L. Dorn).

Vermilion Flycatcher
Pyrocephalus rubinus (Boddaert)   [471]   (Plate 25, facing page 344)

The Vermilion Flycatcher is a bit smaller than the Eastern Phoebe. The male has a black back, tail, bill, and streak through the eye, and its *head* and *under parts* are a *brilliant vermilion-red*. The *female* is dark brown above with a black bill and a dark streak through the eye, and is streaked below with a *pinkish belly*. Immature birds are similar to the female but they have a yellowish belly. Although female and immature birds strikingly resemble the Myrtle Warbler in color, they act very much like a small phoebe. The call of the Vermilion Flycatcher is also like that of a phoebe.

This western flycatcher is casual in winter on the Gulf Coast of Alabama, and it has been recorded once in winter inland. It is not known to nest here. In general it occurs in about the same habitats in winter as does the Eastern Phoebe, and it particularly prefers to perch low over water, especially in live oaks.

[357]

NESTING AND FOOD. This bird usually lays three whitish eggs, heavily marked with dark brown and lavender. The nest of twigs lined with finer materials is in a small horizontal fork or crotch from eight to twenty feet above the ground, and near water. The bird subsists mainly on flying insects including small beetles, flies, bees, and grasshoppers.

DISTRIBUTION. The Vermilion Flycatcher breeds from southern Nevada, New Mexico, and southern Texas south to Chile and Argentina. In winter North American birds fly irregularly west to San Diego and east to Tallahassee.

OCCURRENCE IN ALABAMA. (November 1 to mid-January.) *Tennessee Valley*: No record. *Mountain Region*: No record. *Piedmont*: No record. *Upper Coastal Plain*: January 1, 1960, a young male (Marion Fish Culture Station, D. C. Holliman, T. A. Imhof, and Joseph Imhof). *Lower Coastal Plain*: No record. *Gulf Coast*: November 1, 1958 (immature specimen in Univ. of Ala. collection, Fort Morgan, B. L. Monroe, Jr. and F. M. Weston); November 6, 1948, a male (Elberta, F. M. Weston); November 15, 1943 (Fort Morgan, J. L. Dorn); December 29, 1956, a female (Dauphin Island, Grace Snead and Clustie McTyeire); and mid-January 1954 (Gulf State Park, M. H. Fisher).

FAMILY ALAUDIDAE: LARKS

Horned Lark
Eremophila alpestris (Linnaeus) [474] (Plate 43, facing page 568)

The Horned Lark is a buffy-brown bird, lighter-colored on the belly, and slightly larger than a sparrow in size. Its small, black, feathered horns are often inconspicuous. *A broad black stripe extends* down *from the eye almost to a broad chest band, also black.* This bird has a yellowish throat and face, and over its eye is another broad stripe, which may be yellow or white. The young bird is duller but still easily recognizable as a Horned Lark. In flight, the species can be recognized by the pale belly, *black tail,* and the frequent, shrill flight calls. Its song is longer and more elaborate than the flight call but of the same general quality. This bird never perches in trees; it walks but never hops when on the ground; and it sings both in flight and on the ground.

In Alabama this species is a local, breeding, summer resident in the Tennessee Valley and the eastern part of the Mountain Region. It is uncommon in most places, but it is common in Limestone County. In winter it is abundant in the Tennessee Valley, common to locally abundant in the Black Belt, common but local in the intervening area, and casual on the Gulf Coast. (See Map 61.) It often becomes more numerous in severe weather when regions to the north are snow covered. It is a bird of the open country, such as prairies, golf courses, airports, large pastures, extensive lawns, newly-plowed fields, bare shorelines, or other bare or sparsely-grown places.

NESTING. This lark builds its nest of grasses in a depression it digs in bare ground. It is usually somewhat sheltered on the windward (north-westerly) side. The two to five gray eggs are finely-spotted throughout with cinnamon-brown.

FOOD. A large proportion of this bird's food is seed, for the most part weed seeds, especially those of bristlegrass and ragweed, and waste grain. It also eats insects, particularly in August, when it takes grasshoppers, ants, flies, beetles (including weevils), and wasps.

DISTRIBUTION. The Horned Lark is circumpolar, occurring south to North Africa and northern South America. In North America it breeds from Alaska and Baffin Island south into Mexico except for the Atlantic Coastal Plain south of North Carolina and the Gulf Coastal Plain east of western Louisiana, in which region it usually occurs only irregularly in winter. It also retires from more northerly regions in winter.

OCCURRENCE IN ALABAMA.
(Throughout the year.) *Tennessee Valley*: Permanent resident; abundant from late October to March; most seen, summer, 29 adults, May 4, 1957 (southern Limestone Co., T. A. Imhof and others), winter, "thousands," February 10, 1951 (Bridgeport Airport, Adele West) and 1000, January 17, 1959 (Huntsville, Margaret Robinson). *Mountain Region*: Permanent resident; occurs at places where it does not breed from early November to late February; most seen, summer, 8, June 4, 1954 (Fort Payne, T. A. Imhof and many others), winter, 100+, most of January 1944 (Camp Sibert, Etowah Co., T. A. Imhof) and 60-70, December 12 to 27, 1917 (Longview, Shelby Co., L. S. Golsan). *Piedmont*: January 2, 1954 (14 birds, Auburn, Christmas Count). *Upper Coastal Plain*: November 15 (1957, 160+ birds, Marion, Lois McCollough) to February 26 (1959, Montgomery, R. W. Skinner); most seen, 355, December 27, 1957 (Christmas Count, Marion). *Lower Coastal Plain*: No record. *Gulf Coast*: A mounted specimen in the Glennon collection in the Point Clear Hotel, obtained locally prior to 1916 (*fide* A. H. Howell) and a few during the severe freeze of January 1940 on the Spring Hill College Golf Course (J. L. Dorn).

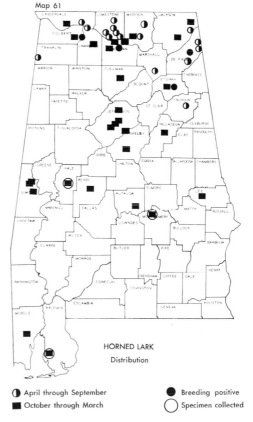

Map 61

HORNED LARK
Distribution

◑ April through September   ● Breeding positive
■ October through March   ○ Specimen collected

[360]

Richard A. Parks

TIME OF BREEDING. Data on 3 nestings: Eggs, May 22 and 25; young flying by June 4.

SUBSPECIES. Local observers are cautioned *not* to identify Horned Larks in the field in Alabama as to subspecies. Although the local breeder is probably *E. a. praticola* (Henshaw), no breeding specimen to my knowledge has been collected in the state. While *alpestris* and *praticola* are the only forms collected in winter in Alabama, collecting has by no means been exhaustive, and a confusing array of western and northern forms, looking like either of the substantiated races, may possibly occur.

FAMILY HIRUNDINIDAE: SWALLOWS

Swallows are small, long-winged birds of graceful flight. Their bills, wide at the base, are shaped like those of the flycatchers, and their feet are weak. They usually nest in protected places and often build with mud, lining the nest with feathers. The greater part of their day is spent coursing about over open spaces, especially over water or short-grass areas, to catch the flying insects which almost exclusively form their food. They migrate mostly by day, generally in river valleys and along coastlines.

Tree Swallow

Iridoprocne bicolor (Vieillot)　[614]　(Plate 26, facing page 360)
OTHER NAME: White-bellied Swallow

The Tree Swallow has an iridescent blue-black back, in some lights appearing greenish, and *immaculately white under parts* from bill to tail. The *immature* bird is *brown above,* but it is as *white* on the *belly as* the *adult.*

This is the only swallow on the Alabama list not known to breed in the state. On migration it is common nearly throughout, especially in river valleys, and it is locally abundant in the Tennessee Valley and on the Gulf Coast. In winter it is locally abundant on the Gulf Coast, especially near the head of Mobile Bay and the north shore of Mississippi Sound, but inland it has been recorded only a few times in winter. It frequents open areas—extensive fields, ponds, rivers, marshes, and the like.

NESTING AND FOOD. The Tree Swallow lays four to six pure white eggs in a nest of straw lined with feathers. It finds tree holes, other natural cavities, and nest boxes, especially those in open areas, for the nest. The bird lives largely on insects, particularly flies, beetles, ants, bees, wasps, and bugs, and in smaller amounts moths, grasshoppers, dragonflies, other insects, and spiders. In fall and winter it turns to berries for a good part of its food, and particularly favors bayberries, gallberries, and those of wax myrtle, red cedar, and dogwood.

[361]

DISTRIBUTION. The Tree Swallow breeds from northern Alaska and northern Quebec south to southern California, Utah, Kansas, Tennessee, and Virginia, casually south to Louisiana and Mississippi. It winters from southern California, southern Texas, and the northern Gulf Coast, and along the Atlantic Coast to Virginia, and occasionally to southern New England, south to Honduras and Cuba.

OCCURRENCE IN ALABAMA. (July 8 to May 16.) *Tennessee Valley*: Last week in March (Leighton, F. W. McCormack) to May 4 (1957, Wheeler Refuge, Ala. Orn. Soc.) and August 21 (1953, Wheeler Refuge, D. C. Hulse and 1957, Wheeler Refuge, T. A. Imhof, T. Z. Atkeson, Jr., and W. M. Depreast) to October 10 (1959, 200 birds, Wheeler Refuge, T. A. Imhof); also December 8, 1940 (Wheeler Refuge, Clarence Cottam, J. H. Steenis, and T. Z. Atkeson, Jr.). *Mountain Region*: April 2 (1936, Birmingham, H. M. Stevenson) to May 8 (1953, Birmingham, T. A. Imhof) and July 8 (1949, Birmingham, T. A. Imhof) to September 25 (1953, Birmingham, T. A. Imhof); most seen, 24, April 27, 1952 (Fort Payne, Blanche Dean and T. A. Imhof). *Piedmont*: March 30 (1955, Auburn, H. G. Good) to April 30 (1955, Auburn, H. G. Good and T. A. Imhof); no fall dates. *Upper Coastal Plain*: March 7 (1953, Marion, T. A. Imhof) to May 1 (1956, bird found dead, Montgomery Co., R. W. Skinner) and September 19 (1956, Clanton, T. A. Imhof) to November 6 (1954, Marion, Lois McCollough); also January 26, 1958 (Marion, Lois McCollough); most seen, spring, 215, April 11, 1956 (Marion, Lois McCollough), fall, 700+, October 8, 1959 (Montgomery, T. A. Imhof and R. W. Skinner). *Lower Coastal Plain*: September 20 (1957, Andalusia, T. A. Imhof and Lovett Williams) to October 20 (1956, Lake Tholloco, T. A. Imhof and L. C. Crawford) and February 26 (1955, Florala, T. A. Imhof) to May 1 (1952, Andalusia, W. R. Middleton). *Gulf Coast*: August 24 (1956, Theodore, H. M. Stevenson, M. W. Gaillard, and T. A. Imhof) to May 16 (1958, Dauphin Island, T. A. Imhof, M. W. Gaillard, and J. C. Gray); most seen, spring, 3100, April 21, 1956 (Cochrane Causeway, H. M. Stevenson and Lovett Williams), fall, 10,000+, October 18, 1959 (Mobile Co., T. A. Imhof and others), winter, 1512, December 30, 1960; 1350, December 27, 1958; and 1050, December 28, 1956 (Christmas Counts, Dauphin Island).

Bank Swallow

Riparia riparia (Linnaeus) [616] (Plate 26, facing page 360)
OTHER NAME: Sand Martin

This swallow is dark *brown above* and clear *white below* with a *narrow,* well-defined *brown breast band.* The Rough-winged Swallow and the immature Tree Swallow also have brown backs, but the former has a dusky throat to distinguish it, and the latter has clear white under parts and lacks the breast band.

On migration in Alabama the Bank Swallow is common and sometimes abundant on the Gulf Coast and in the Tennessee Valley, especially in fall, and uncommon to fairly common elsewhere in the state. It breeds rarely and irregularly in the northern half of the state, but it is probably frequently over-looked among the many Rough-winged Swallows which are similar in appearance and also nest in banks. On migration the Bank Swallow occurs over most open areas with other swallows.

NESTING. This swallow nests in colonies near water and almost always in holes it digs near the top of a bank. The nest proper is usually higher in the tunnel than the entrance, and is made of grasses and lined with finer materials, generally including feathers. The typical clutch is five pure white eggs.

FOOD. Like other swallows, the Bank Swallow lives almost entirely on insects. These include beetles, a large number of boll weevils, flying ants, wasps, leafhoppers, treehoppers, plant lice, house flies, crane flies, dragonflies, a few spiders, and even some caterpillars.

DISTRIBUTION. In the Western Hemisphere the Bank Swallow breeds from northern Alaska and southern Labrador south to southern California, Texas, northern Alabama, and eastern Virginia. It winters from Colombia and British Guiana south to Peru and northern Argentina.

OCCURRENCE IN ALABAMA. (April 6 to October 15.) *Tennessee Valley*: Bred at Wilson and probably also Wheeler dams; occurrence away from these places: April 19 (Wheeler Refuge, *fide* T. Z. Atkeson, Jr.) to May 22 (1959, Decatur, T. A. Imhof, D. C. Hulse, and R. W. Skinner) and July 23 (Wheeler Refuge, *fide* T. Z. Atkeson, Jr.) to September 12 (1958, Wheeler Refuge, T. A. Imhof and others); most seen, spring, 120, May 4, 1957 (Wheeler Refuge, Ala. Orn. Soc.), fall, 500, August 21, 1957 (Wheeler Refuge, T. A. Imhof, T. Z. Atkeson, Jr., and W. M. Depreast). *Mountain Region*: April 6 (1959, 15 birds, Lamar Co., Owen Davies) to June 4 (1954, Fort Payne, T. A. Imhof and others) and July 26 (1949, Birmingham, T. A. Imhof) to September 24 (1936, Eason-ville, St. Clair Co., H. M. Stevenson); most seen, 50+, May 6, 1958 (Birmingham, T. A. Imhof and Idalene Snead). *Piedmont*: April 16 (1952, Auburn, H. G. Good) to May 5 (1952, Auburn, F. W. Fitch and Dillon). *Upper Coastal Plain*: April 19 (1955, Marion, T. A. Imhof) to May 5 (1957, Marion, Lois McCollough) and August 29 (1938, Tusca-loosa, H. M. Stevenson) to October 15 (1956, Elmore Co., J. E. Keeler); bred in Autauga Co., in 1895 (L. S. Golsan); most seen, 375, May 4, 1957 (Marion, Lois McCollough). *Lower Coastal Plain*: May 9, 1958 (Florala, T. A. Imhof); September 20, 1957 (Lake Tholloco, T. A. Imhof and Lovett Williams); and September 20, 1958 (5 birds, Camden, Lovett Williams). *Gulf Coast*: April 7 (1959, 3 birds, Dauphin Island, Owen Davies) to May 17 (1958, Cochrane Causeway, T. A. Imhof and M. W. Gaillard) and July 14 (1955, Bay Minette, Mrs. A. L. Whigham) to October 6 (1956, 4 birds, Fall Count, Mobile Bay Area); most seen, "many thousands," September 14, 1929 (Cochrane Causeway, Helen Edwards), 180, August 28, 1958 (Cochrane Causeway, H. M. Stevenson).

TIME OF BREEDING. Data on 2+ nestings: One or 2 fresh eggs, May 5 (1895, Washington Ferry, Autauga Co., L. S. Golsan); building or feeding young, June 10 (1955, Wilson Dam, T. A. Imhof, Malcolm Harden, and Alfred Walker).

Rough-winged Swallow

Stelgidopteryx ruficollis (Vieillot) [617] (Plate 26, facing page 360)
OTHER NAMES: Sand Martin, Gully Martin, Bank Swallow, Gully Bird

This swallow has a dark *brown back* and white under parts with a *dusky throat*. It is distinct from Alabama's other brown-backed swallows, the immature Tree Swallow and the Bank Swallow, which, except for the narrow brown breast band of the latter, are clear white below, including the throat.

The Rough-winged Swallow is a common to abundant, breeding, summer resident almost throughout Alabama. It is less common as a breeder near the coast and is not known to breed south of Mobile, but it is common to abundant there on migration, and it winters occasionally in small numbers. It frequents the neighborhood of rivers, creeks, and ponds, especially near exposed banks, and on migration flocks over such open areas as cultivated fields, lakes, rivers, and marshes.

NESTING. The nest is usually in a burrow in an exposed bank, but the Rough-winged Swallow uses almost any other reasonable substitute. The nest proper is usually a bulky, loose affair of pine straw and dead leaves, but when it is built outside a cavity it is more sturdy. One nest was built on a buttress on the boat that daily ran the 24 miles between Guntersville and Hobbs Island in 1913, and the birds followed the boat all the way to care for their young (A. H. Howell, 1928:268-269). This swallow usually lays five to seven white eggs.

FOOD. Flies make up a large part of the diet of this swallow. Ants, wasps, bugs, and beetles (including boll weevils) are frequent items, and to a lesser extent it eats moths, caterpillars, dragonflies, May flies, grasshoppers, and spiders.

DISTRIBUTION. The Rough-winged Swallow breeds from British Columbia and southwestern Quebec south to Peru and Argentina. It winters north to southern California, Texas, the northern Gulf Coast, and Florida, casually to coastal South Carolina.

OCCURRENCE IN ALABAMA. (Normal: March 8 to November 6; Out-of-season: December 21 and 27 and January 2.) *Tennessee Valley*: March 22 (1941, Florence, H. M. Stevenson) to October 18 (1959, Wheeler Refuge, J. C. and Margaret Robinson); most seen, spring, 500, May 4, 1957 (Wheeler Refuge, Ala. Orn. Soc.), fall, 600, August 29, 1949 (Wheeler Refuge, T. A. Imhof). *Mountain Region*: March 13 (1955, Birmingham, Blanche Dean) to September 25 (1953, Oak Mountain State Park, T. A. Imhof and others); most seen, 53, June 18, 1950 (Birmingham, T. A. Imhof). *Piedmont*:

March 25 (1959, Auburn, Lovett Williams) to at least June 26 (1950, Roanoke, H. M. Stevenson). *Upper Coastal Plain*: March 8 (1959, Marion, Lois McCollough) to October 15 (1955, Marion, Lois McCollough); most seen, summer, 250+, July 13, 1957 (Demopolis, T. A. Imhof and others), fall, 300+, October 8, 1959 (Montgomery, T. A. Imhof and R. W. Skinner). *Lower Coastal Plain*: March 15 (1958, Jackson, W. U. Harris and 1959, Camden, Lovett Williams) to October 1 (1957, Jackson, W. U. Harris). *Gulf Coast*: March 13 (1938, specimen in U. S. National Museum, Bayou La Batre, T. D. Burleigh) to

November 6 (1948, Fort Morgan, F. M. Weston); also 1, December 21, 1957 (Cedar Point, Lois McCollough), 20, December 27, 1958 (Alabama Port, Idalene Snead and others) and 2, January 2, 1960 (Alabama Port and Bayou La Batre, T. A. Imhof) and a few in winter at Spring Hill (J. L. Dorn); most seen, 300, August 27, 1946 (Gulf Shores, T. Imhof).

TIME OF BREEDING. Data on 55+ nestings: Building, April 9 to 27; eggs, May 1 to 26; young in nest, May 7 to June 19; young just out of nest, June 4 to July.

Barn Swallow

Hirundo rustica Linnaeus [613] (Plate 26, facing page 360)

The Barn Swallow has *dark-blue upper parts*, a *reddish throat*, and salmon-pink under parts. Some birds, particularly on the Gulf Coast, have whitish under parts. This is the only swallow native to Alabama with a *deeply-forked tail*.

In this state, the Barn Swallow is common to abundant on migration and a fairly common but local, breeding, summer resident at both ends of the state, that is, the Tennessee and other nearby valleys and the Gulf Coast. (See Map 62.) The species usually occurs near water, but from time to time it frequents open crop or pasture land, especially that in the vicinity of barns or bridges, dams, piers, and other structures built over or near water.

NESTING. The Barn Swallow nests, often in colonies, around almost any building, especially preferring those near water. In the Tennessee Valley, it chooses bridges and dams and occasionally barns and other outbuildings, but at Fort Morgan it builds inside the fort itself, or when driven away, in other buildings in the vicinity. It builds with mud and straw and lines the nest with feathers. Usually it lays three to four white eggs marked with reddish-brown and darker-brown.

FOOD. This species subsists almost entirely on insects caught on the wing. Flies of various sorts make up almost half, and beetles, wild bees, wasps, ants, bugs, moths, and a few grasshoppers, crickets, dragonflies, and May flies make up the remainder.

DISTRIBUTION. In North America the Barn Swallow breeds from northern Alaska and southern Quebec south to central Mexico, southern Texas, northwestern Florida, and coastal North Carolina. It winters from Panama to Chile and Argentina, and irregularly north to southeastern California, central Arizona, and the northern Gulf Coast.

[365]

OCCURRENCE IN ALABAMA. (March 24 to November 8.) *Tennessee Valley*: April 1 (1951, Wheeler Refuge, D. C. Hulse) to October 18 (1959, Wheeler Refuge, J. C. and Margaret Robinson); most seen, 1500, May 4, 1957 (Wheeler Refuge, Ala. Orn. Soc.). *Mountain Region*: April 5 (1946 and 1952, Birmingham, T. A. Imhof) to May 30 (1955, Fairfield, T. A. Imhof) and August 7 (1949, Birmingham, T. A. Imhof) to October 25 (1958, Birmingham, T. A. Imhof); also July 3, 1946, a pair (St. Bernard College, Cullman, T. A. Imhof) and summer resident in DeKalb Co., most seen, 200+, May 6, 1948 (Birmingham, T. A. Imhof and Idalene Snead). *Piedmont*: April 6 (1952, Auburn, Dillon) to May 11 (1960, Auburn, Edith Clark) and August 11 (1943, Opelika, H. M. Stevenson) to October 12 (1957, Hatchett Creek, Coosa Co., Harriett Wright); also a pair, July 4, 1951 (8 miles south of Opelika, H. G. Good). *Upper Coastal Plain*: March 24 (1939, Prattville, L. S. Golsan) to May 31 (1957, Marion, Lois McCollough) and August 5 (1890, Greensboro, C. S. Brimley) to November 6 (1954, Marion, Lois McCollough); most seen, spring, 600, May 4, 1957 (Marion, Lois McCollough), fall, 300+, October 8, 1959 (Montgomery, T. A. Imhof and R. W. Skinner). *Lower Coastal Plain*: April 13 (1957, Jackson, W. U. Harris) to May 25 (1956, McIntosh, T. A. Imhof and W. F. Colin) and September 14 (1958, Camden, Lovett Williams) to October 20 (1956, Opp and Ozark, T. A. Imhof and L. C. Crawford and 1957, Jackson, W. U. Harris). *Gulf Coast*: March 28 (1931, Fairhope, D. H. McIntosh) to November 8 (1959, Dauphin Island, Ala. Orn. Soc.); most seen, summer, 250, early July 1952 (Fort Morgan, C. W. Summerour), migration, 979, October 19, 1957 (Fall Count, Mobile Bay Area); has bred at Fort Morgan since at least 1940 (T. D. Burleigh, 1941,

Auk 58:261-262), however, June and July 1914 records of Howell (1924:264) seem to indicate that the species has been breeding on the Alabama Gulf Coast for a much longer time.

TIME OF BREEDING. Data on 88+ Tennessee Valley and vicinity nestings: Building, April 22 and 23; eggs, May 15 to June 22; dependent young, June 7 to July 9. Data on 95+ Gulf Coast nestings: Eggs, June 3 to 28; dependent young, June 3 to July 4.

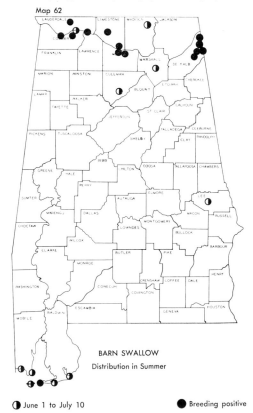

Map 62

BARN SWALLOW
Distribution in Summer

◑ June 1 to July 10   ● Breeding positive

Cliff Swallow

Petrochelidon pyrrhonota (Vieillot)   [612]   (Plate 26, facing page 360)

This is the swallow that "comes back to Capistrano." It is dark-bluish on the back and on the top of its head, dark-brown on the wings and tail, *white* on the *forehead* and belly, and red on the throat. Its *rump is buffy* and its *tail*,

CLIFF SWALLOW NESTS. These birds breed sparingly in extreme north Alabama. Here they chose the underside of a bridge.

square. Except for the rump and tail it resembles the Barn Swallow in pattern, but the flight of the Cliff Swallow is more level and coursing, unlike the darting and flitting of the fork-tailed Barn Swallow.

In the Tennessee Valley of Alabama, the Cliff Swallow is common on migration and remains to breed in at least two colonies in Colbert and Marshall counties. Elsewhere in the state it is uncommon on migration, but it sometimes occurs in fair-sized flocks. It frequents the same places as other swallows, and has the same liking for being near water.

NESTING. This swallow builds an unusual gourd-shaped nest of mud, sometimes reinforced with horsehair and straw. In the chamber of this mud gourd it makes a small nest of a few grass stems and feathers. Cliffs, dams, bridges, barns, or abandoned buildings are typical sites for the Cliff Swallows' nesting colonies. The nest is always protected from the weather, usually by eaves or some other overhang, but from time to time by being placed inside a building. Alabama sites for colonies are a concrete bridge, a transformer tunnel, and a cliff, the last being an old one.

[367]

FOOD. Like other swallows, the Cliff Swallow eats almost entirely insects caught on the wing. About half of its food consists of beetles, particularly weevils (including boll weevils), and bugs, especially the chinch bug. Prominent in the remainder of its diet are green flesh flies, mosquitoes, other flies, ants, and bees, and it also eats grasshoppers, caterpillars, moths, spiders, and rarely juniper berries. The young are fed on soft-bodied flies, wasps, bees, and ants, with few of the hard-bodied bugs and beetles of the adult diet.

DISTRIBUTION. The Cliff Swallow breeds rather locally from central Alaska, Mackenzie, southern Quebec, and Nova Scotia south to central Mexico, southern Texas, northern Alabama, and North Carolina. It winters from central Brazil to central Argentina and casually in southeastern California and Arizona.

OCCURRENCE IN ALABAMA. (April 4 to October 21.) *Tennessee Valley*: April 4 (1959, 3 birds, Huntsville, J. C. and Margaret Robinson) to October 18 (1954, Wheeler Refuge, D. C. Hulse); most seen, breeding, 100 pair, June 1913 (Fort Deposit, Madison Co., A. H. Howell), migration, about 100, April 30, 1912 (Leighton, A. H. Howell). *Mountain Region*: April 20 (1947, Birmingham, T. A. Imhof) to May 23 (1931, Jasper, H. M. Stevenson) and August 19 (1936, Birmingham, H. M. Stevenson) to September 22 (1936, St. Clair Co., H. M. Stevenson and 1956, Birmingham, T. A. Imhof and others); most seen, 246, May 12, 1960 (Talladega, C. T. Hornady) and 120+, May 6, 1958 (Birmingham, T. A. Imhof and Idalene Snead). *Piedmont*: April 13 (1940, specimen, Auburn, D. H. McIntosh) to at least May 7 (Auburn, A. H. Howell) and September 13, 1956 (75 birds, Lanett, Grace Whiteman). *Upper Coastal Plain*: April 20 (1956, 50 birds, Marion, Lois McCollough) to May 22 (1914, Seale, A. H. Howell); also September 20, 1923 (30 birds, Autauga Co., L. S. Golsan) and September 25, 1959 (Montgomery, R. W. Skinner). *Lower Coastal Plain*: September 14, 1956 (2 birds, Jackson, W. U. Harris and T. A. Imhof) and September 20, 1958 (Camden, Lovett Williams). *Gulf Coast*: April 13 (1957, Dauphin Island, H. A. J. and Cora Evans) to June 1, 1914 (Petit Bois Island, J. L. Peters) and August 24 (1939, Foley, H. M. Stevenson) to October 21 (1958, Cochrane Causeway, Peter Petersen and Dennis Sheets); most seen, 75, September 16, 1960 (Dauphin Island, J. L. Dorn).

TIME OF BREEDING. Data on 250+ nestings in 3 colonies: Building, May 5; young in nest, June 7 to July 2.

Purple Martin

Progne subis (Linnaeus) [611] (Plate 26, facing page 360)
OTHER NAMES: Gourd Martin, Black Martin

The Purple Martin, almost the size of a robin, is Alabama's largest swallow. The male is solid deep purple, and it has a slightly forked tail. The female is like the male except that it has a grayish breast and is almost white on the belly. Immatures are whitish below.

This is the state's most widespread swallow, for it is a common to abundant, breeding, summer resident throughout Alabama. It is one of the earliest of the migrant birds to arrive and depart. It occurs over the same open areas as other swallows, but seems to prefer farmland more than areas near water, for it feeds frequently over row crops and pastures.

NESTING. The Purple Martin habitually nests in hollow gourds, which ordinarily are hung from a crossarm on a pole nine or more feet up from the ground. Sometimes a farmer hangs a gourd for its nest from a limb of a dead tree as the Choctaw and Chickasaw Indians did. The Purple Martin uses almost any kind of box from the crudest to the most elaborate, and occasionally it nests in hollow trees, woodpecker holes, mail boxes, traffic lights, or other cavities. Dimensions for individual compartments should be about eight by eight inches by six inches high, with a hole two inches in diameter one and one-half inches above the floor. Boxes should be placed in the open at least seven and preferably twenty feet above the ground. Inside the box or cavity selected, the female lays three to six pure white eggs in a nest of grass, twigs, leaves, mud, and trash.

FOOD. Except for a few spiders, this martin eats only insects. Ants, wasps, beetles (especially weevils), bugs, flies of all sorts (including mosquitoes), dragonflies, and an occasional bee, moth, or butterfly, comprise the bulk of its diet.

DISTRIBUTION. The Purple Martin breeds from British Columbia, southern Quebec, and Nova Scotia south to northern Mexico, southern Texas, and southern Florida. It winters from Venezuela and British Guiana to southern Brazil.

OCCURRENCE IN ALABAMA. (January 26 to October 6.) *Tennessee Valley*: March 14 (1959, Decatur, B. L. Gaines) to September 19 (1959, Decatur, B. L. Gaines); most seen, 5000, July 22 (Wheeler Refuge, T. Z. Atkeson, Jr.) and "many thousands," August 3, 1889 (Leighton, F. W. McCormack). *Mountain Region*: February 27 (1954, McCalla, Jefferson Co., T. A. Imhof and others) to September 26 (1959, Talladega, T. A. Imhof); most seen, 6000, August 1956 (Birmingham, F. B. Daniel), 5000, June to August 1950 to 1955 (Pell City, roosting, F. B. Daniel) and "approximately 100,000," August 9, 1927 (Anniston, W. H. Hoffman). *Piedmont*: February 6 (1956, Lanett, Grace Whiteman) to October 4 (1957, Auburn, Lovett Williams). *Upper Coastal Plain*: January 29 (1933, Cottonwood, W. S. Gilmore and 1960, Selma, Ava Tabor and Electa Levi) to September 25 (1959, Montgomery, R. W. Skinner); most seen, 25,000 at roost, July 26,

1950 (Montgomery, C. W. Summerour). *Lower Coastal Plain*: Last week in January (1956, Finchburg, Monroe Co., R. B. Williams, Jr.) to September 21 (1957, Henry Co. and Geneva Co., T. A. Imhof and Lovett Williams); most seen, 35,000, September 20, 1957 (Lake Tholloco, T. A. Imhof and Lovett Williams). *Gulf Coast*: January 26 (1947, 8 birds, Cochrane Causeway, T. A. Imhof) to October 6 (1956, 3 birds, Spanish Fort, Barbara Lund); most seen, 10,000+, July 6, 1929 (Cochrane Causeway, Helen Edwards).

TIME OF BREEDING. Data on 120+ nestings: Building, March 28 to April 18; eggs, April 20 to June 13; young in nest, May 23 to June 5; dependent young out of nest, June 8 to July.

BANDING. Three banded Purple Martins have been recovered in Alabama as follows: One from Nashville, Tenn., banded as a nestling, July 4, 1954, was found at Guntersville, September 7, 1954; another, marked at McMillan, Mich., May 10, 1933, was found at Clayton, Barbour Co., April 16, 1936; and a third, banded at Fairhope as a nestling, June 5, 1935, was found at Mobile, April 2, 1937.

FAMILY CORVIDAE: JAYS, MAGPIES, AND CROWS

Birds of this family are robust, with stout bills and feet and rather long, rounded tails. Adaptable, they eat a wide variety of foods and live in an equally wide variety of places. Their voices, too, are adaptable, for the birds are accomplished imitators. While they sometimes eat the eggs and young of other birds and rather frequently damage agricultural crops, they also destroy large numbers of injurious insects. They are among our most intelligent birds.

SUBFAMILY GARRULINAE: JAYS AND MAGPIES

Blue Jay
Cyanocitta cristata (Linnaeus)   [477]   (Plate 30, facing page 408)
OTHER NAME: Jaybird

The Blue Jay has a blue back, grayish-white under parts, a prominent crest and black and white markings on the wings, tail, and face. Its most common call is a raucous scream, but some of its calls are quite different, for the Blue Jay is a fair mimic. It imitates the call of the Red-shouldered Hawk especially well and often.

In Alabama, this species is abundant the year round and is possibly a little more numerous in winter. Although particularly abundant in oaks, the Blue Jay is widespread, for it occurs in pines and near houses as well as in remote woodlands. It nests in all parts of the state. This is a bold, noisy, active, strong, and hardy bird, but during the nesting season it can be quite silent. It harasses hawks, owls, and other predators and by screaming and pecking forces them to leave the vicinity.

NESTING. Generally the Blue Jay builds a large nest, using small twigs, bark, moss, lichens, paper, rags, wool, leaves, string, or dry grass. Sometimes it cements with mud and lines with finer materials, usually rootlets. This nest is often hidden by foliage in a crotch from four to forty feet up in an evergreen or hardwood, particularly an oak. Ordinarily it holds three to five olive or buff eggs spotted with darker olive and brown.

[371]

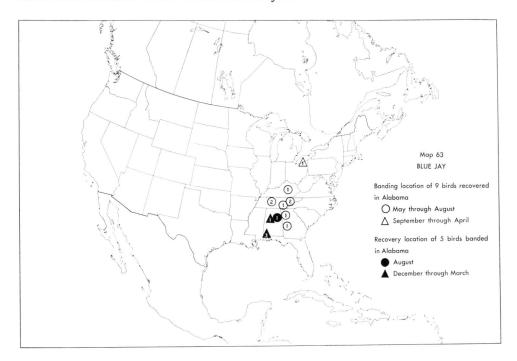

Map 63
BLUE JAY

Banding location of 9 birds recovered
in Alabama

○ May through August

△ September through April

Recovery location of 5 birds banded
in Alabama

● August

▲ December through March

FOOD. The nuts of oak, hickory, pecan, and beech trees are the principal foods of this jay. Prominent among a great variety of other items in its diet are corn, other grains, wild fruit, some cultivated fruit, beetles, grasshoppers, caterpillars, other large insects, spiders, mollusks, crustaceans, mice, fish, frogs, salamanders, and occasionally the eggs and young of other birds. At feeding stations it eats many foods but especially likes peanuts.

DISTRIBUTION. The Blue Jay occurs throughout the year east of the Rocky Mountains from central Alberta, southern Quebec, and Newfoundland south to southern Texas and southern Florida. Many individual birds, particularly immatures, move southward for the winter.

ABUNDANCE IN ALABAMA (*most seen in a day*). Wheeler Refuge, 72, December 31, 1954 (Christmas Count); Birmingham, 170, December 26, 1960 (Christmas Count), migration, 125 in two flocks, October 7, 1960 (T. A. Imhof, Idalene Snead, and Emmy Brownlie); Mobile Bay Area, 390, October 6, 1956 (Fall Count), Dauphin Island, winter, 244, December 27, 1958 (Christmas Count).

TIME OF BREEDING. Data on 75+ nestings: Building, March 13 to April 24; eggs, March 17 to June 23; young in nest, April 10 to August 4; dependent young out of nest, May 15 to August 15.

BANDING. In Alabama, over 45 banded Blue Jays have been recaptured at the place of banding 1 to 5 years later. Another 14 Blue Jays, however, have traveled as below: Anniston to Lineville; Anniston to Clanton; Fairhope to Silverhill; Fairhope to 15 miles above Mobile; Fairhope to Wagar; West Point, Ga. to Lanett; Rome, Ga. to Centre; Chattanooga, Tenn. to Thorsby; Nashville, Tenn. to

Sheffield; Nashville, Tenn. to Florence; Knoxville, Tenn. to Florence; Knoxville, Tenn. to Billingsley, Autauga Co.; Berea, Ky. to Springville, St. Clair Co.; and Painesville, Ohio to Piedmont, Calhoun Co. (See Map 63.)

SUBFAMILY CORVINAE: RAVENS AND CROWS

These black, long-winged birds are generally larger than jays and have deeper voices.

[Common Raven]

Corvus corax Linnaeus   [486]   (Plate 27, facing page 368)

The totally black Common Raven, largest of the perching birds, has nearly twice the bulk of the Common Crow and when perched closely resembles a crow. Relative size is unreliable for identifying birds in the field, but the Common Raven can be distinguished by its bigger bill, more ample tail, and *shaggy throat feathers.* In flight this bird looks more like a hawk than a crow, for its wings are held flat and it often soars. Crows rarely soar and usually bend their wing tips upward. In addition, the *tail* of the Common Raven is distinctly *wedge-shaped,* somewhat like that of the Blue Jay. The call of the Common Raven is a loud and deep guttural croaking.

Formerly this species was a rare, permanent resident in the wildest and most rugged mountain country of northern Alabama—in Winston, Cullman, Walker, Jackson, and DeKalb counties. Outside of Alabama, it also occurs in other types of wild and barren country, for instance, desert, tundra, and seacoast. Although it has not been recorded in Alabama since 1915, a few birds may still persist as they do in nearby states. Only one instance of its nesting in the state is known.

NESTING. The nest is either in the highest substantial crotch of a tall tree, usually a conifer, or on a cliff ledge, generally one that has more than a fifty-foot sheer drop and is in the shade of an evergreen or an overhang. The nest is made of sticks, often very large ones, and is lined with shredded bark and hair, usually that of deer. The dark bluish-green eggs marked with browns and olives generally number four or five, and except for being larger are identical to those of the Common Crow.

FOOD. This raven eats almost any kind of food, but it is particularly attracted to dead or dying animals of all sorts. It captures small mammals, small marine life, and insects, and sometimes it eats large numbers of berries.

[373]

DISTRIBUTION. In North America the Common Raven is resident principally along seacoasts and in mountains from northwestern Alaska and northern Greenland to within 500 miles of the North Pole, south to Nicaragua and northern Georgia. It is generally absent from the Mississippi Valley and Gulf and Atlantic coastal plains.

OCCURRENCE IN ALABAMA. *Mountain Region only*: It bred in the wilder parts of western Cullman Co., northern Walker Co., and southern Winston Co., mostly near Logan, Ardell, and Natural Bridge, up to 1915 (R. R. Bottoms, L. J. Goldman, E. G. Holt, J. L. Peters, and A. H. Howell; specimen in the U S. National Museum, April 15, 1915, L. J. Goldman). It was seen at Long Island Creek Gulch, Jackson Co., May 4 and 11, 1912; April 23, 1913; and last seen, 2 birds, April 16, 1914 (E. W. Graves and A. H. Howell). On Lookout Mountain in Mays Gulf (Little River Canyon), 7 birds were seen in early June 1890 (*fide* Col. Woolsey Finnell of Tuscaloosa, *Alabama Conservation* 25:8).

TIME OF BREEDING. Data on 1 nesting: Sipsey Fork of Warrior River just north of the mouth of Rock Creek, Winston Co., 2 nearly featherless young, 60 feet up on cliff, April 4, 1915 (L. J. Goldman).

Common Crow
Corvus brachyrhynchos Brehm   [488]   (Plate 27, facing page 368)

The familiar Common Crow is all black. It can be distinguished from the Fish Crow by its larger size and by its cawing, which lacks the nasal quality characteristic of the Fish Crow's voice.

The Common Crow is an abundant, breeding, permanent resident in all parts of Alabama, but it seems to shun the deeper woods and to be partial to farming areas. Near the Gulf the Fish Crow replaces it to a large extent. Like the Blue Jay, the Common Crow worries hawks, owls, and other large birds. This species is extremely wary, highly resourceful, and probably more intelligent than most birds.

NESTING. Usually this crow builds a nest of sticks lined compactly with soft, finer material such as hair and bark strips. In Alabama this nest is ordinarily placed next to the trunk of a pine or another conifer from ten to seventy feet from the ground. The typical, well-built, bulky nest, located in the uppermost branches of a tall pine, is said to be the origin of the name "crow's nest" for the lookout position on the mainmast of a sailing vessel. This bird lays four to six eggs, bluish-green to olive-buff with irregular blotches of browns and grays.

FOOD. The Common Crow eats almost any kind of food, its diet depending on local availability. For this reason, this bird may be highly beneficial or highly injurious according to season and locality. About three-fourths of its diet is vegetable matter, chiefly corn, but also other grains, wild fruits and seeds, and some cultivated fruits and vegetables. The remaining fourth is animal matter—insects, spiders, mollusks, millipedes, crustaceans, fish, snails, reptiles, amphibians, wild and domestic birds and their eggs, small mammals, and carrion.

DISTRIBUTION. The Common Crow breeds from British Columbia, central Quebec, and Newfoundland south to Lower California, central Texas, and southern Florida, but it is uncommon in the west. More northerly birds retire southward in winter, and those on the plains migrate a considerable distance.

ABUNDANCE IN ALABAMA (*most seen in a day*). Wheeler Refuge, 250,-000, winter of 1955-56 in roost (*fide* T. Z. Atkeson, Jr.); Birmingham, 117, December 28, 1957 (Christmas Count); Marion, 500+, October 26, 1957 (Lois McCollough); Theo-dore, 500, December 29, 1956 (J. L. Dorn and C. M. Valentine).

TIME OF BREEDING. Data on 20+ nestings: Building, February 26 to April 11; eggs, March 16 to April 19; dependent young, April 7 to June 7.

Fish Crow
Corvus ossifragus Wilson   [490]   (Plate 27, facing page 368)

The Fish Crow is slimmer and smaller than the Common Crow, and has more pointed wings and a slightly longer tail. Estimating these differences of degree, however, can not be relied upon in field identification. A more reliable indication is the distinctive nasal quality characteristic of the cawing of the Fish Crow. Young Common Crows sometimes sound a bit like the Fish Crow, but the begging actions of young crows betray their age.

In Alabama, the Fish Crow is a breeding, permanent resident in the coastal plain, abundant on the Gulf Coast and common farther inland in river valleys. Close to the Fall Line and slightly north of it, the Fish Crow becomes less numerous and widespread, and fewer birds remain in winter. (See Map 64.) This crow generally frequents the vicinity of water and often forages on beaches and mudflats. Inland it also occurs frequently on farms.

NESTING. The nesting habits are much like those of the Common Crow, but the Fish Crow nests in smaller groups, closer to water, later in the year, and generally in pines or cedars, sometimes at a great height. Frequently the nest contains feathers of water birds, and although it rests in a conifer, hardwood twigs are often used exclusively for construction. The usual clutch is three to five eggs colored bluish-green to olive-buff like those of the Common Crow.

FOOD. The Fish Crow eats nearly all kinds of food, but naturally much of its diet is marine life. It takes a variety of fish and other sea animals dead or alive, and also eats large insects, waste grain, and many wild fruits. It victi-

PLATE 28

BROWN-HEADED NUTHATCH
Sexes Alike
Page 383

CAROLINA CHICKADEE
Sexes Alike
Page 378

RED-BREASTED NUTHATCH
Sexes Alike
Page 381

TUFTED TITMOUSE
Sexes Alike
Page 379

BROWN CREEPER
Sexes Alike
Page 384

WHITE-BREASTED NUTHATCH
Sexes Alike
Page 380

Richard A. Parks

mizes many water birds, and apparently eats more eggs and young birds than the Common Crow, for in southern heronries it sometimes does great damage.

DISTRIBUTION. The Fish Crow is resident along the Atlantic and Gulf coasts from Rhode Island to Texas, and, in the southeastern states, inland sometimes as much as 300 miles or more, especially along the larger rivers, and almost exclusively in the Coastal Plain.

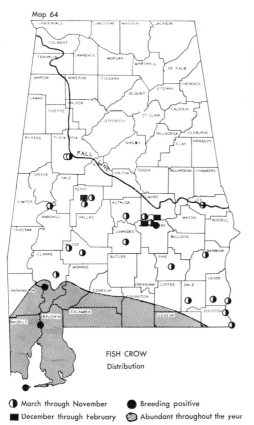

Map 64

FISH CROW
Distribution

◐ March through November   ● Breeding positive
■ December through February   ◉ Abundant throughout the year

ABUNDANCE IN ALABAMA (*most seen in a day*). Auburn, 60, May 9, 1957 (J. E. Keeler); Marion, 48, October 1, 1955 (Lois McCollough); Andalusia, 110, September 20, 1957 (T. A. Imhof and Lovett Williams); Cochrane Causeway, Mobile, 650, January 21, 1955 (C. S. Robbins); Dauphin Island, 358, December 31, 1957 (Christmas Count).

TIME OF BREEDING. Data on 10 nestings: Building, February to April 5; eggs, April 13 to June 20; dependent young, May 20 to July 10; on the wing by June 19.

FAMILY PARIDAE: TITMICE, VERDINS, AND BUSHTITS

SUBFAMILY PARINAE: TITMICE

Among our smallest birds, the curious, trustful, and almost intelligent titmice, have short, stout bills, rather long tails, and rather short wings. These birds have endeared themselves by frequent visits to feeding stations and by allowing

[377]

humans to approach them closely. They are usually non-migratory, and often in the dead of winter their voices are the only bird sounds to be heard in the woods.

Carolina Chickadee
Parus carolinensis Audubon   [736]   (Plate 28, facing page 376)

This tiny titmouse is gray above, whitish below, with rusty flanks, a *black cap,* and a *black bib.* It has a rapid six-syllabled call reminiscent of its name, more rapid and higher pitched than that of the Black-capped Chickadee of the north, which has almost identical plumage and which does not occur in Alabama. The song is a four-noted, rather plaintive whistle.

The Carolina Chickadee is a common, permanent resident, nowhere abundant, but evenly and thoroughly distributed as a breeder in nearly all woodlands in Alabama. It is equally common in pines and hardwoods, in the wildest areas and around houses, and occurs commonly in partially-wooded residential areas where, because of its trustful ways, it is one of the principal customers at feeding stations. Outside the breeding season, it forms flocks with the Tufted Titmouse and many other insect-eating woodland birds. When bird students are in the woods in winter and locate a chickadee, they can be reasonably certain that other small birds such as warblers, nuthatches, creepers, and woodpeckers are nearby.

NESTING. This bird usually excavates its own nest hole from four to fifteen feet above ground in a dead or decaying stub or fence post. It often uses nest boxes. Such a box should be at least three inches square and eight inches high and have a hole one and one-eighth inches in diameter five inches above the floor. The nest itself has a foundation of moss with strips of bark and grass and is lined with plant downs, feathers, and hair. The eggs are white, dotted with reddish-brown, and number five to eight, commonly six. A parent chickadee disturbed on the nest gives a realistic imitation of the hiss of a copperhead.

FOOD. For the most part insects and spiders are this chickadee's food. These include mainly moths and caterpillars, but also bugs, ants, wasps, wild bees, beetles, cockroaches, and katydids. The much smaller amount of plant food consists of a great variety of seeds and small fruits of which those of poison-ivy are most frequent. This bird is attracted to feeding stations in cold weather with suet, cheese, bread crumbs, and peanuts.

DISTRIBUTION. The Carolina Chickadee is resident from southeastern Kansas, central Missouri, central Indiana, southern Pennsylvania, and central New Jersey south to southeastern Texas and central Florida.

ABUNDANCE IN ALABAMA (*most seen in a day*). Birmingham, 161, December 26, 1960 (Christmas Count); southern Clarke Co., 25, January 11, 1958 (T. A. Imhof and others); Foley, 40, December 27, 1947 (Christmas Count).

TIME OF BREEDING. Data on 35+ nestings: Eggs, March 28 to May 29; young in nest, April 8 to May 26; young out of nest, April 25 to June 27.

BANDING. At least 9 chickadees banded at Birmingham and Gadsden have been retrapped at the same place a year or more later.

Tufted Titmouse

Parus bicolor Linnaeus   [731]   (Plate 28, facing page 376)
OTHER NAME: Tomtit

This titmouse is a larger, plainer relative of the Carolina Chickadee. The Tufted Titmouse has the same body pattern, gray back, white under parts, and rusty flanks, but the head is *gray, crested,* and shows a little black between the black bill and the black eye. This bird has a prominent white eye ring. Its usual call is a two-syllabled, loud, clear, and repetitious whistle, but it has other notes which are like those of the Carolina Chickadee in a more wheezing and complaining mood.

In Alabama the Tufted Titmouse as a breeder is about as common and widespread as the Carolina Chickadee, except that it seems to be more common in oaks and less common in pines. It has the same feeding habits, trustful ways, and other titmouse traits. Tufted Titmice apparently lead most of the bands of insect-eaters common in Alabama woodlands outside the breeding season.

NESTING. The nest is in a hollow tree, stub, fence post, or nest box. Dimensions for a nest box are the same as for the Carolina Chickadee, but the entrance hole should have a diameter of one and one-fourth inches. The Tufted Titmouse builds its nest with leaves, usually includes a snakeskin, and lines it with inner bark, Spanish moss, and mammal hairs. The hairs are often collected from living animals, and in one reported instance the animal was a human being. The four to six white eggs are finely spotted with shades of brown.

FOOD. The Tufted Titmouse eats chiefly insects and spiders, with caterpillars and wasps composing the major part of its diet. Other items include ants, bees, sawfly larvae, bugs, and the eggs of katydids and roaches. Plant food, eaten mainly in fall and winter, is composed mostly of acorns but also includes many other seeds and small fruits, especially berries. At feeding stations, this bird is attracted by suet, cheese, bread crumbs, and peanuts.

DISTRIBUTION. The Tufted Titmouse is resident from central Iowa, southern Wisconsin, southern Ontario, southern New York, and southwestern Connecticut south to central Texas and central Florida. It wanders irregularly farther north in winter to such places as South Dakota and central New England.

ABUNDANCE IN ALABAMA (*most seen in a day*). Birmingham, 125, December 26, 1959 (Christmas Count); southern Clarke Co., 40, January 11, 1958 (T. A. Imhof and others); Gulf Coast, 40, January 2, 1960 (Christmas Count, Dauphin Island).

TIME OF BREEDING. Data on

32+ nestings: Building, March 17 to April 26; eggs, April 13 to July 9; dependent young, April 18 to July 11; out of nest by June 6.

BANDING. At least 4 of these birds, banded at Birmingham and Gadsden, have been recaptured at the same place a year or more later.

FAMILY SITTIDAE: NUTHATCHES

SUBFAMILY SITTINAE: TYPICAL NUTHATCHES

Nuthatches are small birds, related to the titmice and similar in size. They spend most of their time clambering on trunks and limbs of trees *head down*. The bill is sharp and stout, the legs are strong, and the tail, never used as a prop, is short and stubby.

White-breasted Nuthatch

Sitta carolinensis Latham   [727]   (Plate 28, facing page 376)
OTHER NAME: Sapsucker

This species, about the size of the Tufted Titmouse, is the largest of the Alabama nuthatches. It is blue above and white below, with a black crown and a *black, beady eye* which stands out against white cheeks. The under tail coverts are tinged with a small amount of reddish; in contrast, the entire under parts of the Red-breasted Nuthatch are reddish. The call of the White-breasted Nuthatch is two-syllabled, and somewhat nasal, and the song is a series of utterances of the same note repeated rapidly.

In northern Alabama, this bird is a fairly common to common, breeding, permanent resident, but below the Fall Line it is uncommon and local, and its numbers gradually decrease southward so that it is rare on the coast. It spends most of its time in hardwoods and generally frequents the bigger trees, especially oaks. Quite a tame bird, it allows close approach and frequently visits feeding stations. Although it keeps somewhat apart from the wintertime titmice flocks, it still seems to be an integral part of them.

NESTING. Usually this nuthatch nests in a knot-hole, an abandoned woodpecker hole, or another natural cavity, but occasionally it selects a nest box. The nest box should be three inches square by eight inches high and the entrance hole should be one and one-fourth inches in diameter five inches above the floor. The box is best placed twelve to twenty feet above the ground. Inside the chosen cavity, this bird assembles a foundation of bark strips, then fine plant materials such as rootlets, inner bark, and grass, and finally a lining of fur and feathers. The four to six white eggs are heavily marked with reddish-brown.

FOOD. The principal food is mast, such as acorns, beechnuts, and hickory nuts, but this species also feeds on corn, pine seeds, sunflower seeds, berries of Virginia creeper, and other fruits. It consumes a large quantity of injurious insects, especially in summer. Spiders, beetles, bugs, weevils, ants, flies, moths, caterpillars, scale insects, and plant lice are the most frequent items. Suet and peanuts, and of course nuts, will attract it to feeding shelves. It often takes particles of food and stores them in cracks in wood or wedges nuts there for more convenient cracking with the bill. This hacking of nuts probably inspired the name nuthatch.

DISTRIBUTION. The White-breasted Nuthatch is resident from southern British Columbia, southern Quebec, and the Canadian Maritime provinces south to central Mexico and central Florida. In winter, some individuals withdraw from the northern limits and the higher mountains.

ABUNDANCE IN ALABAMA (*most seen in a day*). Monte Sano, 15, June 8, 1957 (T. A. Imhof); Birmingham, 49, December 26, 1959 (Christmas Count); Tuscaloosa, 8, December 23, 1940 (H. M. Stevenson).

TIME OF BREEDING. Data on at least 10 nestings: Building, April 7 to 22; eggs, March 17 to June 14; dependent young, April 14 to June 12.

BANDING. A bird, banded in January in Birmingham, was retrapped there in December.

Red-breasted Nuthatch

Sitta canadensis Linnaeus [728] (Plate 28, facing page 376)

The Red-breasted Nuthatch and the Carolina Chickadee are about the same in body bulk, but the Red-breasted Nuthatch has a very short tail. It is blue above and *rusty-red below,* the *top* of the *head* is *black,* a *black line* runs *through the eye,* and a *white line* runs *over it.* This bird's call is said to be like a tiny tin horn, and is much thinner, weaker, and more nasal than that of the White-breasted Nuthatch.

Every winter at least since 1943 a few Red-breasted Nuthatches have invaded the Mountain Region of Alabama, probably from the vicinity of the Great Smoky Mountains. Since 1955, when the bridge to Dauphin Island was opened, the species has been recorded in this state every year within sight of the Gulf of Mexico. About every three or four years, when cones of spruce and other northern evergreens are scarce, the species becomes locally abundant in winter in the Mountain Region, common in piney areas as far south as the Upper Coastal Plain, and uncommon on the Gulf Coast. It is not known to nest in Alabama. Although sometimes frequenting deciduous trees, this bird usually occurs on conifers. In Alabama these are chiefly Virginia pine, other small-coned pines, and hemlock, where it feeds on the outer twigs and cones.

NESTING AND FOOD. The Red-breasted Nuthatch lays four to seven white eggs spotted with reddish-brown in a nest of fine plant materials. It digs a cavity for the nest in dead wood of a conifer or sometimes a hardwood, at any height from the ground, and invariably smears the outside with pitch. Apparently the main foods of this nuthatch are the seeds of spruces, pines, and other conifers. In summer it feeds on large quantities of injurious forest insects, including flying ones. On migration it sometimes eats ragweed seeds, and around feeding stations it prefers walnuts, peanuts, pecans, and suet, and rarely Brazil nuts and sunflower seeds.

DISTRIBUTION. The Red-breasted Nuthatch breeds from southern Alaska, southern Mackenzie, southern Quebec, and Newfoundland south to southern California, southern Colorado, Wisconsin, New York, and Connecticut, and in mountains to North Carolina. In winter, most individuals retire from more northern areas and from mountains, and some individuals wander south of the breeding range. In flight years when cones of northern conifers are scarce, this species becomes abundant in valleys, coastal areas, and more southern locations south to southern New Mexico, Texas, the northern Gulf Coast, and northern Florida.

OCCURRENCE IN ALABAMA. (September 25 to May 1.) *Tennessee Valley*: December 23, 1943 (3 birds, Wheeler Refuge, H. M. Stevenson). *Mountain Region*: September 25 (1957, Birmingham, Harriett Wright) and September 26 (1954, Birmingham, F. T. Carney) to May 1 (1956, Fairfield, T. A. Imhof); specimen in La. State Univ. collection, March 24, 1944 (M. L. Miles); most seen, 13, December 26, 1953 (Christmas Count, Birmingham), 11, November 23, 1954 (Fairfield, T. A. Imhof). *Piedmont*: December 27 (1954, Goodwater, Blanche Dean) to April 7 (1954, Auburn, H. G. Good). *Upper Coastal Plain*: October 4 (1888, specimen in the Avery collection, Greensboro, W. C. Avery) to April 23 (1919, Prattville, L. S. Golsan). *Lower Coastal Plain*: No record. *Gulf Coast*:

October 20 (1956, Dauphin Island, J. L. Dorn, T. J. Hatrel, and S. A. Gauthreaux) to April 18 (1957, Dauphin Island, S. A. Gauthreaux) and April 23 (1960, Dauphin Island, T. A. Imhof and others); most seen, spring, 13, April 13, 1960 (Dauphin Island, S. A. Gauthreaux and others), fall, 6, November 8, 1959 (Dauphin Island, T. A. Imhof and others), and winter, 6, January 2, 1960 (Christmas Count, Dauphin Island).

Brown-headed Nuthatch
Sitta pusilla Latham   [729]   (Plate 28, facing page 376)
OTHER NAME: Cha-cha

This small nuthatch has a pale blue back, white under parts, a *brown cap* which extends to the eye, and a *white spot* on the *nape*. The rapid, metallic, piping call of either three or four syllables often becomes an excited twitter. The almost constant calls of this bird make a flock easy to locate.

The Brown-headed Nuthatch is a common, breeding, permanent resident in Alabama north to at least Cullman, DeKalb, Etowah, and Calhoun counties. Usually occurring in small flocks in more open woods, this bird spends most of its time clambering around the outer twigs of the tall pine trees which are its favorite habitat.

NESTING. For the nest this bird usually digs a hole in a dead pine tree or in a fence post, but occasionally selects a natural cavity or a nest box. The nest is frequently over water, usually less than twelve feet above the ground. The bird lines it almost entirely with pine seed coats but sometimes uses bark shreds and grass. A clutch consists of four to six white eggs, usually marked with reddish-brown.

FOOD. In Alabama this nuthatch feeds on beetles, cockroaches, caterpillars, ants, scale insects, and pine seeds.

DISTRIBUTION. The Brown-headed Nuthatch is resident from southeastern Oklahoma, the northern parts of the Gulf states, southeastern Virginia, and Delaware south to southern Texas, southern Florida, and Grand Bahama Island.

ABUNDANCE IN ALABAMA (*most seen in a day*). Birmingham, 45, December 28, 1957 (Christmas Count); Mobile Bay Area, 77, October 6, 1956 (Fall Count).

TIME OF BREEDING. Data on 22 nestings: Building, February 15 to March 21; eggs, March 21 to May 11; dependent young, March 23 to June 8; young out of nest by April 25.

BANDING. Three birds, banded in Birmingham, have been recaptured a year or more later at the same place.

FAMILY CERTHIIDAE: CREEPERS

SUBFAMILY CERTHIINAE: TYPICAL CREEPERS

Brown Creeper

Certhia familiaris Linnaeus   [726]   (Plate 28, facing page 376)

The only creeper in Alabama, the Brown Creeper is heavily brown-striped above and white below and about the size of a nuthatch. This creeper has a curved bill, sharp claws, and stiff spines in the tail to aid in climbing. The one-syllabled, high-pitched call is similar to that of the Golden-crowned Kinglet, only slightly more prolonged and never trebled.

This bird is usually fairly common in winter in all types of Alabama woodlands, but at times it is uncommon, especially near the coast. It is not known to nest in this state. It spends most of its time circling a tree trunk from the base upward in search of food and then moving on to the next tree and repeating the procedure. Although usually occurring alone, it sometimes joins small flocks of its own species or remains on the fringes of the titmice groups. Except during the breeding season, it rarely pays attention to anything except the perpetual search for food.

NESTING AND FOOD. The nest of twigs and inner bark is wedged behind a loose section of bark on a dead tree, usually a balsam fir. Each corner is built upward into a sort of horn, a very striking feature. The female lays four to eight white eggs, dotted with brown. This species feeds on a variety of injurious woodland insects that occur in crevices in bark and often eats eggs or larvae so small as to be unnoticed by other birds. Plant lice, weevils, sawflies, ants, caterpillars, and also spiders and pseudo-scorpions are the principal food. Occasionally it varies this diet with mast.

DISTRIBUTION. In the Western Hemisphere the Brown Creeper breeds from southeastern Alaska, central Alberta, southern Quebec, and Newfoundland south to southern California, eastern Nebraska, Minnesota, Pennsylvania, and Massachusetts, and in mountains to Nicaragua and Tennessee. It winters mostly at lower elevations from British Columbia, North Dakota, Minnesota, Ontario, and Nova Scotia south to Nicaragua and southern Florida.

OCCURRENCE IN ALABAMA. (October 5 to May 8.) *Tennessee Valley*: October 16 (1889, Leighton, F. W. McCormack) to April 13 (1891, Leighton, F. W. McCormack); most seen, 9, December 27, 1952 (Triana, Madison Co., T. A. Imhof).

Mountain Region: October 5 (1953, Birmingham, H. M. Stevenson) to April 10 (1956, Fairfield, T. A. Imhof); also a cripple, April 6 to 28, 1940 (Birmingham, H. M. Stevenson); most seen, 13, December 26, 1959 (Christmas Count, Birmingham). *Piedmont*: November 1 (1957, Auburn, Lovett Williams) to March 26 (1953, Auburn, H. G. Good); most seen, 6, December 26, 1959 (Christmas Count, Auburn). *Upper Coastal Plain*: Octo- ber 17 (1938, Tuscaloosa, H. M. Stevenson) to April (1878, Coosada, N. C. Brown); also to May 8, 1934 (Booth, Autauga Co., L. S. Golsan). *Lower Coastal Plain*: October 18 (1958, Camden, Lovett Williams) to March 29 (1957, Jackson, W. U. Harris). *Gulf Coast*: October 16 (1929, Fairhope, Helen Edwards) to March 20 (1960, Daphne, J. L. Dorn); most seen, 7, November 1, 1958 (Fall Count, Mobile Bay Area).

FAMILY TROGLODYTIDAE: WRENS

These small, brownish, agile, highly-nervous birds usually have the wings and tail barred with black, and normally carry the tail cocked over the back. They generally frequent dense tangles and would be difficult to locate but for their loud voices, which are out of proportion to their small size. They nest in cavities or build a ball-like nest with a side entrance. Their eggs, like those of the titmice and nuthatches, are colored, which seems to indicate that only in recent geologic time have they begun to nest in holes and lose the need for protective coloration in their eggs.

House Wren
Troglodytes aedon Vieillot   [721]   (Plate 29, facing page 392)

The Carolina Wren, and sometimes Bewick's Wren, are frequently called House Wren because, like the true House Wren, they live close to houses and often use nest boxes. The House Wren is smaller than Bewick's and Carolina Wrens, is barred grayish-brown above, and is whitish below. The House Wren is best identified by its *plain face*. (Bewick's, Carolina, and Long-billed Marsh Wrens have a white stripe over the eye, the Short-billed Marsh Wren, a finely-striped cap, and the Winter Wren, a dark, striped face.) The Winter Wren, with which the House Wren is usually confused, has a stubby tail and a dark belly with heavily-barred sides. Thus the House Wren is distinct because it *lacks* any *prominent markings*. Throughout the nesting season this bird sings in a gushing, gurgling series of loud, rapid notes, frequently repeated. It also has a chattering call which can be distinguished from those of other wrens only after long experience.

Throughout Alabama, the House Wren is a fairly common transient. In winter, it is uncommon to rare above the Fall Line, fairly common in the

Coastal Plain, and common on the Gulf Coast. During the winter, it lives in dense tangles near the ground, especially in bottomlands. Such places as brush piles, fallen trees, thick vines, palmetto clumps, and heavy brush of any sort are ideal for a House Wren. In Alabama it rarely occurs around houses, its favorite breeding site. In 1959 the House Wren, a species moving westward and southward as a breeder, nested in Tennessee, seven miles from the Alabama line near Bridgeport. Thus, the species may breed in Alabama in the near future.

NESTING. This wren originally nested in tree cavities, but at present it uses almost any available cavity near houses. These include nest boxes, tin cans, jars, pots, clothing (including scarecrows), and the abandoned nests of other birds, hole-nesting or otherwise (including the Belted Kingfisher, Eastern Phoebe, Robin, and Baltimore Oriole). This cavity, regardless of size, is filled with sticks and grass, leaving only a passageway and nestcup. This cup is lined with feathers, hair, wool, or other fine materials. The five to eight whitish eggs are very heavily marked with fine reddish-brown dots. The parents feed the young frequently in enormous amounts and make as many as 111 visits per hour and 1,217 visits per full day (A. C. Bent, *U. S. N. M. Bull.* 195, 1948:130).

FOOD. Almost all the food of this wren consists of a great variety of insects and related small animals. Grasshoppers, bugs, beetles, caterpillars, and spiders make up the major part of the diet which also includes other insects and small animals.

DISTRIBUTION. The House Wren breeds from southern British Columbia, southern Quebec, and New Brunswick south to northern Lower California, Arizona, northern Oklahoma, central Tennessee, northern Georgia, and coastal North Carolina. It winters from southern California, southern Arizona, northeastern Texas, the northern parts of the Gulf states, and coastal South Carolina, occasionally farther north along the Atlantic Coast, south to southern Mexico and southern Florida.

OCCURRENCE IN ALABAMA. (September 17 to May 18.) *Tennessee Valley*: September 26 (1950, Wheeler Refuge, T. A. Imhof) to at least January 18 (1948, Wheeler Refuge, L. S. Givens). *Mountain Region*: September 17 (1946, trapped and banded, Birmingham, T. A. Imhof) to May 4 (1934 and 1940, Birmingham, H. M. Stevenson); most seen, winter, 3, January 1, 1951 (Christmas Count, Birmingham). *Piedmont*: November 27 (1952, Roanoke, H. M. Stevenson) to May 5 (1950, Auburn, H. G. Good). *Upper Coastal Plain*: September 29 (1958, Livingston, Jenkins Jackson) to April 28 (1939, Tuscaloosa, H. M. Stevenson); also May 15 and 18, 1955 (Marion, Lois McCollough). *Lower Coastal Plain*: October 11 (1949, River Falls, Covington Co., W. R. Middleton) to April 27 (1952, Andalusia, W. R. Middleton). *Gulf Coast*: September 24 (1933, northern

Mobile Co., Homer Flagg) to May 2 (1961, Dauphin Island, Owen Davies); most seen, migration, 66, October 19, 1957 (Fall Count, Mobile Bay Area), winter, 27, December 21, 1957 (Christmas Count, Dauphin Island).

BANDING. A House Wren, banded as a nestling at South Bend, Indiana, June 20, 1930, was found at Atmore, January 18, 1931.

Winter Wren

Troglodytes troglodytes (Linnaeus)   [722]   (Plate 29, facing page 392)

Slightly smaller than the Short-billed Marsh Wren, the Winter Wren is Alabama's smallest wren. It has a *dark, striped* face, a *short, stubby tail,* and a *brownish belly, heavily barred on the sides.* The pleasing song is a long, variable, rapid, tinkling warble usually ending in a trill. The call is much like that of the Song Sparrow but differs mainly in being double-noted.

This wren is fairly common in winter in most of the state, but it is rare to uncommon on the Gulf Coast. It is not known to nest in Alabama. The Winter Wren frequents woodlands with low, thick cover such as ravines, canebrakes, vine tangles, and brush piles.

NESTING AND FOOD. This bird builds a round, bulky nest of moss and twigs lined with feathers and fur. A small concealed entrance is a feature of the nest which is usually in the roots of an upturned tree or in or under a rotten stump. The five or six white eggs have small spots of reddish-brown. The species feeds mostly on spiders, beetles, bugs, caterpillars, ants, many other injurious insects (including boll weevils), and rarely red cedar berries.

DISTRIBUTION. The Winter Wren breeds from Alaska, southern Mackenzie, northern Ontario, central Quebec, and Newfoundland south to central California, northern Idaho, central Michigan, New York, and central New England, and in mountains to northern Georgia. It also breeds in Eurasia, the only wren that does so. It winters from southern Alaska to southern California and from Colorado, Iowa, southern Ontario, central New York, and Massachusetts south to central Texas and southern Florida.

OCCURRENCE IN ALABAMA. (October 7 to April 19.) *Tennessee Valley*: October 14 (1947, Wheeler Refuge, L. S. Givens and J. H. Heflin) to April 18 (1948, Russellville, E. O. Willis); most seen, 8, December 22, 1942 (Florence, H. M. Stevenson). *Mountain Region*: October 9 (1935, Birmingham, H. M. Stevenson) to April 18 (1950, Birmingham, T. A. Imhof); most seen, 19, December 19, 1943 (Christmas Count, Birmingham). *Piedmont*: December 24 (1936, Auburn, H. S. Peters and Fay Peters) to March 26 (1908, Woodbine, A. A. Saunders). *Upper Coastal Plain*: October 7 (1938, Tuscaloosa, H. M. Stevenson) to April 8 (1939, Tuscaloosa, H. M. Stevenson); most seen, 10, January 25, 1939 (Tuscaloosa, H. M. Stevenson). *Lower Coastal Plain*: October 13 (1956, Jackson, W. U. Harris) to April 19 (1958, Bilbo Island, Washington Co., T. A. Imhof, J. R. Davis, and W. U. Harris). *Gulf Coast*: October 11 (1958, Dauphin Island, Lovett

Williams and R. W. Skinner) to March 26 (1960, Dauphin Island, Ava Tabor and Electa Levi); most seen, migration, 6, November 1, 1958 (Fall Count, Mobile Bay Area), winter, 6, January 2, 1960 (Christmas Count, Dauphin Island).

Bewick's Wren

Thryomanes bewickii (Audubon)   [719]   (Plate 29, facing page 392)
OTHER NAME: House Wren

Smaller than the Carolina Wren and larger than the House Wren, Bewick's Wren is brown above and white below and has a prominent *white stripe over the eye*. Its long, expressive, fan-shaped *tail* has *white spots near* the *tip*. The song is like that of the Song Sparrow in phrasing, but is higher and thinner and ends on a high trill. The buzzing call has a scolding quality.

This wren breeds uncommonly in the Tennessee Valley and Mountain Region and rarely and locally in the Piedmont and Upper Coastal Plain. (See Map 65.) In winter it is uncommon to fairly common in most of Alabama, but rare to uncommon on the Gulf Coast. In both winter and summer it frequents the vicinity of houses, especially liking dilapidated outbuildings, woodpiles, hedge-rows, and brush piles. Because Bewick's Wren does not get along well with the House Wren, the occurrence of the two together in the breeding season usually results in a battle which lasts until one species is driven away.

NESTING. This wren chooses any kind of cavity around houses, including nest boxes. It fills the cavity with sticks, straw, and coarse grass and lines the nest with feathers, hair, or other soft material. The female lays five to seven white eggs variously marked with reddish-brown, brown, or lavender.

FOOD. An insect-eater like other wrens, this bird consumes large numbers of bugs, beetles, caterpillars, moths, wasps, ants, flies, spiders, and grasshoppers.

DISTRIBUTION. Bewick's Wren breeds from southern British Columbia, southern Utah, southern Iowa, southern Michigan, southern Ontario, and central Pennsylvania south to southern Mexico, central Arkansas, northern Mississippi, central Alabama, and northern Georgia. It winters from southern British Columbia, southern Nevada, southern New Mexico, central Arkansas, southern Illinois, and southwestern Ohio south to southern Mexico and central Florida.

OCCURRENCE IN ALABAMA. (Throughout the year.) *Tennessee Valley*: Permanent resident; most seen, summer, 8, June 15, 1957 (Florence to Wheeler Dam, T. A. Imhof), winter, 3, December 23, 1942 and December 26, 1949 (Christmas Counts, Decatur). *Mountain Region*: Away from breeding localities, September 20 (1946 and 1949, Birmingham, T. A. Imhof) to May 8 (1947, Birmingham, T. A. Imhof); most seen, summer, 10, June 7, 1957 (Flat Rock, Jackson Co., T. A. Imhof), winter, 10, December 26, 1953 (Christmas Count, Birmingham). *Piedmont*: October 21 (1925, Auburn, J. M. Robertson) to May 5 (1952, Auburn, F. W. Fitch, Jr.). *Upper Coastal Plain*: Away from breeding localities, September 17 (1891 Greensboro, W. C. Avery and 1938, Tuscaloosa, H. M. Stevenson) to April 5 (1958, Marion, Lois McCollough); most seen, summer, 9, May 28, 1959 (Sumter Co., T. A. Imhof and Jenkins Jackson), winter, 5, December 24, 1922 (Barachias, E. G. Holt) and 5, December 27, 1957 (Marion, Lois McCollough). *Lower Coastal Plain*: October 7 (1908, Brewton, A. H. Howell) to March 23 (1957, Brooklyn, Conecuh Co., T. A. Imhof and L. C. Crawford). *Gulf Coast*: October 6 (1956, Dauphin Island, S. M. Russell and E. O. Willis and Alabama Point, H. M. Stevenson) to April 12 (1957, Dauphin Island, T. A. Imhof, J. L. Dorn, and H. C. Loesch); most seen, migration, 9, October 19, 1957 (Fall Count, Mobile Bay Area), winter, 5, December 21, 1957 (Christmas Count, Dauphin Island).

TIME OF BREEDING. Data on 9 nestings: Building, April 6 to May 28; eggs, March 26 to April 27; young in nest, April 17 to June 15; young out of nest by June 10.

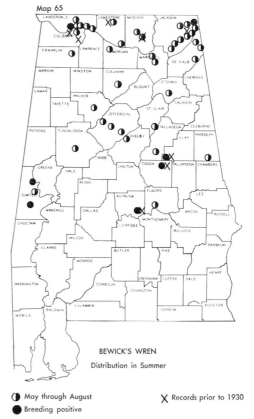

Map 65

BEWICK'S WREN

Distribution in Summer

◑ May through August   X Records prior to 1930
● Breeding positive

Carolina Wren

Thryothorus ludovicianus (Latham)   [718]   (Plate 29, facing page 392)
OTHER NAMES: House Wren, Jenny Wren

The largest and reddest wren in Alabama, the Carolina Wren is *bright reddish-brown above* and lighter underneath, strongly washed with *reddish-brown*, especially on the *belly*. It has a rather long tail and a prominent *white stripe over the eye*. Heard throughout the year, its common song is a loud and ringing refrain of two syllables, but some local birds treble their phrases as is usual farther north. It also has a wide variety of calls and imitations similar in quality to the song.

This bird is the most common and widespread wren in Alabama. It occurs here throughout the year and usually nests wherever found. Except for extensive marshes and prairies, hardly a square mile in the state lacks the Carolina Wren.

[389]

It frequents places near houses, and like other woodland wrens, prefers thick cover near the ground. Although the House and Bewick's Wrens cannot get along together, the Carolina Wren seems to associate amicably with either species.

NESTING. For its nest the Carolina Wren chooses any one of a great variety of situations in and around houses and in woods. It fills with coarse material any sort of cavity or receptacle left undisturbed and lines it with any fine material available. Woodland nests are usually a ball with a side entrance in upturned roots, tree holes, stumps, crotches, stream banks, vine tangles, and often on the ground on slopes. The three to six white eggs are marked with shades of brown, often in rather large spots.

FOOD. This species feeds on large quantities of injurious insects such as caterpillars, moths, beetles (especially boll weevils), ants, wasps, grasshoppers, crickets, cockroaches, and bugs. It often eats spiders and also, surprisingly, lizards and treefrogs, and occasionally berries and seeds. It is attracted to feeding stations by ground peanuts, suet, bone marrow, and hamburger.

DISTRIBUTION. The Carolina Wren is resident from southeastern Nebraska, southern Michigan, southern Ontario, and southern New England south to northeastern Mexico and southern Florida. It periodically extends its range northward to Minnesota, Wisconsin, and Maine, but north of the Ohio and Potomac valleys the species is nearly destroyed by severe winters about every eight to ten years.

ABUNDANCE IN ALABAMA (*most seen in a day*). Wheeler Refuge, 25, December 31, 1954 (Christmas Count); Birmingham, 107, December 20, 1952 (Christmas Count); southern Clarke Co., 60, January 11, 1958 (T. A. Imhof and others); Mobile Bay Area, 48, October 19, 1957 (Fall Count) and 47, January 2, 1960 (Christmas Count, Dauphin Island).

TIME OF BREEDING. Data on 67+ nestings: Building, January 29 to April 21; eggs, March 17 to July 30; young in nest, April 8 to August 9; dependent young out of nest, May 3 to August 10.

BANDING. At least 10 Carolina Wrens, banded at Dauphin Island, Fairhope, Birmingham, and Gadsden, have been recaptured at the same place a year or more later, about half in a different season.

Long-billed Marsh Wren
Telmatodytes palustris (Wilson)   [725]   (Plate 29, facing page 392)
OTHER NAME: Marsh Wren

A medium-sized wren, this bird is generally reddish-brown above with *white stripes* on the *back* and whitish below. A prominent *white line* runs *over* the *eye*. This bird's scolding call is a sharp and rapid ticking of two or three syllables.

PASSERIFORMES: TROGLODYTIDAE: LONG-BILLED MARSH WREN

The song, somewhat like that of the House Wren in composition, is a gurgling and reedy trill, usually with a wavering start.

This wren is a common, sometimes locally abundant, breeding, permanent resident in coastal marshes, whether fresh, brackish, or salt. It frequents tall cover such as cattails, cordgrass, reeds, and rushes, and seems to be a bit more common in salt marshes. This species is also fairly common on migration in much of the state, and it winters in fresh marshes, especially where cattails grow, as far inland as Birmingham. On migration, circumstances may force it to land in a marsh-like spot such as a damp field or a grassy lake shore. Although the Short-billed Marsh Wren often occurs on the periphery and in the drier parts of marshes, the Long-billed Marsh Wren is normally the only wren that frequents the deeper sections.

NESTING. The nest is a globe the size of a softball made by bending over the long blades of marsh grasses and weaving them together. The bird makes several dummy nests, but the real nest contains a lining of finer grasses, cattail or other plant down, and some feathers, and inside the tiny side entrance a ledge or doorsill. The three to five eggs are chocolate-brown, covered almost completely with small darker brown spots.

FOOD. This species eats more beetles and flies than anything else—especially scarabs, diving beetles, crane flies, and mosquitoes. It also consumes ants, bugs, locusts, caterpillars, grasshoppers, wasps, dragonflies, very small mollusks, and snails.

DISTRIBUTION. The Long-billed Marsh Wren breeds from central British Columbia, Saskatchewan, and southwestern Quebec south to central Mexico and southern Florida. It winters almost as far north as it breeds, particularly on the coast, but often only casually inland near the northern limits of its breeding range.

OCCURRENCE IN ALABAMA. (Throughout the year.) *Tennessee Valley*: May 10 and 11, 1941 (3 birds, Florence, H. M. Stevenson) and August 29 (1949, Wheeler Refuge, T. A. Imhof) to September 29 (1953, Wheeler Refuge, D. C. Hulse). *Mountain Region*: September 1 (1954, Birmingham, T. A. Imhof) to May 9 (1955, Fairfield, T. A. Imhof); most seen, winter, 8, February 15, 1955 (Fairfield, T. A. Imhof), migration, 6, May 2, 1949 (Birmingham, T. A. Imhof). *Piedmont*: No record. *Upper Coastal Plain*: October 2 (1954, Marion, Lois McCollough) to May 22 (1914, specimen in U. S. National Museum, Seale, Russell Co., A. H. Howell). *Lower Coastal Plain*: Open Pond, Covington Co., February 25, 1955 (2 birds, T. A. Imhof) and October 19, 1956 (1 bird, T. A. Imhof and L. C. Crawford). *Gulf Coast*: Permanent resident; most seen, winter, 33, January 2, 1960 (Christmas Count, Dauphin Island), migration, 23, October 19, 1957 (Fall Count, Mobile Bay Area).

TIME OF BREEDING. Data on 50+ nestings: Eggs, June 17 and 18; young in nest, June 17 and 18; young on the wing by June 17.

[392]

Richard A Parks

Short-billed Marsh Wren

Cistothorus platensis (Latham) [724] Plate 29, facing page 392)

OTHER NAME: Sedge Wren

In contrast to the Long-billed Marsh Wren, the Short-billed Marsh Wren is more *finely streaked* above, especially on the *crown*, is buffier, particularly on the under tail coverts, has a rather plain face, and is slightly smaller. The song resembles that of the Long-billed Marsh Wren in composition and tempo but not in quality. This wren's song is a dry, less musical staccato ending in a trill. It is somewhat similar to the song of the Dickcissel, but the Dickcissel's song is thicker, heavier, and without a trill. The two-noted call of this wren is of the same quality as the song.

This wren inhabits grassy areas drier than the marshes of the Long-billed Wren, but still rather damp. In Alabama the Short-billed Marsh Wren winters abundantly on the coast, commonly in the remainder of the Coastal Plain, and more locally north of the Fall Line. August records of singing birds suggest that this bird may possibly breed in the state, at least occasionally, but no positive breeding evidence has yet been found. In Alabama it frequents the grassy edges of marshes, boggy areas in pine flats, damp broomsedge, and sometimes dry, grassy places, as long as the cover is at least two or three feet tall. This species is especially active at dawn and dusk.

NESTING. The nest is a globular ball of dry and green grasses. It is usually less than a foot above the ground, mud, or water, well hidden in dense grass such as sedges or rushes. It has a side entrance and is usually lined with plant down and feathers. Like the Long-billed Marsh Wren, this wren builds many unlined dummy nests. The four to eight eggs are usually pure white.

FOOD. In Alabama this bird's diet, consisting of weevils, ants, bugs, grasshoppers, and spiders, differs little from its food elsewhere.

DISTRIBUTION. The Short-billed Marsh Wren breeds from southern Saskatchewan and southern Quebec south to eastern Kansas, Arkansas, and eastern Virginia and also south through Central America to Patagonia. It winters from Texas, Tennessee, and Maryland south to northern Mexico and southern Florida, and occasionally north to Long Island.

OCCURRENCE IN ALABAMA. (August 3 to May 24.) *Tennessee Valley*: August 5 (1952, Wheeler Refuge, Eugene Cypert) to May 16 (1955, Wheeler Refuge, Eugene Cypert); most seen, 7, August 26, 1950 (Wheeler Refuge, T. A. Imhof). *Mountain Region*: September 21 (1936, Easonville, St. Clair Co., H. M. Stevenson) to May 23

(1937, Birmingham, H. M. Stevenson); most seen, 6, December 26, 1959 (Birmingham, T. A. Imhof). *Piedmont*: April 16 (1955, Auburn, H. G. Good) to May 9 (1953, Auburn, C. W. Summerour); no fall or winter dates. *Upper Coastal Plain*: August 3 (1938, singing at Tuscaloosa, H. M. Stevenson) to May 24 (1939, Tuscaloosa, H. M. Stevenson). *Lower Coastal Plain*: March 24, 1958 (Camden, Lovett Williams); April 2, 1953 (2 birds, Point A Lake, Andalusia, W. R. Middleton); and October 3, 1958 (Camden, Lovett Williams). *Gulf Coast*: October 5 (1956, Alabama Port, E. O. Willis and S. M. Russell) to May 3 (1959, Dauphin Island, T. A. Imhof and D. C. Holliman); most seen, 59, December 21, 1957 (Christmas Count, Dauphin Island).

FAMILY MIMIDAE: MOCKINGBIRDS AND THRASHERS

These thrush-like birds usually have long, rounded, expressive tails, long, slightly-curved bills, and well-developed songs. They are generally good imitators.

Mockingbird

Mimus polyglottos (Linnaeus)   [703]   (Plate 30, facing page 408)

This species is a rather plain-looking bird, dark gray above and whitish below with white in the wings and in the long tail. Often on an exposed perch in poor light it is mistaken for a shrike, but the Mockingbird is longer, thinner, long-billed, long-legged, and long-tailed and the shrike has a rounder head and a black mask.

The most remarkable songbird of Alabama, the Mockingbird frequently sings on spring and summer nights, especially when the moon is full. When perched on a chimney, it fills the house with song, to the chagrin of the sleepy occupants. Most ornithologists agree that it is the best singer they know, for it can imitate and often improve on the songs of almost any species, even some water birds. When Edward Bok imported Nightingales for his singing tower at Lake Wales, Florida, the local Mockingbirds soon added perfect imitations of this song to their repertoire. Frequently the Mockingbird goes down the list of songs of local birds, repeating each imitation five or six times and often singing more than one song for each species. In early spring, it even imitates summer-resident birds that have not yet returned from their winter quarters.

In Alabama this bird is a widespread and abundant resident throughout the year. It seems to be most abundant around houses, particularly farms, and least abundant in deep woods, especially on mountains in the northern part of the state. It usually nests wherever found.

[394]

NESTING. The typical nest is durably made of dead twigs lined with grasses and rootlets. It is most commonly three to ten feet above ground in a thick shrub, often near a house, but a great variety of other materials and locations are often selected. The clutch consists of three to five bluish or greenish eggs heavily marked with shades of brown.

FOOD. Wild fruit forms more than half of the yearly diet of the Mockingbird. The principal items are various berries and other fleshy fruits from trees, vines, and shrubs. Occasionally it may eat cultivated fruit, but usually when wild fruit is not available. The remainder of its food includes insects and small animals, eaten mainly in late spring and summer. It takes beetles (including boll weevils), grasshoppers, and caterpillars, and to a lesser extent, ants, bugs, spiders, snails, crawfish, sowbugs, and lizards.

DISTRIBUTION. The Mockingbird is resident from northern California, northern Utah, central Illinois, and central New Jersey south to southern Mexico, Hispaniola, and the Virgin Islands. It is extending its range northward, often as a breeder, to all the southern Canadian provinces, but usually it retires from the more northern parts in winter.

ABUNDANCE IN ALABAMA (*most seen in a day*). Birmingham, 233, December 26, 1959 (Christmas Count); Mobile Bay Area, 295, October 19, 1957 (Fall Count).

TIME OF BREEDING. Data on 105+ nestings: Building, February 12 to July 15; eggs, April 12 to July 26; young in nest, March 28 to August 3; dependent young out of nest, April 15 to August 21.

BANDING. Mockingbirds sometimes travel. One banded at Fairhope in August 1931 was later found at Lower Peachtree, Wilcox Co., 90 miles away. Another, banded at Winfield, Marion Co., July 6, 1931, was recaptured at Leroy, Washington Co., 160 miles away on March 30, 1932. However, 16 other Alabama-banded Mockingbirds were recaptured 1 or 2 years later at the place of banding.

Catbird

Dumetella carolinensis (Linnaeus)   [704]   (Plate 30, facing page 408)

The Catbird is uniformly dark gray with a *black cap* and *reddish under tail coverts*. It is slightly smaller than the Mockingbird which it closely resembles in shape, but the tail of the Catbird is relatively shorter. The call is a loud, cat-like, mewing note. Its song has much of the quality of the songs of the Mockingbird and the Brown Thrasher, but it is less musical and it does not repeat phrases.

The Catbird is a common, breeding, summer resident in most of Alabama, but it breeds in only a few places south of the Black Belt. On migration it is common throughout the state, and on the coast it is abundant in fall. In winter it is uncommon on the coast and rare north to the Tennessee Valley, but it occurs then chiefly south of the Black Belt. It frequents hedgerows, woods borders, and other shrubby or brushy places.

NESTING. The nest is a deep cup made of twigs, sticks, and leaves, lined almost exclusively with rootlets. It is usually well concealed in dense shrubbery close to the ground. The female lays three to four deep greenish-blue eggs.

FOOD. More than half of the food of the Catbird consists of berries and other fruits. It sometimes eats cultivated fruits, especially when wild fruits are not obtainable. A recommended control measure is to plant its favorite fruits, such as mulberry, wild cherry, dogwood, and wild grape, nearby. The remainder of its diet consists mainly of such injurious insects as ants, beetles, caterpillars, and grasshoppers.

DISTRIBUTION. The Catbird breeds from southern British Columbia, central Saskatchewan, southern Quebec, and Nova Scotia south to Arizona, central Texas, and northern Florida. It winters from southeastern Texas, central Alabama, and coastal Virginia, occasionally north to Long Island, south to Panama and the Lesser Antilles.

OCCURRENCE IN ALABAMA. (Throughout the year.) *Tennessee Valley*: April 15 (1891, Leighton, F. W. McCormack) to October 24 (1959, Huntsville, J. C. and Margaret Robinson); also December 23, 1943 (Wheeler Refuge, Paul Bryan and J. H. Steenis) and December 27, 1941 (Wheeler Refuge, T. Z. Atkeson, Jr. and J. H. Steenis); most seen, 10, June 19, 1953 (Wheeler Refuge, T. A. Imhof). *Mountain Region*: March 14 (1931, Jasper, H. M. Stevenson) to November 2 (1935, Birmingham, H. M. Stevenson); also December 20, 1947 (Birmingham, M. H. Perry); December 22, 1956 (3 birds, Birmingham, Idalene Snead); December 26, 1953 (Birmingham, Blanche Chapman) and December 26, 1959 (Birmingham, Malcolm Harden and Alfred Walker); most seen, 36, May 4, 1940 (Birmingham, H. M. Stevenson). *Piedmont*: March 24 (1939, specimen in the Auburn Univ. collection, Auburn, H. G. Good) to October 17 (1959, Waverly, Chambers Co., J. L. Dusi). *Upper Coastal Plain*: Common, March 23 (1956, Montgomery, O. L. Austin, Jr.) to November 8 (1956, Marion, Lois McCollough); most seen in winter, 3, December 27, 1947 (Christmas Count, Marion). *Lower Coastal Plain*: September 14 (1956, Jackson, W. U. Harris and T. A. Imhof) to May 9 (1958, Florala,

T. A. Imhof); also breeds at Greenville (G. A. Carleton); May 25, 1958 (Camden, Lovett Williams); June 1, 1950 and June 6, 1945 (Andalusia, W. R. Middleton) and early July 1957 (southern Henry Co., Lovett Williams). *Gulf Coast*: September 8 (1959, Dauphin Island, T. A. Imhof and J. B. Sullivan) to May 16 (1960, Dauphin Island, J. L. Dorn); most seen, spring, "hundreds" on several dates in April and May 1960 (Dauphin Island, J. L. Dorn), fall, 214, October 6, 1956 (Fall Count, Mobile Bay Area), winter, 7, January 10, 1958 (Bellingrath Gardens, T. A. Imhof and others).

TIME OF BREEDING. Data on 30 nestings: Building, May 19; eggs, April 25 to June 25; young in nest, May 26 to September 1; dependent young on the wing, June 21 to September.

BANDING. A Catbird, banded at Tuscaloosa, July 6, 1945, was found dead in the vicinity in August 1946. Another, banded at Gadsden, May 2, 1956, was recaptured there on April 17, 1960. Two others, both banded in August in Waukegan, Illinois, were recovered in the same county in Alabama, Mount Vernon, November 28, 1929 and Mobile, February 13, 1938, the latter bird, 6 years old.

Brown Thrasher

Toxostoma rufum (Linnaeus)   [705]   (Plate 30, facing page 408)
OTHER NAMES: Brown Thrush, Red Thrush, Thrash, French Mockingbird

This bird is rich reddish-brown above with two white wing bars, and pale yellowish-buff, heavily streaked with dark brown, below. It has a long tail, and its bill is longer and heavier than those of its smaller relatives, the Mockingbird and Catbird. The call of the Brown Thrasher is a loud and emphatic smacking note. Its song is similar to that of the Mockingbird but is less varied and the phrases are repeated only once.

In Alabama the Brown Thrasher is a common to abundant permanent resident. In winter its number greatly increases on the Gulf Coast. During this season this species is more common in the Coastal Plain, but above the Fall Line, particularly on mountains, it is often uncommon. It breeds in this state in woodland borders, shrubbery around houses, and other brushy places.

NESTING. The nest is generally two to ten feet from the ground in hedgerows, vine tangles, shrubbery, or low trees, especially in hawthorn, Osage-

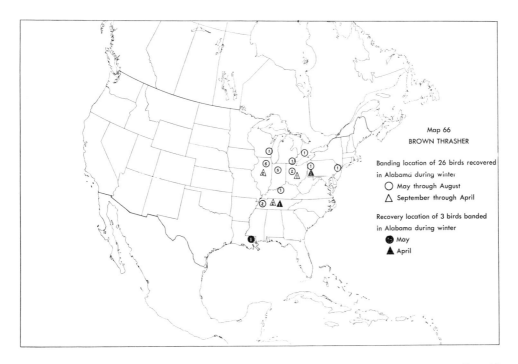

Map 66
BROWN THRASHER

Banding location of 26 birds recovered in Alabama during winter
○ May through August
△ September through April

Recovery location of 3 birds banded in Alabama during winter
● May
▲ April

E. E. and L. E. Foote

NEST OF BROWN THRASHER. Usually located in low shrubs, this rather bulky nest is constructed mainly of sticks and rootlets.

orange, honey-locust, and young oaks. It is built of twigs, dead leaves, and grass, and lined with rootlets. The three to five pale bluish-white eggs are evenly and heavily covered with very fine reddish-brown dots.

FOOD. Most of this bird's food consists of acorns, small berries, cherries, grapes, and beetles. In much smaller amounts, it also takes corn, weed seeds, caterpillars, grasshoppers, crickets, other insects, spiders, and other small animals.

DISTRIBUTION. The Brown Thrasher breeds from southern Alberta, southern Ontario, and southern Quebec south to eastern Texas and southern Florida. It winters in this range regularly north to Oklahoma and southern Maryland and less regularly to the most northern states and southern Ontario.

ABUNDANCE IN ALABAMA (*most seen in a day*). Florence, 27, June 10, 1955 (T. A. Imhof, Malcolm Harden, and Alfred Walker); Birmingham, spring, 34, May 4, 1940 (H. M. Stevenson), winter, 47, December 20, 1958 (Christmas Count); Mobile Bay Area, migration, 116, October 6, 1956 (Fall Count), winter, 60, January 2, 1960 (Christmas Count).

TIME OF BREEDING. Data on 80+ nestings: Building, March 27 to May 14; eggs, March 30 to July 27; young, April 12 to August 2; out of nest by May 11.

BANDING. See Map 66 for place of banding of 26 Brown Thrashers recovered in winter in Alabama and place of recovery of 3 birds banded in winter in Alabama.

[398]

Sage Thrasher

Oreoscoptes montanus (Townsend)　[702]　(Plate 30, facing page 408)

Although this thrasher looks much *like a Mockingbird*, it can be distinguished by its *streaked under parts, short, straight bill,* and *short tail.* It has large white spots under the tip of the dark tail, and its back is a bit more brown than that of the Mockingbird. The Sage Thrasher has many actions like those of the Brown Thrasher and Mockingbird, which help to place it in the right family.

In Alabama this species is accidental in fall on the coast. It usually occurs in dry sagebrush country, and the state's one specimen was found in a dry, shrubby, sandy area on Dauphin Island.

NESTING AND FOOD. The well-hidden, bulky nest of coarse twigs is usually placed close to the ground in sagebrush, thorn, or greasewood. It contains four or five deep blue-green eggs blotched with brown. This thrasher consumes insects and small fruits in considerable variety. Mormon crickets, locusts, alfalfa weevils, bugs, currants, blackberries, and grapes form the principal items in its diet.

DISTRIBUTION. The Sage Thrasher breeds from southern British Columbia and southwestern Saskatchewan south to central California and western Oklahoma. It winters from California and Texas south into northern Mexico, and in fall it occasionally wanders west to the Pacific Ocean and east to New York and Alabama.

OCCURRENCE IN ALABAMA. *Gulf Coast only*: Fort Gaines, Dauphin Island, November 5, 1959, specimen now in the Dept. of Conservation collection (T. A. Imhof and F. B. Daniel).

FAMILY TURDIDAE: THRUSHES, SOLITAIRES, AND BLUEBIRDS

Thrushes have short, rather slender, straight bills, moderate-sized tails, rather long wings, long, stout legs, and large eyes. Most of the thrushes in Alabama are brown with spotted breasts, but mature robins and bluebirds lack the spots on the breast, and it remains for the immatures of these two species to demonstrate this family characteristic. Rather nervous birds, thrushes often flick their tails, but they are usually quiet and rather dainty. Their songs, melodious and pleasing, are among the best music in the bird world.

[399]

Robin

Turdus migratorius Linnaeus   [761]   (Plate 30, facing page 408)
OTHER NAME: Robin Redbreast

The Robin has a gray back and is darker, almost black, on the head and tail. It has a rusty-red breast and belly, white under the tail and around the eye, a yellow bill, and a few dark streaks on the throat. The immature bird has a spotted breast and a duller-colored bill. The song is a clear, loud, robust, rapid, and often long-continued whistle.

In Alabama the Robin is an abundant permanent resident south to the Black Belt, and below this it is uncommon and local, mostly around towns, south to Brewton, Mobile, and Dauphin Island. For breeding it seems to require a lawn and at least one shade tree. In winter, its number reinforced by northern birds, the species is abundant south to the Gulf. It occurs at this time in flocks in many habitats, but seems to favor swamps, farmland, and open woodland, especially where berries are available.

Formerly the Robin nested rarely in Alabama, and then only in the extreme north. Apparently it is a very successful species for it has shown the ability to extend its breeding range southward into suburban areas within the last century. Breeding first around towns, then spreading into the surrounding country about farm houses, it appears to occur in a wider area each year. (See Map 67.)

NESTING. The nest is a deep, bulky cup of mud, reinforced with grasses, twigs, and other materials, and lined with fine grasses. It is usually on a horizontal limb away from the trunk, but it may be in any one of a variety of man-made situations near houses, such as ledges, shelves, and posts, and is about five to thirty-five feet from the ground. The clutch consists of three or four eggs of a plain greenish-blue color which is the original "Robin's-egg blue." The female builds the nest and does almost all the incubating, and the male stands guard and takes charge of feeding the young when they hatch.

FOOD. Most of this bird's food is fruit. Occasionally it becomes a pest around cultivated fruit. The best method of control is to plant native trees or shrubs from the list below that will be in fruit at the same time as the cultivated ones, for the Robin prefers wild fruit if it is available. In the southeastern states, this bird feeds on the fruits of cherry, mulberry, dogwood, holly, persimmon, black gum, sumac, hackberry, blackberry, chinaberry, red cedar, corn, Virginia creeper, greenbrier, blueberry, grape, French mulberry, rattan, and others. It consumes more animal food in summer, and animal life is also probably the main food of the young. Principal items are caterpillars, beetles, and earthworms, but it also eats true bugs, flies, sowbugs, snails, grasshoppers, spiders, termites, millipedes, and centipedes.

DISTRIBUTION. The Robin breeds from the tree limit in Alaska, northern Quebec, and Newfoundland south to central Mexico, the northern Gulf Coast, and northern Florida. This species winters mainly from southwestern British Columbia, southern South Dakota, the Ohio and Potomac valleys, southern New England, and southern Newfoundland south to southern Mexico, Cuba, and Bermuda.

OCCURRENCE IN ALABAMA.

(Throughout the year.) *Tennessee Valley*: Permanent resident; most seen, 500, February 5, 1955 (Marshall Co. and Jackson Co., T. A. Imhof and others). *Mountain Region*: Permanent resident; most seen, winter, 4000+ in roost, December 1960 and January 1961 (Birmingham, T. A. Imhof), spring, 820, February 28, 1953 (Birmingham, T. A. Imhof). *Piedmont*: Permanent resident. *Upper Coastal Plain*: Away from breeding stations, October 15 (1938, Tuscaloosa, H. M. Stevenson) to April 21 (1937, Tuscaloosa, H. M. Stevenson); most seen, "thousands," late February 1921 (Montgomery, P. A. Brannon). *Lower Coastal Plain*: Away from breeding stations, September 18 (1958, Camden, Lovett Williams) to March 26 (1959, Coffeeville, J. E. Keeler and 1960, Florala, H. M. Stevenson); most seen, "millions" in swamp roost near Luverne in 1930-32 (*Bird-Lore* 33:221-223), 400+, February 25, 1955 (Conecuh Co., T. A. Imhof). *Gulf Coast*: Away from breeding stations, October 19 (1957, Foley, H. M. Stevenson) to April 16 (1950, Elberta, H. M. Stevenson); most seen, fall, 10,000+, November 5, 1929 (Fairhope, E. C. Wolcott), winter, 3771, December 30, 1960 (Christmas Count, Dauphin Island).

TIME OF BREEDING. Data on over 110 nestings: Building, February 5 to May 3; eggs, March 22 to July 16; young in nest, March 30 to August 11; dependent young out of nest, April 15 to August 22.

BANDING. Of 116 banded Robins recovered in Alabama, 20 were recovered in

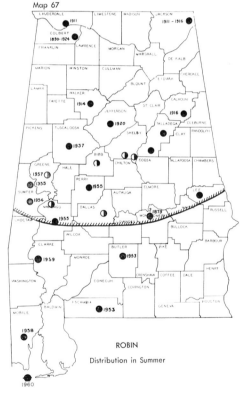

Map 67

ROBIN

Distribution in Summer

⚏⚏⚏ Species widespread as a breeder north of this line but common only in towns indicated southward

◑ May through August
● Breeding positive

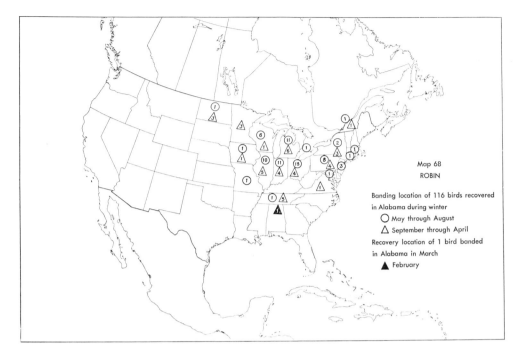

Map 68
ROBIN

Banding location of 116 birds recovered
in Alabama during winter

○ May through August
△ September through April

Recovery location of 1 bird banded
in Alabama in March

▲ February

the Tennessee Valley, 22 in the Mountain Region, 1 in the Piedmont, 26 in the Upper Coastal Plain, 36 in the Lower Coastal Plain, and 11 on the Gulf Coast. For place of banding see Map 68. Another Robin was banded at Auburn and recovered in the Tennessee Valley.

Wood Thrush

Hylocichla mustelina (Gmelin) [755] (Plate 29, facing page 392)
OTHER NAMES: Brown Thrush, Swamp Sparrow, Branch Bird

This thrush has a reddish-brown back, *redder* on the *head,* and large, round, dark brown spots on the under parts. It is larger and heavier than the other Alabama representatives of its genus. The song of the Wood Thrush is louder and more varied and has rounder phrases than the songs of the other brown thrushes of Alabama.

In Alabama, the Wood Thrush is a common and well-distributed summer resident. It frequents primarily the lower parts of low, moist, shaded hardwoods, but it also occurs in mixed woods and rarely in pure pine stands. Although it breeds south to the Gulf, it becomes thinly scattered near the coast as proper habitat becomes scarce.

NESTING. The nest is a deep cup of mud, dead leaves, and moss, reinforced with grass and lined with rootlets. The average nest is in a crotch of a sapling or shrub, or on a horizontal limb of a tree about ten feet from the ground. The two to four eggs are greenish-blue, smaller and darker than those of the robin.

FOOD. In spring this thrush eats insects, chiefly beetles, ants, caterpillars, and grasshoppers, and some flies, bugs, sowbugs, snails, and earthworms. As fall approaches and more plants mature, their fruits constitute the major part of its diet, and chiefly it eats those of spicebush, dogwood, cherry, grape, blackberry, black gum, mulberry, Virginia creeper, and a host of others, depending on what is locally available.

DISTRIBUTION. The Wood Thrush breeds east of the Great Plains from Minnesota and southern Maine south to southeastern Texas and northern Florida. It winters from southern Texas, and sometimes Florida, through Central America to Panama.

OCCURRENCE IN ALABAMA. (Normal: March 11 to November 7; Out of season: December 30.) *Tennessee Valley*: April 5 (1948, Russellville, E. O. Willis) to October 13 (1960, netted, Brownsboro, J. C. and Margaret Robinson). *Mountain Region*: March 11 (1950, Talladega, C. T. Hornady) to October 20 (1958, Birmingham, Harriett Wright); most seen, 50, June 10, 1943 (Mentone, H. M. Stevenson). *Piedmont*: March 25 (1908, Woodbine, A. A. Saunders and 1948, Auburn, H. G. Good) to October 17 (1959, Waverly, Chambers Co., J. L. Dusi). *Upper Coastal Plain*: March 17 (1956, Marion, Lois McCollough) to October 29 (1916, Bear Swamp, Autauga Co., L. S. Golsan). *Lower Coastal Plain*: March 27 (1959, Coffeeville, J. E. Keeler) to October 21 (1958, Camden, Lovett Williams); also March 11 (see BANDING.) *Gulf Coast*: March 17 (1960, Dauphin Island, J. L. Dorn) to November 7 (1959, Dauphin Island, Edith Clark); also December 30, 1960 (Dauphin Island, Clustie McTyeire and many others); most seen, spring, 40, April 15, 1961 (Dauphin Island, T. A. Imhof and others), fall, 17, October 6, 1959 (Fall Count, Mobile Bay Area).

TIME OF BREEDING. Data on 67 nestings: Building, May 17; eggs, April 19 to July 25; young in nest, April 29 to July 25; dependent young out of nest, May 26 to August 8.

BANDING. A Wood Thrush, banded in Baltimore, Md. as a nestling, June 18, 1949, was found at Andalusia, March 11, 1950.

Hermit Thrush

Hylocichla guttata (Pallas)   [759]   (Plate 29, facing page 392)

OTHER NAME: Swamp Sparrow

The Hermit Thrush has a brown back, a moderate amount of spotting on the breast, and a *reddish-brown tail* which is often raised rapidly and lowered slowly.

[403]

This thrush is said to have the most melodious song of all North American birds. It starts with a *long key note* and continues with four or five long phrases in *different pitches,* separated by rather long *pauses.* The song is heard in Alabama only occasionally, but the call, a low chuck, is useful in locating birds in winter.

Throughout Alabama, the Hermit Thrush is common to abundant on migration and in winter, but is not known to nest in the state. It occurs in all types of wooded areas but especially in moist places and shrubby or brushy spots. Like other thrushes, it generally lives on the ground, or close to it.

NESTING AND FOOD. This thrush lays three to six pale greenish-blue eggs in a compact nest of twigs, grasses, bark, moss, and ferns, lined with pine needles and other fine plant fibers, and almost always on the ground among ferns or evergreen boughs. It eats more insects than the other brown thrushes. These include mainly beetles, ants, caterpillars, bees, wasps, flies, bugs, grasshoppers, and crickets. In fall and winter it adds wild fruits and some seeds, including holly, greenbrier, dogwood, serviceberry, sumac, grape, and many others.

DISTRIBUTION. The Hermit Thrush breeds from central Alaska, southern Mackenzie, central Quebec, and Newfoundland south to southern California, northern New Mexico, central Minnesota, Pennsylvania, and Long Island, and in mountains to West Virginia and Maryland. It winters from Vancouver Island, Colorado, Texas, Missouri, the Ohio Valley, and Long Island, rarely southern New England, south to Guatemala and southern Florida.

OCCURRENCE IN ALABAMA. (October 6 to April 28.) *Tennessee Valley*: October 16 (1889, Leighton, F. W. McCormack and 1953, Wheeler Refuge, D. C. Hulse) to April 23 (Wheeler Refuge, *fide* T. Z. Atkeson, Jr.). *Mountain Region*: October 10 (1953, Birmingham, T. A. Imhof) to April 28 (1937, Birmingham, H. M. Stevenson); most seen, 38, December 20, 1952 (Christmas Count, Birmingham). *Piedmont*: November 10 (1936, Auburn, H. G. Good) to April 19 (1958, Auburn, R. W. Skinner and others). *Upper Coastal Plain*: October 15 (1938, Tuscaloosa, H. M. Stevenson) to April 24 (1958, Livingston, Jenkins Jackson). *Lower Coastal Plain*: October 8 (1957, Jackson, W. U. Harris) to April 12 (1958, Camden, Lovett Williams). *Gulf Coast*: October 6 (1956, Coden, M. W. Gaillard, R. T. Lynn, and Mrs. R. T. Lynn) to April 19 (1958, Dauphin Island, S. A. Gauthreaux and others); most seen, 15, December 27, 1947 (Christmas Count, Foley).

Swainson's Thrush

Hylocichla ustulata (Nuttall)   [758]   (Plate 29, facing page 392)
OTHER NAME: Olive-backed Thrush

Swainson's Thrush has a gray-brown or olive back, moderate spotting on the breast, *buffy-brown cheeks,* and a *buffy eye ring.* The song, sometimes heard in May in Alabama, is composed of a phrase repeated many times, each time in a new and higher key. The bird sounds like a Veery in reverse. The call is a low, sharp note, and the flight call, often heard in this state at night, is short and far-carrying.

In Alabama Swainson's Thrush is a common, often abundant, transient which is not known to nest here. It occurs in spring and fall in almost all the wooded areas of the state. Like other thrushes it usually occurs on or near the ground, but Swainson's Thrush occasionally ranges higher in the trees. Migrating birds are usually silent and retiring.

NESTING AND FOOD. The usual clutch contains three or four pale greenish-blue eggs rather evenly spotted with brown. These are laid in a bulky but well-built nest, ordinarily on a horizontal branch near the trunk of a balsam fir or spruce about seven feet from the ground. A distinctive feature of the lining is the dark, fibrous mass of *Hypnum* moss. In spring and summer, this thrush subsists principally on insects, and in fall and winter, on fruits. Favorites are those of wild cherry, dogwood, elderberry, Virginia creeper, and grape. In Alabama it frequently feeds on black gum.

DISTRIBUTION. Swainson's Thrush breeds from central Alaska, central Quebec, and Newfoundland south to southwestern California, Colorado, northern Minnesota, West Virginia, and southern New England. It winters from southern Mexico to northwestern Argentina.

OCCURRENCE IN ALABAMA. (April 4 to May 28 and August 28 to November 10.) *Tennessee Valley:* April 23 (1914, specimen in U. S. National Museum, Muscle Shoals, J. L. Peters) to May 16 (1959, Huntsville, J. C. and Margaret Robinson) and September 7 (1960, Brownsboro, Madison Co., J. C. and Margaret Robinson) to October 12 (1960, Brownsboro, J. C. and Margaret Robinson). *Mountain Region:* April 19 (1947, Birmingham, T. A. Imhof) to May 28 (1960, Birmingham, T. A. Imhof) and August 28 (1935, Camp Winnetaska, St. Clair Co., H. M. Stevenson) to October 26 (1956, Birmingham, J. B. Sullivan); most seen or heard, spring, 67, flying over in one hour, night of April 30, 1953 (Fairfield, T. A. Imhof), fall, 245, flying over, night of October 4, 1954; and 145 ceilometer casualties, October 8, 1954 (Birmingham, T. A. Imhof and F. B. Daniel). *Piedmont:* April 8 (1936, Beehive, Lee Co., H. S. Peters) to May 21 (1960, Mitchell Lake, Harriett Wright) and September 10 (1958, Auburn, Lovett Williams) to October 18 (1959, Waverly, Chambers Co., J. L. Dusi). *Upper Coastal Plain:* April 7 (1937, Tuscaloosa, H. M. Stevenson) to May 22 (1954, Eutaw, Harriett Wright) and September 3 (1890, specimen, Greensboro, W. C. Avery) to October 22 (1915, specimen, Autaugaville, L. S. Golsan). *Lower Coastal Plain:* April (*fide* several observers) to May 10 (1954, Grove Hill, G. A. Carleton and Julia Helms) and September 19 (1957, Andalusia, T. A. Imhof and Lovett Williams) to October 25 (1954, Greenville, G. A. Carleton and Stanley). *Gulf Coast:* April 4 (1959, Spring Hill, J. L. Dorn) to May 16 (1960, Dauphin Island, J. L. Dorn and Hurricane, D. D. Stamm) and September 10 (1959, Dauphin Island, T. A. Imhof and J. B. Sullivan) to November 10 (1957, Dauphin Island, Ava Tabor); most seen, 125, September 16, 1960 (after Hurricane Ethel, Dauphin Island, J. L. Dorn).

Gray-cheeked Thrush

Hylocichla minima (Lafresnaye) [757] (Plate 29, facing page 392)

This thrush has a gray-brown back, moderate amount of breast spotting, *gray cheeks,* and an incomplete or very *indistinct eye ring.* The song resembles that of the Veery but is thin and nasal and usually rises abruptly at the end. The flight call, nasal and two-syllabled, is sometimes heard in Alabama at night during migration.

In Alabama, this species is uncommon to common on migration and casual in winter but is not known to nest. Usually it occurs with Swainson's Thrush at the same season and in the same habitat. Occasionally it sings on migration.

NESTING AND FOOD. The female lays three to five greenish-blue eggs, faintly marked with brown, in a compact and sturdy nest of mud and grass. The nest is built on or close to the ground among the stunted trees of the subarctic forest. Insects, particularly beetles, ants, wild bees, wasps, and caterpillars, form a large portion of the diet, especially in summer. Wild fruits, although eaten at whatever season they mature, constitute most of the fall diet and include those of dogwood, cherry, and black gum, and grapes, blueberries, and mulberries.

DISTRIBUTION. The Gray-cheeked Thrush breeds from northeastern Siberia, northern Alaska, and northern Quebec south to northeastern British Columbia, central Saskatchewan, southeastern New York, and central New England. It winters on the island of Hispaniola and from Nicaragua to northern Peru and northwestern Brazil.

OCCURRENCE IN ALABAMA. (Normal: March 26 to May 25 and September 6 to November 10; Out-of-season: December 27 and 31 and January 1.) *Tennessee Valley:* May 4 (1957, Wheeler Refuge, Blanche Dean and J. E. Keeler) to May 25 (1941, Florence, H. M. Stevenson) and September 5 (1960, Brownsboro, Madison Co., J. C. and Margaret Robinson) to October 18 (1958, Huntsville, J. C. and Margaret Robinson). *Mountain Region:* April 23 (1937, Birmingham, H. M. Stevenson) to May 17 (1940, Birmingham, H. M. Stevenson) and September 6 (1935, Birmingham, H. M. Stevenson) to October 19 (1949, Birmingham, T. A. Imhof); also December 27, 1960, December 31, 1949, and January 1, 1951 (Birmingham, Blanche Dean and Larry Rosen); most seen, 42 (39 ceilometer casualties and 3 survivors); October 8, 1954 (Birmingham, T. A. Imhof and F. B. Daniel). *Piedmont:* April 17 (1954, Chewacla State Park, H. G. Good) to May 3 (1950, Auburn, H. G. Good) and September 10 (1958, Auburn, Lovett Williams) to October 17 (1959, Waverly, Chambers Co., J. L. Dusi). *Upper Coastal Plain:* April 23 (1912, specimen, Barachias, E. G. Holt) to May 14 (1939, Tuscaloosa, H. M. Stevenson) and September 10 (1891, specimen in the Avery collection, Greensboro, W. C. Avery) to October 20 (1890, specimen in the Avery collection, Greensboro, W. C. Avery and 1956, Marion, Lois McCollough). *Lower Coastal Plain:* No spring dates; September 14 (1956,

Jackson, W. U. Harris and T. A. Imhof and 1958, Camden, Lovett Williams) to October 25 (1957, Jackson, W. U. Harris); also December 27, 1957 (dead bird in yard, Jackson, W. U. Harris). *Gulf Coast*: March 26 (1961, Dauphin Island, Ava Tabor and others) to May 22 (1960, netted, Hurricane, D. D. Stamm) and September 16 (1960, 15 birds after Hurricane Ethel, Dauphin Island, J. L. Dorn) to November 10 (Spring Hill, J. L. Dorn).

Veery
Hylocichla fuscescens (Stephens)   [756]   (Plate 29, facing page 392)
OTHER NAME: Wilson's Thrush

The Veery is a brown thrush which is *uniformly reddish-brown* on all the *upper parts* and has a *very few* small reddish-brown *spots* which are *confined* to the *throat*. The song has about four phrases, which suggest the bird's name, and is characterized by its gradual progression down the scale, each phrase lower in key than the one before. The call, also used as an alarm note, is a low-pitched whistle which may be recognized from time to time among thrushes migrating overhead at night in Alabama.

In this state, the Veery is uncommon to fairly common on migration. It appears to be the least common of the brown thrushes, but this may be due to its shorter stay here. It has been noted twice on Lookout Mountain and once in Birmingham in summer, but no instance of its breeding here is known. Usually it occurs low in the wetter hardwoods with the other brown thrushes, and it is reputed to be the tamest of them.

NESTING. The nest of the Veery is ordinarily on the ground in a wet place at the base of a shrub. The cup itself is small and protected from the moisture by a thick foundation of dead leaves. The four eggs are pale greenish-blue, rarely spotted.

FOOD. About half of the Veery's food consists of insects, largely injurious kinds. Prominent items in its diet are beetles, ants, wasps, sawflies, grasshoppers, and caterpillars, but it also frequently eats spiders, sowbugs, and snails. The rest is made up of wild fruits, especially Juneberries, strawberries, blackberries, cherries, the fruits of sumac and dogwood, and blueberries, wild grapes, and elderberries.

DISTRIBUTION. The Veery breeds from British Columbia and Newfoundland south to northern Arizona, South Dakota, northern Ohio, in mountains to northern Georgia, and near the coast rarely to Washington, D. C. It migrates through Central America to winter from Colombia and Venezuela to Brazil.

OCCURRENCE IN ALABAMA. (Normal: April 12 to May 28 and August 23 to October 25; Out-of-season: June 19 to July 21 and August 6.) *Tennessee Valley*:

[407]

[408]

Richard A. Park

April 23 (1914, Muscle Shoals, A. H. Howell) to May 15 (Wheeler Refuge, *fide* T. Z. Atkeson, Jr.) and September 6 (1948, Florence, H. M. Stevenson) to October 1 (1889, Leighton, F. W. McCormack). *Mountain Region:* April 19 (1960, Birmingham, Harriett Wright) to May 28 (1960, Birmingham, T. A. Imhof) and August 23 (1936, Birmingham, H. M. Stevenson) to October 23 (1949, Talladega, Carrie Henderson); also June 19 to July 21, 1961 (a singing bird, Birmingham, Emmy Lou Grimley and Harriett Wright); June 21 to July 13, 1957 (a singing bird, Gadsden, Edith Clark); and August 6, 1936 (Camp Cloudmont, DeKalb Co., J. F. Denton); most seen, 6, April 28, 1950 and September 14, 1959 (Birmingham, T. A. Imhof and J. B. Sullivan). *Piedmont:* April 27 (1940, Auburn, H. G. Good) to May 3 (1951, Auburn, H. G. Good); no fall dates. *Upper Coastal Plain:* April 21 (1957, Marion, Lois McCollough) to

May 18 (1938, Tuscaloosa, H. M. Stevenson) and August 26 (1891, specimen in the Avery collection, Greensboro, W. C. Avery) to October 22 (1915, specimen, not preserved, Autaugaville, L. S. Golsan); most seen, 35-40, September 17 and 18, 1915 (Bear Swamp, L. S. Golsan). *Lower Coastal Plain:* May 9, 1958 (Florala, T. A. Imhof) and September 15 (1956, Grove Hill, T. A. Imhof and others and 1958, Camden, Lovett Williams) to October 8 (1957, 4 birds, Jackson, W. U. Harris). *Gulf Coast:* April 12 (1959, dead bird at TV tower, northern Baldwin Co., Lovett Williams) to May 16 (1960, Dauphin Island, J. L. Dorn) and September 6 (1958, Spring Hill, J. L. Dorn) to October 25 (1941, Spring Hill, J. L. Dorn); most seen, spring, 22, April 26, 1952 (Bear Point, H. M. Stevenson), fall, 91, September 16, 1960, after Hurricane Ethel (Dauphin Island, J. L. Dorn).

Eastern Bluebird

Sialia sialis (Linnaeus)   [766]   (Plate 30, facing page 408)

This familiar thrush is deep azure *blue above,* rusty *red* on the *under parts,* and *white* on the *lower belly.* The female is less brightly colored, and the young bird is heavily spotted on the chest, but in any plumage they show sufficient blue in the wings and tail to be easily recognized. The Eastern Bluebird has a soft, musical, two-syllabled call, and the song is a warbling, gurgling rendition of the same notes used in the call. This bird perches on wires with the head tilted to one side, and this characteristic posture is useful in identification.

In Alabama, the Eastern Bluebird is a well-distributed, abundant, permanent resident. In winter it becomes less common in the northern counties and more abundant in the southern. It is scarce in the deep woods and in cities, but occupies nearly all other dry-land habitats, especially in farming areas and along roads. It breeds throughout the state.

Since about 1957, the species has become considerably reduced in numbers in most of the East, and the winter population of Alabama has likewise suffered a decline. The breeding population in this state seems to be holding its own. There seem to be four causes for the decline: (1) the natural habitat is being destroyed by the conversion of rural areas to suburban areas; (2) the Starling has been introduced, and this hole-nesting bird competes powerfully for breeding sites; (3) many bluebirds have not survived the winter in the

[409]

Map 69
EASTERN BLUEBIRD

Banding location of 9 birds recovered
in Alabama during winter
O May through August

South during periods of prolonged freezes; and (4) insecticides are now being dispersed indiscriminately on an area-wide basis blanketing large sections of both wintering and breeding grounds.

NESTING. The Eastern Bluebird nests in cavities such as natural ones in trees, deserted woodpecker holes, nest boxes, or other artificial ones like seldom-used mail boxes. Five by five by eight inches high are the desirable dimensions for a nest box, and it should be situated from eight to twelve feet above the ground on a pole in an open area. The entrance hole, one and one-half inches in diameter, is best cut six inches above the floor. The Starling, this bluebird's chief competitor, is apt to take over a nest box with a larger entrance. In Alabama, this bluebird's clutch usually consists of three to five eggs of a very pale blue.

FOOD. Animal matter, chiefly insects, which it eats mainly in spring and summer, constitutes most of the food of this bird. Grasshoppers, crickets, katydids, beetles, and caterpillars are most preferred, but the species takes a great variety of other insects and small animals—spiders, sowbugs, and snails, for example. Wild fruit, especially berries, make up most of the vegetable food, which it consumes principally in fall and winter. At feeding stations, suet and peanut butter attract it.

DISTRIBUTION. The Eastern Bluebird breeds from southern Saskatchewan, southern Quebec, and Nova Scotia south to southern Mexico and southern Florida, and also in Arizona. In winter it usually retires from the northern half of the breeding range, the northern limit depending on the severity of the weather.

ABUNDANCE IN ALABAMA (*most seen in a day*). Wheeler Refuge, 100, November 22, 1952 (T. A. Imhof); Birmingham, 158, December 20, 1952 (Christmas Count); Dallas Co., 100, February 25, 1955 (T. A. Imhof); southern Baldwin Co., 200, February 13, 1946 and January 25, 1947 (T. A. Imhof and others); southern Mobile Co., 162, December 21, 1957 (Christmas Count, Dauphin Island).

TIME OF BREEDING. Data on 68 nestings: Building, February 7 to March 22; eggs, March 17 to June 26; dependent young, April 6 to July 23; out of nest, May 13 to August 8.

BANDING. One bluebird, banded at Fairhope, July 9, 1926, was recaptured there, November 11, 1927. Nine others, banded between May 1 and August 10 in states to the north, were recaptured in Alabama, mostly in the Upper Coastal Plain, between November 8 and March 24. For place of banding, see Map 69.

FAMILY SYLVIIDAE: OLD WORLD WARBLERS, GNATCATCHERS, AND KINGLETS

Although they closely resemble the wood warblers (*Parulidae*) in many ways, the *Sylviidae* differ principally in having ten, instead of nine primaries, and in being much plainer in coloring. The long-tailed gnatcatchers and the short-tailed kinglets are generally smaller in body than wood warblers.

SUBFAMILY POLIOPTILINAE: GNATCATCHERS

Blue-gray Gnatcatcher
Polioptila caerulea (Linnaeus) [751] (Plate 31, facing page 424)

About the size of the Carolina Chickadee, this bird is *bluish-gray above* and has a *white eye ring, white under parts,* and a *white border* on its *long, expressive tail.* It is almost constantly on the move, flitting and tumbling through trees and rapidly moving its tail. The seldom-heard song is distinctive—a low, soft, pleasing warble. The call is a high-pitched, nasal mewing.

Throughout Alabama this gnatcatcher is a common, breeding, summer resident which also winters commonly on the coast, rarely inland in the Coastal Plain, and even once slightly above the Fall Line at Auburn. It occurs in almost any type of woodland except pure pines and seems to prefer white oaks, especially post oaks. In winter it usually associates with flocks of titmice, kinglets, and other insect-eaters.

[411]

NESTING. The beautiful nest is a well-constructed cup of various plant downs, bound together by spider and caterpillar silk and covered with lichens. It usually straddles a horizontal limb of a hardwood and occasionally a pine. This gnatcatcher often completes the nest about ten days before the first egg is laid. The four or five pale bluish eggs are rather sparingly marked with fine reddish-brown or dark brown dots. The young are fed at an amazing rate, often more than twice a minute.

FOOD. This species subsists almost entirely on insects, especially small flying insects and those that feed on foliage. Most of these are injurious to field crops and forests.

DISTRIBUTION. The Blue-gray Gnatcatcher breeds from northern California, Colorado, central Minnesota, southern Ontario, and northern New Jersey south to central Mexico, central Florida, and the Bahamas. It winters from southern California, southern Texas, and coastal South Carolina, rarely from coastal Virginia, south to Guatemala and Cuba.

OCCURRENCE IN ALABAMA. (Throughout the year.) *Tennessee Valley*: March 20 (Wheeler Refuge, T. Z. Atkeson, Jr.) to September 26 (1950, Wheeler Refuge, T. A. Imhof); most seen, 17, September 6, 1948 (Florence, H. M. Stevenson). *Mountain Region*: March 11 (1898, Shelby, *fide* A. H. Howell) to October 19 (1959, Birmingham, Harriett Wright); most seen, 25, April 18, 1950 (Short Creek, Jefferson Co., T. A. Imhof). *Piedmont*: March 15 (1908, Woodbine, A. A. Saunders) to October 1 (1957, Auburn, Lovett Williams); also December 26, 1960 (2 birds, Auburn, Christmas Count). *Upper Coastal Plain*: March 9 (1956, Demopolis, T. A. Imhof and W. W. Beshears) to October 12 (1957, Chilton Co., Harriett Wright); also December 27, 1945 (Tusca-loosa, S. R. and Isabel Tipton); December 22, 1956 and December 27, 1957 (Marion, Lois McCollough and others) and January 2, 1955 (Christmas Count, Montgomery). *Lower Coastal Plain*: March 16 (1959, Camden, Lovett Williams) to November 5 (1957, Jackson, W. U. Harris); most seen, 27, May 25, 1956 (McIntosh, Washington Co., T. A. Imhof and W. F. Colin). *Gulf Coast*: Permanent resident; most seen, spring, "hundreds," March 18, 1959 (Spring Hill, J. L. Dorn), fall, 100+, September 3, 1960 (Daphne, J. L. Dorn), winter, 20, January 2, 1960 (Christmas Count, Dauphin Island).

TIME OF BREEDING. Data on 50+ nestings: Building, March 29 to June 25; eggs, April 5 to June 4; dependent young, May 8 to July 21.

SUBFAMILY REGULINAE: KINGLETS

Small in body and with short tails, these birds are named for the bright feathers in the crown.

Golden-crowned Kinglet

Regulus satrapa Lichtenstein [748]   (Plate 31, facing page 424)

Except for the two hummingbirds, this kinglet is the smallest bird that occurs in Alabama. It is green above, white below, and has a *white line over* the *eye,* with a black one above it. *Males* have a *bright orange crown, females,* a *yellow* one. The high, thin, and rapid call of three syllables differs from that of the Brown Creeper in being trebled but never drawn out. The song, which resembles that of the Ruby-crowned Kinglet, is a series of high, thin notes like the call, followed by chattering sounds.

In winter this kinglet is abundant in wooded areas almost throughout Alabama, but it is not known to nest here. In this state it prefers pines, especially Virginia pine, which most closely resembles the spruce of its breeding haunts. It frequently associates with woodland titmice bands, often forming the major portion of such flocks.

NESTING AND FOOD. This bird lays eight or nine whitish eggs marked with brown in a thick-walled, oblong nest that resembles a ball with a hole in the top. Usually in a spruce or other conifer, the nest is made of mosses, silks, twigs, and other fine materials, and lined with feathers. The species feeds extensively on small crawling insects such as plant lice, caterpillars, beetles, and bugs which are abundant on the bark, leaves, and twigs of conifers. It also consumes many small flying insects, and in winter eats many of their eggs and pupae. It rarely eats vegetable matter.

DISTRIBUTION. The Golden-crowned Kinglet breeds from Alaska and southern Quebec south to southern California, Guatemala, and North Carolina (in mountains). It winters from southern Alaska, southern Ontario, and New-foundland south to Guatemala and northern Florida.

OCCURRENCE IN ALABAMA. (October 4 to May 7.) *Tennessee Valley*: October 9 (1892, Leighton, F. W. McCormack) to April 20 (Wheeler Refuge, *fide* T. Z. Atkeson, Jr.). *Mountain Region*: October 8 (1935, Birmingham, H. M. Stevenson) to April 7 (1948, Birmingham, T. A. Imhof and 1953, Gadsden, Edith Clark); also 2 birds until May 7, 1947 (Birmingham, T. A. Imhof); most seen, 219, December 29, 1946 (Christmas Count, Birmingham). *Piedmont*: October 13 (1957, Hatchet Creek, Coosa Co., Harriett Wright) to April 27 (1948, Auburn, H. G. Good); most seen, 68, January 2, 1954 (Christmas Count, Auburn). *Upper Coastal Plain*: October 4 (1925, Booth, Autauga Co., L. S. Golsan) to April 5 (1958, Marion, Lois McCollough). *Lower Coastal Plain*: November 1 (1957, Jackson, T. A. Imhof and W. U. Harris) to March 26 (1960, Florala, H. M. Stevenson). *Gulf Coast*: October 19 (1957, Gulf Shores, B. L. Monroe, Jr. and F. M. Weston and Dauphin Island, Ala. Orn. Soc.) to April 1 (1960, Spring Hill, J. L. Dorn); most seen, 54, January 2, 1960 (Christmas Count, Dauphin Island).

Ruby-crowned Kinglet
Regulus calendula (Linnaeus) [749] (Plate 31, facing page 424)

This kinglet is a little larger and more plainly marked than the Golden-crowned

Kinglet. Olive-green above, grayer on the head, and white below, the Ruby-crowned Kinglet has *two white wing bars* and a broken *white eye ring*. On the crown of the male is a patch of bright ruby-red, usually hidden. The habit of flitting the wings frequently while perched is a good clue to identification of this bird. In pattern the Ruby-crowned Kinglet resembles the *Empidonax* flycatchers, the Chestnut-sided Warbler, and the Solitary and Bell's Vireos. Several groups of species from the warbler, vireo, flycatcher, and kinglet families have very similar patterns. For this reason the novice will find it profitable to learn to place a bird in its proper family, best done by studying the members of the family which are most easily recognized. Once family recognition is achieved, identification of the more difficult, individual species is far easier.

The call of the Ruby-crowned Kinglet is a wren-like chatter, though perhaps not so harsh. The song, remarkably loud and prolonged for so small a bird, may be heard in Alabama in late March and April.

This kinglet is abundant in winter in all parts of Alabama in all types of woodland but is not known to breed in the state. It prefers hardwoods to pines, and it often occurs in weedy or brushy border areas such as ragweed growths. Small groups of these birds usually associate with the titmice flocks in winter.

NESTING AND FOOD. This bird lays five to eleven tiny whitish eggs marked with brown in a rather deep, hanging cup suspended from twigs of a conifer, usually a spruce. The nest is made of fine plant fibers in which green mosses and lichens seem to be distinctive. Primarily an insect-eater, this kinglet consumes large numbers of wasps, bugs of all sorts, beetles, and flies. Less extensively it eats ants, caterpillars, butterflies, moths, spiders, and pseudo-scorpions, and a small amount of vegetable matter, especially elderberries and poison-oak berries.

DISTRIBUTION. The Ruby-crowned Kinglet breeds from Alaska, northern Manitoba, central Quebec, and Newfoundland south to Lower California, central New Mexico, northern Michigan, southern Ontario, and Nova Scotia. It winters from southern British Columbia, southern Missouri, and Maryland, occasionally farther north, south to Guatemala and southern Florida.

OCCURRENCE IN ALABAMA. (Normal: September 27 to May 12; Out-of-season: September 13.) *Tennessee Valley*: October 2 (1960, Brownsboro, J. C. and Margaret Robinson) to May 4 (1957, Wheeler Refuge, M. F. Prather). *Mountain Region*: September 27 (1947, Birmingham, T. A. Imhof) to May 12 (1960, 6 birds, Fairfield, T. A. Imhof); most seen, 125, December 22, 1956 (Christmas Count, Birmingham). *Piedmont*: November 3 (1939, Auburn, H. G. Good) to April 30 (1955, Auburn, H. G. Good and T. A. Imhof); most seen, 72, December 26, 1960 (Christmas Count, Auburn). *Upper Coastal Plain*: October 8 (1938, Tuscaloosa, H. M. Stevenson) to May 5 (1956, Marion, Lois McCollough and others). *Lower Coastal Plain*: October 14 (1958, Camden, Lovett Williams) to April 15 (1957, Jackson, W. U. Harris). *Gulf Coast*: October 6 (1932, Fairhope, Homer Flagg and 1956, Fall Count, Mobile Bay Area) to May 1

(1933, Fairhope, Helen Edwards); also September 13, 1959 (Dauphin Island, H. A. J. and Cora Evans); most seen, fall, 55, October 19, 1957 (Fall Count, Mobile Bay Area), winter, 71, December 30, 1960 (Christmas Count, Dauphin Island).

FAMILY MOTACILLIDAE: WAGTAILS AND PIPITS

These ground birds of open country have rather long straight bills, long tails, and long pointed wings. The hind toe is well developed and has a claw equally as long. They walk instead of hop, frequently pump the tail, and in many of their actions resemble the larks. The flight of these birds is wavering and erratic and their two-syllabled call, which suggests the family name, Pipit, is usually given while the birds are flying.

Water Pipit

Anthus spinoletta (Linnaeus) [697] (Plate 43, facing page 568)
OTHER NAMES: American Pipit, Titlark, Prairie Sparrow

This pipit resembles a sparrow in color and size, but it is distinguished by its family characteristics. It is dark grayish-brown above and buffy, heavily brown streaked below. It has a *thin, black bill, white outer tail feathers,* and black legs. The Water Pipit repeats its two-syllabled call often. This bird *wags its tail, walks* on the ground, and dips up and down in the air as it flies, habits which along with its call are good clues to identify it.

In winter the Water Pipit is common, often abundant and widespread in Alabama, but it is not known to breed here. It frequents open country such as farmland, especially where the ground is bare. Beaches, mudflats, plowed fields, and barren shorelines are favored places.

NESTING AND FOOD. The nest is a grassy cup in a hollow in moss on the tundra or on mountains above timberline. It contains four to seven dull white eggs very heavily marked with chocolate-brown. Insects comprise most of the food of this pipit, and the remainder is weed seeds, waste grain, and wild berries. It takes many injurious insects from the ground, particularly cotton-boll weevils and various larvae, especially of beetles, turned over by the plow. Principal items of its diet are beetles, caterpillars, bugs (mostly plant bugs, aphids, and leafhoppers), spiders, flies, and ants.

DISTRIBUTION. In the Western Hemisphere the Water Pipit breeds from northern Alaska and northern Greenland south in mountains to California, northern New Mexico, Manitoba, and northern Maine. It winters from southwestern British Columbia, Utah, Texas, Arkansas, and Virginia, often north on the coast to Massachusetts, south to Guatemala and southern Florida.

OCCURRENCE IN ALABAMA. (October 6 to May 4.) *Tennessee Valley*: October 15 (1949, Wheeler Refuge, T. A. Imhof and others) to March 17 (Leighton, F. W. McCormack); most seen, 135, March 6, 1950 (Wheeler Refuge, T. A. Imhof and others). *Mountain Region*: October 13 (1947, Birmingham, T. A. Imhof) to May 4 (1956, Birmingham, T. A. Imhof, Idalene Snead, and Emmy Brownlie); most seen, 220, January 1, 1951 (Christmas Count, Birmingham). *Piedmont*: November 29 (1952, Stroud, H. M. Stevenson) to April 11 (1952, Auburn, H. G. Good). *Upper Coastal Plain*: October 12 (1957, Marion, Lois McCollough) to April 25 (1959, Montgomery, R. W. Skinner); most seen, 300, December 18, 1954 (Marion, Lois McCollough). *Lower Coastal Plain*: November 10 (1958, Camden, Lovett Williams) to March 22 (1958, Camden, Lovett Williams); most seen, 220, February 10, 1956 (Monroe Co., T. A. Imhof and W. F. Colin). *Gulf Coast*: October 6 (1956, Cochrane Causeway, H. M. Stevenson) to April 27 (1919, Spring Hill, E. W. Graves); most seen, 125, December 27, 1947 (Christmas Count, Foley).

Sprague's Pipit
Anthus spragueii (Audubon)   [700]   (Plate 43, facing page 568)

Sprague's Pipit and the Water Pipit naturally differ in protective coloration because their habitats differ. Sprague's Pipit is a grass dweller, and therefore is generally paler, more buffy, and heavily *streaked above* and much less streaked, almost whitish in spring, below. It has a pale bill, *straw-colored legs,* and a little more white in the tail, which it seldom wags. In pattern this bird resembles the Vesper Sparrow, but the sparrow hops and has a conical bill. The call of this pipit is similar to that of a weak, gravel-voiced Water Pipit.

In Alabama Sprague's Pipit is rare on migration and more often noted in spring. It is not known to nest here. The preferred habitat seems to be airports and short-grass pastures, and it usually occurs alone, in pairs, or in small flocks, seldom, if ever, with the Water Pipit.

NESTING AND FOOD. This species lays four to five grayish eggs spotted with brown in a nest of grass, usually concealed by an overhanging arch of grass, or in a hollow or a grass tussock. Its principal foods are grass-dwelling insects and the seeds of weeds and grasses. The Alabama specimen contained two large *Hemiptera*, probably squash bugs.

DISTRIBUTION. Sprague's Pipit breeds from northern Alberta and central Manitoba south to Montana and northwestern Minnesota. It winters from Arizona, Texas, Arkansas, and northwestern Mississippi, rarely to South Carolina, south to southern Mexico.

OCCURRENCE IN ALABAMA. (September 29, October 17, and February 5 to April 15.) *Tennessee Valley*: No record. *Mountain Region*: Gadsden, February 18 to

26, 1956, 8 birds, and September 29, 1956 (Edith Clark); Birmingham, April 15, 1958 and October 17, 1956 (specimen in Univ. of Ala. collection, T. A. Imhof). *Piedmont*: No record. *Upper Coastal Plain*: February 5, 1959 (Montgomery, R. W. Skinner). *Lower Coastal Plain*: No record. *Gulf Coast*: February 21, 1959 (Loxley, F. M. Weston and A. M. McMillan) and April 13, 1957 (Foley, H. M. Stevenson).

FAMILY BOMBYCILLIDAE: WAXWINGS

Cedar Waxwing

Bombycilla cedrorum Vieillot [619]   (Plate 30, facing page 408)
OTHER NAMES: Seal, Cedar Bird, Hammerlock

The Cedar Waxwing is a trim, silky-brown, *crested* bird about the size of a bluebird. The wings and tail are dark blue-gray, the belly and tip of the tail are yellow, and the bill and the *mask* through the eye are *black*, the latter with a white border. A red spot, which looks like a drop of sealing wax, is usually present on the tip of a few secondaries. The immature bird is streaked above and below and is whiter on the face, but it closely resembles the adult. In flight, this bird has a shape like a small Starling. It is called Seal in imitation of its rather high-pitched, drawn-out call.

This species is common to abundant in winter in Alabama, and in certain years when it is especially numerous it breeds rarely in a few northern counties. It occurs in flocks, usually in berry-bearing trees in towns and woodlands. Hackberries, mulberries, and cedars are favorites. In fall it is usually rather uncommon before December, but from January to mid-March it becomes exceptionally abundant, especially on hackberries. In late April and May, flocks of up to 100 linger on red mulberries, often into the first week in June. During the winter following the exceptionally late and severe freeze of March 27, 1955, which destroyed fruit buds, the species was scarce in this state.

NESTING. The Cedar Waxwing builds a rather bulky nest of twigs and grass and lines it compactly and neatly with moss and other fine materials. Most often it is in a conifer, and frequently several pairs nest close together. The three to five pale bluish-gray eggs are sparingly marked with black or dark brown.

FOOD. Wild fruits are the staple of this species, and of the many kinds it eats, hackberries, mulberries, privet, cedar berries, Juneberries, strawberries, and wild cherries are most important in its diet. It often feeds on flowers, in Alabama particularly crab apple blossoms. It varies this diet, particularly

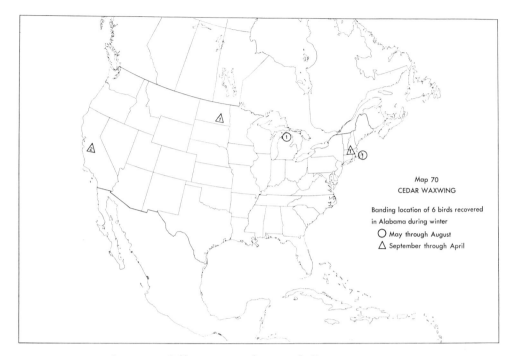

Map 70
CEDAR WAXWING

Banding location of 6 birds recovered
in Alabama during winter

○ May through August
△ September through April

in summer, with many different crawling and flying insects, of which beetles and canker worms are most frequent.

DISTRIBUTION. The Cedar Waxwing breeds, often locally and sporadically, from southeastern Alaska, northern Alberta, southern Quebec, and Newfoundland south to northern California, northern Utah, Oklahoma, the Ohio Valley, and coastal Maryland, and in mountains to northern Georgia and rarely Alabama. It winters from British Columbia, Colorado, southern Michigan, southern Ontario, and Massachusetts south to the northern Gulf Coast and central Florida, occasionally to Panama, northern South America, and the Greater Antilles.

OCCURRENCE IN ALABAMA. (September 4 to June 4, sometimes summers and breeds.) *Tennessee Valley*: September 4 (1957, Florence, J. E. Keeler) to May 25 (1893, Leighton, F. W. McCormack and 1941, Florence, H. M. Stevenson and 1948, Russellville, E. O. Willis); most seen, 125, December 27, 1952 (Christmas Count, Decatur). *Mountain Region*: September 11 (1933, Birmingham, H. M. Stevenson) to June 4 (1935, Birmingham, H. M. Stevenson); also in summer, see nesting data; most seen, 800, March 3, 1950 (Birmingham, T. A. Imhof).

Piedmont: September 11 (1943, Auburn, H. M. Stevenson) to May 23 (1953, Auburn, F. W. Fitch). *Upper Coastal Plain*: September 20 (1936, Autaugaville, L. S. Golsan) to May 31 (1956, Marion, Lois McCollough); also June (Autauga Co., L. S. Golsan); most seen, 500, March 10, 1925 (Autaugaville, L. S. Golsan) and 300, May 24, 1914 (Autaugaville, L. S. Golsan). *Lower Coastal Plain*: November 26 (1958, Camden, Lovett Williams) to May 27 (1958, Jackson, W. U. Harris). *Gulf Coast*: November 6 (1959, Dauphin Island, F. B. Daniel) to May 31

[418]

(1940, Elberta, H. M. Stevenson and 1958, Mobile, M. W. Gaillard); also September 6, 1959 (Dauphin Island, S. A. Gauthreaux and others) and September 28, 1931 (Fairhope, Ruth Connolly); most seen, 230, December 30, 1960 (Christmas Count, Dauphin Island).

TIME OF BREEDING. Data on 4 nestings: Nest, contents unknown, June 1947 and July 1946 (Birmingham, M. H. Perry and S. R. Tipton); dependent young just out of nest, July 3, 1946 (Cullman, T. A. Imhof) and July 11, 1949 (Fairfield, T. A. Imhof).

BANDING. Six banded Cedar Waxwings have been recovered in Madison, Franklin, Winston, Tuscaloosa, and Russell counties of Alabama during the period about December 11 to March 29. Map 70, which shows the place of banding of these birds, is an illustration of the remarkable wanderings of this species.

FAMILY LANIIDAE: SHRIKES

SUBFAMILY LANIINAE: TYPICAL SHRIKES

Loggerhead Shrike

Lanius ludovicianus Linnaeus   [622]   (Plate 30, facing page 408)
OTHER NAMES: French Mockingbird, Catbird, Butcher Bird

The Loggerhead Shrike is often confused with the Mockingbird because they are about the same color and size and both use exposed perches. But the shrike is dark bluish-gray above and white below, and has a *black, hooked bill, black mask,* and *black wings and tail* with small white areas. In general, the shrike is chunkier, with a big, round head and a short bill, while the Mockingbird is long and thin. On the coast in summer the Loggerhead Shrike may be confused with the Gray Kingbird, which acts like a flycatcher and has an even bigger head, longer, heavier bill, and is more uniformly dark gray than the shrike.

The flight of the Loggerhead Shrike is usually fast and direct, often low over the ground until with a final upward swoop it comes to its perch. Its call is said to be guttural, harsh, and unmusical, but its song is a series of suprisingly soft and liquid phrases reminiscent of the Mockingbird.

In Howell's time (1924), this shrike was resident in Alabama and bred as far north as Shelby County, and in winter birds of the northern race occupied the whole state. Now, it is known in summer as a breeder throughout the state, even on the higher mountains around farms. The species is common and well distributed throughout the year, more abundant in winter, and possibly most abundant in the Black Belt. It occupies exposed perches usually on wires and fences, along roadsides, in open country around farmlands, woods borders, and meadows.

[419]

F. S. Barkalow, Jr.

YOUNG LOGGERHEAD SHRIKES. Better known in Alabama by the name of Butcherbird or French Mockingbird.

NESTING. The nest is well made of heavy twigs or grass and is lined with rootlets and plant fibers, often padded with cotton or feathers. Usually it is in the dense part of a tall shrub or small tree, frequently an oak or hawthorn. The four to six dull white to light gray eggs are variously marked with gray, yellow, and brown.

FOOD. This bird eats small animals, mainly insects, which are its summer staple, and less importantly vertebrates, eaten mostly in winter. Grasshoppers and crickets, beetles, caterpillars, miscellaneous insects, and spiders all comprise a part of the diet. Of the vertebrates, it eats chiefly mice, and adds a few small birds, reptiles (frequently including snakes), fish, and others. The shrike frequents thorny trees and shrubs, where it impales its prey on the thorns, either for ease in tearing it to smaller pieces or for storage. This is why it is called Butcher Bird.

DISTRIBUTION. The Loggerhead Shrike breeds from British Columbia and southern Quebec south to central Mexico and southern Florida. It winters north to northern Washington, southern Utah, Kansas, southern Illinois, and New Jersey, occasionally farther north.

[420]

ABUNDANCE IN ALABAMA (*most seen in a day*). Lauderdale Co. and Limestone Co., 26, June 10, 1955 (T. A. Imhof, Malcolm Harden, and Alfred Walker); Birmingham, 24, December 26, 1955 (Christmas Count); Sumter Co., 40, February 7, 1958 (T. A. Imhof and others); Dallas Co., 30, February 25, 1955 (T. A. Imhof); Covington Co. and Conecuh Co., 41, October 19, 1956 (T. A. Imhof and L. C. Crawford); Mobile Bay Area, 121, October 19, 1957 (Fall Count).

TIME OF BREEDING. Data on 32 nestings: Eggs, March 29 to June 14; dependent young, March 28 to July 28.

BANDING. Banding records reveal the dual status of permanent resident and winter visitor. One shrike, banded as a nestling at Whittemore, Michigan, June 9, 1929 was recovered at Ramer, Montgomery Co., September 5, 1929. Four others were captured at the place of banding in Alabama as follows: Wheeler Refuge, August 1 to February 26; Auburn, March 13 to February 24; Fairhope, April 27 to January 12; and Dauphin Island, October 31 to "winter."

FAMILY STURNIDAE: STARLINGS

Starling

Sturnus vulgaris Linnaeus [493] (Plate 27, facing page 368)
OTHER NAME: Blackbird

The Starling is a stocky, glossy *black* bird with a *short tail* and a rather long, dull *yellow bill.* In the breeding season, the bill turns bright yellow and the bird is dark, glossy greenish and purplish on the head and under parts. At all seasons, whitish or buffy dots cover the body, but in fall they are more prominent. Although the young bird is dark gray, it is easy to recognize if one knows the adult. The Starling has many harsh, guttural, and squeaky notes, but it can also whistle very clearly. It imitates other birds, especially those that whistle—for example, the Bobwhite, Killdeer, Eastern Wood Pewee, and Eastern Meadowlark.

Between 1850 and 1900 many attempts were made to introduce this species from Europe into the United States. Apparently the only successful one was the 1890-1891 effort in New York. From there the species spread rapidly. Reports show that it reached Alabama in 1918 (Montgomery, January 14, P. A. Brannon) and the Gulf Coast in 1932, where one of a flock of twenty was shot (Fairhope, December 22, Paul Titus). It has been found on the coast in summer since 1942 (F. M. Weston). Nesting was first reported at Anniston and Auburn in 1930. At present it has occupied nearly all of the continental United States.

The Starling is an abundant and widespread permanent resident which breeds throughout Alabama and in winter is much more numerous. It is equally common around cities and farms, and seems to be least common in heavy

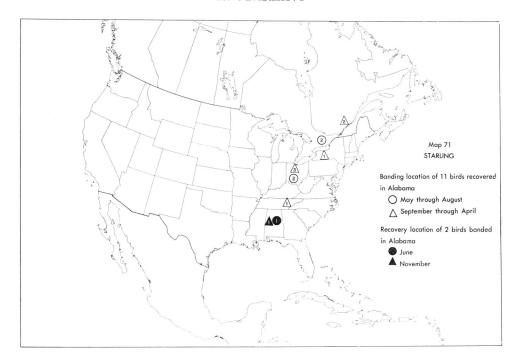

Map 71
STARLING

Banding location of 11 birds recovered
in Alabama
○ May through August
△ September through April

Recovery location of 2 birds banded
in Alabama
● June
▲ November

woods, on mountains, and near salt water. In fall and winter it often joins flocks of blackbirds, and usually it roosts with them by the thousands on public buildings, in evergreens, or in other protected places.

NESTING. Almost any cavity suits this bird for a nest, but it prefers natural tree holes or fresh woodpecker holes. Starlings often wait for a woodpecker to complete an excavation and then gang up on the owner, forcibly evict him, and take over the hole. The Starling lines its cavity with grasses, twigs, feathers, and many other materials, and lays three to five bluish-white or greenish-white eggs.

FOOD. Most of the food of this bird is animal matter, a major part of it insects. The chief item is beetles, and others are grasshoppers, crickets, caterpillars, spiders, millipedes, and earthworms. Vegetable food includes principally wild fruits and additionally seeds, grains, and some cultivated fruits, especially cherries. The bird forages extensively on lawns, pastures, and other short-grass areas where it obtains beetle grubs and other foods.

DISTRIBUTION. In North America, the Starling breeds from British Columbia, Quebec, and Newfoundland south to eastern Oregon, central Texas, and central Florida. In winter, it withdraws from more northern portions, and occurs then in all states west of the Rocky Mountains, into Mexico, and farther south in Florida. Apparently it is still expanding its breeding range.

ABUNDANCE IN ALABAMA (*most seen in a day*). Marshall Co. and Jackson Co., 6000, February 5, 1955 (T. A. Imhof and others); Decatur, 15,000, January 11, 1957 (T. A. Imhof and T. Z. Atkeson, Jr.); Birmingham, 18,400, December 28, 1957 (Christmas Count); Auburn, 40,000, December 26, 1960 (Christmas Count); Montgomery, 10,000+, winter 1955-56 (O. L. Austin, Jr., J. E. Keeler, and J. M. Rice); Mobile, 2700, December 28, 1956 (Christmas Count).

TIME OF BREEDING. Data on 75+ nestings: Building, March to July; eggs, March 27 to June; young in nest, March 19 to August; dependent young on the wing, May 15 to August.

BANDING. Near Birmingham, 1 winter-banded Starling was found near the place of banding the following winter, and a June-banded bird was found nearby in June three years later. For place of banding of 11 others banded outside the state and recovered in Alabama during the period November 29 to February 1, see Map 71.

FAMILY VIREONIDAE: VIREOS

SUBFAMILY VIREONINAE: TYPICAL VIREOS

The word vireo, taken from Latin, refers to the olive-green color of the upper parts of most birds of this group. They are rather similar to warblers, although they have stubby bills, much plainer coloring and the sexes are alike in appearance. The Red-eyed, Black-whiskered, Warbling, and Philadelphia Vireos lack wing bars and have a whitish stripe over the eye. The other Alabama members of this family have two wing bars and spectacles—a light line extending from the bill around the eye. These birds are slower and more deliberate feeders than the highly active warblers, and a particular feature of their foraging habits is the search for insects on the *underside* of leaves.

White-eyed Vireo
Vireo griseus (Boddaert)   [631]   (Plate 31, facing page 424)

This vireo has a *white eye* and *yellow spectacles,* but the eyes of the immature are brown. This species is white below, especially on the throat, and has yellow flanks, whereas the Yellow-throated Vireo has a yellow throat and a white belly. The White-eyed Vireo has a distinctive and strongly accented song of usually five to seven phrases. Sometimes it imitates other birds, but the quality of the song always betrays the vireo.

Throughout Alabama this vireo is a common, breeding, summer resident which winters uncommonly on the coast and rarely farther inland in the Coastal Plain. It lives in brushy and shrubby places, especially along woods borders.

[423]

PLATE 31

BLACK-WHISKERED VIREO
Adult, Sexes Alike
Page 429

RED-EYED VIREO
Adult, Sexes Alike
Page 430

YELLOW-THROATED VIREO
Adult, Sexes Alike
Page 426

WHITE-EYED VIREO
Adult, Sexes Alike
Page 423

BELL'S VIREO
Adult, Sexes Alike
Page 425

SOLITARY VIREO
Adult, Sexes Alike
Page 428

WARBLING VIREO
Adult, Sexes Alike
Page 433

PHILADELPHIA VIREO
Adult, Sexes Alike
Page 431

GOLDEN-CROWNED KINGLET
Adult Male
Page 412

BLUE-GRAY GNATCATCHER
Adult, Sexes Similar
Page 411

RUBY-CROWNED KINGLET
Adult Male
Page 413

[424]

Richard A. Parks

NESTING. The nest is a deep cup shaped like an inverted cone and is about one to eight feet above ground in a fork in shrubs or saplings. It is made of grasses, leaves, and inner bark, lined with fine plant fibers, and ornamented on the outside with bark, papers, lichens, mosses, and spider webs. The usual clutch consists of three to five white eggs with a few small dark brown or black spots around the larger end.

FOOD. This bird subsists mainly on insects, but it also consumes berries and other wild fruits in fall and winter. Principal insects taken are caterpillars, moths, bugs, beetles, wasps, wild bees, flies and grasshoppers.

DISTRIBUTION. The White-eyed Vireo breeds from southeastern Nebraska, southern Wisconsin, New York, and southern New England south to northern Mexico, southern Florida, and in Bermuda. It winters from southern Texas, central Alabama, coastal South Carolina, and Bermuda south to Honduras and Cuba.

OCCURRENCE IN ALABAMA. (Throughout the year.) *Tennessee Valley*: March 20 (1948, Russellville, E. O. Willis) to October 22 (1935, Wheeler Dam, J. Bamberg); most seen, 60, May 4, 1957 (Wheeler Refuge, Ala. Orn. Soc.). *Mountain Region*: March 18 (1956, Birmingham, M. H. Perry) to November 2 (1947, Birmingham, T. A. Imhof); specimen in La. State Univ. collection, March 24, 1944 (Birmingham, M. L. Miles); most seen, 32, May 4, 1940 (Birmingham, H. M. Stevenson). *Piedmont*: March 17 (1908, Weogufka, A. A. Saunders) to October 12 (1939, specimen in the Auburn Univ. collection, Auburn, H. G. Good). *Upper Coastal Plain*: March 19 (1937, Booth, L. S. Golsan and 1952, Montgomery, C. W. Summerour) to October 18 (1890, Greensboro, W. C. Avery); also December 25, 1937 (Tuscaloosa,

H. M. and T. F. Stevenson); February 21, 1913 (Barachias, E. G. Holt) and March 2, 1937 (Booth, L. S. Golsan); most seen, 26, April 23, 1955 (Autauga Co., E. G. Holt and T. A. Imhof). *Lower Coastal Plain*: March 22 (1957, Samson, Geneva Co., T. A. Imhof) to October 19 (1956, Andalusia, T. A. Imhof); also January 11, 1958 (singing, Jim Burr Lake, Clarke Co., T. A. Imhof and others). *Gulf Coast*: Common, March 18 (1912, specimen in U. S. National Museum, Mobile, A. H. Howell) to November 1 (1958, Dauphin Island, S. M. Russell and others); most seen, 138, April 13, 1957 (Spring Count, Mobile Bay Area).

TIME OF BREEDING. Data on 21 nestings: Building, April 23 to May 4; eggs, April 11 to July 12; young, May 1 to July 29.

[Bell's Vireo]
Vireo bellii Audubon   [633]   (Plate 31, facing page 424)

This plain-looking vireo differs from the White-eyed Vireo in being smaller and in having a *dark eye* and *white spectacles*. The young White-eyed Vireo also has a dark eye, but it always shows some yellow in the spectacles. Since these two vireos are alike in appearance, their very different songs are the best means of identification. A distinctive feature of the song of Bell's Vireo is its similarity to a musical question and answer. The rising inflection at the end of the first three syllables is followed by three more notes, the last of which is lowered.

This species is casual on migration in Alabama and has been recorded twice in spring and twice in fall, but it is not known to breed here. It frequents willows and other streamside thickets.

NESTING AND FOOD. In shrubs and often near water, the nest is a small deep cup of bark, leaves, grass, and other plant fibers, usually lined with grass stems and often adorned on the rim with cocoons. The three to five white eggs have a few small dots of dark brown or black. This species feeds almost exclusively on insects, especially bugs, grasshoppers, locusts, beetles, and caterpillars. The number of large insects taken by so small a bird is surprising.

DISTRIBUTION. Bell's Vireo breeds from central California, Colorado, South Dakota, and northeastern Illinois south to southern Mexico and western Louisiana. It winters from Mexico to northern Nicaragua, casually in Louisiana.

OCCURRENCE IN ALABAMA. (April 28, August 19 to 31, and September 2.) *Tennessee Valley*: April 28, 1961 (a pair, male singing, Brownsboro, Madison Co., J. C. and Margaret Robinson). *Mountain Region*: April 28, 1937 (Birmingham, H. M. Stevenson) and August 19 to 31, 1932 (Birmingham, H. M. Stevenson and H. E. Wheeler). *Piedmont*: No record. *Upper Coastal Plain*: No record. *Lower Coastal Plain*: No record. *Gulf Coast*: September 2, 1959 (Dauphin Island, O. B. Miles).

Yellow-throated Vireo
Vireo flavifrons Vieillot   [628]   (Plate 31, facing page 424)

This vireo is *bright yellow below,* white on the belly, and has *yellow spectacles* and two white wing bars. It is sometimes confused with the Pine Warbler, but the Pine Warbler is streaked, has no spectacles, and has a thin bill. The song of the Yellow-throated Vireo is similar to that of the Red-eyed Vireo but is louder, more musical, and has a distinct burr. The call is a thick, heavy, wren-like chatter.

This vireo is a common, breeding, summer resident in Alabama, except on the Gulf Coast where it is uncommon and local in summer, common on migration, and rare in winter. It is a woodland bird which usually frequents large deciduous trees and occasionally pines.

NESTING. The nest is a very well-made, handsome, deep cup decorated on the outside with lichens and lined with fine grass tops on the inside. It is usually over twenty feet from the ground in a fork of a small sturdy branch of a hardwood or occasionally a pine. The female lays three or four white eggs rather heavily spotted with various shades of brown around the larger end.

J. L. Dusi

NEST OF YELLOW-THROATED VIREO. This vireo adorns its well constructed nest with lichens and cocoons fastened by spider webs.

FOOD. This vireo is primarily an insect-eater, but in fall it feeds rarely on sassafras berries, wild grapes, and other fruits. The main insect fare consists of caterpillars, moths, bugs, beetles, and flies. The remainder of its food is spiders and other insects.

DISTRIBUTION. The Yellow-throated Vireo breeds from southern Manitoba and southern Quebec south to central Texas and central Florida. It winters from central Mexico to Colombia and Venezuela, and rarely in southern Texas, southern Alabama, and southern Florida.

OCCURRENCE IN ALABAMA. (Normal: March 17 to November 5; Out-of-season: December 2 and 29 and January 3.) *Tennessee Valley*: March 25 (1948, Russellville, E. O. Willis) to September 27 (1947, Russellville, E. O. Willis). *Mountain Region*: March 21 (1955, Gadsden, Edith Clark) to November 2 (1955, Gadsden, Edith Clark); most seen, 14, April 18, 1950 (Birmingham, T. A. Imhof). *Piedmont*: March 22 (1923, Auburn, J. M. Robertson) to November 5 (1936, specimen, Auburn, F. S. Barkalow).

Upper Coastal Plain: March 20 (1913, Autaugaville, L. S. Golsan) to October 1 (1938, Tuscaloosa, H. M. Stevenson). *Lower Coastal Plain*: March 17 (1959, Camden, Lovett Williams) to September 21 (1957, Geneva Co. and Henry Co., T. A. Imhof and Lovett Williams); also December 2, 1954 (Clayton, Barbour Co., trapped and banded, J. E. Keeler). *Gulf Coast*: March 20 (1937, Gulf Shores, F. S. Barkalow) to May 11 (1960, Dauphin Island, J. L. Dorn) and August 24 (1960, Spring Hill, J. L. Dorn) to No-

[427]

vember 1 (1958, Bellingrath Gardens, T. A. Imhof), in summer at Spring Hill (M. W. Gaillard and others) and Nigger Lake (T. A. Imhof and J. R. Davis), in winter, December 29, 1956 (Dauphin Island, Idalene Snead, Grace Snead, and Clustie McTyeire) and January 3, 1957 (Fairhope, Rosemary Gay-mer); most seen, 36, March 29, 1958 (Dauphin Island, S. A. Gauthreaux and others).

TIME OF BREEDING. Data on 18 nestings: Building, April 7 to 19; eggs, April 25 to June 1; young in nest, May 17 to June 19; dependent young out of nest, June to late July.

Solitary Vireo
Vireo solitarius (Wilson)   [629]   (Plate 31, facing page 424)
OTHER NAME: Blue-headed Vireo

This vireo has a *blue head, greenish or grayish back, white wing bars, white spectacles,* white under parts, and yellowish flanks. The song is phrased like that of the Red-eyed Vireo, but it is slower, sweeter, and higher pitched. In Alabama, this bird often sings on warm, sunny days in winter.

The Solitary Vireo is common on migration throughout the state, and it winters fairly commonly in the Coastal Plain and rarely but regularly north at least as far as Jefferson County. Although it breeds quite far south in Georgia, it is not known to nest in Alabama. It is a woodland bird that is about equally common in pines and hardwoods. In winter it rarely joins the loose bands of titmice and other small insect-eaters, but it may associate with Myrtle and Orange-crowned Warblers.

NESTING. The nest is a woven basket suspended rather insecurely by the rim in a fork of a hardwood or conifer, either tree or sapling, usually less than fifteen feet from the ground. It is made of inner bark, lichens, and various other fine plant materials, and is lined with fine grass stems, pine needles, fur, or feathers. The three to five white eggs are marked with a few dark brown spots.

FOOD. This vireo eats insects and other small animals such as caterpillars, moths, bugs, spiders, and snails. Most of them are obtained from the foliage of trees and shrubs, but it frequently catches flying insects on the wing. In winter, especially in January, it eats a fair portion of wild, fleshy fruits.

DISTRIBUTION. The Solitary Vireo breeds from British Columbia, southern Quebec, and Newfoundland south to El Salvador, northern North Dakota, northern Ohio, northern Georgia, northern New Jersey, and southern New England. It winters from Arizona, southern Texas, the central parts of the Gulf states, and coastal South Carolina south to Nicaragua and Cuba.

OCCURRENCE IN ALABAMA. (September 12 to May 16.) *Tennessee Valley:* April 29 (1960, Huntsville, Ala. Orn. Soc.) to May 16 (1959, Huntsville, J. C. and Margaret

Robinson) and September 26 (1950, Wheeler Refuge, T. A. Imhof) to October 12 (1953, Wheeler Refuge, D. C. Hulse). *Mountain Region*: September 14 (1946, Birmingham, T. A. Imhof) to May 9 (1935, Birmingham, H. M. Stevenson), unrecorded from mid-November to early March north of Jefferson Co. *Piedmont*: March 14 (1908, specimen, Woodbine, A. A. Saunders) to April 17 (1940, Auburn, R. J. Wheeler, Jr.) and December 24, 1936 (Auburn, H. S. Peters and Fay Peters), no fall dates. *Upper Coastal Plain*: September 17 (1959, Livingston, Jenkins Jackson) to April 18 (1958, Livingston, Jenkins Jackson). *Lower Coastal Plain*: Early September (1937, found dead, Columbia, T. Z. Atkeson, Jr.) to April 5 (1957, Jackson, W. U. Harris). *Gulf Coast*: September 12 (1937, Spring Hill, J. L. Dorn) to April 23 (1960, Delchamps, J. L. Dorn); most seen, 5, December 27, 1947 (Christmas Count, Foley) and December 27, 1958 (Bellingrath Gardens, T. A. Imhof).

Black-whiskered Vireo
Vireo altiloquus (Vieillot)   [623]   (Plate 31, facing page 424)

This vireo looks much like the Red-eyed Vireo except for a *thin, black whisker mark* on each side of the throat. Its other head markings are not as distinct as those of the Red-eyed Vireo. The Black-whiskered has a bigger bill, and it is more brownish above, but only close examination will disclose these differences. Immature birds show much brown on the head, especially the cheeks, and they have a trace of a yellow wing bar. The song, easily recognized as that of a vireo, is a two-syllabled phrase, often prolonged by adding several additional churring notes.

This subtropical vireo is accidental on the coast of Alabama in spring. Since it is frequently recorded on other northern Gulf coasts, it is probable that this species is regular on the Alabama Coast but passes by unnoticed among the host of Red-eyed Vireos that swarm through coastal live oaks each spring. In its breeding range, the Black-whiskered Vireo is most frequent in mangroves, but it often occurs in nearby hardwoods.

NESTING AND FOOD. The neatly-built nest is suspended from a horizontal fork of a mangrove or hardwood and usually holds three white eggs sparingly dotted. As far as is known, most of this bird's food is spiders, caterpillars, beetles, earwigs, bugs, and flies, varied with small fruits.

DISTRIBUTION. The Black-whiskered Vireo breeds from subtropical Florida and the Bahamas south through the West Indies. It winters from Hispaniola south through the West Indies and northern South America to the western Amazon basin. During migration, it occurs on the northern coast of the Gulf of Mexico, especially in spring.

OCCURRENCE IN ALABAMA. *Gulf Coast only*: April 10, 1959, specimen in Dept. of Conservation collection, collected from a large flock of Red-eyed Vireos in a live oak (Dauphin Island, T. A. Imhof and others).

NEST OF RED-EYED VIREO. A small pensile nest is typical of the vireo family.

Red-eyed Vireo

Vireo olivaceus (Linnaeus) [624] (Plate 31, facing page 424)

OTHER NAME: Hanging Bird

This vireo, the most common of those which have a *white line* over the *eye and lack wing bars,* can be readily distinguished by the bluer crown and the *heavy black lines outlining* the *white eye stripe.* The eye of adults is seen in good light and at close range to be brighter red than that of other Alabama vireos. The song of this species is a monotonous series of slow robin-like phrases often repeated. It is probably the most common bird sound in summer in the eastern deciduous woodlands. The novice will find it easier to learn this vireo song first and then to learn the others by comparison. The call is a nasal and querulous note.

The Red-eyed Vireo is probably the most abundant bird in eastern deciduous forests. In Alabama it is an abundant, breeding, summer resident wherever hardwoods are dominant. It almost never occurs in pines, for even where pines are dominant it seeks out hardwoods. This species apparently maintains a rigid migration schedule, for in Alabama no record of any stragglers exists, and the arrival and departure dates of each of the six regions are remarkably even in the progression from north to south.

NESTING. The nest is a well-woven, dainty cup suspended from a horizontal fork at almost any height from the ground in a hardwood. It is made of fine grasses, rootlets, and bits of bark, held together by numerous strands of spider and caterpillar silk. The three or four white eggs are sparingly marked with brown spots around the larger end.

FOOD. This bird destroys caterpillars to such an extent that a typical vireo posture is the one it assumes when hunting these insects on the underside of a leaf. Other insects it consumes in quantity are moths, beetles, bugs, wasps, ants, and flies, and it also feeds on spiders and gives a surprising number of land snails to its young. It eats many berries, especially blackberries, elderberries, and those of spicebush, dogwood, Virginia creeper, sassafras, and magnolia.

DISTRIBUTION. The Red-eyed Vireo breeds from British Columbia, southern Mackenzie, and central Quebec south to Oregon, Colorado, central Texas, and central Florida. It winters from Colombia and Venezuela to Peru and Brazil.

OCCURRENCE IN ALABAMA. (March 20 to November 1.) *Tennessee Valley*: April 6 (1948, Russellville, E. O. Willis) to October 22 (1935, Wheeler Dam, J. Bamberg); most seen, 70, June 7, 1957 (south shore of Tennessee River, Marshall Co., T. A. Imhof). *Mountain Region*: March 28 (1936, Birmingham, H. M. Stevenson) to October 17 (1956, 4 birds, Birmingham, T. A. Imhof and others); most seen, spring, 100, May 2, 1949 (Birmingham, T. A. Imhof), summer, 82, June 10, 1943 (Mentone, H. M. Stevenson) and 129, June 6 and 7, 1958 (Cheaha, T. A. Imhof and C. T. Hornady), fall, 105, October 8, 1954 (Birmingham, T. A. Imhof and F. B. Daniel). *Piedmont*. March 25 (1948, Auburn, H. G. Good) to October 17 (1959, Waverly, Chambers Co., J. L. Dusi). *Upper Coastal Plain*: March 25 (1916, Autauga Co., L. S. Golsan) to October 18 (1890,

specimen not preserved, Greensboro, W. C. Avery). *Lower Coastal Plain*: March 23 (1957, Choctaw Bluff, Clarke Co., M. W. Gaillard) to October 19 (1956, Andalusia, T. A. Imhof); most seen, spring, 70, April 18, 1958 (Jackson, T. A. Imhof, W. U. Harris, and J. R. Davis), fall, 80+, September 20, 1957 (Covington Co. and Dale Co., T. A. Imhof and Lovett Williams). *Gulf Coast*: March 20 (1937, Gulf Shores, F. S. Barkalow) to November 1 (1958, Dauphin Island, T. A. Imhof and S. A. Gauthreaux); most seen, spring, 93, April 13, 1957 (Spring Count, Mobile Bay Area), fall, 210, September 16, 1960 (after Hurricane Ethel, Dauphin Island, J. L. Dorn)

TIME OF BREEDING. Data on 34 nestings: Building, April 29 to May 17; eggs, May 6 to July 14; young, May 10 to July 2.

Philadelphia Vireo
Vireo philadelphicus (Cassin)   [626]   (Plate 31, facing page 424)

This small vireo has a rather obscure eye stripe, no wing bars, and *pale yellowish under parts*. The Warbling and Red-eyed Vireos also lack wing bars and may have a touch of yellowish on the flanks or under tail coverts, but they have no yellow on the breast as does the Philadelphia Vireo. Several warblers, notably the Orange-crowned and Tennessee, closely resemble this one in color pattern, and until the novice can tell a warbler from a vireo, he will not easily identify the Philadelphia Vireo. The song of this vireo differs from that of the Red-eyed Vireo in being slower and higher in pitch.

The Philadelphia Vireo is a quiet, shy, and retiring bird which frequents the middle and upper parts of hardwoods. Because it is also difficult to identify, it probably is more common than the records indicate. Certainly it is more common than the Warbling Vireo everywhere in Alabama except in the Tennessee Valley in summer. As a migrant, mainly in fall in Alabama, the Philadelphia Vireo is uncommon to fairly common in the Mountain Region and rare to uncommon in the rest of the state. It is not known to breed here.

NESTING AND FOOD. This vireo lays three to five white, brown-spotted eggs in a deep cup hanging by its rim from the fork of a deciduous tree, usually over ten feet from the ground. The nest is made of bark shreds, *Usnea* moss, and numerous other plant fibers, and is lined with fine grasses or pine needles. The bulk of the diet is caterpillars, beetles, wasps, moths, ants, flies, bugs, other insects, and spiders. Chiefly in fall it eats wild fruits such as bayberries, wild rose hips, and grapes.

DISTRIBUTION. The Philadelphia Vireo breeds from northeastern British Columbia, central Ontario, southern Quebec, and Newfoundland south to North Dakota, southern Ontario, northern New England, and New Brunswick. It winters from Guatemala to Colombia.

OCCURRENCE IN ALABAMA. (April 6 to May 6 and August 28 to October 18.) *Tennessee Valley*: May 6, 1912 (specimen in the U. S. National Museum, Florence, A. H. Howell); October 2, 1959 (2 birds, Huntsville, J. C. and Margaret Robinson); October 5, 1960 (netted, Brownsboro, J. C. and Margaret Robinson); and October 18, 1959 (3 birds, Huntsville, J. C. and Margaret Robinson). *Mountain Region*: April 6 (1955, Gadsden, Edith Clark) to May 4 (1935, Birmingham, H. M. Stevenson and 1953, Fairfield, T. A. Imhof) and September 21 (1936, Easonville, St. Clair Co., H. M. Stevenson and 1948, Fairfield, T. A. Imhof) to October 13 (1954, Gadsden, Edith Clark); most seen, 40 (39 ceilometer casualties and 1 survivor, 2 specimens preserved at Auburn Univ. collection and Auburn Wildlife collection), October 8, 1954 (Birmingham, T. A. Imhof and F. B. Daniel). *Piedmont*: No record. *Upper Coastal Plain*: April 30, 1959 (Livingston, Jenkins Jackson) and September 17, 1959 (Livingston, Jenkins Jackson). *Lower Coastal Plain*: September 21, 1957 (Columbia, T. A. Imhof and Lovett Williams) and October 2, 14, and 16, 1958, a specimen not preserved on October 14 (Camden Lovett Williams). *Gulf Coast*: April 26, 1958 (Bellingrath Gardens, T. A. Imhof); May 2 and 3, 1961 (Dauphin Island, Owen Davies); August 28, 1946 (Gulf Shores, T. A. Imhof); October 4, 1939 (Spring Hill College, J. L. Dorn); and October 14 and 15, 1960 (Dauphin Island, Margaret Robinson and others).

Warbling Vireo

Vireo gilvus (Vieillot) [627] (Plate 31, facing page 424)

This vireo is rather difficult to identify because it lacks any prominent field marks. A *white line over* the *eye*, rather wide especially *between* the *eye* and the *bill*, and *without* a *thick dark line* above it, separates the bluish cap from the *whitish throat* and *under parts*. Although the Warbling Vireo has some yellow on the flanks, and young Red-eyed Vireos have dark eyes, the italicized field marks separate this species from other vireos having no wing bars. As suggested by its name, this bird has a leisurely, pleasing warble, not broken up into phrases as are the songs of other vireos. It consists of a long note, then three short ones, each of which is repeated three times in a successively higher key, and a long, high note at the end. Though slower, the song somewhat resembles that of a Purple Finch or a more musical Orchard Oriole.

In Alabama the Warbling Vireo, uncommon north of the Fall Line and rare south of it, has been recorded as a migrant more often in spring. It breeds rarely in the Tennessee Valley, usually within sight of the river. (See Map 72.) The species frequents tall shade trees, and in Alabama prefers those near water, particularly hackberries and sycamores.

NESTING. Usually thirty to fifty feet from the ground the nest is a well-made, deep cup suspended by its rim from a fork in a shade tree. It is built of leaves, bits of bark, and other plant fibers, and is lined with fine plant stems. The clutch consists of three to five whitish eggs with a few dark brown spots.

FOOD. Caterpillars and moths form most of the food of this vireo. The remainder consists of beetles, grasshoppers, other insects, and wild berries.

DISTRIBUTION. The Warbling Vireo breeds from northern British Columbia, southern Mackenzie, southern Quebec, and Nova Scotia south to central Mexico, central Texas, southern Louisiana, northern Alabama, and southern Virginia. It winters from Mexico to El Salvador.

OCCURRENCE IN ALABAMA. (April 7 to September 29.) *Tennessee Valley*: April 24 (1914, specimen in the U. S. National Museum, Muscle Shoals, J. L. Peters and 1959, Huntsville, J. C. and Margaret Robinson) to September 29 (1940, Wheeler Refuge, Clarence Cottam). *Mountain Region*: April 7 (1953, Gadsden, Edith Clark) to May 21 (1957, Gadsden, Edith Clark) and September 17 (1957, Birmingham, Harriett Wright) to September 28 (1959, Birmingham, Harriett Wright); also July 22 and 23, 1957 (Gadsden, Edith Clark). *Piedmont*: Auburn, April 9, 1926 (H. G. Good); April 19, 1958 (Edith Clark and R. W. Skinner); and April 28, 1928 (H. G. Good). *Upper Coastal Plain*: April 30, 1959 (Livingston, Jenkins Jackson) and August 19, 1959 (Livingston, Jenkins Jackson). *Lower Coastal Plain*: First week of August 1956 (Grove Hill, G. A. Carleton). *Gulf Coast*: April 18 (1959, Dauphin Island, H. A. J. and Cora Evans) to May 13 (1960, Dauphin Island, J. L. Dorn) and September 13, 1959 (Dauphin Island, H. A. J. and Cora Evans).

TIME OF BREEDING. Data on 1 nesting at Florence: Building, May 7, 1936; nest collected for the Auburn Univ. collection after young left on July 11 (C. R. Mason, H. S. Peters, and N. H. Giles).

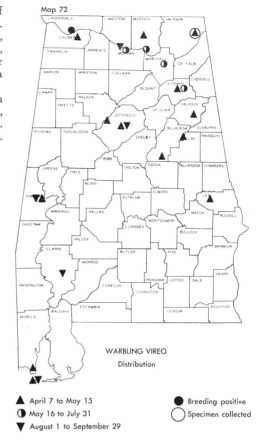

Map 72

WARBLING VIREO
Distribution

▲ April 7 to May 15
◑ May 16 to July 31
▼ August 1 to September 29

● Breeding positive
○ Specimen collected

FAMILY PARULIDAE: WOOD WARBLERS

These small, brightly-colored birds are energetic, highly nervous, and almost constantly on the move. Their bills, adapted to their insect fare, are usually short, straight, and slender. The dependence on insects makes them highly migratory, for, although 20 of the 41 species of warblers recorded in Alabama breed in the state, most of the individuals breed far north of here and winter far south. In fall the confusing array of dull plumages of these birds is a challenge to the bird-watcher. Perhaps the key to identifying the warblers in fall is to learn the spring plumages exceptionally well. At any rate, long experience will help. Many warblers, especially in the breeding season, occur high up in dense foliage, often in rugged country, for this family is most abundant in heavily-wooded areas such as swamps, bottomlands, and timbered hilly country. Because they occur in such inaccessible spots, a knowledge of the songs of these birds is essential in making any comprehensive list of local warblers. Many wood warblers have much yellow in their plumage, and they are often called wild canary or goldfinch in Alabama, but the wild canary has a conical bill.

Black-and-white Warbler
Mniotilta varia (Linnaeus) [636] (Plate 32, facing page 440)

The Black-and-white Warbler is *heavily streaked* with *black on white,* and has a prominent white stripe in the middle of the crown. The male is streaked heavily below, especially on the throat, but the female is streaked below almost solely on the sides. The immature bird shows a brownish wash on the belly. No other warbler is entirely black and white. The song is a series of at least seven very thin, two-noted phrases, usually with the first note accented and higher in pitch. Variations of this song make some individuals difficult to identify by voice alone.

Throughout Alabama this warbler is a common migrant which winters rarely on the coast. In summer as a breeder it is fairly common in hardwoods or mixed woods north of the Fall Line and rare south of it. (See Map 73.) Often hopping with its head down, it forages on the trunks and larger branches of trees, rarely in pines. Although other warblers may occasionally perch or even forage on trunks, this species consistently feeds there.

NESTING. The nest is always concealed from above and is usually on the ground in a sheltered situation against a tree or shrub or under a bank or over-hanging bough. It is made of dry leaves, coarse grass, inner bark, pine needles and rootlets, and is lined with finer grasses, rootlets, and horsehair. The four to five whitish eggs are heavily marked with brown or purplish-brown.

FOOD. Principally an insect-eater, this bird feeds on beetles, caterpillars, ants, and spiders in large amounts, and moths, flies, and bugs to a lesser extent. It eats very little vegetable food.

DISTRIBUTION. The Black-and-white Warbler breeds from southwestern Mackenzie, southern Quebec, and Newfoundland south to central Texas, southern Louisiana, central Alabama, and central South Carolina. It winters from Lower California, southern Texas, and central Florida, irregularly from California, southern Alabama, and southern South Carolina, south through Central America and the West Indies to Ecuador and Venezuela.

OCCURRENCE IN ALABAMA. (Normal: March 6 to November 1; Out-of-season: November 23, December 27, and February.) *Tennessee Valley*: March 20 (1948, Russellville, E. O. Willis) to October 18 (1959, Huntsville, J. C. and Margaret Robinson). *Mountain Region*: March 11 (1955, Birmingham, Harriett Wright) to October 25 (1935, Birmingham, H. M. Stevenson); also November 23, 1958 (Gadsden, Edith Clark); most seen, summer, 14, June 10, 1943 (Mentone, H. M. Stevenson), migration, 30, August 23, 1948 (Fairfield, T. A. Imhof). *Piedmont*: March 6 (1940, Auburn, H. G. Good) to October 3 (1958, Wedowee, T. A. Imhof and C. T. Hornady). *Upper Coastal Plain*: March 12 (1939, Tuscaloosa, H. M. Stevenson) to May 13 (1939, Tuscaloosa, H. M. Stevenson) and July 1 (1938, Tuscaloosa, H. M. Stevenson) to October 20 (1938, Tuscaloosa, H. M. Stevenson); summers at Greensboro (W. C. Avery) and Autaugaville (L. S. Golsan), see Map 73. *Lower Coastal Plain*: March 16 (1959, Camden, Lovett Williams) to May 9 (1958, Lake Tholloco, T. A. Imhof) and July 10 (1958, Camden, Lovett Williams) to October 14 (1958, Camden, Lovett Williams). *Gulf Coast*: March 16 (1960, Spring Hill, J. L. Dorn) to May 16 (1960, Dauphin Island, J. L. Dorn) and July 8 (1932, Fairhope, D. H. McIntosh) to November 1 (1958, Dauphin Island, Lois McCollough); also December 27, 1958 (Dauphin Island, D. C. Holliman and Clustie McTyeire and Bellingrath Gardens, T. A. Imhof) and February 1931 and 1932 (Fairhope, Ruth Connolly); most seen, 65, September 16, 1960, after Hurricane Ethel (Dauphin Island, J. L. Dorn).

TIME OF BREEDING. Data on 17 nestings: Eggs, April 25 to May 15; young in nest, April 29 to June 24; dependent young out of nest, May 23 to June 17.

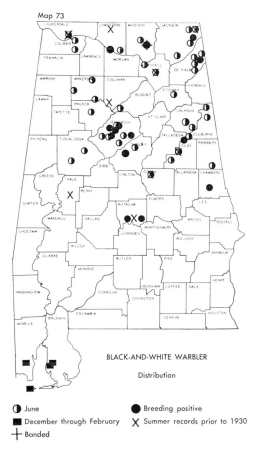

Map 73

BLACK-AND-WHITE WARBLER

Distribution

◗ June   ● Breeding positive
■ December through February   ✗ Summer records prior to 1930
+ Banded

Prothonotary Warbler

Protonotaria citrea (Boddaert)   [637]   (Plate 35, facing page 464)

OTHER NAMES: Golden Swamp Warbler, Swamp Yellowbird

This strikingly-colored warbler has a *blue-gray back, wings,* and *tail,* and rich *golden-yellow head* and *under parts.* The female is duller, and in fall and immature plumages both sexes have browner upper parts and lemon-yellow under parts. The tail has prominent white spots. The song is loud and emphatic and consists of five or six notes alike in sound and pitch, while the call is a loud, sharp chip similar to that of a waterthrush.

In Alabama, this warbler is a common to abundant, breeding, summer resident in the Coastal Plain and Tennessee Valley, but in the Mountain Region and Piedmont it breeds usually only locally along rivers. It inhabits river swamps and swampy ponds and lakes, and occurs in almost all Coastal Plain bottomlands. On migration the Prothonotary Warbler occasionally frequents uplands with other warblers.

NESTING. This species is the only warbler in the eastern United States that habitually nests in cavities. It is not particular as to species of tree or size or condition of the hole, although it most often chooses a dead stub between five and ten feet above the ground or water. It often uses a nest box. Dimensions for a box are these: three inches square by eight inches high, with an entrance hole one and one-half inches in diameter, five inches above the floor. The bird fills the cavity almost to the top with moss which it uses in the cup and lining along with other fine materials such as rootlets, hair, grass, and leaf stems. The three to six eggs are rich creamy to rose-colored and are boldly and handsomely marked with browns, grays, and purples.

FOOD. This species is known to eat flies, beetles, caterpillars, ants, and snails. Other than the fact that it feeds chiefly on insects, little is known of its food habits.

DISTRIBUTION. The Prothonotary Warbler breeds from southeastern Minnesota, rarely southern Ontario, central New York, and New Jersey south to southeastern Texas and central Florida. It winters from Yucatan to Colombia and Venezuela.

OCCURRENCE IN ALABAMA. (March 12 to October 12.) *Tennessee Valley*: April 13 (1957, Wheeler Refuge, M. F. Baker) to August 26 (1889, Leighton, F. W. McCormack); most seen, 13, June 19, 1953 (Wheeler Refuge, T. A. Imhof and T. Z. Atkeson, Jr.). *Mountain Region*: April 6 (1936, Birmingham, H. M. Stevenson) to September 1 (1936, Birmingham, H. M. Stevenson); most seen, 27, May 30, 1949 (Warrior River above Lock 14, T. A. Imhof and others). *Piedmont*: March 31 (1936, Auburn, H. S. Peters) to September 22 (1957, Auburn, Lovett Williams); also October 12, 1957 (Hatchet Creek, Harriett Wright). *Upper Coastal Plain*: April 1 (1939, Tuscaloosa, H. M. Stevenson and 1950, Tuscaloosa, T. A. Imhof) to August 21 (1949, Tuscaloosa, H. M. Stevenson); most seen, 11, April 23, 1955 (Autauga Co., E. G. Holt and T. A. Imhof). *Lower Coastal Plain*: March 25 (1958, Jackson, W. U. Harris and M. H. Fisher) to September 20 (1957, Florala, Lovett Williams and T. A. Imhof); most seen, 95, May 25, 1956 (McIntosh, T. A. Imhof and W. F. Colin). *Gulf Coast*: March 12 (1960, Daphne, J. L. Dorn) to September 29 (1960, dead at TV tower, Mobile, J. L. Dorn); most seen, 95, May 26, 1956 (Mount Vernon, T. A. Imhof and W. F. Colin).

TIME OF BREEDING. Data on 22 nestings: Building, April 28; eggs, April 21 to June 16; young in nest, May 22 to June 22; dependent young out of nest, July 1 to August 4.

Swainson's Warbler
Limnothlypis swainsonii (Audubon) [638] (Plate 36, facing page 488)

Swainson's Warbler is one of the *plainest*-colored warblers. It is olive-brown above and pale brownish to buffy below with a *reddish-brown crown* and a conspicuous *white line* over the *eye*. The head markings are less distinct in the female, immature, and fall plumages. In shape, the bird much resembles the Worm-eating Warbler, for the head and bill are large, the body plump, and the tail short. The song is sweet, loud, and clear and suggests a Louisiana Waterthrush in quality and a Hooded Warbler in composition. It usually consists of five or six phrases—two or three slurred notes, two lower ones, and then a higher one.

Swainson's Warbler is an uncommon and local summer resident in the Coastal Plain and Tennessee Valley of Alabama. Elsewhere it is a rare migrant. (See Map 74.) Although breeding evidence is positive from only two nests in the same locality, the species probably breeds in Alabama wherever it occurs in June. In the breeding season it inhabits river swamps, usually where cane (*Arundinaria*) grows. In the Allegheny Mountains it occurs in summer along branches in the rhododendron and laurel thickets growing under hemlocks, and it has been recorded at least once in this habitat in Alabama. This plainly-colored species lives in dense thickets and is often motionless or voiceless for long periods of time. Hence bird-watchers often fail to record it even when making a special search for it.

NESTING. The bulky, loosely-built nest is usually in a clump of cane from three to ten feet from the ground and often looks like a bunch of leaves lodged there by high water. The lining is generally of fine rootlets, pine needles, cypress leaves, moss, and sometimes horsehair. The two or three eggs are very round and usually dull white but on rare occasions they are spotted.

FOOD. Little is known about the food of this bird. It is primarily an insect-eater, and the stomach contents of four specimens collected in Alabama show that it eats caterpillars, spiders, ants, and bees.

DISTRIBUTION. Swainson's Warbler breeds locally from Oklahoma, the Ohio Valley, and southeastern Maryland south to southern Louisiana and northern Florida. It winters in eastern Mexico, British Honduras, Jamaica, and Cuba.

OCCURRENCE IN ALABAMA. (March 29 to October 19). *Tennessee Valley:* April 23 (1948, Beaverdam Creek, Limestone Co., H. H. Grammer and L. S. Givens) to August 20 (1940, Wheeler Refuge, T. Z. Atkeson, Jr.). *Mountain Region:* May 1, 1914 (specimen in U. S. National Museum, Mellville, Winston Co., A. H. Howell and others); May 7, 1955 (DeSoto Park, D. W. Speake); June 7, 1957 (Long Island Gulf, 1150 feet elevation, singing in rhododendrons, T. A. Imhof); and September 4, 1954 (Birmingham, T. A. Imhof and others). *Piedmont*: April 19, 1940 (2 birds, Downdell's Swamp, Auburn, D. H. McIntosh). *Upper Coastal Plain*: Bear Swamp, April 3 (1914, specimen, L. S. Golsan) to September 19 (1916, specimen not preserved, L. S. Golsan); Tuscaloosa, April 22 (1939, H. M. Stevenson) to August 17 (1939, H. M. Stevenson); elsewhere, April 1 (1914, Teasley Mill, Montgomery Co., A. H. Howell) to September 13 (1957, specimen in Dept. of Conservation collection, Catoma Creek Swamp, Montgomery Co., R. W. Skinner). *Lower Coastal Plain*: April 30 (1951, River Falls, Covington Co., W. R. Middleton) to October 4 (1957, Sepulga River, R. W. Skinner). *Gulf Coast*: March 29 (1958, Dauphin Island, T. A. Imhof) to October 19 (1957, Mon Luis Isle, R. W. Skinner); most seen, 9 singing birds in May 1911, May 1914, and July 1913, "in the big river swamps above Mobile" (A. H. Howell 1928:284), 6 singing birds, June 20 and 21, 1958 (Raft River to Nigger Lake, T. A. Imhof and J. R. Davis).

TIME OF BREEDING. Data on 2 nestings at Florence: Three slightly incubated eggs and 1 recently-completed nest, May 8, 1912 (A. H. Howell).

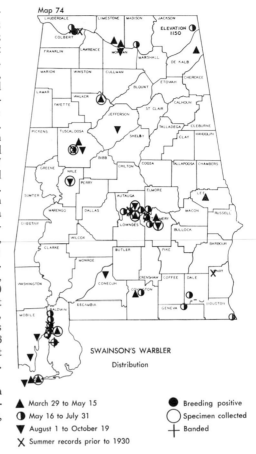

Map 74

ELEVATION 1150

SWAINSON'S WARBLER

Distribution

▲ March 29 to May 15
◐ May 16 to July 31
▼ August 1 to October 19
✕ Summer records prior to 1930

● Breeding positive
○ Specimen collected
+ Banded

Worm-eating Warbler
Helmitheros vermivorus (Gmelin)   [639]   (Plate 36, facing page 488)

This rather *plain* warbler is olive-brown above and buffy below with prominent *black stripes* on its *buffy head*. It has a big bill, long for a warbler, a rather large head, and a plump body. The song is a thin, rapid, short, unmusical buzz with an *abrupt ending*. It closely resembles the more variable and slightly more musical song of the Chipping Sparrow.

In Alabama the Worm-eating Warbler is an uncommon and local summer resident which breeds in the Mountain Region and in a few other scattered places in the state. (See Map 75.) As a migrant it is fairly common to common in the Mountain Region and on the Gulf Coast and uncommon to rare in the

Richard A. Parks

rest of the state. It lives close to the ground, often near tree trunks, on shrubby, wooded hillsides and ravines.

NESTING. This warbler builds its nest on the ground on hillsides deeply shaded with hardwoods, or in stream bottoms bordered by steep slopes. The nest is hidden in leaves, usually under a leafy shrub, and the outside is made of dead leaves, often skeletonized. Very fine grass stems, rootlets, or the thread-like stalks of the hair-moss line the interior. The four to six eggs are white, spotted around the larger end with various shades of brown.

FOOD. This warbler is known to eat weevils, other beetles, bugs, cater-pillars, wasps, grasshoppers, locusts, sawfly larvae, spiders, and dragonflies.

DISTRIBUTION. The Worm-eating Warbler breeds from Kansas, northern Illinois, central Ohio, central New York, and southern New England south to northern Texas, central Louisiana, central Alabama, and northwestern South Carolina. It winters from northeastern Mexico, central Florida, and the Bahamas south to Panama and Jamaica.

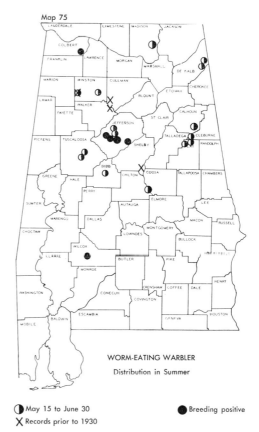

Map 75

WORM-EATING WARBLER

Distribution in Summer

◑ May 15 to June 30   ● Breeding positive

✗ Records prior to 1930

OCCURRENCE IN ALABAMA. (March 31 to October 8.) *Tennessee Valley*: April 20 (1940, Wheeler Refuge, Clarence Cottam) to September 9 (1890, Leighton, F. W. McCormack). *Mountain Region*: April 3 (1957, Birmingham, Amy Mason and Marjorie Ayres) to October 8 (1954, ceilometer casualty, Birmingham, T. A. Imhof and F. B. Daniel); most seen, 8, April 18, 1950 (Short Creek, Jefferson Co., T. A. Imhof). *Piedmont*: March 31 (1950, Auburn, H. G. Good) to May 7 (1937, singing at Mitchell Dam, H. M. Stevenson) and September 10 (1937, Roanoke, H. M. Stevenson and 1958, Auburn, Lovett Williams); also May 22, 1960 (singing at Mitchell Dam, Harriett Wright). *Upper Coastal Plain*: April 4 (1958, Marion, Lois McCollough and Montgomery, R. W. Skinner) to May 1 (1913, specimen not preserved, Barachias, E. G. Holt) and August 9 (1891, specimen not preserved, Greensboro, W. C. Avery) to September 18 (1915, specimen not preserved, Bear Swamp, L. S. Golsan). *Lower Coastal Plain*: April 5 (1957, 3 birds, Jackson, T. A. Imhof and W. U. Harris) to May 9 (1958, Lake Tholloco, T. A. Imhof) and August 10 (1958, Camden, Lovett Williams) to September 29 (1958, Camden, Lovett Williams); bred at Camden in 1958 (Lovett Williams). *Gulf Coast*: April 4 (1958, Dauphin Island, Ava Tabor) to May 11 (1960, Dauphin Island, J. L. Dorn) and

July 23 (1956, 8 birds, Spring Hill, J. L. Dorn) to September 16 (1960, 120 birds after Hurricane Ethel, Dauphin Island, J. L. Dorn); most seen, spring, 55, April 15, 1960 (Dauphin Island, S. A. Gauthreaux and others).

TIME OF BREEDING. Data on 7 nestings: Building, April 28; eggs, April 29 and June 21; dependent young, May 26 to July 12.

Golden-winged Warbler

Vermivora chrysoptera (Linnaeus)   [642]   (Plate 33, facing page 448)

This handsome warbler is pearl gray above and white below with a *golden-yellow crown* and *wing bars* and a *black bill, throat,* and *cheeks.* Females, immatures, and fall-plumaged birds have the black feathers obscured by white edges. The song of the Golden-winged Warbler, similar to that of the Blue-winged Warbler, is a series of mechanical sounds like buzzes, the first syllable long and high in pitch. The number of phrases may vary, and the bird may utter them in a different order. Sometimes this warbler sings the song of the Blue-winged Warbler.

In Alabama the Golden-winged Warbler is fairly common on migration in nearly all parts of the state. It is then found generally in saplings or in the lower branches of large deciduous trees. In the nesting season, it occurs about the edges of woodland openings, especially where the ground is damp. This species is not known to nest in Alabama, although it nested within a mile or two of the border at Rising Fawn, in northwest Georgia.

NESTING. The nest is on dead leaves on the ground, usually among the stems of herbs, grasses, or shrubs, and ordinarily it is well concealed. It is made of long strands of dry grass and strips of grapevine bark, and is coarsely lined with a few hairs. The four or five eggs are white marked with purples and browns.

FOOD. This warbler feeds mainly on small hairless caterpillars and also on spiders and butterflies. Little else is known of its diet.

DISTRIBUTION. The Golden-winged Warbler breeds from southern Manitoba, southern Ontario, and Massachusetts south to southeastern Iowa, southern Ohio, in mountains to northern Georgia, and near the coast to northern New Jersey. It winters from Guatemala to Colombia and Venezuela.

OCCURRENCE IN ALABAMA. (April 9 to May 7 and August 1 to October 14.) *Tennessee Valley*: April 18 (1947, Wheeler Refuge, L. S. Givens) to May 2 (1937, 6 birds, Guntersville, C. R. Mason) and August 23 (1893, specimen, Leighton, F. W. McCormack) to October 3 (1947, Russellville, E. O. Willis). *Mountain Region*: April 17 (1960, Mentone, Edith Clark) to May 7 (1955, DeSoto Park, Ala. Orn. Soc.)

and August 2 (1959, Fort Payne, Harriett Wright) to September 29 (1948, Birmingham, T. A. Imhof). *Piedmont*: April 9 (1940, Auburn, H. G. Good) to May 7 (1908, Woodbine, A. A. Saunders) and August 22 (1934, Roanoke, H. M. Stevenson) to September 11 (1958, Auburn, Lovett Williams). *Upper Coastal Plain*: April 12 (1912, specimen, Barachias, A. H. Howell) to May 1 (1937, Tuscaloosa, H. M. Stevenson) and August 11 (1890, specimen in the Avery collection, Greensboro, W. C. Avery) to October 14 (1956, Marion, Lois McCollough). *Lower Coastal Plain*: April 19, 1958 (2 birds, Jackson, T. A. Imhof, J. R. Davis, and W. U. Harris) and September 15 (1956, 2 birds, Grove Hill, T. A. Imhof and W. U. Harris) to September 21 (1957, Bellwood, Geneva Co., Lovett Williams and T. A. Imhof). *Gulf Coast*: April 14 (1957, Dauphin Island, Lovett Williams and others) to May 3 (1961, Dauphin Island, Owen Davies) and August 1 (1959, Daphne, J. L. Dorn) to October 6 (1956, Romar Beach, H. M. Stevenson); most

seen, 32, September 16, 1960 (after Hurricane Ethel, Dauphin Island, J. L. Dorn).

HYBRIDS. The Golden - winged Warbler frequently breeds with the Blue-winged Warbler. The resulting fertile hybrids include a dominant Brewster's Warbler which looks like a Blue-winged Warbler with yellow wing bars and white instead of yellow under parts. The rarer recessive Lawrence's Warbler looks like a Golden-winged Warbler with yellow under parts and white wing bars. (See Plate 33.) Brewster's Warbler has been recorded twice in Alabama, April 25, 1961 (specimen in Dept. of Conservation collection, Brownsboro, Madison Co., J. C. and Margaret Robinson) and October 10, 1958 (specimen, Dauphin Island, Lovett Williams, R. W. Skinner, and T. A. Imhof). Lawrence's Warbler has been noted three times in Alabama: Decatur, April 20, 1958 (Robert Helle); Birmingham, about April 20, 1957 (Dorothy Roberts) and Marion, April 16, 1955 (Lois McCollough).

Blue-winged Warbler
Vermivora pinus (Linnaeus) [641] (Plate 33, facing page 448)

This warbler is olive-yellow above and bright yellow below with bluish-gray wings crossed by two white wing bars. It has a narrow *black line through the eye.* The Pine Warbler is similar but darker, lacks the black eye line, and is streaked below. One song of the Blue-winged Warbler is a long, two-noted buzz, as if the singer inhaled and exhaled, but this species has other more musical songs, and it and the Golden-winged Warbler sometimes sing each other's songs.

In Alabama, this species is an uncommon to fairly common local summer resident in the Tennessee Valley and Mountain Region. Records of birds that spent the summer in the Piedmont and Upper Coastal Plain indicate that it may breed farther south than is so far known. (See Map 76.) As a migrant, the species is uncommon to fairly common in most of the state. Around Birmingham it breeds near water in long-abandoned fields which have usually a scattered growth of saplings about six to eight feet tall. After a few years, apparently when the sapling growth becomes too tall for it, the bird deserts the place for another less overgrown field, preferably one nearby.

[443]

PASSERIFORMES: PARULIDAE: BLUE-WINGED WARBLER

NESTING. Like the Golden-winged Warbler, this warbler nests on the ground, usually among stems of herbs, grasses, or shrubs. Nests of the Blue-winged Warbler, however, are more substantial, and the deep cup has a lining of fine grass or grapevine bark. The three to four eggs are white, finely and sparingly spotted with reddish-brown and gray, usually around the larger end.

FOOD. As far as is known, this species lives on small hairless caterpillars, beetles, spiders, and locusts, but it probably eats a much greater variety of insect food.

DISTRIBUTION. The Blue-winged Warbler breeds from eastern Nebraska, southern Minnesota, southern Michigan, and Massachusetts south to northern Arkansas, northern Alabama, and northern Georgia. It winters from the Valley of Mexico to northern Colombia.

OCCURRENCE IN ALABAMA. (March 27 to October 20.) *Tennessee Valley*:

Map 76

BLUE-WINGED WARBLER
Distribution

◖ May 15 to July 31   ✕ Records prior to 1930
● Breeding positive

April 7 (1948, Russellville, E. O. Willis) to September 26 (1959, Huntsville, J. C. and Margaret Robinson). *Mountain Region*: April 1 (1936, Birmingham, H. M. Stevenson) to October 8 (1954, ceilometer casualty, Birmingham, T. A. Imhof and F. B. Daniel); most seen, 9, April 12, 1958 (Short Creek, Jefferson Co., T. A. Imhof and C. W. Summerour). *Piedmont*: March 27 (1908, Woodbine, A. A. Saunders) to at least June 9 (1908, Woodbine, A. A. Saunders) and September 11 (1958, Auburn, Lovett Williams) to October 3 (1958, Wedowee, T. A. Imhof and C. T. Hornady). *Upper Coastal Plain*: March 27 (1939, Tuscaloosa, H. M. Stevenson) to May 5 (1961, Lamar Co., Owen Davies) and August 18 (1939, Tuscaloosa, H. M. Stevenson) to September 24 (1938, Tuscaloosa, H. M. Stevenson); also at Autaugaville, a pair, April 16 to July 10, 1912 (L. S. Golsan). *Lower Coastal Plain*: April 18, 1958 (3 birds, Jackson, T. A. Imhof, W. U. Harris, and J. R. Davis) and September 14 to October 2, 1958 (Camden, Lovett Williams). *Gulf Coast*: April 10 (1959, 2 birds, Dauphin Island, A. J. Murphy and 1960, Dauphin Island, J. L. Dorn) to May 11 (1960, Dauphin Island, J. L. Dorn) and August 22 (1939, Spring Hill College, J. L. Dorn) to October 20 (1957, Dauphin Island, Lovett Williams); most seen, 18, September 16, 1960 (after Hurricane Ethel, Dauphin Island, J. L. Dorn).

TIME OF BREEDING. Data on 7 nestings: Building, April 27; eggs, May 13 to 23; young in nest, June 2; dependent young out of nest, May 23 to June 3.

[444]

Bachman's Warbler

Vermivora bachmanii (Audubon)   [640]   (Plate 33, facing page 448)

This is probably the rarest of North American songbirds. Bachman's Warbler is a small olive-green bird with bright yellow under parts. The male has a *black bib,* a *black cap,* and a *yellow forehead,* and thus resembles a male Hooded Warbler with an incomplete hood. The female, rather nondescript, lacks the black and closely resembles a female Hooded or Wilson's Warbler except that it is dull whitish below. But the *yellow eye ring* of the female Bachman's Warbler, standing out against the *blue-gray* of the *cap* and cheeks, is distinct. The song is a buzzy trill, all on one pitch but sometimes with a higher introductory note, and so ventriloquial as to make the singer difficult to locate. Although the song resembles those of the Parula and Worm-eating Warblers, its buzzing quality strongly suggests the kinship of Bachman's Warbler to the Golden-winged and Blue-winged Warblers.

Bachman's Warbler is a local and erratic summer resident in the Coastal Plain of Alabama, particularly near the Fall Line and on the lower Tombigbee River. Thus far it is known to nest only in Tuscaloosa and Autauga counties. Elsewhere in the state, it is a rare spring transient, particularly in the Mountain Region. (See Map 77.) It inhabits the borders of swamps, especially where the forest crown is open and blackberry bushes are frequent. The transient nature of this habitat probably explains the erratic movements and local abundance of the species. After the young have left the nest and the male stops singing, the species is extremely difficult to find. Migrants in the Mountain Region of Alabama are usually reported as occurring in small trees on a river or stream bank next to a field.

NESTING. The nest is one to three feet from the ground in dense shrubs, usually blackberry. The outside of the nest consists mainly of grass stems and dead leaves (often *Magnolia* and *Persea* bay), many of which are decayed and partially skeletonized. The lining is usually made of black plant fibers, most of which are probably threads of pendent lichens. The female lays three or four white eggs.

FOOD. The contents of five stomachs examined in Alabama provide what is apparently the only information on the food of this species. Caterpillars and the remains of *Hymenoptera,* probably ants, were found.

DISTRIBUTION. Bachman's Warbler breeds usually in the upper part of the Coastal Plain and in the Mississippi Valley from southern Indiana and eastern Missouri south to Louisiana, east through the Gulf states, and north to coastal Virginia. Because it frequently moves its nesting locality, has secretive habits, lacks a distinctive song, and generally frequents places of difficult access, the species is often undetected for many years in much of this range. It migrates through the Florida Keys, occasionally also the Bahamas, to winter in western Cuba, the Isle of Pines, and rarely Mississippi, Georgia, and Florida.

Map 77

BACHMAN'S WARBLER
Distribution

◗ Coastal Plain, March 20 to August 26   ● Breeding positive
▲ North of the Fall Line, April 7 to   ○ Specimen collected
May 3

OCCURRENCE IN ALABAMA. (March 20 to August 26.) *Tennessee Valley*: No record. *Mountain Region*: April 23, 1954 (a singing male, Gadsden, Edith Clark and Naomi Banks); May 2 and 3, 1914 (2 male specimens in U. S. National Museum, Mellville, Cullman Co., J. L. Peters and A. H. Howell); April 18, 1959 (a singing male, Jacksonville, Calhoun Co., W. J. Calvert); April 9 to 13, 1936 (Birmingham, H. E. Wheeler and H. M. Stevenson) and April 7, 1917 (a singing male, Longview, Shelby Co., L. S. Golsan). *Piedmont*: March 20, 1908 (male specimen, Woodbine, Coosa Co., A. A. Saunders). *Upper Coastal Plain*: Tuscaloosa (present in 1937 and 1939), March 25 (1939, H. M. Stevenson) to May 1 (1937, H. M. Stevenson and H. E. Wheeler); Autauga Co. (mostly Bear Swamp, present from 1912 to 1937), March 24 (1916, L. S. Golsan) to August 26 (1912, L. S. Golsan); most seen, 7, March 24 and 25, 1916 and April 9, 1915 (L. S. Golsan). *Lower Coastal Plain*: April 17, 1958 (a singing male, Jackson, W. U. Harris) and April 17, 1940 (Salt Springs Sanctuary, Clarke Co., R. J. Wheeler, Jr.). *Gulf Coast*: May 27, 1914 (male specimen in U. S. National Museum, Stiggins Lake near Mount Vernon, J. L. Peters).

TIME OF BREEDING. Data on 2 nestings: Four fresh eggs, May 25, 1919 (Bear Swamp, Autauga Co., E. G. Holt and L. S. Golsan); 3 young about a week old in nest, May 1, 1937 (Tuscaloosa, H. M. Stevenson and H. E. Wheeler).

Tennessee Warbler
Vermivora peregrina (Wilson)   [647]   (Plate 36, facing page 488)

The Tennessee Warbler is *green* on the *back, wings,* and *tail*. The spring male has a *grayish head* with a *white eye stripe* and is white below from bill to tail. In female, immature, and fall plumages, the crown is as green as the back, and the breast is suffused with yellow. This bird then resembles the Philadelphia Vireo in pattern, but the warbler has a thin bill and is much more active. This species also resembles the Orange-crowned Warbler, but the Tennessee Warbler has an *unstreaked breast, white* or *whitish under tail coverts,* and a *trace* of a *yellowish wing bar.* The song is a loud and rapid staccato series of unmusical notes, the last part never quite a trill.

In Alabama, this warbler is a common spring and abundant fall migrant, not known to breed in the state. Except for the Myrtle Warbler, during fall migration the Tennessee Warbler is often the most abundant warbler in the state. It occurs in almost any woodland, pine or hardwood, dense or thin. Although it occurs frequently on shrubs, it usually forages in the upper half of the taller trees, particularly in spring.

NESTING AND FOOD. This species lays four to six white eggs spotted with reddish-brown in a nest of dried grasses lined with finer grasses, rootlets, and hairs and well hidden in moss and grass at the base of a sapling or shrub. Principal insect foods are caterpillars, beetles, leafhoppers, plant lice, flies, and wasps, and it eats in smaller numbers spiders, ants, caddis flies, snails, bugs, and locusts. Vegetable food, eaten chiefly in fall and winter, includes grapes and the fruits of goldenrod, ragweed, sumac, poison-ivy, pokeberry, and French mulberry.

DISTRIBUTION. The Tennessee Warbler breeds from southern Yukon, northern Manitoba, northern Quebec, and Newfoundland south to British Columbia, northern Minnesota, northern New York, central New England, and Nova Scotia. It migrates mainly through the Mississippi Valley to winter from Mexico south to Colombia and Venezuela.

OCCURRENCE IN ALABAMA. (Normal: April 1 to May 16 and August 29 to November 8; Out-of-season: June 9 and November 22.) *Tennessee Valley:* April 20 (Wheeler Refuge, *fide* T. Z. Atkeson, Jr.) to May 16 (1960, Wheeler Refuge, Demett Smith) and August 29 (1949, Wheeler Refuge, T. A. Imhof) to October 26 (1945, Guntersville, H. M. Stevenson). *Mountain Region:* April 5 (1937, Birmingham, H. M. Stevenson) to May 15 (1954, Birmingham, T. A. Imhof and others) and September 4 (1954, Birmingham, T. A. Imhof and others) to November 8 (1939, Birmingham, H. M. Stevenson); also June 9, 1954 (Birmingham, F. B. Daniel) and November 22, 1949 (Birmingham, M. H. Perry); most seen, 250+ (198 of them ceilometer casualties), October 8, 1954 (Birmingham, T. A. Imhof and F. B. Daniel). *Piedmont:* April 1 (1926, Auburn, J. M. Robertson) to May 9 (1908, Woodbine, A. A. Saunders) and September 10 (1958, Auburn, Lovett Williams) to October 21 (1939, specimen in Auburn Univ. collection, H. G. Good). *Upper Coastal Plain:* April 7 (1937, Tuscaloosa, H. M. Stevenson) to May 14 (1939, Tuscaloosa, H. M. Stevenson) and September 16 (1959, Montgomery, R. W. Skinner) to November 6 (1938, Tuscaloosa, H. M. Stevenson). *Lower Coastal Plain:* April 19, 1958 (13 birds, McIntosh, T. A. Imhof, W. U. Harris, and J. R. Davis) and September 14 (1958, Camden, Lovett Williams) to November 5 (1957, Jackson, W. U. Harris). *Gulf*

PLATE 33

BREWSTER'S WARBLER
Hybrid
Adult Male, Sexes Similar
Page 443

PINE WARBLER
Adult Male, Sexes Similar
Page 473

LAWRENCE'S WARBLER
Hybrid
Adult Male, Sexes Similar
Page 443

GOLDEN-WINGED WARBLER
Adult Male, Sexes Similar
Page 442

BLUE-WINGED WARBLER
Adult Male, Sexes Similar
Page 443

CONNECTICUT WARBLER
Adult Female
Page 483

PALM WARBLER (WESTERN)
Adult, Spring, Sexes Alike
Page 476

CONNECTICUT WARBLER
Adult Male
Page 483

PALM WARBLER (YELLOW)
Adult, Spring, Sexes Alike
Page 476

KIRTLAND'S WARBLER
Adult Male, Spring, Sexes Similar
Page 474

YELLOW WARBLER
Adult Male, Sexes Similar
Page 452

MOURNING WARBLER
Adult Male
Page 484

MOURNING WARBLER
Adult Female
Page 484

BACHMAN'S WARBLER
Adult Female
Page 445

WILSON'S WARBLER
Adult Male, Sexes Similar
Page 491

BACHMAN'S WARBLER
Adult Male
Page 445

[448]

Richard A. Parks

Coast: April 6 (1957, Dauphin Island, S. A. Gauthreaux and 1960, Dauphin Island, J. L. Dorn) to May 13 (1960, Dauphin Island, J. L. Dorn) and September 13 (1959, Dauphin Island, H. A. J. and Cora Evans) to November 7 (1959, Dauphin Island, T. A. Imhof and others); most seen, spring, 70, April 15, 1960 (Dauphin Island, T. A. Imhof and others), fall, 175, September 16, 1960 (after Hurricane Ethel, Dauphin Island, J. L. Dorn) and 92, November 1, 1958 (Fall Count, Mobile Bay Area).

Orange-crowned Warbler
Vermivora celata (Say)   [646]   (Plate 36, facing page 488)

The Orange-crowned Warbler is a *plain greenish* bird that is often as *dark green below*, particularly on the breast, as it is above. The orange crown patch of the male is rarely useful in identification because it is usually hidden. *Immature birds* are plain dark *gray* above, and often on the breast also, but in any plumage the species is best distinguished, especially from the Tennessee Warbler, by the *faint,* poorly-defined *streaks* on the *breast* and the *yellowish-green under tail coverts.* The much less noticeable eye stripe, no trace of a wing bar, and the darker under parts are further good clues. The song of the Orange-crowned Warbler is a series of loud, musical notes much like that of the Chipping Sparrow but higher in pitch and ending with two slower notes. The call is a sharp chip.

In winter in Alabama, this warbler is common on the Gulf Coast, fairly common in most of the Coastal Plain, and uncommon to rare as far north as Birmingham and occasionally Gadsden. On migration it is uncommon to fairly common nearly throughout the state. The species is not known to breed in Alabama. It is partial to evergreen oaks, especially live oaks, but it also frequents a variety of other hardwoods, particularly other oaks and magnolias. Transients may be found almost anywhere, often in tall weeds such as ragweeds, but at any season in Alabama this bird seems to avoid pines.

NESTING AND FOOD. This species lays three to six white eggs spotted with reddish-brown in a nest of leaves and grasses lined with finer grasses, mosses, hair, or feathers. This nest is usually on the ground among dead leaves at the base of a shrub or within four feet of the ground in a low fork. This warbler feeds on leafhoppers, plant lice, scale insects, beetles, caterpillars small wasps, ants, flies, and spiders. This diet is varied with seeds, leafgalls, and wild fruit. At feeding stations, it is known to eat suet, peanut butter, and doughnuts.

DISTRIBUTION. The Orange-crowned Warbler breeds from northern Alaska, northwestern Mackenzie, and northwestern Quebec south, particularly in moun-

[449]

tains, to Lower California, southwestern Texas, southern Manitoba, and central Ontario. It winters from northern California, southern Nevada, southern Texas, central Alabama, and South Carolina, occasionally north to Wisconsin, Michigan, and coastal New England, south to Guatemala and southern Florida.

OCCURRENCE IN ALABAMA. (Normal: October 7 to May 1; Out-of-season: September 11 and 22.) *Tennessee Valley*: October 10, 1959 (Wheeler Refuge, T. A. Imhof and others); April 29, 1951 (3 birds, Wheeler Refuge, D. C. Hulse); and April 30, 1957 (Wheeler Refuge, D. C. Hulse). *Mountain Region*: October 13 (1954, Gadsden, Edith Clark) to May 1 (1940, Birmingham, H. M. Stevenson); also September 11, 1957 and September 22, 1956 (Gadsden, Edith Clark) and a bird visited a Gadsden feeder throughout the winter of 1955-56 and February 1, 1959 (Edith Clark); most seen, 20, October 25, 1952 (Birmingham, T. A. Imhof). *Piedmont*: January 3 (1959, Auburn, Lovett Williams) and January 9 (1958, Auburn, Lovett Williams) to April 19 (1959, Auburn, Lovett Williams). *Upper Coastal Plain*: October 12 (1956, Marion, Lois McCollough) to April 15 (1878, Coosada, N. C. Brown). *Lower Coastal Plain*: October 19 (1958, Camden, Lovett Williams) to April 5 (1957, Jackson, T. A. Imhof and W. U. Harris); most seen, 8, January 11, 1958 (Hal's Lake and vicinity, T. A. Imhof and others). *Gulf Coast*: October 7 (1956, Dauphin Island, H. A. J. and Cora Evans and others) to April 16 (1959, Spring Hill, J. L. Dorn); most seen, migration, 48, October 19, 1957 (Fall Count, Mobile Bay Area), winter, 25, January 2, 1960 (Christmas Count, Dauphin Island).

Nashville Warbler
Vermivora ruficapilla (Wilson)   [645]   (Plate 36, facing page 488)

The Nashville Warbler has an *olive-green back*, wings, and tail, *bright yellow under parts*, and a *bluish-gray head* with a *white eye ring*. The male has a reddish crown patch, but this is rarely useful in identification because it is concealed. This warbler lacks any markings on the wings, tail, or under parts, and their absence makes the species distinct from other yellow-bellied warblers with greenish or olive backs. The usual song of the Nashville Warbler begins with a slow phrase of six syllables and continues with a much faster trill in a lower pitch, the trill resembling those of the Chipping Sparrow and Tennessee Warbler.

In spring, the Nashville Warbler is known only north of the Fall Line and on the Gulf Coast, where it is rare. In fall, it is uncommon in the Tennessee Valley, Mountain Region, and Gulf Coast, rare in the Upper Coastal Plain, and unrecorded elsewhere. It is unknown as a breeder in Alabama. The species usually frequents the lower parts of tall deciduous trees and the upper parts of shrubs and saplings.

NESTING AND FOOD. This bird hides its nest of moss, ferns, and dried grass on the ground, near the base of a small shrub, and lays four to five creamy-white eggs marked with reddish-brown. Included in the food of this species are flies, grasshoppers, locusts, leafhoppers, plant lice, caterpillars, beetles, and other small insects especially in the larval and egg stages.

DISTRIBUTION. The Nashville Warbler breeds from southern British Columbia, southern Manitoba, southern Quebec, and Nova Scotia south to central California, northern Utah, southern Minnesota, northern West Virginia, northern New Jersey, and southern New England. It winters from northern Mexico, southern Texas, and rarely southern Florida south to Guatemala.

OCCURRENCE IN ALABAMA. (April 13 to May 4 and September 14 to November 1.) *Tennessee Valley*: April 26 (1961, Brownsboro, Madison Co., Margaret Robinson) to May 2 (1937, Guntersville, C. R. Mason) and September 28 (1940, Wheeler Refuge, Clarence Cottam) to October 10 (1959, Wheeler Refuge, T. A. Imhof and others). *Mountain Region*: April 30 (1934, Birmingham, H. M. Stevenson) to May 4 (1940, Birmingham, H. M. Stevenson) and September 14 (1952, Gadsden, Edith Clark) to October 25 (1948, Birmingham, T. A. Imhof); most seen, 6, ceilometer casualties, October 8, 1954 (Birmingham, T. A. Imhof and F. B. Daniel). *Piedmont*: April 18, 1908 (specimen not preserved, Hollins, A. A. Saunders). *Upper Coastal Plain*: September 17 (1959, Livingston, Jenkins Jackson), to October 17 (1958, Livingston, Jenkins Jackson). *Lower Coastal Plain*: No record. *Gulf Coast*: April 13 (1957, Alabama Point, Lovett Williams) to May 2 (1961, Dauphin Island, Owen Davies) and October 7 (1956, specimen in the Florida State Univ. collection, Dauphin Island, Lovett Williams) to November 1 (1958, Dauphin Island, T. A. Imhof and S. A. Gauthreaux).

Parula Warbler
Parula americana (Linnaeus) [648] (Plate 32, facing page 440)

The Parula Warbler is *blue above* with two *white wing bars* and a *greenish patch* in the *middle* of the *back*. It is unstreaked *below* and *mostly yellow*, but the lower belly is white. In spring plumage the white eye ring is prominent, and the male has a chestnut ring across the throat. In fall the wing bars, the unstreaked under parts, and the lack of prominent marks in the rump and tail distinguish it from several other similar warblers. The song of the Parula Warbler is a buzzing trill that rises in pitch and falls on the last note.

In the Coastal Plain of Alabama this warbler is a common to abundant summer resident in swampy woods wherever Spanish moss grows. On the Gulf Coast a few birds sometimes remain in winter principally in mossy live oaks. North of the Fall Line, the species is uncommon and local in summer in moist woods where *Usnea* moss hangs from the trees. As a transient it is uncommon to fairly common in spring and common to abundant in fall throughout the state. It breeds in Alabama generally wherever found in early June.

NESTING. North of the Fall Line, the nest is a pocket in *Usnea* moss sparingly lined with fine grass, pine needles, hair, or fern down. In the Coastal

[451]

Plain this bird selects Spanish moss, building its nest in the same way. In regions where neither moss is available, the nest is often in a cluster of leaves and is a hanging affair made of any fine plant materials locally obtainable. The four or five white eggs are normally marked with various shades of reddish-brown.

FOOD. This species feeds on caterpillars, beetles, bugs, small flies, plant lice, spiders, ants, and probably many other insects, including their eggs and larvae. In winter it occasionally eats a few seeds.

DISTRIBUTION. The Parula Warbler breeds from southern Manitoba, southern Quebec, and Nova Scotia south to eastern Texas, the northern Gulf Coast, and central Florida. It winters from northeastern Mexico, rarely the northern Gulf Coast, Florida, and the Bahamas south to Nicaragua and the Lesser Antilles.

OCCURRENCE IN ALABAMA. (Normal: March 7 to November 1; Out-of-season: December 27 and 30, January 2, and February 28.) *Tennessee Valley*: April 2 (1890, Leighton, F. W. McCormack) to September 26 (1959, Huntsville, J. C. and Margaret Robinson). *Mountain Region*: March 28 (1950, Fairfield, T. A. Imhof) to October 24 (1936, Easonville, St. Clair Co., H. M. Stevenson); most seen, 12, August 23, 1948 and August 20, 1949 (Fairfield, T. A. Imhof). *Piedmont*: March 20 (1908, Woodbine, A. A. Saunders) to September 11 (1958, Auburn, Lovett Williams). *Upper Coastal Plain*: March 11 (1950 and 1951, Catoma Creek, Montgomery Co., C. W. Summerour) to October 14 (1938, Tuscaloosa, H. M. Stevenson and 1950, Montgomery, C. W. Summerour); most seen, 17, April 23, 1955 (Autauga Co., T. A. Imhof and E. G. Holt). *Lower Coastal Plain*: March 15 (1959, Camden, Lovett Williams) to October 19 (1956, Open Pond, T. A. Imhof and L. C. Crawford); most seen, 55, May 12, 1956 (Choctaw Bluff, T. A. Imhof, M. W. Gaillard, and G. A. Carleton) and May 25, 1956 (McIntosh, T. A. Imhof and W. F. Colin). *Gulf Coast*: March 7 (1933, Fairhope, Homer Flagg) to November 1 (1958, 6 birds, Fall Count, Mobile Bay Area); also December 27, 1958, 2 birds (Bellingrath Gardens, T. A. Imhof); December 30, 1960 (Bellingrath Gardens, T. A. Imhof); January 2, 1960 (Bellingrath Gardens, T. A. Imhof) and February 28, 1959 (Dauphin Island, S. A. Gauthreaux and others); most seen, summer, 65, May 26, 1956 (Mount Vernon, T. A. Imhof and W. F. Colin), fall, 45, September 16, 1960, after Hurricane Ethel (Dauphin Island, J. L. Dorn).

TIME OF BREEDING. Data on 14+ nestings: Building, April 9 to May 25; eggs, April 23 to June 25; dependent young, May 12 to June 29.

Yellow Warbler
Dendroica petechia (Linnaeus)   [652]   (Plate 33, facing page 448)

In Alabama the Yellow Warbler is the only small bird that *appears to be entirely yellow*. It is a little darker on the back, wings, and tail, and in *spring* the *bright yellow male* has *reddish-brown streaks* on the *breast,* and the female often is sparingly streaked. Immature birds in fall are often quite dull. The species can always be identified by the *yellow spots near* the *tip* of the *tail* which are a brighter yellow than the rest of the plumage. The usual song of this species consists of about seven rather loud and lively notes, which are often clipped in Alabama.

This warbler is a common summer resident in the Tennessee Valley and uncommon, but sometimes locally abundant, south to a short distance beyond the Fall Line. (See Map 78.) As a migrant it is common and occasionally abundant throughout the state. Usually it occurs in small trees and shrubs in relatively open areas, around houses, in orchards, streamside thickets, and other similar situations. It almost always breeds near water and in Alabama most often in willow thickets along creeks and rivers.

NESTING. This bird places its neat, well-built nest in a fork of a shrub or tree. It uses various plant materials such as grass, cotton, and herb strands for the outer cup and lines it with finer plant materials. The two to four whitish eggs are spotted and blotched around the larger end with shades of brown, olive, and gray.

FOOD. Like other warblers, this species feeds almost entirely on insects from the foliage of trees and shrubs. Frequent items are caterpillars, weevils, other beetles, moths, and plant lice. Less often it takes flies, spiders, locusts, small wasps, bugs, grasshoppers, millipedes, and centipedes, and occasionally a few small fruits such as raspberries.

DISTRIBUTION. The Yellow Warbler breeds from northern Alaska, northern Mackenzie, northern Quebec, and Newfoundland south to Peru and Trinidad. It winters from northern Mexico, southern Florida, and the Bahamas south to Peru and Brazil.

OCCURRENCE IN ALABAMA. (March 31 to October 23.) *Tennessee Valley*: April 6 (1893, Leighton, F. W. McCormack) to September 12 (1958, Wheeler Refuge, T. A. Imhof and others); also October 11, 1954, 1 found dead (Wheeler Refuge, D. C. Hulse); most seen, spring, 18, May 4, 1957 (Wheeler Refuge, Ala. Orn. Soc.), fall, 17, September 2, 1943 (Wheeler Refuge, H. M. Stevenson). *Mountain Region*: April 2 (1935, Birmingham, H. M. Stevenson) to September 25 (1953 and 1956, Birmingham, T. A. Imhof and E. G. DeLoach); most seen, 41, May 4, 1940 (Birmingham, H. M. Stevenson). *Piedmont*: April 4 (1925, Auburn, J. M. Robertson) to September 11 (1958, Auburn, Lovett Williams); most seen, 10, April 30, 1955 (Auburn, H. G. Good and T. A. Imhof). *Upper Coastal Plain*: April 3 (1958, Livingston, Jenkins Jackson) to May 11 (1957, Marion, Lois McCollough) and August (many observers, no definite dates) to October 18 (1924, Prattville, L. S. Golsan); also May 29, 1949 (6 birds, Tuscaloosa, T. A. Imhof and others). *Lower Coastal Plain*: April 5 (1958, Jackson, W. U. Harris) to May 1 (1952, Andalusia, W. R. Middleton) and September 12 (1958, Camden, Lovett Williams) to September 20 (1957, Andalusia, T. A. Imhof and Lovett Williams and 1958, Camden, Lovett Williams). *Gulf Coast*: March 31 (1958, Tensaw, W. U. Harris and M. H. Fisher) to May 14 (1950, Gulf Shores, H. M. Stevenson) and July 28 (1960, 6 birds, Spring Hill, J. L. Dorn) to October 23 (1949, Cochrane Causeway, T. A. Imhof); most seen, 89, after Hurricane Ethel, September 16, 1960 (Dauphin Island, J. L. Dorn).

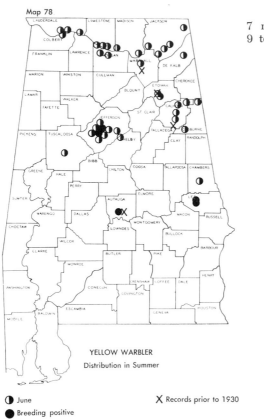

Map 78

YELLOW WARBLER

Distribution in Summer

◑ June   X Records prior to 1930

● Breeding positive

TIME OF BREEDING. Data on 7 nestings: Building, April 19; eggs, May 9 to 20; dependent young, June 28.

Magnolia Warbler

Dendroica magnolia (Wilson)   [657]   (Plate 32, facing page 440)

This brightly-colored warbler is mainly dark gray above and bright yellow below and has white patches on the head, wings, and tail. In any plumage the *square white patch*es on the *black tail* distinguish this species from other warblers which have dark backs and yellow under parts. In *spring* the *male* is almost entirely black above and has a black cheek patch and *heavy black streaks* on the *breast*. Females and immatures have much less streaking, and it is usually confined to the sides. The song is a rather slow one of six syllables with the last note either higher or lower than the preceding one. It closely resembles songs of the Hooded and Yellow Warblers.

[454]

PASSERIFORMES: PARULIDAE: MAGNOLIA WARBLER

The Magnolia Warbler is a transient in Alabama. In spring it is common north of the Black Belt and rare to uncommon south of it and in fall it is common and sometimes locally abundant throughout the state. It is not known to breed here. Its scarcity in southern Alabama in spring is probably due to the fact that it is a late migrant which apparently crosses the Gulf and southern Alabama at a season when it seldom encounters cold fronts that force it to land. This species is so named because one of the first known specimens was collected from a magnolia in coastal Mississippi, but it generally frequents young evergreen growth, especially spruces, in the breeding season and on migration usually occurs in hardwoods.

NESTING AND FOOD. This species lays four whitish eggs marked with brown in a rather poorly-built nest of small twigs, coarse grasses, and weed stalks lined with fine black rootlets. The nest is often placed against the trunk of a young spruce, hemlock, balsam fir or other evergreen within five feet of the ground. Its food consists chiefly of caterpillars, beetles, and flies, but it also eats leafhoppers, plant lice, sawfly larvae, ants, scale insects, spiders, and locusts.

DISTRIBUTION. The Magnolia Warbler breeds from southwestern Mackenzie, central Quebec, and Newfoundland south to British Columbia, central Wisconsin, northern Ohio, Virginia in mountains, and central New England. It winters from central Mexico to Panama and in the Bahamas and the Greater Antilles.

OCCURRENCE IN ALABAMA. (April 15 to May 29 and September 1 to November 7.) *Tennessee Valley*: April 20 (1947, Russellville, E. O. Willis) to May 29 (1948, Russellville, E. O. Willis) and September 1 (1948, Russellville, E. O. Willis) to October 26 (1947, Russellville, E. O. Willis). *Mountain Region*: April 17 (1956, Gadsden, Edith Clark) to May 23 (1940, Birmingham, H. M. Stevenson and 1957, Gadsden, Edith Clark) and September 1 (1934 and 1936, Birmingham, H. M. Stevenson) to October 26 (1947, Birmingham, T. A. Imhof); most seen, 118 ceilometer casualties, October 8, 1954 (Birmingham, T. A. Imhof and F. B. Daniel), 38+, October 4, 1948 (Fairfield, T. A. Imhof). *Piedmont*: April 15 (1926, Auburn, H. G. Good) to May 5 (1926, Auburn, H. S. Peters) and September 10 (1938, Roanoke, H. M. Stevenson and 1958, Auburn, Lovett Williams) to October 27 (1925, Auburn, J. M. Robertson). *Upper Coastal Plain*: April 19 (1958, Marion, Lois McCollough) to May 18 (1938, Tuscaloosa, H. M. Stevenson) and September 3 (1939, Tuscaloosa, H. M. Stevenson) to October 31 (1957, Livingston, Jenkins Jackson); most seen, 16, October 13 and 20, 1956 (Marion, Lois McCollough). *Lower Coastal Plain*: May 15, 1954 (Grove Hill, G. A. Carleton) and September 17 (1958, Camden, Lovett Williams) to November 2 (1956, Gordon, Houston Co., H. M. Stevenson). *Gulf Coast*: May 2 (1961, Dauphin Island, Owen Davies and J. L. Dorn) to May 16 (1960, Dauphin Island, J. L. Dorn) and September 11 (1937, Spring Hill College, J. L. Dorn) to November 7 (1959, 4 birds, Dauphin Island, Ala. Orn. Soc.); most seen, 140+, October 17, 1959 (Dauphin Island, T. A. Imhof and others).

[456]

Cape May Warbler

Dendroica tigrina (Gmelin)   [650]   (Plate 34, facing page 456)

The Cape May Warbler is dark olive-green streaked with black above and has a dull, poorly-defined *yellow rump patch*. It has a *suffused patch* of *yellow* on the *side* of the *neck*, and it is *yellow heavily streaked* with *black below*. The *male* has a dark cap, a *large, triangular, chestnut cheek patch,* and a larger, brighter-yellow neck patch. Females and immature birds are much duller with much less yellow below. But in any plumage, the species can always be distinguished from other yellow-rumped warblers because it retains the heavy streaking of its under parts, and its yellow neck patch. The most distinctive song of this warbler is a series of high, very thin notes, but it has other songs which are easily confused with those of other warblers.

An Atlantic Coast migrant, the Cape May Warbler occurs commonly in Alabama only on the eastern edge of the state—at Auburn, Gadsden, and Jacksonville in spring, for example, and in the eastern half of the Tennessee Valley in spring and fall. In the remainder of the state its occurrence is usually preceded by sustained easterly winds of several days duration. Thus in spring it is uncommon and in fall it is rare, noted most often in the Mountain Region and on the Gulf Coast. It is not known to breed in Alabama. On migration it usually occurs in hardwoods, but in the breeding season it inhabits spruces.

NESTING AND FOOD. This species lays five to seven creamy-white eggs spotted and blotched with brown in a bulky, well-camouflaged nest. The Cape May Warbler usually builds against the trunk of a spruce or other conifer toward the top. The exterior of the nest is made of plant fibers, twigs, and moss, but the inside is lined with smoothly-felted hair and feathers. This warbler feeds on wasps, flies, small moths, beetles (including weevils), small crickets, leafhoppers, plant lice, termites, caterpillars, dragonflies, and spiders. In fall it occasionally feeds on small fruits, especially grapes.

DISTRIBUTION. The Cape May Warbler breeds from northeastern British Columbia, southern Mackenzie, northern Ontario, and southern Quebec south to North Dakota, northern Wisconsin, northern New York, southern Maine, and Nova Scotia. It migrates through Florida, avoiding the lower Mississippi Valley to winter in the West Indies from Cuba and the Bahamas south to St. Lucia and from Yucatan to Honduras.

OCCURRENCE IN ALABAMA. (April 2 to May 12 and September 26 to November 1.) *Tennessee Valley*: April 27 (1961, Brownsboro, Madison Co., J. C. and

[457]

Margaret Robinson) to May 7 (1960, Wheeler Refuge, Demett Smith) and September 26 (1947, Wheeler Refuge, L. S. Givens) to October 18 (1959, 4 birds, Huntsville, J. C. and Margaret Robinson). *Mountain Region:* April 5 (1935, Birmingham, H. M. Stevenson) to May 12 (1955, Birmingham, J. B. Sullivan); also October 10, 1954 (Gadsden, Edith Clark); October 15, 1954 (Fairfield, T. A. Imhof) and October 16, 1949 (Birmingham, T. A. Imhof). *Piedmont:* April 2 (1955, Auburn, H. G. Good) to April 30 (1955,

Auburn, H. G. Good and T. A. Imhof); no fall dates. *Upper Coastal Plain:* April 13 to 29, 1958 (a male, Montgomery, J. E. Keeler). *Lower Coastal Plain:* No record. *Gulf Coast:* April 10 (1959, Dauphin Island, T. A. Imhof and others) to May 3 (1961, Dauphin Island, Owen Davies); also November 1, 1958 (Dauphin Island, R. W. Skinner); most seen, 12, April 26, 1958 (Dauphin Island, Lovett Williams and D. W. Speake and Fort Morgan, B. L. Monroe, Jr. and F. M. Weston).

Black-throated Blue Warbler
Dendroica caerulescens (Gmelin) [654] (Plate 32, facing page 440)

The *male* of this species is aptly named, for it is *dark blue* on all the *upper parts*, and it has a *black face, throat, breast,* and sides, and a white belly. The *female* and *immature* birds are quite different, for they are *dark olive-brown above* and have an *olive-brown cheek patch*. The throat, a line over the eye, and the under tail coverts are white, and much of the under parts are yellowish. This species has a *small, square, white wing patch* which identifies it in *most plumages,* but some immature birds lack this mark. They, however, have a dark-cheeked look which points them out to those who know the other plumages of the species well. The song is a thick, slow buzz.

Like the Cape May Warbler, this species is an Atlantic Coast migrant and is thus more common on the eastern edge of the state—Auburn, Cheaha, Gadsden, and Lookout Mountain, for instance. Elsewhere in Alabama, the Black-throated Blue Warbler is an uncommon to rare migrant, and nowhere in the state is it known to breed. This warbler usually frequents tall shrubs and small trees such as laurel and dogwood and normally occurs between five and fifteen feet from the ground. In the breeding season it seems to prefer northern hardwoods with a few pines and much evergreen undergrowth.

NESTING AND FOOD. The well-made nest of bark, leaves, and other plant fibers, lined with fine rootlets, pine needles, hair, or fur, and often containing pieces of dead wood, is very close to the ground in a broad-leafed evergreen shrub, evergreen sapling, small maple, or small beech. The four eggs are creamy-white, marked with brown and gray. This warbler feeds chiefly on flying and crawling insects including many kinds of flies, caterpillars, beetles, moths, dragonflies, winged ants, plant lice, and locusts. It also eats spiders and occasionally slugs and seeds.

[458]

DISTRIBUTION. The Black-throated Blue Warbler breeds from western Ontario, southern Quebec, and Nova Scotia south to Minnesota, northern Wisconsin, northern Ohio, northern Georgia mountains, northern New Jersey, and southern New England. It winters mainly in the Greater Antilles from islands off Yucatan, Cuba, and the Bahamas southeast to the Virgin Islands.

OCCURRENCE IN ALABAMA. (Normal: April 4 to May 7 and September 20 to October 26; Out-of-season: November 25.) *Tennessee Valley*: April 13, 1940 (Wheeler Refuge, Clarence Cottam); May 2, 1937 (Guntersville, C. R. Mason); September 26, 1959 (Huntsville, J. C. and Margaret Robinson); and October 17, 1959 (Huntsville, J. C. and Margaret Robinson). *Mountain Region*: April 20 (1960, Gadsden, Edith Clark) to May 4 (1940, Birmingham, H. M. Stevenson) and September 22 (1953, Gadsden, Edith Clark) to October 26 (1952, Gadsden, Edith Clark). *Piedmont*: April 6 (1940, Auburn, H. G. Good) to May 3 (1908, Hollins, A. A. Saunders); no fall dates. *Upper Coastal Plain*: April 4, 1954 (Livingston, Juanita Ennis); April 26, 1878 (Coosada, N. C. Brown); and May 7, 1911 (2 birds, Montgomery, A. H. Howell). *Lower Coastal Plain*: No record. *Gulf Coast*: April 8, 1939 (Gulf Shores, H. G. Good); April 26, 1958 (Dauphin Island, Lovett Williams and D. W. Speake); May 2, 1961 (6 birds, Dauphin Island, Owen Davies) and September 10 (1960, Dauphin Island, J. L. Dorn) to October 20 (1957, Dauphin Island, Lovett Williams and H. G. Loftin); also November 25, 1960 (Dauphin Island, H. A. J. and Cora Evans).

Myrtle Warbler

Dendroica coronata (Linnaeus)   [655]   (Plate 32, facing page 440)

This warbler is mainly dark gray streaked with black above, and white lightly streaked with black below. It has a prominent, *well-defined, bright yellow rump*. Spring adults have yellow patches on the crown and on each side of the breast also. In spring plumage the male has a black ear patch, and black spreads over much of the chest and runs into the streaks on the sides. The female is brownish-gray in spring wherever the male is dark gray and black. In fall and winter, all ages and both sexes are much plainer, but they retain the bright yellow rump, the badge of the species.

Many warblers have similar call-notes, probably because they often travel in mixed flocks, and hence a distinctive call for each species is seldom necessary. But the Myrtle Warbler has a distinctive call, a single loud, sharp note, and an obvious need for it, because this species frequently occurs in pure flocks, especially in winter when few other warblers remain in the state. Its song is a rather low, weak, spiritless, irregular warble which resembles that of the Pine Warbler but varies in pitch.

The Myrtle Warbler is the most numerous of its family in Alabama, but it is not known to breed here. It is abundant on migration and in winter throughout the state, and adapts itself to all wooded and brushy habitats. Often it feeds over water, especially in trees and shrubs which grow in flooded lakes and bottomlands. It feeds in both hardwoods and pines, and although it sometimes associates with the wintertime titmouse flocks, it seems to have a flock organization of its own.

NESTING AND FOOD. The nest, made of small twigs, grasses, rootlets, mosses, and other plant materials and lined with hair and feathers, is almost always in an evergreen, usually a cedar, and ordinarily less than fifteen feet above the ground. The four or five eggs are creamy-white marked with brown and gray. The species feeds on a variety of insects including caterpillars, beetle grubs, sawfly larvae, flies of many kinds, scale insects, plant lice, grasshoppers, locusts, bugs, and ants, especially in the egg and larval stages. In winter it subsists largely on a great variety of berries and seeds, the fruit of the bayberry or wax myrtle being important enough in its diet to give the species its name. Its ability to survive on fruits is undoubtedly the reason why large numbers can winter farther north than other warblers. At feeding stations in Alabama it eats suet and peanut butter.

DISTRIBUTION. The Myrtle Warbler breeds from the limit of trees in northern Alaska and northern Canada south to northern British Columbia, southern Alberta, northern Minnesota, central Ontario, northeastern Pennsylvania, central New England, and southern Maine. It winters from Oregon to Lower California and from Kansas, the southern Great Lakes area, and southern New England south to Panama and Puerto Rico.

OCCURRENCE IN ALABAMA. (September 23 to May 16.) *Tennessee Valley*: October 10 (1889, Leighton, F. W. McCormack) to May 16 (Wheeler Refuge, *fide* T. Z. Atkeson, Jr.); most seen, 150+, February 5, 1955 (Marshall Co., T. A. Imhof). *Mountain Region*: September 23 (1953, Gadsden, Edith Clark) to May 16 (1956, Fairfield, T. A. Imhof and 1960, Birmingham, Harriett Wright); most seen, 117, December 26, 1955 (Christmas Count, Birmingham). *Piedmont*: October 3 (1958, Wedowee, T. A. Imhof and C. T. Hornady) to May 13 (1953, Auburn, H. G. Good). *Upper Coastal Plain*: October 7 (1925, Autaugaville, L. S. Golsan and 1938, Tuscaloosa, H. M. Stevenson) to May 10 (1939, Tuscaloosa, H. M. Stevenson); most seen, winter, 270, December 31, 1956 (Marion, Lois McCollough), spring, 220, March 19, 1960 (Marion, T. A. Imhof and others).

Lower Coastal Plain: October 18 (1958, Camden, Lovett Williams) to May 1 (1952, Andalusia, W. R. Middleton); most seen, 200, February 26, 1955 (Covington Co. and Geneva Co., T. A. Imhof). *Gulf Coast*: October 5 (1956, Dauphin Island, Lois McCollough and T. A. Imhof) to May 2 (1961, Dauphin Island, Owen Davies); most seen, 1500, December 29, 1956 (Christmas Count, Dauphin Island).

BANDING. A Myrtle Warbler banded at Zion, Illinois (40 miles north of Chicago), October 20, 1948, was recovered in Birmingham on November 13, 1948, 23 days later. Another banded at Fairhope, December 1, 1930, was retrapped on December 7, 1931 at the same place. A third, banded at Gadsden, March 13, 1954, was retrapped there on April 24, 1956.

Audubon's Warbler
Dendroica auduboni (Townsend)   [656]   (Plate 32, facing page 440)

This bird is the southwestern counterpart of the Myrtle Warbler, from which it differs in having a *bright yellow throat* and white in four or five tail feathers instead of two or three. *Adult males* have a *broad white wing patch* instead of two white wing bars. The song is much like that of the Myrtle Warbler, and the call, though softer and lower, is also similar; yet the two can be distinguished by an observer with sharp ears.

Audubon's Warbler is casual in fall and winter in Alabama in the Mountain Region and on the Gulf Coast, and it does not breed here. It frequents the same places as does the Myrtle Warbler.

NESTING AND FOOD. The nest and eggs are similar to those of the Myrtle Warbler. Audubon's Warbler feeds mainly on insects, supplemented in fall and winter with fruit and seeds. Items taken are ants, bugs, flies, plant lice, caterpillars, beetles, poison-oak seeds, weed seeds, wax myrtle berries, and raisins.

DISTRIBUTION. Audubon's Warbler breeds from British Columbia and southwestern Saskatchewan south to Lower California and southern New Mexico and in mountains in Mexico to Durango. It winters from coastal British Columbia, Utah, and southern Texas, casually east of the Mississippi River, south to Costa Rica.

OCCURRENCE IN ALABAMA. (November 1 and March.) *Tennessee Valley*: No record. *Mountain Region*: A male, which was photographed in color, spent most of March 1959 at or near the feeding station of Harriett Wright in Birmingham. *Piedmont*: No record. *Upper Coastal Plain*: No record. *Lower Coastal Plain*: No record. *Gulf Coast*: T. A. Imhof observed 1 in Bellingrath Gardens at 15 feet on November 1, 1958.

Black-throated Gray Warbler
Dendroica nigrescens (Townsend)   [665]   (Plate 32, facing page 440)

This warbler is dark gray above and white below and has a *black cap*, *black cheek patch*, and *black throat*. Adults have a tiny *yellow spot between* the *eye* and the *bill*. Females are gray instead of black and lack the black throat, and fall and immature birds are duller but still easily recognized. Although this species resembles the Carolina Chickadee and the Black-and-white and Blackpoll Warblers, the head pattern makes it sufficiently distinctive for easy identification.

[461]

In Alabama the Black-throated Gray Warbler is casual on migration, and it is not known to breed here. It frequents low shrubby growth, especially in openings in evergreens on dry slopes.

NESTING AND FOOD. The nest of well-bleached plant fibers is either out on a high limb of a conifer or low in a shrub in a clump of leaves. The clutch consists of four white eggs spotted with brown. The major food of this warbler consists of insects obtained from low shrubbery.

DISTRIBUTION. The Black-throated Gray Warbler breeds from southern British Columbia and southwestern Wyoming south in mountains to northern Lower California and southern New Mexico. It winters in most of Mexico, also southern California, southern Arizona, and rarely in southern Texas, Louisiana, and Florida.

OCCURRENCE IN ALABAMA. *Gulf Coast only*: Dauphin Island, October 7, 1956 (specimen in the Florida State Univ. collection, R. T. Lynn, Lovett Williams, and others) and October 18, 1957 (T. A. Imhof, M. W. Gaillard, and Harriett Wright).

Black-throated Green Warbler
Dendroica virens (Gmelin) [667] (Plate 34, facing page 456)

This warbler has olive-green upper parts, yellow cheeks, black throat, white wing bars, and white under parts. The female has less black on the throat and the immature shows no black. Fall immatures closely resemble Blackburnian Warblers of the same age, but the Black-throated Green Warbler has a whitish, not yellow, breast, an unstreaked back, and a prominent *yellow* area on the whole *side* of the *head*, the mark of the species. The streaking on the flank extends upward to the head to help frame this area. The two songs are pleasing melodies of five or six alternating high and low notes, distinctive in quality.

This species is common on migration in Alabama except for the Lower Coastal Plain where it has not as yet been recorded in spring. It is also a locally common summer resident in many parts of the Mountain Region and in Coosa County. It has been recorded in summer within a few miles of the Fall Line and at elevations down to 400 feet or a little less. In winter it has been recorded once on the Gulf Coast. (See Map 79.) At the southern ends of the Appalachian Plateau in Walker, Jefferson, Tuscaloosa, and Coosa counties, it is decidedly more common as a breeder than it is farther north along the ridges. On migration the species mixes with other warblers and shows no noticeable habitat preferences. For nesting, however, it favors mixed woodlands and seems to be equally common in the upper parts of pines and hardwoods, especially oaks.

PASSERIFORMES: PARULIDAE: BLACK-THROATED GREEN WARBLER

Birds breeding near Birmingham usually frequent the many bluffs in the region where Virginia pine grows abundantly.

NESTING. The nest, usually built in a conifer or, almost as often, in a hardwood, is quite high and is generally difficult to find. It is a well-built, deep cup made of fine twigs, bark, weed stems, and other plant fibers. The only nest described from Alabama was 25 feet from the ground and four feet from the trunk of a shortleaf pine in an area where almost pure pines gave way to hardwoods. This loosely-made affair, saddled lightly with cobwebs on a thick limb, was made of gray plant fibers and lined with the same golden plant fibers as those commonly used by the Prairie Warbler. It contained an incomplete set of two fresh eggs.

FOOD. Caterpillars, beetles, and small flies appear to be the main foods eaten by this warbler. Other items taken are ants, moths, bugs, locusts, spiders, mites, and plant lice, of which it prefers primarily crawling rather than flying kinds. Occasionally it eats a few berries of poison-ivy and juniper.

DISTRIBUTION. The Black-throated Green Warbler breeds from southern Mackenzie, northern Ontario, southern Quebec, and southern Labrador south to central Alberta, central Minnesota, southern Michigan, northern New Jersey, and Long Island, in mountains to central Alabama and also near the coast in Virginia and the Carolinas. It winters from southern Texas to Panama and from southern Florida and the Bahamas to Cuba.

OCCURRENCE IN ALABAMA. (Normal: March 17 to November 9; Out-of-season: January 21.) *Tennessee Valley*: March 25 (1948, Russellville, E. O. Willis) to May 22 (1948, Russellville, E. O. Willis) and August 28 (1940, Florence, H. M. Stevenson) to October 26 (1947, Russellville, E. O. Willis). *Mountain Region*: March 18 (1944, specimen in the La. State Univ. collection, Birmingham, M. L. Miles) to November 2 (1947, Birmingham, T. A. Imhof); most seen, summer, 11 singing males, May 30, 1949 (Pegee's Creek, elevation 500 ft., northern Tuscaloosa Co., T. A. Imhof and others) and June 7, 1958 (eastern slope of Cheaha, T. A. Imhof and C. T. Hornady), migration, 42+, October 18, 1948 (Fairfield, T. A. Imhof). *Piedmont*: March 17 (1908, Woodbine, A. A. Saunders) to April 30 (1936, Auburn, H. S. Peters) and September 26 (1957, Auburn, Lovett Williams) to October 14 (1925, banded at Auburn, J. M. Robertson); sum-

mers in Coosa Co. *Upper Coastal Plain*: March 25 (1939, Tuscaloosa, H. M. Stevenson and 1957, Marion, Lois McCollough) to May 14 (1939, Tuscaloosa, H. M. Stevenson) and September 18 (1951, Montgomery, C. W. Summerour) to November 3 (1957, Blue Creek, Chilton Co., Harriett Wright). *Lower Coastal Plain*: September 20 (1957, Samson, Geneva Co., T. A. Imhof and Lovett Williams) to November 3 (1958, Camden, Lovett Williams); no spring records. *Gulf Coast*: April 6 (1957, Dauphin Island, S. A. Gauthreaux and others) to May 13 (1960, Dauphin Island, J. L. Dorn) and September 3 (1960, 3 birds, Daphne, J. L. Dorn) to November 9 (1932, Fairhope, Homer Flagg and Helen Edwards); also January 21, 1961 (female specimen in Dept. of Conservation collection, Dauphin Island, R. W. Skinner); most seen, 23, November 1, 1958 (Fall Count, Mobile Bay Area).

[464]

Richard A Parks

TIME OF BREEDING. Data on 4 nestings: Building, April 18 to 23; eggs, April 23 (C. W. Summerour); dependent young out of nest, June 7 and July 17.

Cerulean Warbler
Dendroica cerulea (Wilson)   [658]   (Plate 32, facing page 440)

The *upper parts* of this warbler are a beautiful shade of rather *pale blue,* unlike the color of any other American warbler. This bird has two white wing bars and a few streaks on the flanks. *Adults* are *white below,* and the *male* has a *narrow, pale blue breast band.* Immature birds and fall females have a white eye line and are tinged below with very pale yellow, never the deep yellow of the Parula Warbler. The buzzy and rather hurried song of about five notes suggests that of the Parula Warbler except that it is louder and rises at the end.

More numerous in the western half of Alabama, this warbler is a locally common, breeding, summer resident in river and creek valleys and mountain

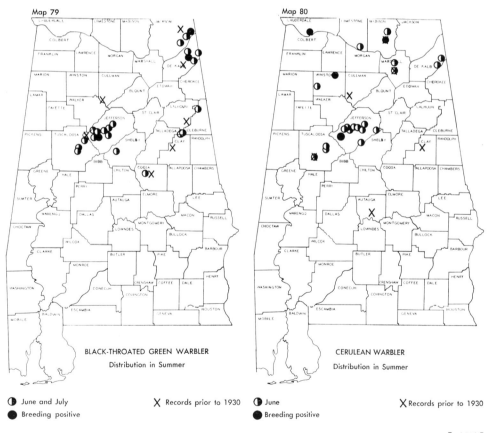

Map 79

BLACK-THROATED GREEN WARBLER

Distribution in Summer

Map 80

CERULEAN WARBLER

Distribution in Summer

◐ June and July   ✕ Records prior to 1930
● Breeding positive

◐ June   ✕ Records prior to 1930
● Breeding positive

[465]

coves south to just below the Fall Line. (See Map 80.) In the breeding season it frequents tall hardwoods near water, especially along creeks rather than rivers or streams where the cover may be too open or too dense. As a migrant it is fairly common in the Mountain Region and on the Gulf Coast and uncommon elsewhere in the state.

NESTING. The nest is difficult to find because it is usually twenty to sixty feet from the ground well out from the trunk of a tall hardwood, often on a substantial limb. It is a very shallow cup made chiefly of bark strips decorated with lichens and lined with moss and is well woven together but poorly attached to the tree. The four pale greenish-white or grayish-white eggs are speckled and spotted with shades of brown.

FOOD. In Alabama this warbler is known to eat ants, wasps, bees, weevils, other beetles, sawflies, and caterpillars.

DISTRIBUTION. The Cerulean Warbler breeds from southeastern Nebraska, southeastern Minnesota, southern Michigan, and central New York south to eastern Texas, southern Louisiana, central Alabama, central North Carolina, and Delaware. It winters from Colombia and Venezuela to Peru and Bolivia.

OCCURRENCE IN ALABAMA. (March 26 to September 24.) *Tennessee Valley*: April 18 (1959, Huntsville, J. C. and Margaret Robinson) to September 9 (1889, Leighton, F. W. McCormack). *Mountain Region*: March 28 (1950, Fairfield, T. A. Imhof) to September 21 (1948, Birmingham, T. A. Imhof); most seen, 17 singing males, May 29, 1950 (Short Creek, Jefferson Co., T. A. Imhof). *Piedmont*: April 10 (1908, Woodbine, A. A. Saunders) to August 15 (1958, Auburn, Lovett Williams). *Upper Coastal Plain*: March 26 (1890, specimen, Greensboro, W. C. Avery) to May 19 (1887, Greensboro, W. C. Avery) and August 8 (1889, Greensboro, W. C. Avery) to August 21 (1958, specimen in the Dept. of Conservation collection, Bear Creek, Autauga Co., R. W. Skin-ner). *Lower Coastal Plain*: April 18, 1958 (Jackson, T. A. Imhof, W. U. Harris, and J. R. Davis); April 19, 1958 (McIntosh, T. A. Imhof, W. U. Harris, and J. R. Davis); September 20, 1957 (4 birds, Florala, T. A. Imhof and Lovett Williams) and September 24, 1958 (Camden, Lovett Williams). *Gulf Coast*: April 8 (1939, specimen, Gulf Shores, H. G. Good) to April 21 (1956, 2 birds, Mobile Co., T. A. Imhof and Baldwin Co., H. M. Stevenson) and August 9 (1953, Bon Secour, H. M. Stevenson) to September 16 (1960, 17 birds after Hurricane Ethel, J. L. Dorn).

TIME OF BREEDING. Data on 3 nestings: Building, April 28 to May 6; eggs, May 6; young in nest, June 2 and 18; dependent young out of nest, July 9.

Blackburnian Warbler
Dendroica fusca (Müller) [662] (Plate 34, facing page 456)

The male Blackburnian Warbler is black above with white streaks on the back and white below with black streaks on the sides. It has a wide white wing patch and *brilliant orange* on the crown, cheeks, and *throat*. The orange of the female is duller and a little more extensive. In fall, immature birds are much duller and resemble Black-throated Green Warblers of the same age, but Blackburnian Warblers can be distinguished by the *streaks* on the *back, pale orange* or *yellowish under parts,* and a dark cheek patch. The high, thin, and wiry song resembles that of the Black-and-white Warbler, but it also has a buzzy quality and a final high note like that of the Parula Warbler. This high note, which sometimes also ends each phrase, is probably the best clue to the identity of the Blackburnian Warbler.

This species is common on migration especially in the northern half of the state. June and July records indicate that it may possibly breed somewhere in the northern part of Alabama, and it has been noted once in winter. In the breeding season this warbler lives in tall evergreens, especially hemlocks and spruces, but in the southern Appalachians it frequently occurs in pure stands of hardwoods. On migration it forages with other warblers in hardwoods.

NESTING. The rather large, substantial, and deeply-cupped nest is almost always well hidden in the thick part of a conifer and well away from the trunk ten to fifty feet from the ground. In the South this bird sometimes chooses a hardwood. (Two nests in Georgia, one sixty miles from the Alabama line at Burnt Mountain, Pickens County, at an elevation of about 2,700 feet, were both on high substantial limbs well away from the trunk of white oaks growing beside springs at the head of a cove. Burleigh, 1958:526-527.) The nest is built of small twigs often interwoven with *Usnea* moss and lined with fine grasses, horsehair, and soft plant fibers. The four whitish eggs are handsomely marked with brown.

FOOD. This warbler eats mainly caterpillars, beetles, and flies, but it also consumes leafhoppers, ants, and aphids, and sometimes when insects are scarce, it eats a few berries.

DISTRIBUTION. The Blackburnian Warbler breeds from southern Saskatchewan, northern Ontario, central Quebec, and Nova Scotia south to central Minnesota, northeastern Ohio, and northern New Jersey, and in mountains to northern Georgia. It winters from Guatemala to Venezuela and Peru.

OCCURRENCE IN ALABAMA. (Normal: March 29 to May 30 and August 31 to October 26; Out-of-season: June 11, July 23, 24, 25, and 26, and December 23.) *Tennessee Valley:* April 18 (1959, Huntsville, J. C. Robinson) to May 26 (1948, Russellville, E. O. Willis) and September 1 (1948, Russellville, E. O Willis) to October 26 (1956, Scottsboro, T. A. Imhof and M. W. Gaillard). *Mountain Region:* April 1 (1954, Birmingham, T. A. Imhof) to May 30 (1952, Birmingham, T. A. Imhof) and September 2 (1935 and 1940, Birmingham, H. M. Stevenson) to October 25 (1948, Fairfield, T. A. Imhof); also June 11, 1954 (Fairfield, T. A. Imhof); July 25, 1949 (Fairfield, T. A. Imhof); July 24 to 26, 1944 (Cheaha, J. L. Dorn) and December 23, 1956 (Huffman,

Birmingham, Adele West); most seen, 50, September 17, 1934 (Birmingham, H. M. Stevenson). *Piedmont*: April 4 (1908, Woodbine, A. A. Saunders) to May 14 (1959, Auburn, Lovett Williams) and September 11 (1958, Auburn, Lovett Williams) to October 21 (1939, specimen, Auburn, D. H. McIntosh); also late August 1932 (Roanoke, H. M. Stevenson). *Upper Coastal Plain*: April 4 (1937, Bridge Creek, Autauga Co., L. S. Golsan) to May 12 (1912, Autaugaville, L. S. Golsan) and September 17 (1951, Montgomery, C. W. Summerour and 1959, Livingston, Jenkins Jackson) to October 19 (1913, specimen, Bear Swamp, L. S. Golsan). *Lower*

Coastal Plain: March 29, 1959 (Camden, Lovett Williams); April 5, 1912 (3 birds, Jackson, E. G. Holt) and September 14 (1958, Camden, Lovett Williams) to October 14 (1956, Jackson, W. U. Harris). *Gulf Coast*: April 10 (1937, Gulf Shores, H. G. Good) to May 20 (1945, specimen not preserved, Gulf Shores, M. W. Gaillard) and August 31 (1958, Dauphin Island, S. A. Gauthreaux and others) to October 20 (1956, Dauphin Island, J. L. Dorn and others); also July 23, 1956 (3 birds, Spring Hill, J. L. Dorn); most seen, 113, September 16, 1960 (after Hurricane Ethel, Dauphin Island, J. L. Dorn).

Yellow-throated Warbler

Dendroica dominica (Linnaeus)   [663]   (Plate 32, facing page 440)

OTHER NAME: Sycamore Warbler

This warbler has a plain *gray back* and *white under parts,* and the head and flanks have some black markings which outline a *bright yellow throat.* The female and immature birds closely resemble the male. The song is a loud and clear repetition of several slurred whistles, accented on the second syllable, and has a high, sharp ending.

The Yellow-throated Warbler is a common, breeding, summer resident throughout Alabama except in southern Mobile County. It is a common migrant throughout the state and winters sparingly on the Gulf Coast and rarely inland. (See Map 81.) In most of Alabama it frequents pines, especially tall ones near water, but in the western part of the state it often occurs in sycamores northward and cypress southward. Much of the time it forages on and around the trunks of large trees.

NESTING. The nest is usually in a clump of Spanish moss when it is available, fifteen to fifty-five or more feet from the ground, and generally well away from the trunk of a large pine, cypress, or hardwood. Where no moss occurs, this bird hides its nest in a cluster of leaves, usually in a pine. Into the Spanish moss or leaves it weaves fine grasses, bark strips, other plant fibers, and silk of caterpillars or spiders. The nest is lined with plant down, feathers, or hair and there are four or five whitish eggs rather heavily marked, chiefly around the larger end, with reddish-brown, lavender, and gray.

FOOD. This warbler is known to feed on flies, beetles, ants, caterpillars, spiders, moths, bugs, grasshoppers, locusts, crickets, and scale insects.

DISTRIBUTION. The Yellow-throated Warbler breeds from Nebraska, southern Wisconsin, northern Ohio, southeastern New York, and Connecticut south to eastern Texas, central Florida, and the Bahamas. It winters from southern Texas, southern Alabama, coastal South Carolina, and the Bahamas south to Costa Rica and the Lesser Antilles.

OCCURRENCE IN ALABAMA. (Throughout the year.) *Tennessee Valley*: April 8 (Wheeler Refuge, *fide* T. Z. Atkeson, Jr.) to October 18 (1959, Wheeler Refuge, J. C. and Margaret Robinson). *Mountain Region*: March 13 (1961, West Blocton, Bibb Co., C. W. Summerour) to October 16 (1935, Birmingham, H. M. Stevenson); also December 24, 1935 (Birmingham, H. M. and T. F. Stevenson); most seen, 25, May 7, 1955 (DeSoto Park, Ala. Orn. Soc.). *Piedmont*: March 15 (1938, specimen, Auburn, D. H. McIntosh) to September 11 (1958, Auburn, Lovett Williams). *Upper Coastal Plain*: March 10 (1951, Bear Swamp, Autauga Co., C. W. Summerour) to October 14 (1938, Tuscaloosa, H. M. Stevenson). *Lower Coastal Plain*: March 16 (1959, Camden, Lovett Williams) to October 8 (1958, Camden, Lovett Williams); also January 7, 1937 (Slocomb, Geneva Co., H. S. Peters and A. G. Watkins); most seen, 20, April 19, 1958 (McIntosh, T. A. Imhof, W. U. Harris, and J. R. Davis). *Gulf Coast*: Common, March 11 (1955, Fort Morgan Peninsula, 2 birds, F. M. Weston and others) to November 3 (1940, specimen in the U. S. National Museum, Mobile, T. D. Burleigh); most seen, spring, 7, March 29, 1952 (Bear Point, H. M. Stevenson), fall, 23, September 16, 1960 (after Hurricane Ethel, Dauphin Island, J. L. Dorn).

TIME OF BREEDING. Data on 16 nestings: Building, March 31 to May 13; eggs, April 18 to May 22; young in nest, May 4 to 9; dependent young out of nest, May 6 to July 22.

SUBSPECIES. See Map 81 for location of specimens of *D. dominica dominica* and *D. dominica stoddardi* Sutton which have been collected in Alabama.

Map 81

YELLOW-THROATED WARBLER
Specimens and Winter Records

♂ Subspecies dominica
♪ Subspecies stoddardi
△ March and April
○ May through July

▽ August through October
☐ November through February
(unidentified)
◯ Specimen collected

Chestnut-sided Warbler
Dendroica pensylvanica (Linnaeus) [659] (Plate 34, facing page 456)

This warbler is *white below* and *yellowish-green above* with yellow wing bars

[469]

and a white eye ring. Spring adults also have black streaks on the back, a lemon-yellow crown, and *chestnut-brown flanks*. Some of this chestnut is retained by fall adults. The song is rather loud and closely resembles those of the Yellow and Magnolia Warblers except for slightly different phrasing.

On migration this warbler is fairly common to common in spring and common to abundant in fall in Alabama. In the breeding season it frequents the borders of second-growth woods and shrubby pastures and forages between the ground and the lower branches of tall trees. It occurs in similar places on migration. Since the chestnut blight began its attack, large areas along ridge tops in the southern Appalachian Mountains contain chestnut sprouts ten to fifteen feet high which are killed before they become trees. In this habitat the Chestnut-sided Warbler is abundant as a breeder and is increasing southwestward so that it now breeds in Georgia sixty miles from the Alabama line (Burleigh, 1958: 532-534). Thus far it is not known to breed in this state.

NESTING. Usually close to the ground in a shrub, the rather flimsy nest is a deep cup of bark strips, fine grasses, and other plant fibers, lined with very fine grasses and hair. The four whitish eggs are speckled with brown.

FOOD. Most of this bird's food apparently consists of such leaf-eating insects as caterpillars, beetles, aphids, leafhoppers, bugs, grasshoppers, and locusts. It also feeds on ants and spiders and, when insects are difficult to obtain, a few seeds or berries.

DISTRIBUTION. The Chestnut-sided Warbler breeds from central Saskatchewan, southern Quebec, and northern Nova Scotia south to eastern Nebraska, northern Ohio, central New Jersey, and in mountains to northern Georgia. It winters from southern Nicaragua to Panama.

OCCURRENCE IN ALABAMA. (Normal: April 3 to May 26 and August 8 to November 2; Out-of-season: June 2.) *Tennessee Valley*: April 3 (1940, Wheeler Refuge, Clarence Cottam) to May 22 (1948, Russellville, E. O. Willis) and September 2 (1908, specimen, Scottsboro, A. H. Howell and 1943, Wheeler Refuge, H. M. Stevenson) to October 2 (1959, Huntsville, J. C. and Margaret Robinson); most seen, 8, September 19, 1959 (Huntsville, J. C. and Margaret Robinson). *Mountain Region*: April 16 (1916, Anniston, R. H. Dean and 1947, Birmingham, T. A. Imhof) to May 26 (1958, Birmingham, T. A. Imhof and Idalene Snead) and August 8 (1936, Birmingham, H. M. Stevenson) to October 27 (1956, DeSoto State Park, 2 birds, G. L. Hight and Idalene Snead); also June 2, 1949 (a singing male, Cullman Co., F. J. Buchmann); most seen, 125, ceilometer casualties, October 8, 1954 (Birmingham, T. A. Imhof and F. B. Daniel) and 50, September 21, 1948 (Fairfield, T. A. Imhof). *Piedmont*: April 17 (1948, specimen, Auburn, H. G. Good) to May 3 (1908, Hollins, A. A. Saunders) and September 10 (1937, Roanoke, H. M. Stevenson and 1958, Auburn, Lovett Williams) to October 1 (1957, Auburn, Lovett Williams). *Upper Coastal Plain*: April 22 (1939, Tuscaloosa, H. M. Stevenson) to May 18 (1938, Tuscaloosa, H. M. Stevenson) and August 13 (1956, Cottondale, R. L. Chermock) to October 23 (1954, Valley Creek State Park, Blanche Chapman). *Lower Coastal Plain*: April 5, 1957 (Jackson, T. A. Imhof and W. U. Harris) and September 14 (1958,

Camden, Lovett Williams) to November 2 (1956, specimen in Florida State Univ. collection, Gordon, Houston Co., H. M. Stevenson). *Gulf Coast*: April 12 (1957, Dauphin Island, J. L. Dorn, T. A. Imhof, and H. C. Loesch) to May 13 (1960, Dauphin Island, J. L. Dorn) and September 16 (1960, 178 birds after Hurricane Ethel, Dauphin Island, J. L. Dorn) to October 20 (1956, Dauphin Island, S. A. Gauthreaux and others).

Bay-breasted Warbler
Dendroica castanea (Wilson)   [660]   (Plate 34, facing page 456)

The male Bay-breasted Warbler is striped olive-green above with two white wing bars. It is *black* on the *face,* dark *chestnut-brown* on the *crown, breast,* and *flanks,* and has a large pale *buff* area *on* the *side* of the *neck.* The female is similar but duller with less extensive chestnut areas. Fall birds are much duller, with the striped olive-green of the back extending onto the head, and, except for the chestnut on the lower flanks, which most adults retain, they closely resemble the fall Blackpoll Warbler. Immature birds are darker and less streaked than the Blackpoll Warbler. A fall Bay-breasted Warbler of any age can be distinguished from the Blackpoll by its pale *yellowish-green,* instead of white, *under tail coverts* and its *dark legs,* unlike the yellowish legs of the Blackpoll. Since the Blackpoll Warbler is rare this far west in fall, it is reasonably safe to assume that questionable birds are Bay-breasted Warblers. The double-noted song is high pitched, thin, and rather wiry and resembles that of the Black-and-white Warbler in composition and that of the Blackpoll in quality.

The Bay-breasted Warbler is common on migration in Alabama, particularly in the northern half and in fall, but it is not known to breed here. It usually occurs in flocks of other migrant warblers that forage through hardwoods.

NESTING AND FOOD. Usually in a conifer about fifteen to forty feet from the ground, the nest is rather large and loosely built of coarse straw and fine conifer twigs and neatly lined with finer materials. A clutch consists of four to six whitish eggs handsomely marked with reddish-brown and gray. This species feeds mainly on caterpillars, beetles, leafhoppers, moths, locusts, ants, and probably other insects and occasionally a few small berries.

DISTRIBUTION. The Bay-breasted Warbler breeds from central Manitoba, central Quebec, and Nova Scotia south to southern Manitoba, northern Wisconsin, southern Ontario, northern New York, central New England, and southern Nova Scotia. It winters from the Panama Canal Zone to Colombia and Venezuela.

OCCURRENCE IN ALABAMA. (April 17 to May 22 and September 2 to November 14.) *Tennessee Valley*: April 25 (1914, specimen in U. S. National Museum,

Muscle Shoals, A. H. Howell) to May 15 (1948, Russellville, E. O. Willis) and October 17 (1959, 6 birds, Huntsville, J. C. and Margaret Robinson) to October 22 (1935, 9 birds, Wheeler Dam, J. Bamberg). *Mountain Region*: April 20 (1914, Sand Mountain near Long Island, E. W. Graves) to May 22 (1910, near Long Island, E. W. Graves) and September 2 (1958, Gadsden, Edith Clark) to November 4 (1959, Birmingham, Harriett Wright); most seen, 40, ceilometer casualties, October 8, 1954 (Birmingham, T. A. Imhof and F. B. Daniel). *Piedmont*: April 17 (1940, specimen, Auburn, H. G. Good) to May 18 (1954, Auburn, H. G. Good) and September 23 (1957, Auburn, Lovett Williams) to No-vember 14 (1939, Auburn, F. S. Barkalow). *Upper Coastal Plain*: April 28 (1939, Tus-caloosa, H. M. Stevenson) to May 9 (1939, Tuscaloosa, H. M. Stevenson) and October 21 (1950, Montgomery, C. W. Summerour) to November 1 (1938, Tuscaloosa, H. M. Steven-son). *Lower Coastal Plain*: October 9, 1958 (Camden, Lovett Williams); October 17, 1957 (Jackson, W. U. Harris); and October 19, 1958 (Camden, Lovett Williams). *Gulf Coast*: April 18 (1959, Dauphin Island, H. A. J. and Cora Evans) to May 14 (1950, Gulf Shores, H. M. Stevenson) and October 6 (1956, Gulf Shores, F. M. Weston and L. E. Goodnight) to November 7 (1959, Dauphin Island, J. C. and Margaret Robinson).

Blackpoll Warbler

Dendroica striata (Forster)   [661]   (Plate 34, facing page 456)

This warbler is *heavily streaked olive-green above* with *two white wing bars*. In *spring*, *adults* are *white below* with prominent dark streaks on the sides, and the *male* has a *solid black cap* and *white cheeks*. In fall, immature birds are *streaked greenish below*. The Pine Warbler is somewhat similar above, but is usually bright yellow below with only a few streaks on the sides, and gray imma-ture Pine Warblers have even less streaking. The Blackpoll Warbler has *white under tail coverts* and light *yellowish legs* which distinguish it in any plumage from the Bay-breasted Warbler, but this difference is sometimes difficult to see, especially in poor light. The usual song of the Blackpoll Warbler is a thin, meas-ured series of notes on the same pitch, becoming louder in the middle and lessen-ing in volume near the end. As a variation of this song it sometimes sings the notes very rapidly and runs them together.

This warbler is a common spring transient throughout Alabama, often abun-dant north of the Fall Line. Although it is not known to breed in the state, it has been recorded once in summer in the Mountain Region. In fall it is rare and has been noted only in the Tennessee Valley and Mountain Region. On migration the species mixes with other warblers in hardwoods.

NESTING AND FOOD. The solid, bulky nest, well-hidden on the ground or close to it in a shrub or small spruce, is usually built of spruce twigs, dry grass, moss, and weeds and lined with fine rootlets, plant down or hair, and many feathers. The four or five white eggs are marked with brown. This insect-eater feeds on caterpillars, sawflies, weevils, other beetles, plant lice,

May flies, mosquitoes, termites, locusts, gnats, ants, and others. It also takes many spiders, and occasionally a few small berries and seeds.

DISTRIBUTION. The Blackpoll Warbler breeds from northern Alaska, northern Mackenzie, northern Quebec, northern Labrador, and Newfoundland south to southern Alaska, central Alberta, central Manitoba, northern New York, central New England, and southern Nova Scotia. In fall it migrates along the Atlantic Seaboard through Florida and the West Indies to winter in South America from Colombia and Venezuela to northern Chile and western Brazil.

OCCURRENCE IN ALABAMA. (Normal: April 7 to May 24 and September 7 to October 20; Out-of-season: June 11.) *Tennessee Valley*: April 8 (1955, Wheeler Refuge, D. C. Hulse) to May 17 (1951, Wheeler Refuge, D. C. Hulse) and September 26, 1959 (4 birds, Meridianville, Madison Co., J. C. and Margaret Robinson); most seen, 20, May 3, 1957 (Wheeler Refuge, T. A. Imhof and others). *Mountain Region*: April 18 (1955, Gadsden, Edith Clark and others and 1960, Birmingham, T. A. Imhof and others) to May 24 (1934 and 1940, Birmingham, H. M. Stevenson) and September 7, 1948 and September 21, 1946 (Birmingham, T. A. Imhof); October 9, 1955, October 10, 1954, and October 20, 1957 (Gadsden, Edith Clark); also June 11, 1961 (Cheaha, Lois McCollough and others); most seen, 16, April 21 and May 2, 1949 (Birmingham, T. A. Imhof). *Piedmont*: April 7 (1954, Auburn, H. G. Good) to May 15 (1937, female specimen, Auburn, D. H. McIntosh). *Upper Coastal Plain*: April 17 (1955, Marion, Lois McCollough) to May 14 (1939, Tuscaloosa, H. M. Stevenson). *Lower Coastal Plain*: April 19, 1958 (McIntosh, T. A. Imhof, W. U. Harris, and J. R. Davis) and May 1, 1952 (2 birds, Andalusia, W. R. Middleton). *Gulf Coast*: April 10 (1937, Gulf Shores, H. G. Good) to May 17 (1958, Cedar Point, T. A. Imhof and M. W. Gaillard); most seen, 25, May 2, 1959 (Spring Count, Mobile Bay Area).

Pine Warbler
Dendroica pinus (Wilson)   [671]   (Plate 33, facing page 448)

The Pine Warbler is *unstreaked olive-green above* with two *white bars* on the *gray wings* and a few streaks on the sides of the *bright yellow under parts*. The *immature* bird is dull mouse *gray*, and it is best learned by its association with adults and its general resemblance to them in pattern, for it also has the *gray wing* with two *white bars* and the *absence* of *streaks* on the under parts and back. The song is a pleasing musical trill much like that of the Chipping Sparrow but slower and more melodious. It is the only warbler in Alabama that habitually begins singing in January.

This warbler is an abundant, breeding, permanent resident in pines throughout the state. In winter it is more numerous in the southern counties and less so in the northernmost, and at this season it often flocks with other insect-eating woodland birds. Rarely does it occur at any season in hardwoods or in dense pine plantations.

[473]

NESTING. The nest, usually ten to fifty feet from the ground, may be saddled on a horizontal limb of a pine or hidden in a cluster of needles or cones. It is generally compact and well built of weed stems, grasses, bark strips, and other similar material and is lined with plant down, animal hair, or feathers. The female lays three to five whitish eggs spotted and blotched with various shades of reddish-brown and gray.

FOOD. This species eats a great variety of insects, especially those that infest pines. Caterpillars, beetles, grasshoppers, locusts, moths, ants, wasps, bugs, boll weevils, scale insects, and aphids (including eggs and larvae) form a major part of its insect diet. In winter it often eats wild fruits such as those of dogwood, wild grape, Virginia creeper, and sumac. Quite often it feeds on the ground, probably on grass and weed seeds. At feeding stations it eats suet and peanut butter.

DISTRIBUTION. The Pine Warbler breeds from southern Manitoba, central Ontario, and southern Quebec south to southeastern Texas and southern Florida, but it is local and rare where pines are scarce such as in the southern Great Lakes area and the Mississippi and Ohio valleys. It winters in the southern part of the breeding range north to Arkansas, Tennessee, and South Carolina, and irregularly north along the coast to New Hampshire.

ABUNDANCE IN ALABAMA (*most seen in a day*). Birmingham area, summer, 50+, August 23, 1948 (Fairfield, T. A. Imhof), winter, 67, December 26, 1955 (Christmas Count); Mobile Co., 123, December 29, 1956 (Christmas Count, Dauphin Island); Baldwin Co., 102, December 27, 1947 (Christmas Count, Foley).

TIME OF BREEDING. Data on 26 nestings: Building, March 17 to 26; eggs, March 24 to June 28; young in nest, March 29 to June 12; dependent young out of nest, April 7 to June 16.

BANDING. A bird banded at Gadsden, March 5, 1954 was shot by a small boy near Dothan about December 10, 1954. Another banded in Birmingham, September 7, 1955 was retrapped at the same place, February 12, 1956.

[Kirtland's Warbler]
Dendroica kirtlandii (Baird)   [670]   (Plate 33, facing page 448)

This rare warbler is streaked bluish-gray above with two rather faint wing bars. Below, it is bright yellow with black streaks on the flanks. The male has a black mask with a partial white eye ring. In fall the species is dull brownish-gray above except for the gray rump. The bird habitually *wags its tail*, and this trait in combination with a *gray rump* identifies the species in any plumage. The quite variable song is very loud and low pitched for a warbler and suggests those of the Northern Waterthrush and the House Wren.

[474]

This bird is casual on spring migration in Alabama. It occurs on the ground in about the same places as does the Palm Warbler or in trees where it acts much like a Pine Warbler. Its breeding grounds are confined to the jack pine barrens in Michigan.

NESTING AND FOOD. The nest, on the ground close to a jack pine, has a side entrance, and is made of dried grasses and other plant fibers and lined with moss, hair, and fine grasses. The four or five eggs are creamy white marked with reddish-brown. This species feeds mainly on caterpillars, flies, moths, grasshoppers, crickets, ant lions, and other insects that it obtains from pitch pines and oaks. It drinks pine pitch and is not known to drink water.

DISTRIBUTION. Kirtland's Warbler breeds in a 60 by 100 mile area in north-central Michigan (lower peninsula). It winters in the Bahamas and has been recorded on migration from nearly all intervening states.

OCCURRENCE IN ALABAMA. (May 7 and 10.) *Tennessee Valley*: No record. *Mountain Region*: May 7, 1936 (a female, Municipal Airport, Birmingham, H. M. Stevenson). *Piedmont*: May 10, 1908 (Woodbine, Coosa Co., watched for 10 or 15 minutes, A. A. Saunders). *Upper Coastal Plain*: No record. *Lower Coastal Plain*: No record. *Gulf Coast*: No record.

Prairie Warbler
Dendroica discolor (Vieillot)　　[673]　　(Plate 35, facing page 464)

The Prairie Warbler is *yellowish-green above* and *bright yellow below* with dark streaks confined to the sides. Adults have a *black line through* the *eye* and a *V-shaped one below it*. In immature birds these lines are gray and indistinct and sometimes lacking but the *olive-green* of the *back* comes to a *point* on the *shoulder* and this marking is a good clue. This species wags its tail, but not as frequently as does the Palm Warbler, and this is another good mark. Adults have some fine reddish streaks on the back, more pronounced in the male, but these are difficult to see and therefore seldom useful in field identification. The distinctive song is a series of at least seven thin, buzzy notes which ascend the chromatic scale.

This warbler is a common and widespread summer resident in Alabama, except in Baldwin and Mobile counties where it is rare in summer. It is a common migrant on the Gulf Coast and throughout the state. In late winter it has been noted in Mobile and Monroe counties. In Alabama this species breeds in saplings and shrubs in openings and borders of woodlands, especially in rather open, scrubby oak-pine woods, on hillsides, overgrown pastures, or cut-over woodlands.

[475]

NESTING. This warbler hides its nest in dense foliage within ten feet of the ground, most often selecting a small hardwood and only occasionally using a pine. In Alabama it has used sweetgum, farkleberry, and elm most commonly. It builds with fine grass, bark shreds, and other plant materials and lines with fern down, thistle down, a kind of fine golden plant fiber, hair, and feathers. The three to five eggs are usually white spotted with reddish-brown.

FOOD. In Alabama this warbler is known to eat beetles, bugs, bees, ants, wasps, caterpillars, and spiders. Elsewhere it also consumes grasshoppers, locusts, and plant lice.

DISTRIBUTION. The Prairie Warbler breeds from South Dakota, southern Wisconsin, southern Ontario, southern New York, and central New England south to northeastern Texas, southern Louisiana, southern Alabama, and southern Florida. It winters from central Florida and the Bahamas, casually southern Alabama and coastal South Carolina, south to Corn Island off Nicaragua and the Lesser Antilles to Martinique.

OCCURRENCE IN ALABAMA. (Normal: March 25 to October 20; Out-of-season: February 10 and March 3.) *Tennessee Valley*: April 4 (1948, Russellville, E. O. Willis) to September 19 (1947, Russellville, E. O. Willis). *Mountain Region*: March 30 (1948, Birmingham, T. A. Imhof and 1959, Birmingham, Harriett Wright) to October 15 (1916, Anniston, R. H. Dean); most seen, 20, May 30, 1952 (Short Creek, Jefferson Co., T. A. Imhof) and June 25, 1949 (Fort Payne, T. A. Imhof and M. H. Perry). *Piedmont*: March 25 (1948, Auburn, H. G. Good) to at least August 29 (1943, Auburn, H. M. Stevenson). *Upper Coastal Plain*: March 27 (1878, Coosada, N. C. Brown) to September 23 (1939, Montgomery, H. M. Stevenson). *Lower Coastal Plain*: March 29 (1959, Camden, Lovett Williams) to at least August (several observers, no dates); also February 10, 1956 (Perdue Hill, Monroe Co., T. A. Imhof and W. F. Colin). *Gulf Coast*: April 6 (1957, Dauphin Island, S. A. Gauthreaux and others) to May 14 (1950, Gulf Shores, H. M. Stevenson) and July 30 (1959, Dauphin Island, H. M. Stevenson) to October 20 (1957, Dauphin Island, E. O. Willis and G. L. Carter); also March 3, 1943 (Spring Hill, J. L. Dorn).

TIME OF BREEDING. Data on 56+ nestings: Building, May 5 to June 10; eggs, April 27 to July 3; young in nest, May 12 to June 29; dependent young out of nest, June 3 to July 29.

Palm Warbler
Dendroica palmarum (Gmelin) [672] (Plate 33, facing page 448)

This warbler has a dark, *reddish-brown* crown, is dark olive-brown above and whitish or yellow below, and is rather finely streaked with dark brown above and below. It can be identified in any plumage by the *yellow upper* and *under tail coverts* and its *almost constant tail wagging*. In spring the crown is brighter and the under parts are bright yellow, but in fall all markings except the tail coverts are obscured in a plain, streaked dark brownish plumage. At this time the slightly reddish-brown color of the back and crown is an aid to identification, but the yellow tail coverts and the wagging of the tail are the best marks. The song is a weak, colorless trill similar to that of the Chipping Sparrow, but more musical and not as loud or as strong.

Throughout Alabama this species is a migrant, abundant in spring and usually uncommon in fall, and it is not known to breed here. The eastern race, recognizable in the field at all seasons by its brighter yellow under parts from bill to tail, is common in winter, especially on the coast, and local north of the Fall Line. The duller western race, which always has some whitish color on the belly, is rare in winter on the coast but comprises most of the transients north of the coastal area. The Palm Warbler forages on or near the ground in open scrubby woods or woodland borders. These open, second-growth, piney and oak-pine woods with an abundance of saplings and shrubs resemble the stunted subarctic spruce woods of the far north where it breeds.

NESTING AND FOOD. The nest of this warbler, well-concealed on the ground in moss, grass, or ferns or close to it in a small spruce, is chiefly made of fine plant fibers and lined with finer plant materials. The four or five white eggs are marked with gray and reddish-brown. Small flying and crawling insects taken on or near the ground form the bulk of the diet of this warbler. It takes beetles (including weevils), many kinds of flies (including gnats and mosquitoes), bugs, ants, plant lice, caterpillars (including cotton worms), small wasps, May flies, and grasshoppers. Spiders also are eaten, and when insects are dormant, raspberries, seeds, and other small fruits enable this bird to survive in cold weather.

DISTRIBUTION. The Palm Warbler breeds from southern Mackenzie, northern Manitoba, southern Quebec, and southern Newfoundland south to northeastern British Columbia, central Saskatchewan, northern Minnesota, central Michigan, southern Ontario, Maine, and Nova Scotia. It winters from northern Louisiana, Tennessee, and North Carolina, sometimes north to Ohio, Indiana, and coastal Massachusetts, south to Honduras, Jamaica, Puerto Rico, and the Virgin Islands.

OCCURRENCE IN ALABAMA. (September 3 to May 20.) *Tennessee Valley*: October 2 (1947, Russellville, E. O. Willis) to May 13 (Wheeler Refuge, *fide* T. Z. Atkeson, Jr.); most seen, 110+, April 24, 1950 (Wheeler Refuge, T. A. Imhof). *Mountain Region*: September 17 (1952, Birmingham, T. A. Imhof) to May 12 (1949, 1954, and 1960, Birmingham, T. A. Imhof); most seen, winter, 75, December 25, 1916 (Anniston, R. H. Dean), migration, 65, April 7, 1947 (Birmingham, T. A. Imhof and M. H. Perry). *Piedmont*: September 25 (1939, specimen, Auburn, F. S. Barkalow) to May 10 (1937, Auburn, H. G. Good). *Upper Coastal Plain*: September 15 (1893, specimen in the Avery collection, Greensboro, W. C. Avery) to May 12 (1878, specimen in the Harvard Museum of Comparative Zoölogy, Coosada, N. C. Brown) and May 20 (Prattville, L. S. Golsan). *Lower Coastal Plain*: October 19 (1956, Open Pond, Covington Co., T. A. Imhof and L. C. Crawford) to April 27 (1952, Andalusia, W. R. Middleton). *Gulf Coast*: September 27 (1931, Fairhope, D. H. McIntosh) to May 2 (1959, Dauphin Island, R. W. Skinner); also September 3, 1960 (2 birds, Daphne, J. L. Dorn) and September 13, 1959 (Dauphin Island, H. A. J. and Cora Evans); most seen, 82, December 27, 1947 (Christmas Count, Foley).

SUBSPECIES. The eastern race, *Dendroica palmarum hypochrysea* Ridgway, is more yellow and easily recognized in the field. The paler western nominate race breeds generally west of Hudson Bay but winters mostly in Florida. The two races cross on migration in such a way that in Alabama the western subspecies is the common migrant throughout the state and the eastern form is common only within 50 or so miles of the coast and rare farther north (one *hypochrysea* specimen in U. S. National Museum, Sand Mountain, April 12, 1914, A. H. Howell). In winter, however, the eastern bird is common in the Coastal Plain and local farther north, while only a few of the western birds winter, chiefly on the coast. This statement is based on numerous specimens in the Avery collection, those of Univ. of Ala., Auburn Univ., U. S. National Museum, Harvard Museum of Comparative Zoölogy, and of the Dept. of Conservation. Further evidence comes from sight identification in the hand, during banding, and in the field. This is one of the few species with races easily recognized in the field.

Ovenbird
Seiurus aurocapillus (Linnaeus)　[674]　(Plate 36, facing page 488)

This warbler is unstreaked olive-brown above and buffy below, heavily streaked with dark brown. Because it often walks around on the forest floor, it is sometimes mistaken for a thrush, but the Ovenbird is smaller, has many warbler actions, and is easily recognized by the *black-bordered orange crown* and the *white eye ring*. The song is a rapid series of six to twelve phrases which increase dramatically in volume until the sound seems to fill the woods. The song of northern birds consists of two-syllabled phrases which southern birds shorten to one syllable.

This species is a common migrant in Alabama and is a little more numerous in the northern half of the state. It is also a common summer resident on the higher ridges of the Mountain Region and the Tennessee Valley, usually above 1,000 feet elevation, and it breeds here in summer. (See Map 82.) This bird lives on the ground in deciduous woods both in summer and on migration and is much more often heard than seen.

NESTING. The Ovenbird gets its name from the shape of its nest, a covered structure of dead leaves, dead grass, weed stems, pine straw, moss, rootlets, bits of bark, or other vegetable fibers. It is so well blended and hidden on the forest floor that usually the nest is discovered only by flushing the female. The lining, ordinarily of horsehair, generally holds four or five white eggs marked with gray and reddish-brown.

FOOD. This bird feeds mainly on insects and other small life which it finds primarily on the ground in the woods. Frequent items taken are caterpillars, moths, weevils, other beetles, spiders, snails, slugs, centipedes, millipedes, earthworms, crickets, ants, flies, aphids, grasshoppers, and locusts. Occasionally it eats wild fruits such as red mulberry.

DISTRIBUTION. The Ovenbird breeds from northeastern British Columbia, southern Mackenzie, northern Ontario, southern Quebec, and Newfoundland south to southeastern Colorado, Oklahoma, Arkansas, and the northern parts of the Gulf states. It winters from northeastern Mexico, the northern Gulf Coast, coastal South Carolina, and the Bahamas south to northern Venezuela and in the Lesser Antilles to Martinique.

OCCURRENCE IN ALABAMA. (Normal: April 4 to November 8; Out-of-season: March 17.) *Tennessee Valley*: April 24 (1950, Wheeler Refuge, T. A. Imhof) to October 16 (1889, Leighton, F. W. McCormack). *Mountain Region*: April 5 (1956, Birmingham, Harriett Wright) to October 23 (1957, Gadsden, Edith Clark); most seen, spring, 20, April 24, 1953 (Cheaha, Ala. Orn. Soc.), summer, 61, June 6 and 7, 1958 (Cheaha and vicinity, T. A. Imhof and C. T. Hornady) and 25, June 10, 1943 (Mentone, H. M. Stevenson), fall, 145, ceilometer casualties, October 8, 1954 (Birmingham, T. A. Imhof and F. B. Daniel). *Piedmont*: April 7 (1925, Auburn, J. M. Robertson) to May 4 (1955, Auburn, H. G. Good) and October 3 (1958, Wedowee, T. A. Imhof and C. T. Hornady) to October 17 (1959, 3 birds, Waverly, Chambers Co., J. L. Dusi); also June 27, 1950 (singing, Wedowee, H. M. Stevenson). *Upper Coastal Plain*: April 6 (1922, Autaugaville, L. S. Golsan) to May 19 (1955, Marion, Lois McCollough) and August 17 (1939, Tuscaloosa, H. M. Stevenson) to October 19 (1890, specimen in the Avery collection, Greensboro, W. C. Avery). *Lower Coastal Plain*: September 15 (1958, Camden, Lovett Williams) to November 1 (1957, Jackson, T. A. Imhof and W. U. Harris); no spring dates. *Gulf Coast*: April 4 (1959, Dauphin Island, Ava Tabor and others) to May 16 (1960, Dauphin Island, J. L. Dorn) and August 11 (1944, Spring Hill, J. L. Dorn) to November 8 (1959, 1 banded, Dauphin Island, T. A. Imhof and others); also March 17, 1960 (Dauphin Island, J. L. Dorn); most seen, spring, 15, May 3, 1960 (Dauphin Island, J. L. Dorn), fall, 137, September 16, 1960 (after Hurricane Ethel, Dauphin Island, J. L. Dorn).

Map 82

OVENBIRD
Distribution in Summer

◐ June and July
● Breeding positive

X Records prior to 1930

TIME OF BREEDING. Data on 8 nestings: Building, April 25; eggs, May 7, June 30, and July 3; dependent young, June 1 to 12.

Northern Waterthrush

Seiurus noveboracensis (Gmelin)   [675]   (Plate 36, facing page 488)

This warbler is *olive-brown above including* the *crown,* and below it is pale yellowish or whitish, heavily streaked with dark brown. Birds with yellowish under parts are readily separated from the white-bellied Louisiana Waterthrush but those with pale bellies can be distinguished by the *yellowish line over* the *eye* and the fact that the more extensive *streakings* of the *under parts include* the *throat.* The loud and sweet song consists of a series of short staccato notes.

In Alabama this ground warbler is uncommon in spring and common in fall and it is common both seasons on the Gulf Coast, where it is particularly numerous. It is not known to breed in this state. On migration, as on the breeding ground, it almost always occurs close to water, for example, in swamps, bogs, along streams, and on the shores of lakes and ponds.

NESTING AND FOOD. This species usually nests among the roots of a large tree or stump. It builds with leaves, moss, rootlets, twigs, and inner bark and lines the nest with fine grass, moss, or hair. The clutch consists of four to six whitish eggs marked with gray and brown. The Northern Waterthrush feeds on small aquatic life and other small animals which live close to water. It eats most aquatic stages of insects, beetles and their larvae, moths, small worms, mosquitoes, tiny mollusks, and even an occasional small minnow.

DISTRIBUTION. The Northern Waterthrush breeds from north-central Alaska, northwestern Mackenzie, northern Manitoba, north-central Quebec, and Labrador south to central British Columbia, northern Idaho, North Dakota, northern Ohio, West Virginia, and southern New England. It winters from northern Mexico, Cuba, the Bahamas, and Bermuda south including most of Central America and the West Indies to northern Peru and French Guiana.

OCCURRENCE IN ALABAMA. (March 22 to May 26 and July 30 to November 2.) *Tennessee Valley*: April 13 (1940, Wheeler Refuge, Clarence Cottam) to May 26 (1948, Russellville, E. O. Willis) and August 30 (1940, Florence, H. M. Stevenson) to October 4 (1939, Wheeler Refuge, Clarence Cottam). *Mountain Region*: April 9 (1936, Birmingham, H. M. Stevenson) to May 16 (1956, specimen in Univ. of Ala. collection, Birmingham, Idalene Snead and Emmy Brownlie) and August 24 (1934, Birmingham, H. M. Stevenson) to October 17 (1935, Birmingham, H. M. Stevenson); most seen, 6, September 22, 1956 (Birmingham, T. A. Imhof and others). *Piedmont*: April 9 (1926, Auburn, H. G. Good) to May 3 (1908, Hollins, A. A. Saunders) and August 21 (1934, Roanoke, H. M. Stevenson) to October 3 (1958, Lineville, T. A. Imhof). *Upper Coastal Plain*: March 31 (1929, Bridge Creek, Autauga Co., L. S. Golsan) to May 10 (1939,

Tuscaloosa, H. M. Stevenson) and August 17 (1958, Montgomery, R. W. Skinner) to October 8 (1959, Livingston, Jenkins Jackson). *Lower Coastal Plain*: April 23, 1954 (3 birds, Andalusia, W. R. Middleton) and July 30 (1960, specimen in Univ. of Ala. collection, Grove Hill, D. C. Holliman) to November 2 (1956, Gordon, Houston Co., H. M. Stevenson). *Gulf Coast*: March 22 (1958, Dauphin Island, S. A. Gauthreaux and others) to May 16 (1958, Dauphin Island, T. A. Imhof, M. W. Gaillard, and J. C. Gray) and July 30 (1955, Foley, H. M. Stevenson) to October 20 (1956, Dawes, Mobile Co., M. W. Gaillard and Dauphin Island, J. L. Dorn and T. J. Hatrel); most seen, spring, 10, April 12, 1957 (Dauphin Island, T. A. Imhof, J. L. Dorn, and H. C. Loesch), fall, 75, September 16, 1960 (after Hurricane Ethel, Dauphin Island, J. L. Dorn).

Louisiana Waterthrush
Seiurus motacilla (Vieillot)   [676]   (Plate 36, facing page 488)

The Louisiana Waterthrush closely resembles the Northern Waterthrush in size and color pattern and in Alabama the two species are even more similar because most of the Northern Waterthrushes which occur in this state have a pale belly. The Louisiana Waterthrush, however, can always be distinguished by the *white line over* the *eye* and the *unstreaked throat*. The loud, wild, and sweet song consists of two to four high-pitched, slurred notes followed by a rapid series of descending notes.

In Alabama the Louisiana Waterthrush is a common, breeding, summer resident south to the Lower Coastal Plain. On the Gulf Coast it is a migrant, fairly common in spring and rare in fall. It frequents streams and creeks, particularly those flowing with a noticeable current through well-developed woodlands.

NESTING. This waterthrush builds in the roots of a tree, usually upturned, on the side of a bank, or occasionally in a stump or on a rock ledge but always close to water. The well-built, shallow cup on a foundation of leaves is made of small twigs, moss, rootlets, and weed stems, and has a lining of fine grass, fine rootlets, and hair. Shades of gray and brown variously mark the four to six white eggs.

FOOD. This species subsists mainly on aquatic insect larvae, other small water animals, and other kinds of insects. Its diet includes bugs, beetles, ants, caterpillars, scale insects, locusts, spiders, small mollusks, small fish, scorpions, treefrogs, worms, snails, and rarely a few seeds and small wild fruits.

DISTRIBUTION. The Louisiana Waterthrush breeds from eastern Nebraska, eastern Minnesota, southern Ontario, and central New England south to eastern Texas, the southern parts of the Gulf states, and northwestern Florida. It winters from southern Mexico, Cuba, the Bahamas, and Bermuda south to Colombia and Trinidad.

[481]

OCCURRENCE IN ALABAMA. (March 9 to October 22.) *Tennessee Valley*: March 15 (1948, Russellville, E. O. Willis) to October 12 (1889, Leighton, F. W. McCormack). *Mountain Region*: March 12 (1961, Birmingham, Harriett Wright) to October 22 (1935, Birmingham, H. M. Stevenson); most seen, 11, May 30, 1949 (Warrior River, northern Tuscaloosa Co., T. A. Imhof and others). *Piedmont*: March 9 (1908, Woodbine, A. A. Saunders) to October 5 (1936, Auburn, W. A. Rosene and others). *Upper Coastal Plain*: March 13 (1878, Coosada, N. C. Brown) to September 29 (1957, Livingston, Jenkins Jackson). *Lower Coastal Plain*: March 15 (1959, Camden, Lovett Williams) to September 28 (1958, Camden, Lovett Williams). *Gulf Coast*: March 17 (1960, Dauphin Island, J. L. Dorn) to May 16 (1960, Dauphin Island, J. L. Dorn) and July 11 (1913, swamp north of Mobile, *fide* A. H. Howell) to September 16 (1960, 63 birds, after Hurricane Ethel, Dauphin Island, J. L. Dorn).

TIME OF BREEDING. Data on 15 nestings: Eggs, May 9 to June 12; young in nest, April 29 to June 12; dependent young out of nest, April to June 6.

Kentucky Warbler
Oporornis formosus (Wilson) [677] (Plate 35, facing page 464)

This warbler is *olive-green above* and *bright yellow below*. It is *black* on *part* of the *crown*, the *sides* of *head*, and *sides* of the *neck*, and has a *yellow line* which extends from the *bill* to and *around* the *eye*. Fall, female, and immature plumages are somewhat duller. The song, suggestive of the Carolina Wren, is a loud, clear, whistle about six phrases in length, but often each phrase sounds like a single syllable. The loud and sharp call somewhat resembles that of the Hooded Warbler.

The Kentucky Warbler is a common, breeding, summer resident in Alabama south to the northern parts of our Gulf Coastal counties. It lives on or near the ground in shaded shrubs and saplings in deciduous woods, often bottomlands. It can live in drier woods than can the Hooded Warbler, and it does not forage as high.

NESTING. The nest of the Kentucky Warbler is very well concealed either on the ground or close to it in shrubby woods, usually in a rather open place such as near a path or a road. On a bulky foundation of dead leaves this bird builds an open cup of rootlets and other plant fibers, such as inner bark, weed stems, and grass, and lines it with finer rootlets and often horsehair. The white eggs, usually marked finely with reddish-browns and grays, generally number three to five in a clutch in Alabama, but in one instance numbered six.

FOOD. In Alabama this species is known to eat bugs, beetles, ants, wasps, while data from elsewhere show that it also eats caterpillars, grasshoppers, locusts, moths, plant lice, grubs, spiders, and occasionally a few berries.

DISTRIBUTION. The Kentucky Warbler breeds from southeastern Nebraska, southern Wisconsin, central Ohio, and southeastern New York south to Texas,

E. E. and L. E. Foote

NEST OF KENTUCKY WARBLER. The nest of this species is usually located close to or on the ground.

the northern Gulf Coast, and northern Florida. It winters from eastern Mexico to northern Colombia and northern Venezuela.

OCCURRENCE IN ALABAMA. (March 26 to October 21.) *Tennessee Valley*: April 11 (1948, Russellville, E. O. Willis) to September 24 (1959, Huntsville, J. C. and Margaret Robinson). *Mountain Region*: April 4 (1956, Gadsden, Edith Clark) to October 21 (1954, Birmingham, Idalene Snead); most seen, 32, May 30, 1949 (northern Tuscaloosa Co., T. A. Imhof and others). *Piedmont*: April 5 (1959, Auburn, Lovett Williams) to September 10 (1937, Roanoke, H. M. Stevenson and 1958, Auburn, Lovett Williams). *Upper Coastal Plain*: March 30 (1914, Teasley Mill, Montgomery Co., *fide* A. H. Howell) to October 9 (1958, Livingston, Jenkins Jack-son); most seen, 15, May 29, 1949 (Tuscaloosa, T. A. Imhof and others). *Lower Coastal Plain*: April 5 (1957, Jackson, T. A. Imhof and W. U. Harris) to October 4 (1958, Camden, Lovett Williams). *Gulf Coast*: March 26 (1960, Dauphin Island, J. L. Dorn) to October 9 (1931, Fairhope, Ruth Connolly); most seen, spring, 25, April 12, 1959 (Dauphin Island, Lovett Williams), fall, 35, September 16, 1960 (after Hurricane Ethel, Dauphin Island, J. L. Dorn).

TIME OF BREEDING. Data on 20 nestings: Building, April 25 to 27; eggs, April 22 to June 27; dependent young, May 26 to July 2.

[Connecticut Warbler]
Oporornis agilis (Wilson) [678] (Plate 33, facing page 448)

The Connecticut Warbler is *olive-green above* and *bright yellow below*, and it

[483]

has a *blue-gray hood* and a *white eye ring*. In fall the species is difficult to identify because its plumage is very plain and it skulks in the brush and is hard to see. At this time the hood is usually reduced to a brown ring across the chest. It is quite similar to three other species in fall plumage but the Yellowthroat is whitish on the lower belly, the Nashville Warbler has a bright yellow throat, and the slightly smaller Mourning Warbler has an incomplete eye ring, broken between the eye and the bill. A good field mark of the Connecticut Warbler in any plumage is the *very long under tail coverts* which extend almost to the end of the tail. The loud and ringing song resembles those of the Ovenbird in composition and the Kentucky Warbler in quality.

The spring migration route of the Connecticut Warbler apparently extends up through Florida and diagonally across to the Mississippi Valley, so that this species rarely occurs southwest of Atlanta, Chattanooga, and Nashville. In Spring the Connecticut Warbler has been recorded three times just southwest of this area in northeastern Alabama and once on the Coast. It is not known to breed in this state, nor has it been recorded in fall. It occurs most often on the ground or in low bushes in moist places in rather open woodlands.

NESTING AND FOOD. This warbler lays four or five white eggs marked with reddish-brown and gray. The nest of leaves, grasses, and rootlets is completely hidden on or near the ground, usually in a sunken hollow of moss or dried grass. The species is known to eat spiders, beetles, snails, and sometimes seeds and berries, but very little is known of its food habits.

DISTRIBUTION. The Connecticut Warbler breeds from eastern British Columbia, central Manitoba, and northwestern Quebec south to northern Minnesota, northern Wisconsin, and central Ontario. It winters from northern Venezuela to central Brazil.

OCCURRENCE IN ALABAMA. (April 24, May 2, 17, and 20.) *Tennessee Valley*: April 24, 1950 (Wheeler Refuge, Blackwell Spring, a male, T. A. Imhof). *Mountain Region*: May 17, 1940 and May 20, 1936 (Birmingham, H. M. Stevenson). *Piedmont*: No record. *Upper Coastal Plain*: No record. *Lower Coastal Plain*: No record. *Gulf Coast*: May 2, 1961 (Dauphin Island, Owen Davies).

[Mourning Warbler]
Oporornis philadelphia (Wilson) [679] (Plate 33, facing page 448)

Although very much like the Connecticut Warbler, this species can always be identified because its eye ring is not complete and it lacks the long under tail coverts. In *spring* the Mourning Warbler has *no eye ring* and in *fall* it has a *partial one, interrupted between* the *eye* and the *bill.* The *black* throat of the *spring male* and the *blue-gray* hood have the combination of mourning colors which gives this species its name. Its song is like those of the Kentucky and Connecticut Warblers in quality and composition, but it terminates on two lower notes.

In Alabama this warbler is a rare migrant which has been recorded almost as often in spring as in fall. It has thus far been noted in the Tennessee Valley and Mountain Region, and once in fall on the coast, but it is not known to breed in this state. Like the Connecticut Warbler, it is a skulker in thick brush, and it is usually noted on or near the ground in heavy shrubbery in open woodlands. Because it is a skulker, it may be more common than so far recorded.

NESTING AND FOOD. The nest of leaves, weed stalks, and grasses is well concealed in thick shrubbery or herbage on or near the ground in damp open woodlands. The female lays four white eggs spotted with reddish-brown. This species is known to eat beetles and spiders, and although little else is known of its food habits, it probably subsists on insects gathered on or near the ground.

DISTRIBUTION. The Mourning Warbler breeds from central Alberta, southern Quebec, and Newfoundland south to North Dakota, central Wisconsin, northern Ohio, in mountains to Maryland and West Virginia, central New England, and Nova Scotia. It winters from southern Nicaragua to Ecuador and Venezuela.

OCCURRENCE IN ALABAMA. (May 20 to 24, September 4 and 28, and October 7.) *Tennessee Valley*: May 20, 1948 (Russellville, E. O. Willis); September 28, 1960 (a female banded at Brownsboro, Madison Co., J. C. and Margaret Robinson) and October 7, 1954 (a badly mutilated specimen picked up on the road, not preserved, Wheeler Refuge, D. C. Hulse). *Mountain Region*: May 22, 1954 (Cardiff, Jefferson Co., T. A. Imhof and Barto Country) and May 24, 1940 (Birmingham, H. M. Stevenson). *Piedmont*: No record. *Upper Coastal Plain*: No record. *Lower Coastal Plain*: No record. *Gulf Coast*: September 4, 1960 (Dauphin Island, J. L. Dorn).

Yellowthroat
Geothlypis trichas (Linnaeus) [681] (Plate 35, facing page 464)
OTHER NAMES: Maryland Yellowthroat, Common Yellowthroat

The small Yellowthroat has an *olive-green back* and a *yellow breast,* and the male is easily distinguished by a *gray-bordered black mask.* Females and immature birds lack the mask, but they are identified by their *dull whitish bellies.* Other warblers with an olive-green back and yellow under parts are either yellow all the way to the under tail coverts or have distinctive markings else-

[485]

where on the body. As is true with many other warblers, the best method in identifying the Yellowthroat is to learn the spring male first. The song is a distinctive ditty of two or more three-syllabled phrases, and the call, equally distinctive, is a single note, low in pitch and volume.

This species is a common, sometimes locally abundant, summer resident throughout Alabama. It winters commonly throughout the Coastal Plain, but farther north, at least as far as Birmingham, it is uncommon and local. In summer it nests in Alabama in almost any type of sunlit thicket that is in or near water. In winter, however, it retires to a similar habitat such as cattails and shrubby or grassy wet areas that are either evergreen or contain sufficient dead vegetation to provide protection from the weather.

NESTING. The well-hidden nest is on or near the ground in dense vegetation, often near a shrub or small tree, and is very difficult to locate. This bird builds a rather large, bulky affair of dead grass, dead leaves, weed stems, and bark and lines it with fine grasses, fine bark fibers, and hair. The clutch consists of usually three to five white eggs lightly marked around the larger end with brown, gray, and black.

FOOD. Principal items in the diet of this species are caterpillars, moths, butterflies, beetles and their grubs, true flies, spiders, leafhoppers, plant lice,

NEST OF YELLOWTHROAT. Usually well-hidden, this nest is built in low bushes or grass clumps.

C. W. Summerour

locusts, ants, May flies, caddis flies, and dragonflies. It also eats other insects and in winter a few small seeds.

DISTRIBUTION. The Yellowthroat breeds from southeastern Alaska, northern Alberta, northern Ontario, central Quebec, and southern Newfoundland south to central Mexico and southern Florida. It winters from northern California, southern Arizona, southern Texas, the northern parts of the Gulf states, and coastal North Carolina, rarely north on the coast to Massachusetts, south to Panama and Puerto Rico.

OCCURRENCE IN ALABAMA. (Throughout the year.) *Tennessee Valley*: March 29 (1938, Decatur, Paul Bryan) to October 10 (1959, Wheeler Refuge, T. A. Imhof and others); also March 6, 1950 (Wheeler Refuge, T. A. Imhof and Lucien Fievet); most seen, 100+, May 1, 1948 (Wheeler Refuge, T. A. Imhof and others). *Mountain Region*: Permanent resident; widespread, March 14 (1949, Birmingham, T. A. Imhof) to October 26 (1954, Birmingham, T. A. Imhof); most seen, migration, 35, October 8, 1954 (Birmingham, T. A. Imhof and F. B. Daniel), winter, 7, February 15, 1955 (Fairfield, T. A. Imhof and others). *Piedmont*: Permanent resident; common, March 2 (1951, singing, Auburn, F. W. Fitch) to October 3 (1958, 6 birds, Clay Co. and Randolph Co., T. A. Imhof and C. T. Hornady); most seen, winter, 11, January 2, 1954 (Christmas Count, Auburn). *Upper Coastal Plain*: Permanent resident. *Lower Coastal Plain*: Permanent resident. *Gulf Coast*: Permanent resident; most seen, migration, 54, October 19, 1957 (Fall Count, Mobile Bay Area), winter, 27, December 21, 1957 (Christmas Count, Dauphin Island) and 24, December 27, 1947 (Christmas Count, Foley).

TIME OF BREEDING. Data on 15 nestings: Eggs, April 26 to July 6; dependent young, May 9 to July 10.

Yellow-breasted Chat
Icteria virens (Linnaeus) [683] (Plate 35, facing page 464)

This bird differs from other warblers to such an extent that many bird students feel it should not be placed in the warbler family. The Yellow-breasted Chat is about the *size* of a *towhee* and is plain *olive-green above* and *bright yellow below* with a white belly. Its *bill* is *black* and thick, the *tail is long*, and a *white stripe* runs *over and around* the *eye*. This bird has a great variety of calls including some imitations, which it gives a distinctive quality. It chucks, squeaks, whistles, hoots, and cackles, and often utters all these sounds in succession but with a distinct pause between phrases. Sometimes the singer is in plain view, but more often it hides in shrubbery.

The Yellow-breasted Chat is a common to abundant summer resident throughout Alabama except on the immediate coast where it is rare in summer but common on migration. It occasionally winters, but because it is so secretive it is probably more common then than recorded. In Alabama the species usually

[487]

PLATE 36

ORANGE-CROWNED WARBLER
Adult Male, Sexes Similar
Page 449

ORANGE-CROWNED WARBLER
Immature, Fall
Page 449

TENNESSEE WARBLER
Adult Male, Sexes Similar
Page 446

NASHVILLE WARBLER
Adult Male, Sexes Similar
Page 450

TENNESSEE WARBLER
Immature, Fall
Page 446

NASHVILLE WARBLER
Immature, Fall
Page 450

WORM-EATING WARBLER
Adult, Sexes Alike
Page 439

LOUISIANA WATERTHRUSH
Adult, Sexes Alike
Page 481

SWAINSON'S WARBLER
Adult, Sexes Alike
Page 438

NORTHERN WATERTHRUSH
Adult, Sexes Alike
Page 480

OVENBIRD
Adult, Sexes Alike
Page 478

[488]

Richard A. Parks

NEST OF YELLOW-BREASTED CHAT. This species, the largest member of the warbler family, builds its nest in a dense thicket.

breeds in rather dense sunlit thickets such as those along woods borders, hedgerows, and shrubby pastures.

NESTING. The nest is rather loosely attached to a thick shrub or small tree and is made of dead leaves, dead grass, and weed stems and lined with grapevine bark and finer plant fibers. This species lays three or four white eggs usually heavily marked with reddish-brown and grayish-brown.

FOOD. Insect food of this bird includes bees, bugs, ants, caterpillars, beetles (including cotton-boll weevils), wasps, May flies, and grasshoppers. It also eats spiders and a few crustaceans and many wild berries, including mulberries.

DISTRIBUTION. The Yellow-breasted Chat breeds from southern British Columbia, southern Saskatchewan, North Dakota, southern Minnesota, southern Ontario, central New York, and central New England south to central Mexico, the northern Gulf Coast, and northern Florida. It winters from Lower California and southern Texas, rarely farther north, especially along the Atlantic Coast, south to Panama.

OCCURRENCE IN ALABAMA. (Normal: March 25 to November 2; Out-of-season: March 1, December 23 and 28.) *Tennessee Valley*: April 11 (1947, Wheeler

Refuge, L. S. Givens) to September 7 (1948, Russellville, E. O. Willis); most seen, 55, May 4, 1957 (Wheeler Refuge, Ala. Orn. Soc.). *Mountain Region*: April 8 (1953, Gadsden, Edith Clark) to October 23 (1955, trapped and banded, Birmingham, J. B. Sullivan); also December 23, 1956 (Gadsden, Edith Clark); most seen, 40, May 30, 1952 (Birmingham, T. A. Imhof). *Piedmont*: March 25 (1933, Auburn, H. G. Good) to October 17 (1959, Waverly, Chambers Co., J. L. Dusi). *Upper Coastal Plain*: April 8 (1893, specimen in the Avery collection, Greensboro, W. C. Avery) to September 30 (1938, Tuscaloosa, H. M. Stevenson). *Lower Coastal Plain*: March 28 (1956, Barbour Co., J. E. Keeler) to October 7 (1957, Jackson, W. U. Harris); most seen, 30, May 1, 1952 (Andalusia, W. R. Middleton). *Gulf Coast*: March 29 (1952, Bear Point, H. M. Stevenson) to November 2 (1958, Dauphin Island, Lovett Williams and R. W. Skinner); also March 1, 1949 (Bellingrath Gardens, T. A. Imhof) and December 28, 1959 (Spring Hill, J. L. Dorn), recorded in summer on the immediate coast at Gulf State Park (H. M. Stevenson and others) and at Grand Bay, Mobile Co. (T. A. Imhof and M. W. Gaillard); most seen, 9, April 21, 1956 (Spring Count, Mobile Bay Area).

TIME OF BREEDING. Data on 26 nestings: Building, May 1 to 23; eggs, May 6 to July 3; dependent young, May 17 to July 4.

Hooded Warbler

Wilsonia citrina (Boddaert)   [684]   (Plate 35, facing page 464)

The Hooded Warbler is olive-green above and bright yellow below. The *adult male* has a *black hood* which extends onto the throat and *outlines* its *bright yellow cheeks* and *forehead*. The adult female, like the young, lacks this hood, and looks very much like an immature Wilson's Warbler. The Hooded Warbler, however, is larger and has *white spots* in the *tail*. This bird has two pleasing and distinct songs, one a five-syllabled phrase and the other, thinner, higher in pitch, and seven-syllabled. The call is a sharp, high-pitched chink.

Few shrubby bottomland deciduous woods in Alabama are without breeding Hooded Warblers, for the species is a common summer resident throughout the state. Occasionally it visits dry, unshaded, or shrubless woodlands, especially during migration.

NESTING. The well-camouflaged and often well-hidden nest is a neat, compact structure usually one to four feet from the ground in a shrub or sapling. This bird makes the outside of the nest of dead leaves and other dry plant fibers, reinforces it with bark strips and spider silk, and lines it with fine grasses, other fine plant fibers, and horsehair. The three to four white eggs in the Hooded Warbler's clutch are marked variously with reddish-brown and grayish-brown.

FOOD. This warbler lives mostly on insects caught on the wing in the forest undergrowth. It is known to eat grasshoppers, locusts, caterpillars, plant lice, beetles, flies, ants, wasps, bugs, moths, caddis flies, and spiders.

[490]

DISTRIBUTION. The Hooded Warbler breeds from Iowa, southern Michigan, southern Ontario, central New York, and southern New England south to southeastern Texas, the northern Gulf Coast, and northern Florida. It winters from eastern Mexico to the Panama Canal Zone.

OCCURRENCE IN ALABAMA. (Normal: March 16 to November 7; Out-of-season: November 21.) *Tennessee Valley*: March 31 (1948, Russellville, E. O. Willis) to October 17 (1959, Huntsville, J. C. and Margaret Robinson). *Mountain Region*: March 28 (1953, Birmingham, T. A. Imhof and 1956, Gadsden, Edith Clark) to October 22 (1935, Birmingham, H. M. Stevenson); most seen, 30, April 18, 1950 (Birmingham, T. A. Imhof). *Piedmont*: March 25 (1948, Auburn, H. G. Good) to October 3 (1958, Wedowee, T. A. Imhof and C. T. Hornady). *Upper Coastal Plain*: March 24 (1916, Bear Swamp, Autauga Co., L. S. Golsan) to October 15 (1938, Tuscaloosa, H. M. Stevenson); most seen, 27, April 23, 1955 (Autauga Co., E. G. Holt and T. A. Imhof). *Lower Coastal Plain*: March 22 (1957, Florala, T. A. Imhof) to October 19 (1958, Camden, Lovett Williams). *Gulf Coast*: March 16 (1933, Fairhope, Homer Flagg and 1960, Spring Hill, J. L. Dorn) to November 7 (1959, Dauphin Island, T. A. Imhof and others); also November 21, 1959 (1 netted and banded, Hurricane, D. D. Stamm); most seen, spring, 136, April 13, 1957 (Spring Count, Mobile Bay Area), fall, 73, September 16, 1960 (after Hurricane Ethel, Dauphin Island, J. L. Dorn).

TIME OF BREEDING. Data on 15 nestings: Building, May 4; female specimen about to lay, April 28; eggs, May 7 to July 15; dependent young, May 15 to July 9; out of nest by May 20.

Wilson's Warbler

Wilsonia pusilla (Wilson) [685] (Plate 33, facing page 448)
OTHER NAME: Black-capped Warbler

Although it is slightly smaller, Wilson's Warbler looks like a Hooded Warbler without the white on the tail. The *black* on the head of the male Wilson's Warbler is reduced to a *square patch on the crown*. The female has a much smaller cap and until her second summer lacks a cap entirely, but the female's *beady black eye* on a deep yellow background is a good mark. The loud and lively song of Wilson's Warbler is a rapid series of short staccato notes which drop in pitch.

This warbler is a migrant in Alabama, fairly common near Auburn in spring and near Birmingham and on Dauphin Island in fall. Elsewhere in Alabama it is rare and most of the records are north of the Fall Line. It is not known to breed in the state. The bird appears mostly in small trees or in the lower parts of tall trees.

NESTING AND FOOD. The nest is hidden on the ground in moss, usually at the base of a small tree or shrub, and is generally made of fine grass, moss, dead leaves, and weed stems. The four to six white eggs are marked with

[491]

reddish-brown and grayish-brown. This warbler eats insects, especially flying ones, and occasionally it takes small amounts of vegetable matter.

DISTRIBUTION. Wilson's Warbler breeds from along the tree limit in northern Alaska and Labrador south to southern California, northern New Mexico, northern Minnesota, southern Ontario, and northern New England. It winters from northern Mexico and southeastern Texas, occasionally Florida and Louisiana, south to Panama.

OCCURRENCE IN ALABAMA. (April 9 to May 15 and August 23 to October 14.) *Tennessee Valley*: May 1, 1937 (Florence, C. R. Mason); May 15, 1960 (3 birds, Wheeler Refuge, Demett Smith); September 4, 1948 (Florence, H. M. Stevenson); September 12, 1958 (Wheeler Refuge, T. A. Imhof and J. B. Sullivan); and September 26, 1959 (Meridianville, Madison Co., J. C. and Margaret Robinson). *Mountain Region*: May 13, 1952 (Birmingham, T. A. Imhof); May 14, 1936 (Birmingham, H. M. Stevenson) and August 23 (1948, Fairfield, T. A. Imhof) to October 8 (1954, 6 ceilometer casualties, Birmingham, T. A. Imhof and F. B. Daniel). *Piedmont*: April 9 (1926, Chewacla State Park, H. G. Good) to May 2 (1908, Hollins, A. A. Saunders) and October 1, 1957 (Auburn, Lovett Williams). *Upper Coastal Plain*: May 10, 1939 and September 30, 1938 (Tuscaloosa, H. M. Stevenson). *Lower Coastal Plain*: No record. *Gulf Coast*: October 5 (1956, specimen in Univ. of Ala. collection, Dauphin Island, T. A. Imhof and Lois McCollough) to October 14 (1960, Dauphin Island, Ala. Orn. Soc.); most seen, 6, October 6, 1956 (Fall Count, Mobile Bay Area.)

Canada Warbler

Wilsonia canadensis (Linnaeus)   [686]   (Plate 32, facing page 440)

This warbler is dark *blue-gray above* and *bright yellow below*. It has a *yellow line* which runs from the bill *to* and *around* the *eye* and a *necklace* of *black stripes,* sharply defined in the spring male and dull or sometimes lacking in other plumages. The song is a pleasing and quite variable warble which sounds somewhat like that of the American Goldfinch.

In the northern half of Alabama this warbler is uncommon in spring and fairly common to common in fall. South of the Black Belt it is recorded mostly in fall and only on the immediate coast is it fairly common and recorded in spring. The species is not known to breed in the state. It generally occurs among tall shrubs or small trees in the woods and darts about like a flycatcher to obtain insects on the wing.

NESTING AND FOOD. This species selects a spot in moss on the ground, on a moss-covered stump or log, or among the roots of a fallen tree for nesting. It lays three to five white eggs marked with shades of brown in a nest of dead leaves thickly lined with fine plant materials. Most of its food consists of insects caught on the wing, but it supplements these with others gleaned from foliage. Moths, flies, beetles, grubs, smooth hairless caterpillars, locusts, and the eggs of insects and spiders are known to be items in its diet.

DISTRIBUTION. The Canada Warbler breeds from northern Alberta, northern Ontario, and southern Quebec south to central Minnesota, northern Ohio, northern New Jersey, and southern New England, and in mountains, to northern Georgia. It winters from northern Colombia and northern Venezuela to central Peru.

OCCURRENCE IN ALABAMA. (April 14 to June 1 and August 5 to November 2.) *Tennessee Valley*: April 25 (1914, specimen in U. S. National Museum, Leighton, A. H. Howell) to June 1 (1948, Russellville, E. O. Willis) and August 18 (1891, specimen, Leighton, F. W. McCormack) to October 4 (1958, Huntsville, J. C. and Margaret Robinson); most seen, 6, September 12, 1958 (Wheeler Refuge, T. A. Imhof and J. B. Sullivan). *Mountain Region*: April 24 (1937, Birmingham, H. M. Stevenson) to May 23 (1940, Birmingham, H. M. Stevenson) and August 5 (1935, Camp Winnetaska, St. Clair Co., H. M. Stevenson) to October 8 (1954, 22 birds at ceilometer, Birmingham, T. A. Imhof and F. B. Daniel). *Piedmont*: April 14 (1952, Auburn, H. G. Good) to May 14 (1908, Woodbine, A. A. Saunders); also September 10, 1958 (Auburn, Lovett Williams). *Upper Coastal Plain*: April 25 (1912, specimen in U. S. National Museum, Barachias, A. H. Howell) to May 18 (1938, Tuscaloosa, H. M. Stevenson) and August 17 (1958, specimen in Dept. of Conservation collection, Montgomery, R. W. Skinner) to September 24 (1938, Tuscaloosa, H. M. Stevenson). *Lower Coastal Plain*: September 17 (1958, Camden, Lovett Williams) to September 29 (1958, Camden, Lovett Williams). *Gulf Coast*: April 15, 1961 (specimen in Florida State Univ. collection, Dauphin Island, H. M. Stevenson) and May 2, 1961 (3 birds, Dauphin Island, Owen Davies) and August 29 (1958, Fort Morgan, H. M. Stevenson, F. M. Weston, and B. L. Monroe, Jr.) to November 2 (1958, Dauphin Island, Lovett Williams and R. W. Skinner).

American Redstart

Setophaga ruticilla (Linnaeus) [687] (Plate 34, facing page 456)

The adult *male* American Redstart has a vivid color pattern of *black, flaming orange,* and *white.* It is mostly black, but bright orange glows on both sides of the breast and flashes in the wings and in the tail. The belly is white. *Female and immature* birds are *gray* where the male is black, and *yellow* where he is orange. The usual song of this warbler is a rapid series of four or more high-pitched notes ending on the same pitch or higher or lower. Other songs are similar but with two-noted phrases. Although many other warblers have two or more songs, this species is the only one that habitually sings different ones in succession.

In Alabama the American Redstart is a common summer resident south to within five miles of the city of Mobile. (See Map 83.) As a breeder in this

[493]

state it inhabits rich deciduous woods, especially bottomland hardwoods and swamps. Foraging often on the outermost twigs of tall hardwoods, it darts downward in long loops in pursuit of its prey. On migration it occurs in all wooded habitats except pines.

NESTING. The beautifully-constructed, thin-walled nest is usually in an upright fork of a hardwood, often a sapling, and from four to twenty feet from the ground. This warbler builds with such plant fibers as inner bark strips, small rootlets, and grass stems, and lines the interior with fine grasses, weed and bark fibers, and sometimes horsehair, ornamenting it with lichens, seed pods, bud scales, and the like. The three or four whitish eggs are variously marked with browns and grays.

FOOD. A great variety of insects in all stages of growth make up the major portion of its food. Caterpillars, flies, and beetles are most frequent, and it also eats a few spiders and occasionally berries such as barberry, shadbush, and magnolia.

DISTRIBUTION. The American Redstart breeds from southeastern Alaska, southern Mackenzie, central Quebec, and Newfoundland south to Oregon, Utah, northeastern Texas, southern Louisiana, southern Alabama, and northwestern Florida. It winters from central Mexico, Cuba, and Puerto Rico south to Ecuador, northern Brazil, and British Guiana.

OCCURRENCE IN ALABAMA. (Normal: April 1 to November 7; Out-of-season: March 14 and December 17.) *Tennessee Valley*: April 5 (Wheeler Refuge, *fide* T. Z. Atkeson, Jr.) to October 11 (1893, Leighton, F. W. McCormack). *Mountain Region*: April 1 (1936, Birmingham, H. M. Stevenson and 1954, Gadsden, Edith Clark) to October 22 (1935, Birmingham, H. M. Stevenson); also December 17, 1939 (Birmingham, H. M. Stevenson); most seen, 32, May 30, 1949 (northern Tuscaloosa Co., T. A. Imhof and others). *Piedmont*: April 11 (1936, Auburn, H. S. Peters) to October 3 (1957, Auburn, Lovett Williams). *Upper Coastal Plain*: April 1 (1956, Marion, Lois McCollough) to November 2 (1957, Livingston, Jenkins Jackson); also March 14, 1955 (singing, Marion, Lois McCollough); most seen, 21, April 23, 1955 (Autauga Co., E. G. Holt and T. A. Imhof) and September 24, 1959 (Montgomery, R. W. Skinner). *Lower Coastal Plain*: April 17 (1958, Jackson, W. U. Harris) to October 18 (1958, Camden, Lovett Williams); most seen, 75, mostly singing males, May 12, 1956 (Choctaw Bluff, Clarke Co., T. A. Imhof, M. W. Gaillard, and G. A. Carleton). *Gulf Coast*: Away from breeding stations, April 5 (1933, Fairhope, Helen Edwards) to May 27 (1958, Pilot Ship, Mobile Point, J. C. Gray) and July 23 (1956, 7 birds, Spring Hill, J. L. Dorn) to November 7 (1959, Dauphin Island, Ala. Orn Soc.), breeds in the big delta swamp north of Mobile south as far as the hardwoods grow (5 miles north of Cochrane Causeway); most seen, 220, October 17, 1959 (Dauphin Island, T. A. Imhof, A. J. Murphy, and others).

TIME OF BREEDING. Data on 11 nestings: Building, April 28 to May 6; eggs, May 12 to June 6; dependent young, May 30 to June 25.

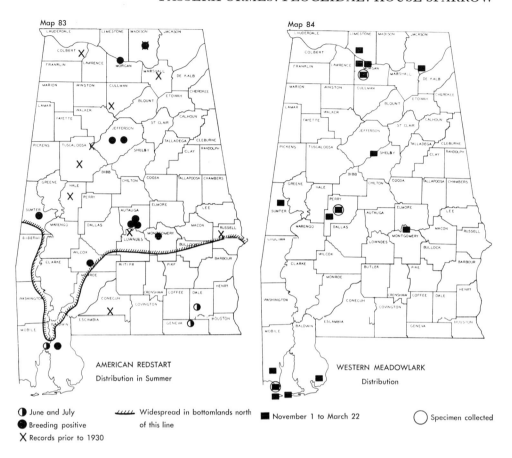

Map 83

AMERICAN REDSTART
Distribution in Summer

Map 84

WESTERN MEADOWLARK
Distribution

◗ June and July
● Breeding positive
✕ Records prior to 1930

〰〰 Widespread in bottomlands north of this line

■ November 1 to March 22

◯ Specimen collected

FAMILY PLOCEIDAE: WEAVER FINCHES

SUBFAMILY PASSERINAE: HOUSE SPARROWS

House Sparrow

Passer domesticus (Linnaeus)   [688.2]   (Plate 27, facing page 368)
OTHER NAMES: English Sparrow, Town Sparrow

The male House Sparrow is a reddish-brown bird with a gray crown, whitish cheeks, black bib, and whitish under parts. Female and immature birds are very plain looking with a light line over the eye. This species is so abundant

[495]

and widespread around houses that almost everyone knows it. The call is a single metallic note and the song is a few chirping sounds that have the same quality.

In Alabama this introduced species is abundant and breeding throughout the year. It occurs almost invariably around houses or other buildings and seems to prosper well in city, small town, or farm.

This species was introduced into America in 1850 at Brooklyn, New York. Its spread in Alabama is documented by the following records which give the first years of observation: 1880 at Athens, Talladega, and Union Springs; 1882, four birds at Eufaula (introduced); 1883 at Auburn, Anniston, Clayton, and Tuscumbia; summer of 1886 at Leighton. Its rapid spread and total occupation of the temperate parts of North America is relatively complete and was favored by a high rate of reproduction, adaptability to human surroundings, and the ability to supplant native birds by taking over their nesting sites. Its economic value is doubtful, for even though its food habits are sometimes beneficial, it is still accused of driving away from houses such native species as the Eastern Bluebird and the Carolina Wren, noted for their pleasing song, pleasing plumage, and useful habits.

NESTING. The usual nest is a disorderly pile of grass, straw, feathers, rags, paper, and the like, in a man-made cavity, often a nest box. The House Sparrow builds on barns, houses, bridges, windmills, or any other man-made structure. Often, too, it builds a bulky, round, tree nest with a side entrance, and as many as thirty such nests have been found close to each other. The four to seven eggs are whitish marked with olive and brown, and this bird is said to raise two to five broods each year. Bird students have observed breeding activity in every month of the year in Alabama. Local ornithologists, however, pay so little attention to the House Sparrow that exact egg dates are few and do not show the very great extent of the breeding season of this species in the South.

FOOD. The natural diet of this bird includes mainly grains, seeds, fruits, and insects, and a large amount of cultivated fruits, grains, and vegetables. Many individual birds live off discarded human and animal food such as garbage, bread crumbs, and the grain and fodder of farm animals, especially in chicken yards.

DISTRIBUTION. The House Sparrow is resident in Eurasia and northern Africa and has been introduced into all the temperate parts of the world. In North America it now commonly occurs in all but the Far North and southern Mexico.

[496]

FAMILY ICTERIDAE: MEADOWLARKS, BLACKBIRDS, AND ORIOLES

At first glance this family would seem to encompass a rather loosely associated group, but these birds actually hold many characteristics in common. They are predominantly black, often with much red, orange, or yellow in their plumage; their feet are very strong; and their bills, sturdy and usually sharply pointed. The flocking habit is strong, and winter roosts of some of them often hold over a million birds. Many species breed in loose colonies. Their principal foods are insects in the summer and grains in the winter, and in winter they sometimes cause economic loss by sheer weight of numbers. Orioles are brighter-colored, winter mostly in the tropics, rarely eat grain, and have the flocking habit less well developed.

Bobolink

Dolichonyx oryzivorus (Linnaeus)   [494]   (Plate 38, facing page 512)
OTHER NAMES: Oatbird, Ricebird, Reedbird, Maybird, Ortolan

In spring the *male* Bobolink is *black* with a large pale yellowish patch on the back of the head and a Y-shaped patch of *white* which extends *across* the *wings* and onto the *lower back* and *base* of the *tail*. It is one of the few birds that are dark below and light-colored above. The *female, immature,* and *fall male* are plain birds, *streaked black* on *buffy brown* and with *prominent head stripes.* Although they then closely resemble female and immature Dickcissels, Bobolinks are slightly larger in size, behave like blackbirds, and lack the reddish shoulders. The call note is a single nasal syllable, best learned in spring when males are well marked and easy to recognize. The song, which it sings on the wing and often in chorus with several others in a flock, is a bubbling cascade of notes similar in quality to the call note. It was this song which inspired William Cullen Bryant's poem, "Robert of Lincoln."

This bird is a common to abundant spring migrant throughout Alabama. In fall it is uncommon, but it has been recorded then, and even in flocks, in most areas of the state where observers are diligent. The species is not known to nest in the state. It occurs, often in large flocks, in fields with a luxuriant growth, particularly of oats, wild rice, or legumes.

[497]

PASSERIFORMES: ICTERIDAE: BOBOLINK

NESTING AND FOOD. The loosely-made cup of grasses, weeds, and rootlets lined with finer grasses is placed in a slight depression in a tall dense stand of meadow grasses. The four to seven eggs are bluish-gray or reddish-brown marked with brown and purple. In summer the Bobolink feeds almost exclusively on insects, chiefly beetles, caterpillars, grasshoppers, wasps, and ants. During the rest of the year, however, seeds, including grains, are the main food. In the South it may be destructive to oats, wild rice, and other grains, but its stay here is short, and it compensates somewhat by eating large amounts of weed seeds.

DISTRIBUTION. The Bobolink breeds from British Columbia, southern Manitoba, southern Quebec, and the Canadian Maritime provinces south to northeastern California, Utah, Missouri, central Indiana, West Virginia, and central New Jersey. It migrates in fall mainly down the Atlantic Coast and through the West Indies, but more and more western birds in recent years seem to be taking the more logical shortcut down the Mississippi Valley. Hence it is increasingly abundant as a fall migrant in Alabama. It winters in South America from Bolivia and Brazil south to Argentina.

OCCURRENCE IN ALABAMA. (April 15 to June 12 and August 22 to October 16.) *Tennessee Valley*: April 21 (1891, Leighton, F. W. McCormack) to June 1 (1951, Wheeler Refuge, D. C. Hulse); also August 31, 1954 (4 birds, Wheeler Refuge, Eugene Cypert) and September 12, 1958 (12 birds, Wheeler Refuge, T. A. Imhof and others); most seen, 1000+, May 10, 1959 (Wheeler Refuge, J. C. and Margaret Robinson), 700+, May 4, 1957 (Wheeler Refuge, Ala. Orn. Soc.) and 450, May 17, 1959 (Moulton to Russellville, B. B. Coffey). *Mountain Region*: April 19 (1940, Birmingham, H. M. Stevenson) to June 1 (1949, Birmingham, T. A. Imhof) and August 26 (1953, Birmingham, T. A. Imhof) to October 8 (1954, 2 ceilometer casualties, Birmingham, T. A. Imhof and F. B. Daniel); most seen, 240, May 2, 1949 (Birmingham, T. A. Imhof). *Piedmont*: April 15 (1914, Dadeville, W. B. Fulton) to May 23 (1914, Dadeville, W. B. Fulton); also August 22, 1934 (Roanoke, H. M. Stevenson); most seen, 500, date un-known, 1914 (Dadeville, W. B. Fulton) and 200, April 29, 1912 (Auburn, A. H. Howell). *Upper Coastal Plain*: April 16 (1959, 10 birds, Montgomery, R. W. Skinner) to June 12 (1956, Macon Co., J. E. Keeler); also September 14, 1958 (150 birds, Marion, Lois McCollough) and October 8, 1959 (Montgomery, T. A. Imhof and R. W. Skinner); most seen, 300, May 8, 1921 (Prattville, L. S. Golsan). *Lower Coastal Plain*: Second week in April (Columbia, T. Z. Atkeson, Jr.) to May 26 (1958, Camden, Lovett Williams), no fall records; most seen, 500, May 10, 1958 (Brundidge, T. A. Imhof). *Gulf Coast*: April 15 (1960 and 1961, Dauphin Island, S. A. Gauthreaux, J. L. Dorn, and others) to May 17 (1958, Grand Bay, Mobile Co., T. A. Imhof and M. W. Gaillard) and August 29 (1958, 10 birds, Fort Morgan, B. L. Monroe, Jr., F. M. Weston, and H. M. Stevenson) to October 16 (1959, Dauphin Island, T. A. Imhof); most seen, 106, May 3, 1961 (Dauphin Island, Owen Davies).

Eastern Meadowlark

Sturnella magna (Linnaeus)   [501]   (Plate 37, facing page 504)
OTHER NAME: Field Lark

The Eastern Meadowlark is *streaked brown above* and *bright yellow* below with streaks on the sides. It has prominent black head stripes, a *black V* on the *breast,* and *white outer tail feathers.* Its flight is unusual, consisting of several quick strokes followed by a glide. The usual call is a sharp note with several succeeding chattering notes, and the song is a slow, clear, slurred whistle, usually of four or five syllables.

Eastern Meadowlarks occur throughout the year in Alabama in almost any field that is at least an acre in size. Throughout the state the species is common as a breeder in summer, and, its numbers swelled by birds from the north, it becomes abundant in winter. It occupies almost all kinds of fields from the broomsedge openings in the piney woods to active or abandoned farmlands and even the salt marshes of the coast. Apparently this species was uncommon as a breeder in the Coastal Plain of Alabama prior to 1900.

NESTING. The nest is a loosely-made, arched-over cup of grasses and weed stems, well concealed in the grass, often at the base of a tussock. The three to five eggs are white marked with reddish-brown.

FOOD. This species obtains almost all of its food on the ground. Insects, particularly grasshoppers, crickets, beetles, and caterpillars, constitute the major portion, and cotton-boll weevils and underground root-feeding larvae comprise a large part of the beetles taken. Weed seeds and waste grain are a large part of the winter and spring diet.

DISTRIBUTION. The Eastern Meadowlark breeds from Arizona, New Mexico, South Dakota, central Ontario, southern Quebec, and Nova Scotia south to Brazil and Cuba. It winters mostly south of the Ohio and Potomac valleys and in southern New Jersey, but often north to the Great Lakes and southern New England.

ABUNDANCE IN ALABAMA (*most seen in a day*). Birmingham, 533, December 31, 1949 (Christmas Count); Auburn, 243, January 2, 1954 (Christmas Count); Sumter Co., 320, February 7, 1959 (T. A. Imhof and others); Marion, 180, December 27, 1957 (T. A. Imhof); Baldwin Co., 260+, February 1, 1958 (T. A. Imhof and others).

TIME OF BREEDING. Data on 17 nestings: Eggs, April 21 to July 13; dependent young, May 20 to July 3.

BANDING. Six banded meadowlarks have been recaptured in Alabama as below: *Banded,* Eveleth, Minnesota, July 23, 1934; *recovered,* Weogufka, Coosa Co., about December 25, 1934; *banded,* Oak Park, Illi-

NEST OF EASTERN MEADOWLARK. This roofed-over nest is very difficult to find.

nois, July 4, 1929; *recovered,* Benton, Lowndes Co., March 1, 1930; *banded,* Nashville, Tennessee, June 17, 1941; *recovered,* Akron, Hale Co., November 6, 1942; *banded,* Birmingham, October 6, 1959; *recovered,* Birmingham, December 15, 1959; *banded,* Montgomery, December 31, 1949; *recovered,* Montgomery, January 22, 1951; *banded,* Montgomery, December 31, 1949; *recovered,* Montgomery, January 31, 1951.

Western Meadowlark
Sturnella neglecta Audubon   [501.1]   (Plate 37, facing page 504)

This bird is noticeably paler and slightly smaller than its eastern relative, and, although several characteristics indicate this species, voice should be relied on for positive identification in the field. The western bird has broken crown stripes, yellow on the cheeks, in winter is much paler yellow below with an irregular, much-reduced V, has much smaller and narrower black bars on the secondaries and tail feathers, and has more direct flight, with none of the sailing of the eastern bird. The song, unlike the clear whistle of the Eastern Meadowlark, is a gurgling flute-like, double-noted one which resembles that of an oriole. This song is often heard on western television programs.

Local in winter in Alabama, this species is rare in the Tennessee Valley, has been noted only once in the Mountain Region, is uncommon in the Black Belt, and fairly common on the Gulf Coast. (See Map 84.) It lives in the same places as does the Eastern Meadowlark, but is not known to breed in the state. Occasionally one or two Western Meadowlarks flock with the eastern species, but as a rule the western birds form flocks of their own.

NESTING AND FOOD. The nest and food are similar to those of the eastern bird. Alabama specimens of the western bird contained ground beetles, grass, and small seeds.

DISTRIBUTION. The Western Meadowlark breeds from British Columbia and southwestern Ontario south to northern Mexico and northwestern Louisiana, and east to Wisconsin, Illinois, and roughly the Mississippi River. In winter it withdraws south of Nebraska and Utah, at which time it occurs east to northern Alabama and northwestern Florida.

OCCURRENCE IN ALABAMA. (November 1 to March 22.) *Tennessee Valley*: January 11 and 12, 1957 (Wheeler Refuge, T. A. Imhof and others); January 16, 1960 (North Sauty Refuge, Demett Smith) and February 17, 1957 (Adele West and others); March 4, 1957 (Limestone Co. and Morgan Co., 10 birds, 1 now specimen in Univ. of Ala. collection, B. L. Monroe, Jr.). *Mountain Region*: December 26, 1959 (Birmingham, near Lake Purdy, T. A. Imhof and Gene Crutcher). *Piedmont*: No record. *Upper Coastal Plain*: Marion and vicinity, December 27 (1957, T. A. Imhof and D. C. Holliman) to March 22 (1958, Lois McCollough); most seen, 20, February 16, 1957 (1 now specimen in Univ. of Ala. collection, T. A. Imhof and Lois McCollough); Gainesville, February 7, 1959 (12 birds, T. A. Imhof and others); Montgomery, January 9, 1959 (R. W. Skinner). *Lower Coastal Plain*: No record. *Gulf Coast*: November 1 (1958, 11 birds, 1 now specimen in the La. State Univ. collection, Cedar Point, S. M. Russell; also Fort Morgan and Lillian, B. L. Monroe, Jr., F. M. Weston, and others) to March 22 (1958, Dauphin Island, S. A. Gauthreaux).

Redwinged Blackbird

Agelaius phoeniceus (Linnaeus) [498] (Plate 37, facing page 504)
OTHER NAME: Redwing

The male Redwinged Blackbird, *black* with orange-bordered *red shoulders,* is unmistakable. Females and immature birds are very *dark* brown, *heavily streaked* with dark brown below so that they look black at a distance. The young male usually shows some red on the shoulders, and the female can be identified by the call notes and associates. The call is sharp and consists of either one or two syllables, while the song is a liquid three-syllabled phrase, and it is accompanied by much physical movement, including fluffing up the feathers, especially the red epaulets.

The Redwinged Blackbird prefers fresh-water marshes, but it is a highly adaptable species and will accept many poor substitutes for a marsh as long as

[501]

NEST OF REDWINGED BLACKBIRD. This bird seems to prefer to nest in loose colonies in marshy areas.

grass or bushes and a little water occur together. Hence, it breeds commonly almost everywhere in Alabama except in woodlands and on mountains. Its numbers bolstered by northern birds, the species becomes abundant throughout in winter, and often occurs in flocks of a thousand or more. It usually feeds on farmlands, particularly grain fields, and frequently associates with Starlings and other blackbirds.

NESTING. This species builds a loosely-woven cup of various grasses and lines it with finer grasses and roots. Whenever possible, it is placed over water in marsh grass, but the bird may substitute a shrub or small tree, or even build on the ground in dense grass. The female lays two to five bluish eggs marked with dark purple or reddish-brown. Large numbers of these blackbirds breed close to one another when the available habitat is limited.

FOOD. This species feeds mainly on waste grain—chiefly corn, wheat, and oats—and weed and grass seeds. This diet is supplemented with beetles, grasshoppers, and caterpillars, and the bird also takes a few wasps, ants, flies, bugs, dragonflies, and occasional snails and crustaceans.

DISTRIBUTION. The Redwinged Blackbird breeds from British Columbia, central Mackenzie, southern Quebec, and Nova Scotia south to central Mexico

Map 85
REDWINGED BLACKBIRD

Banding location of 20 birds recovered in Alabama

○ May through August
△ September through April

Recovery location of 1 bird banded in Alabama in January

▲ February

and southern Florida. It winters from British Columbia, Utah, Kansas, the Ohio Valley, and New Jersey, often north to the Great Lakes and southern New England, south to Costa Rica.

ABUNDANCE IN ALABAMA (*most seen in a day*). Decatur, 60,000, January 11, 1957 (T. A. Imhof); Birmingham, 1012, December 20, 1958 (Christmas Count); Auburn, 400,000, December 26, 1960 and 25,150, December 26, 1959 (Christmas Counts); Montgomery, 10,000+, winter 1955-56 (O. L. Austin, Jr., J. E. Keeler, and J. M. Rice); Baldwin Co., 14,000, October 19, 1957 (H. G. Loftin, B. L. Monroe, Jr., and F. M. Weston).

TIME OF BREEDING. Data on over 100 nestings: Building, March 25 to May 15; eggs, April 15 to July 13; young in nest, May 2 to July 5; dependent young out of nest, May 31 to July 22.

BANDING. For place of banding of 20 birds recovered in Alabama and place of recovery of 1 bird banded in Alabama, see Map 85.

Orchard Oriole

Icterus spurius (Linnaeus)   [506]   (Plate 38, facing page 512)
OTHER NAME: Swinger

The *adult male* Orchard Oriole, smaller than the Redwinged Blackbird, is *black* with *chestnut belly, rump, and shoulders,* some white in the wing, and a silvery

[504]

Richard E. Perks

bill. The female, immature, and first year male also have *silvery bills* but they are plain *greenish-yellow*, grayer above, and have white wing bars. The female and immature Baltimore Orioles show a strong tinge of orange in the yellow. The *first year male* Orchard Oriole is similar to the female, but it has a *black throat*. The call is a single chuck with an unmistakable blackbird quality, while the song, often given on the wing, is a loud and rapid series of gurgling notes, differing from the song of the Baltimore Oriole in its mechanical timbre.

This oriole is a common to abundant, breeding, summer resident in Alabama. Although very few birds are noted after September 1, the species has been recorded twice in winter in Birmingham. (See Map 87.) True to its name, the Orchard Oriole occurs in orchards and also wherever low trees grow rather far apart, particularly about houses and in hedgerows.

NESTING. It hangs a rather deep basket of woven grasses and weed stems from an outer branch or the uppermost fork of a shade tree, orchard tree, tall shrub, or slender sapling, usually ten to twenty feet from the ground. It lines the nest with plant down and feathers and lays three to five pale bluish eggs marked with shades of brown and purple.

FOOD. This oriole feeds almost entirely on insects, the bulk of them injurious to man's welfare, and it takes cotton-boll weevils from the squares in large quantities. It also eats many other beetles, May flies, grasshoppers, bugs, ants, a considerable variety of caterpillars, and rarely a few wild fruits, mainly mulberries.

DISTRIBUTION. The Orchard Oriole breeds from southern Manitoba, southern Ontario, central New York, and Massachusetts south to central Mexico, the northern Gulf Coast, and northern Florida. It winters from central Mexico to Colombia and Venezuela.

OCCURRENCE IN ALABAMA. (Normal: March 29 to September 10; Out-of-season: February 4 to 8 and December 26.) *Tennessee Valley*: April 6 (1938, Wheeler Refuge, Paul Bryan) to September 2 (1948, Russellville, E. O. Willis); most seen, 35, June 10, 1955 (Florence, T. A. Imhof, Malcolm Harden, and Alfred Walker). *Mountain Region*: March 30 (1936, Birmingham, H. M. Stevenson) to September 1 (1948, Birmingham, T. A. Imhof); also February 4 to 8, 1959 (an adult male which sang, Birmingham, Blanche Dean and Ethel Bush) and December 26, 1960 (another adult male, Birmingham, Clustie McTyeire, Walter Coxe, and Margaret Persons); most seen, 45, May 2, 1949 (Birmingham, T. A. Imhof). *Piedmont*: April 3 (1936, Auburn, H. S. Peters) to August 22 (1934, Roanoke, H. M. Stevenson). *Upper Coastal Plain*: March 29 (1939, Tuscaloosa, H. M. Stevenson) to August 27 (1959, Livingston, Jenkins Jackson). *Lower Coastal Plain*: April 2 (1953, Andalusia, W. R. Middleton) to at least July 2 (1958, Grove Hill, T. A. Imhof). *Gulf Coast*: March 29 (1952, Bear Point, H. M. Stevenson) to September 10 (1957, Dauphin Island, H. A. J. and Cora Evans); most seen, spring, 500, April 15, 1961 (Dauphin Island, T. A. Imhof and others), fall, 100, July 15 to 17, 1931 (Fairhope, M. Quarrels).

TIME OF BREEDING. Data on 41+ nestings: Building, mid-April to May 28; eggs, April 27 to June 21; young in nest, May 18 to July 14; dependent young out of nest, May 13 to July.

Baltimore Oriole

Icterus galbula (Linnaeus)   [507]   (Plate 38, facing page 512)

The *male* Baltimore Oriole is chiefly *black,* but it is *brilliant orange* on the under parts, shoulders, lower back, rump, and on the outer edges of the tail, and it has white in the wings. The *female* and *immature* birds are greenish above with two white wing bars and *yellow* below with a *strong orange tinge* throughout. The variable song is a series of rich, low-pitched, loud and clear whistles, and the low call is also a whistle.

This oriole is at present an uncommon to fairly common migrant throughout the state, uncommon and local in summer and rare in winter. (See Maps 86 and 87.) It frequents tall shade trees, especially those around towns. Formerly it bred commonly in the northern half of Alabama, but now it probably breeds at only a few places, primarily in the Tennessee Valley and in the western half of the Black Belt.

NESTING. The nest is a deep basket hung from an outer twig far from the trunk of a tall shade tree usually ten to forty feet from the ground. It is made of weed stems and other plant fibers, twine, horsehair, Spanish moss, and other materials. The four to six grayish-white eggs are marked with dark brown and black.

FOOD. Largely an insect-eater, this bird consumes many caterpillars, beetles, wasps, bugs, flies, grasshoppers, and locusts and destroys almost as many cotton-boll weevils as does the Orchard Oriole. The rest of the diet consists mainly of fruit such as cherries, raspberries, mulberries, huckleberries, elderberries, and Juneberries, and occasionally it feeds on grain and weed seeds. At feeders in Alabama it is known to eat suet, raisins, and bacon fat.

DISTRIBUTION. The Baltimore Oriole breeds from central Alberta, southern Manitoba, southern Quebec, and Nova Scotia south to eastern Texas, southern Louisiana, west-central Alabama, northern Georgia, Maryland, and Delaware. It winters from southern Mexico to Colombia and Venezuela and occasionally near feeding stations in the eastern United States.

OCCURRENCE IN ALABAMA. (Normal: April 6 to November 7; Out-of-season: Balance of year.) *Tennessee Valley*: April 18 (1890, Leighton, F. W. McCormack) to September 27 (1960, netted, Brownsboro, J. C. and Margaret Robinson), summers rarely; most seen, 9, May 22, 1959 (Swan Creek, T. A. Imhof, D. C. Hulse, and R. W.

Skinner). *Mountain Region*: April 7 (1955, Birmingham, Harriett Wright) to May 11 (1955, female netted and banded, J. B. Sullivan) and August 25 (1955, Birmingham, Harriett Wright) to October 18 (1954, Gadsden, Edith Clark); also an immature male, which was banded, almost daily at a feeder, December 7, 1956 to April 19, 1957 (Birmingham, Harriett Wright). *Piedmont*: April 7 (1952, Auburn, C. Otto) to May 10 (1908, Woodbine, A. A. Saunders); also September 11, 1958 (Auburn, Lovett Williams) and early January 1958 (specimen, Auburn, Lovett Williams). *Upper Coastal Plain*: April 9 (1918, Prattville, E. G. Holt) to September 23 (1890, specimen in the Avery collection, Greensboro, W. C. Avery), see Map 86 for breeding stations; also January through April 1952, a male (Livingston, Juanita Ennis) and March 15, 1959 (Tuscaloosa, Marjorie Ayres). *Lower Coastal Plain*: April

16, 1957 (Jackson, W. U. Harris) and September 14 to 20, 1958 (Camden, Lovett Williams). *Gulf Coast*: April 6 (1957, Dauphin Island, S. A. Gauthreaux and others) to May 11 (1960, Dauphin Island, J. L. Dorn) and August 24 (1956, Dauphin Island, T. A. Imhof and others) to November 7 (1959, female specimen in Dept. of Conservation collection, Dauphin Island, T. A. Imhof); also December 31, 1949, a male and 3 unidentified female orioles (Semmes, Mobile Co., William Clark); most seen, 35, April 16, 1961 (Dauphin Island, T. A. Imhof, A. J. Murphy, and others).

TIME OF BREEDING. Data on 5 nestings: Eggs, May 15 to June 20; young in nest, June 28.

BANDING. A male, banded near Schenectady, N. Y. on April 21, 1954, was found dead in the Tri-Cities area in May 1955.

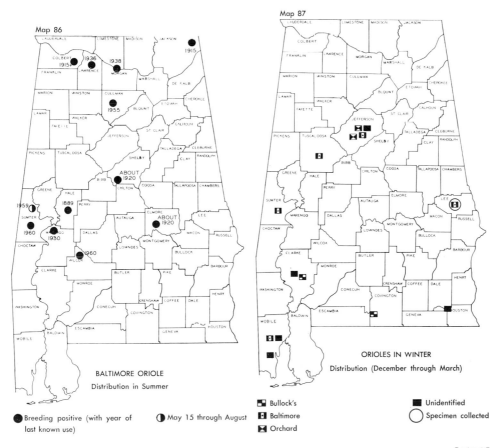

Map 86

BALTIMORE ORIOLE
Distribution in Summer

● Breeding positive (with year of last known use)   ◗ May 15 through August

Map 87

ORIOLES IN WINTER
Distribution (December through March)

▨ Bullock's
▤ Baltimore
▧ Orchard
■ Unidentified
○ Specimen collected

[507]

[Bullock's Oriole]
Icterus bullockii (Swainson)   [508]   (Plate 38, facing page 512)

This western counterpart of the Baltimore Oriole has *more orange* and *less black* than its eastern relative. The sides of the head are orange except for a thin black line through the eye, the tail has more orange, and the *wing* has a *large white patch*. Female and immature birds differ from the female Baltimore Oriole in being grayer above, lighter colored on the cheeks, and yellow rather than orange on the breast which contrasts more with the white belly. Many Bullock's Orioles, however, cannot be identified in the field with any certainty because the difference between them and the Baltimore Oriole is only a matter of degree, and frequent hybridization with this species makes identification more difficult. The young male Bullock's Oriole has a black throat like the Orchard Oriole.

Bullock's Oriole is casual to rare in fall and winter in the southern half of Alabama, but it is not known to breed here. The inability to identify numbers of late fall orioles, many of which are probably hybrids, obscures the exact status of the species in Alabama. The bird occurs in rather open country with scattered trees, such as in orchards, around farm houses, in hedgerows, and woods borders.

NESTING AND FOOD. The nest is a deep, woven bag of vegetable fibers, horsehair, inner bark, and string, heavily lined with wool, plant down, hair, or feathers, and usually located in isolated trees around ranches and along streams. The three to six grayish-white eggs are penciled with dark purple. Insects such as injurious caterpillars and the black olive scale form most of this bird's food. It also eats cherries, apricots, and other small fruit when available.

DISTRIBUTION. Bullock's Oriole breeds from southern British Columbia, southern Saskatchewan, and North Dakota south to central Mexico and east to eastern South Dakota and southern Texas. It winters from southern California, southern Texas, and southern Louisiana, occasionally farther north and east, south to Costa Rica.

OCCURRENCE IN ALABAMA. (September 13 to February 25.) *Tennessee Valley*: No record. *Mountain Region*: No record. *Piedmont*: No record. *Upper Coastal Plain*: No record. *Lower Coastal Plain*: January 15, 1954 (Grove Hill, at a feeder, G. A. Carleton) and February 25, 1955 (Rome, Covington Co., a male, T. A. Imhof). *Gulf Coast*: September 13, 1959 (Dauphin Island, a male, H. A. J. and Cora Evans); October 6, 1956 (S. M. Russell and E. O. Willis) and October 19, 1957 (E. O. Willis and G. L. Carter). A hybrid Baltimore-Bullock's Oriole, immature male specimen, was taken on Dauphin Island, April 25, 1959 by Lovett Williams.

Unidentified orioles, which are very likely immature or female Bullock's or Baltimore Orioles, have been noted in Alabama as follows (see Map 87): East Lake, Birmingham, in a yard, January 15, 1954 (Lee Brewer); 6 miles west of Dothan, in a pecan orchard, December 30, 1953 (Jesse G. Whitfield); Grove Hill, February 20, 1953 (Julia Helms) and most of January 1960 (Julia Helms and others); Semmes, Mobile Co., 3 birds, probably female or immature Baltimore Orioles because an adult male was with them, December 31, 1949 (William Clark); Bellingrath Gardens, December 24, 1957 (W. U. Harris); Dauphin Island, September 10, 1957 (H. A. J. and Cora Evans) and April 18, 1959 (H. A. J. and Cora Evans).

Rusty Blackbird

Euphagus carolinus (Müller)   [509]   (Plate 37, facing page 504)

The Rusty Blackbird is appropriately named, for immature birds show a great deal of *rusty-brown* in their plumage, and the song of the male sounds like the squeaking of a rusty hinge. The adult male is dull black with less gloss than other blackbirds, and the adult female is dark gray. The size and tail length of this species are between those of the Common Grackle and the Redwinged Blackbird. The Rusty Blackbird flies with less up and down motion than does the Redwinged Blackbird, but its flight is not quite as level and direct as that of a grackle. In all plumages this blackbird has a *white* or *pale yellow eye*. The call is a single harsh note.

In Alabama the Rusty Blackbird is common and often locally abundant in winter, but uncommon near the coast. It is not known to breed in the state. This species sometimes frequents grain fields and feeds with other blackbirds, but it more often occurs near water where it feeds along the margins of streams, ponds, and small pools, especially in or near woods.

NESTING AND FOOD. The bulky nest of sticks, grass, leaves, mud, and moss lined with fresh green grass is usually less than ten feet from the ground in dense conifers, alders, or willows near or over water. The four or five pale bluish-green eggs have dark brown spots instead of the penciling of the other blackbirds. This species feeds mainly on insects such as beetles, grasshoppers, and caterpillars, but especially those that live in water. Other food includes grain, weed seeds, and wild fruits.

DISTRIBUTION. The Rusty Blackbird breeds from northwestern Alaska, northern Mackenzie, northern Quebec, and Newfoundland south to central British Columbia, central Manitoba, southern Ontario, northern New York, northern New England, and Nova Scotia. It winters from British Columbia, southern Manitoba, southern Ontario, central New England, and southern Maine south to Colorado, southeastern Texas, and northern Florida.

OCCURRENCE IN ALABAMA. (October 19 to April 23.) *Tennessee Valley*: October 21 (Wheeler Refuge, *fide* T. Z. Atkeson, Jr.) to April 19 (1951, Wheeler Refuge, D. C. Hulse); most seen, 10,000, January 11, 1957 (Decatur, T. A. Imhof). *Mountain Region*: October 22 (1935, Birmingham, H. M. Stevenson) to April 23 (1937, Birmingham, H. M. Stevenson); most seen, 7000, January 30, 1954 (Lane Park, Birmingham, T. A. Imhof). *Piedmont*: From at least December 1 (1957, Auburn, Lovett Williams) to April 5 (1955, Auburn, H. G. Good and others); most seen, 10,000, December 26, 1959 and 20,000, December 26, 1960 (Christmas Counts, Auburn). *Upper Coastal Plain*: October 19 (1913, Autauga Co., L. S. Golsan) to April 12 (1958, 40 birds, Marion, Lois

McCollough); most seen, 5000, December 2, 1938 (Autauga Co., L. S. Golsan). *Lower Coastal Plain*: December (1957, Leroy, Washington Co., W. U. Harris) to March 22 (1957, Troy, T. A. Imhof); most seen, 144, February 25 and 26, 1955 (Covington Co. and Geneva Co., T. A. Imhof). *Gulf Coast*: October 21 (1958, Cochrane Causeway, Peter Petersen and Dennis Sheets) to April 13 (1957, 2 birds, Cochrane Causeway, Karl and Marion Zerbe and others); most seen, 70, December 29, 1956 (Coden, T. A. Imhof and D. C. Holliman).

BANDING. Two banded Rusty Blackbirds have been reported from Alabama. One from Sulligent had been banded in Indiana, and another in Limestone Co. came from Kentucky.

Brewer's Blackbird
Euphagus cyanocephalus (Wagler)   [510]   (Plate 37, facing page 504)

Brewer's Blackbird is the western counterpart of the Rusty Blackbird and is about the same size and shape. The male Brewer's Blackbird is glossier, especially on the *head* where the *gloss* is *bluish* or *purplish*. Although the female is dark gray like the female Rusty Blackbird, it is easier to identify because it has a *dark eye*. Immature birds are dark gray like the female and do not show any rust in the plumage. The call is a single harsh note and the song is as squeaking as that of the Rusty Blackbird.

In Alabama Brewer's Blackbird is abundant in winter on the Gulf Coast, where it outnumbers the Rusty Blackbird. In the remainder of the Coastal Plain Brewer's Blackbird is common but somewhat local, and north of the Fall Line it is uncommon and local. (See Map 88.) It is not known to breed in the state. This species frequents barnyards, city parks, golf courses, grain fields, and freshly-plowed fields, but especially likes pastures where it often feeds *on* or around domestic animals. It rarely flocks with other blackbirds except in the roosts.

NESTING AND FOOD. The nest, in low bushes or occasionally high above the ground, is made of coarse twigs, plant stems, bark, and rootlets cemented with mud or manure and lined with fine grass, hair, and rootlets. The four to six dull whitish eggs are marked with heavy dark brown blotches. In summer this blackbird feeds chiefly on various injurious insects, especially beetle grubs, alfalfa weevils, caterpillars, lygus bugs, leafhoppers, grasshoppers, and ants. It eats fruit when available, and in winter most of its diet consists of weed seeds and waste grain, particularly oats and wheat.

DISTRIBUTION. Brewer's Blackbird breeds from central British Columbia, central Saskatchewan, and western Ontario south to Lower California, southern New Mexico, and northern Texas, and east to Michigan, northwestern Indiana, and Oklahoma. It winters from southern British Columbia, Montana, Kansas, and western Tennessee south to Mexico and east to Georgia and northwestern Florida.

OCCURRENCE IN ALABAMA. (Normal: October 7 to April 10; Out-of-season: May 2.) *Tennessee Valley*: October 7 (1950, a male and female trapped, 1 banded and the other taken as a specimen, Wheeler Refuge, D. C. Hulse) to at least February 20 (1960, 200 birds, Huntsville, J. C. and Margaret Robinson). *Mountain Region*: November 18 (1959, small flock, Talladega, C. T. Hornady) to March 4 (1950, Birmingham, T. A. Imhof); most seen, 45, December 26, 1955 (Gadsden, Edith Clark). *Piedmont*: January 6, 1958 (1 found dead near roost, Auburn, Lovett Williams). *Upper Coastal Plain*: November 30 (1937, 100 birds and a male and a female taken specimen and now in the U. S. National Museum, Montgomery, T. D. Burleigh) to March 19 (1960, 155 birds, Marion, T. A. Imhof and others); most seen, 300, February 7, 1959 (Gainesville, T. A. Imhof and others) and 70, March 7, 1959 (Union Springs, Lovett Williams and R. W. Skinner). *Lower Coastal Plain*: From at least January 11 (1958, Lamison, Wilcox Co., T. A. Imhof) to March 16 (1939, Orion, Pike Co., F. J. Ruff); most seen, 200, March 3, 1957 (Jackson, W. U. Harris) and 70, February 26, 1955 (Hacoda, Geneva Co., T. A. Imhof). *Gulf Coast*: October 31 (1958, Dauphin Island, Lois McCollough and T. A. Imhof) to April 10 (1960, 20 birds, Theodore, J. L. Dorn); also May 2, 1961 (Dauphin Island, Owen Davies); most seen, migration, "thousands," March 17, 1960 (Theodore, J. L. Dorn), winter, 300, January 28, 1959 (Spring Hill, J. L. Dorn).

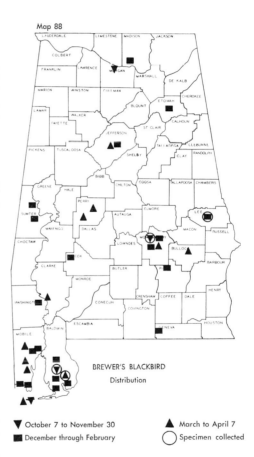

Map 88

BREWER'S BLACKBIRD
Distribution

▼ October 7 to November 30   ▲ March to April 7

■ December through February   ◯ Specimen collected

Richard A. Parks

Boat-tailed Grackle

Cassidix mexicanus (Gmelin)   [513]   (Plate 37, facing page 504)
OTHER NAME: Jackdaw

The Boat-tailed Grackle is the *largest blackbird* in Alabama, for the male is several inches longer than the Common Grackle, and the female, which has a somewhat shorter tail, is just a little larger than the Common Grackle. The male Boat-tailed Grackle is *glossy black* and the *female* is *dark brown above* and *lighter below*. The bill is long and powerful and the *very long tail* is shaped like that of the Common Grackle. The Boat-tailed Grackle has a variety of loud, harsh, squeaking, shrill calls, some clacking, some whistling but all penetrating in quality.

In Alabama this bird is common throughout the year within half a mile of salt or brackish water and it breeds in rather scattered colonies. It is much more numerous in Baldwin County and is more widespread outside the breeding season, yet it occurs only rarely in many apparently suitable places such as Dauphin Island. It forages in marshes, on beaches, on mudflats, and even in shallow water.

NESTING. Breeding in small colonies, this blackbird builds a bulky nest of twigs, reeds, and other dry plant materials usually in reeds or other marsh vegetation but sometimes in nearby grass, trees, or shrubs. The interior is a mud-cemented cup lined with fine grasses. The female lays three or four pale blue or brownish eggs marked irregularly with dark purple or dark brown.

FOOD. The main food items in this bird's diet are beetles (including boll weevils), moths, grasshoppers, cotton-boll worms, aquatic insects, shrimp, crawfish, crabs, snails, lizards, and spiders. It also eats corn, other grains, some fruit such as figs and wild grapes, and occasionally pecans or other nuts. Around beach cottages it feeds on discarded food such as bread crumbs.

DISTRIBUTION. The Boat-tailed Grackle breeds from southern Arizona, western Texas, and coastally from southern New Jersey, south to Peru and Venezuela. It retires slightly southward in winter from the northern part of its range.

ABUNDANCE IN ALABAMA (*most seen in a day*). Cochrane Causeway, 250, December 28, 1956 (T. A. Imhof and others); Mobile Bay Area, 210, November 1, 1958 (Fall Count).

TIME OF BREEDING. Data on 30+ nestings: Building, April to June 21; eggs, May 9 to 16; young in nest, May 9 to July 2.

[513]

Common Grackle

Quiscalus quiscula (Linnaeus)   [511]   (Plate 37, facing page 504)
OTHER NAME: Crow Blackbird

The Common Grackle is a large blackbird which appears entirely black at a distance, but at a closer range and in good light shows glossy purple, green, blue, and bronze in its plumage. The long tail—longer in the male—is carried with the central feathers lower so that it resembles the keel of a boat. This long tail makes the flight of the Common Grackle level, in contrast to the up and down flight of most other blackbirds. The usual call is a loud and thick chuck, but it has various other harsh and creaking notes.

The Common Grackle is a common summer resident throughout Alabama. In winter it becomes abundant, often occurring in flocks of several thousand, and during this season it roosts in large numbers, frequently with the Redwinged Blackbird and the Starling. It spreads out over a large area, often a whole county, to feed during the day. In Alabama it usually breeds in small colonies in tall trees, especially conifers, in towns, in parks, or around farms.

NESTING. Small colonies breed preferably in tall evergreens near water, but any one of a variety of other places, including willows and cavities in trees and buildings, is acceptable. The bulky nest is usually close to a tree trunk and is made of twigs, grasses, weed stems, and often mud and lined with fine grasses. The four to six eggs are pale greenish, bluish, or brownish boldly marked with brown or black.

FOOD. This blackbird subsists on a great variety of food items but it chiefly feeds on grain and many kinds of insects, especially those on the ground. It also consumes small animals, aquatic or otherwise, nuts, fruits, seeds, and even the eggs of other birds.

DISTRIBUTION. The Common Grackle breeds from northeastern British Columbia, southern Mackenzie, northern Ontario, and Newfoundland south to southern Texas and southern Florida. It winters north to Kansas, the Ohio Valley, and New Jersey, sometimes farther.

ABUNDANCE IN ALABAMA (*most seen in a day*). Decatur, 25,000, January 11, 1957 (T. A. Imhof); Birmingham, 15,000, January 1, 1951 (Christmas Count); Auburn, 40,000, December 26, 1960 (Christmas Count); Montgomery, 20,000+, winter 1955-56 (O. L. Austin, Jr., J. E. Keeler, and J. M. Rice); Gulf Coast, 1565, December 30, 1960 (Christmas Count, Dauphin Island).

TIME OF BREEDING. Data on 42 nestings: Building, March 14 to May 7; eggs, April 18 to May 22; young in nest, April 25 to June; dependent young out of nest, May 8 to June 6.

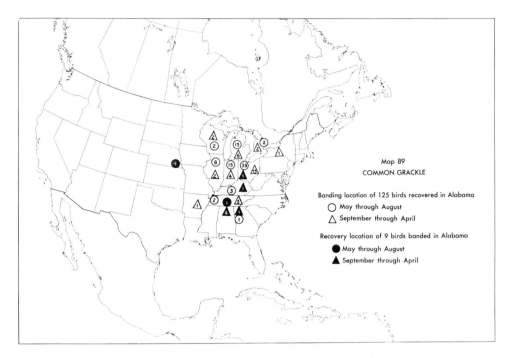

Map 89
COMMON GRACKLE

Banding location of 125 birds recovered in Alabama
○ May through August
△ September through April

Recovery location of 9 birds banded in Alabama
● May through August
▲ September through April

BANDING. At least 134 banded Common Grackles have been recovered in Alabama, 125 from other states, 5 from the immediate vicinity, and 4 from other parts of Alabama. An additional 5 birds banded in Alabama were recovered outside the state. Those banded outside the state were recovered during the period, November 12 to April 25, except for an Illinois bird recaptured September 17 and an Ohio bird recovered June 25. (See Map 89 for out-of-state localities involved.) These recoveries are evenly scattered throughout Alabama except that there are *none* for the two *Gulf Coastal counties*.

Brown-headed Cowbird
Molothrus ater (Boddaert)   [495]   (Plate 37, facing page 504)

This small blackbird is about the size of a towhee. It has a *conical,* finch like *bill* and a relatively *short tail* so that its flight, compared to that of other blackbirds, is very bouncy. The *male* is *glossy black* with a *dark brown head; females* are entirely *dark gray;* and immature birds are more brownish than gray. This bird's call is a shrill penetrating whistle, often followed by a rattle, and its song is a rather liquid but squeaky gurgle.

The Brown-headed Cowbird is abundant in winter throughout Alabama. In Howell's time (1924) no breeding was known in the state, but today it breeds in many places and occurs in the breeding season in almost all of Alabama, commonly south at least to the Black Belt and fairly commonly to the Gulf

[515]

itself. It feeds at all seasons in open grain fields but prefers the vicinity of livestock where it forages in feed lots or at the feet of grazing animals. In summer it often flies over woodlands and calls frequently.

NESTING. This and other cowbirds in the Western Hemisphere lay their eggs in the nests of other birds. The female seeks out the unguarded open nests of small land birds and deposits a white, evenly brown-spotted egg. So far as is known, the number of eggs is four or five and they are laid a day apart, usually in different nests. These eggs have a short incubation period—about eleven days—and the fast-growing young cowbirds crowd out the normal offspring. Usually the young cowbird is the sole survivor of the nest, and its foster parents are as zealous in its care as if it were one of their own. When a bird of another species finds a cowbird egg in its nest, it rarely deserts, but some species build a new nest on top of the old one so that occasionally a nest may contain several layers. Known victims of the Brown-headed Cowbird in Alabama are Blue-gray Gnatcatcher, White-eyed, Yellow-throated, and Red-eyed Vireos, Prothonotary, Blue-winged, Parula, Prairie, and Hooded Warblers, American Redstart, Summer Tanager, Indigo Bunting, and Field Sparrow.

FOOD. This cowbird feeds mainly on weed seeds and grass seeds, and especially those of the yellow foxtail grass when it is available. Waste grain,

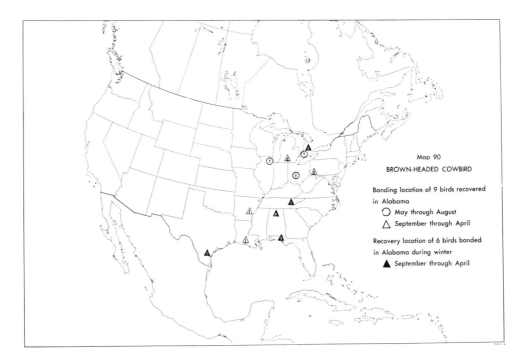

Map 90
BROWN-HEADED COWBIRD

Banding location of 9 birds recovered in Alabama
○ May through August
△ September through April

Recovery location of 6 birds banded in Alabama during winter
▲ September through April

a very small amount of fruit, and insects stirred up by livestock constitute the rest of the diet. These insects include grasshoppers, caterpillars, and boll weevils, but so far as is known, none of the common parasites of domestic animals.

DISTRIBUTION. The Brown-headed Cowbird breeds from central British Columbia, southern Mackenzie, central Ontario, and Nova Scotia south to central Mexico, the northern Gulf Coast, and South Carolina, possibly Florida. It winters from central California, Oklahoma, southern Michigan, and New York south to southern Mexico and southern Florida.

ABUNDANCE IN ALABAMA (*most seen in a day*). Decatur, 40,000, January 11, 1957 (T. A. Imhof); Birmingham, 570, December 20, 1958 (Christmas Count); Auburn, 500,000, December 26, 1960 and 50,000, December 26, 1959 (Christmas Counts); Montgomery, 20,000+, winter 1955-56 (O. L. Austin, Jr., J. E. Keeler, and J. M. Rice); Sumter Co., 2700, February 7, 1959 (Gainesville to Epes, T. A. Imhof and others); Lower Coastal Plain, 2900, February 26, 1955 (Headland, T. A. Imhof); Baldwin Co., 3200, February 1, 1958 (Elberta to Bon Secour, T. A. Imhof and others).

TIME OF BREEDING. Data on 17 nestings: Eggs, May 4 to 17; young in nest, May 16; dependent young out of nest, June 4 to August 23.

BANDING. Six birds banded in Alabama have been recovered, 2 in Alabama and 4 outside the state. Nine other birds banded elsewhere have been recovered in Alabama, mostly in the Upper Coastal Plain, during the period, November 20 to March 11. For localities of banding and recovery, see Map 90.

FAMILY THRAUPIDAE: TANAGERS

SUBFAMILY THRAUPINAE: TYPICAL TANAGERS

Tanagers are sweet-singing, tree-dwelling, fruit-eaters of tropical origin. In many ways they resemble finches, but tanagers have unusual bills, stout, swollen, generally yellow and nearly as long as the head. Males have predominantly red plumage and females, yellowish or greenish.

[Western Tanager]
Piranga ludoviciana (Wilson) [607] (Plate 38, facing page 512)

The male Western Tanager has *black wings* and *tail*, and bright *yellow under parts, rump, upper tail coverts,* and *wing bars.* The *face* and *crown* are bright *red in summer.* The *female* is yellowish-green above and bright yellow on the rump and under parts, and *immature* birds are similar but greener. In these plumages, the *swollen, pale yellowish bill* marks the bird a tanager and two prominent pale *yellowish wing bars* mark it a Western Tanager. Most female and immature orioles have wing bars, usually white, but their bills are sharp, pointed, and silvery or black. The song of the Western Tanager is much like that of the Scarlet Tanager, and the call is a dry, chattering phrase of two or three syllables similar to that of the Summer Tanager.

In fall in Alabama, this tanager is rare on the coast and has been recorded once in the Tennessee Valley. It is not known in Alabama as a breeder. It frequents the upper parts of well-developed but rather open woods.

NESTING AND FOOD. The nest is a loosely-made cup placed away from the trunk of an oak or pine at medium height. It usually holds four blue-green eggs. Primarily an eater of insects, often those caught on the wing, this bird feeds on fruit in fall and winter.

DISTRIBUTION. The Western Tanager breeds from southern Alaska, southern Mackenzie, and central Saskatchewan south to northern Lower California and western Texas and east to South Dakota and Nebraska. It winters from west-central Mexico to Costa Rica and occasionally migrates through or winters near the northern Gulf Coast east to Florida and southern Georgia.

OCCURRENCE IN ALABAMA. (August 30 to October 12.) *Tennessee Valley*: September 19, 1959 (a female, Monte Sano, Margaret Robinson). *Mountain Region*: No record. *Piedmont*: No record. *Upper Coastal Plain*: No record. *Lower Coastal Plain*: No record. *Gulf Coast*: August 30 (1959, Dauphin Island, a male, H. A. J. and Cora Evans) to October 12 (1957, an immature male, Dauphin Island, S. A. Gauthreaux and others); 8 records involving 10 birds, all since October 1956, and all on Dauphin Island.

Scarlet Tanager
Piranga olivacea (Gmelin)   [608]   (Plate 38, facing page 512)

The *male* Scarlet Tanager is brilliant *red* with *black wings* and *tail*, but in fall the red becomes yellowish-green. *Females* and *immature* birds are yellowish-green throughout the year and have *dark green* instead of black *wings* and *tail*. Female and immature orioles often have the same yellowish-green colors but the tanager's swollen, pale yellowish bill is distinct. The call of the Scarlet Tanager is a low, rather sharp, two-noted, burry phrase, and the song is a robin-like, burry warble with a decided nasal or metallic twang.

This tanager is a locally common, breeding, summer resident, usually at higher elevations, in the Tennessee Valley and Mountain Region, southwest to Tuscaloosa (see Map 91) but as yet no record of its summering or breeding in the Piedmont is known. The species is a common migrant throughout the state but appears to be more numerous in the northern half. It occurs in the upper levels of hardwood timber, most often in oaks and hickories.

NESTING. The nest is usually well out on a horizontal limb of a hardwood, generally below thirty feet from the ground. It is a shallow, loosely-built structure of small twigs, weed stems, rootlets, and grass lined with fine rootlets and other fine plant fibers. The three to five eggs are greenish or bluish spotted, sometimes rather faintly, with brown.

FOOD. This tanager feeds principally on leaf-eating insects, especially caterpillars, gall insects, beetles (including weevils and bark-borers), moths, crane flies, and many others. It varies this diet, especially in fall, with fruit, chiefly mulberries, cherries, huckleberries, black gum, and French mulberries.

DISTRIBUTION. The Scarlet Tanager breeds from southern Manitoba and southern Quebec south to Oklahoma, central Arkansas, central Alabama, and northwestern South Carolina. It winters from Colombia to Peru and Bolivia.

OCCURRENCE IN ALABAMA. (March 29 to November 3.) *Tennessee Valley*: April 11 (1941, Wheeler Refuge, J. H. Steenis) to October 9 (1960, Brownsboro, J. C. and Margaret Robinson). *Mountain Region*: March 30 (1953, western Jefferson Co., M. H. Perry and M. F. Prather) to November 3 (1946, Birmingham, T. A. Imhof); most seen, migration, 55 ceilometer casualties, October 8, 1954 (Birmingham, T. A. Imhof and F. B. Daniel), summer, 12, June 9, 1960 (Choccolocco Mountain, Fort McClellan, T. A. Imhof and John Beck) and 10, June 10, 1943 (Mentone, H. M. Stevenson). *Piedmont*: April 2 (1908, Woodbine, A. A. Saunders) to May 23 (1953, Auburn, F. W. Fitch) and October 3 (1939, Auburn, H. G. Good and 1958, Wedowee, T. A. Imhof and C. T. Hornady) to October 17 (1959, Waverly, Chambers Co., J. L. Dusi). *Upper Coastal Plain*: April 2 (1914, Bear Swamp, Autauga Co., L. S. Golsan) to May 16 (1914, Teasley Mill, Montgomery Co., A. H. Howell) and August 28 (1950, Montgomery, C. W. Summerour) to October 16 (1889 and 1890, specimen in the Avery collection, Greensboro, W. C. Avery and 1959, dead at TV tower, Montgomery, R. W. Skinner). *Lower Coastal Plain*: April 12 (1958, Camden, Lovett Williams) to May 16 (1954, Grove Hill, Julia Helms) and September 20 (1957, Florala, T. A. Imhof and Lovett Williams) to November 2 (1956, Columbia, H. M. Stevenson).

Map 91

SCARLET TANAGER

Distribution in Summer

◗ May 30 to July 31   X Records prior to 1930
● Breeding positive

Gulf Coast: March 29 (1958, Bellingrath Gardens, T. A. Imhof) to May 16 (1960, Dauphin Island, J. L. Dorn) and August 19 (1939, Mobile, J. L. Dorn) to October 20 (1956, Dauphin Island, S. A. Gauthreaux and others); most seen, 27, April 26, 1952 (Gulf Shores, H. M. Stevenson).

TIME OF BREEDING. Data on only 2 nestings: Building, April 29 to May 1 (Monte Sano, Ala. Orn. Soc.); young just out of nest, June 25 (DeSoto State Park, T. A. Imhof and M. H. Perry).

Summer Tanager
Piranga rubra (Linnaeus)   [610]   (Plate 38, facing page 512)
OTHER NAME: Summer Redbird

The *male* Summer Tanager is *entirely red,* and it retains this plumage throughout the year. The *female* is *entirely yellow,* darker on the back and with a decided *orange wash,* especially on the under tail coverts. (The female Scarlet Tanager is yellowish-green with darker wings, and female orioles have thin silvery bills and white wing bars.) The call of the Summer Tanager is a loud, rather sharp phrase of either two or four syllables, and the song is a melodious, robin-like warble that has little of the burry quality of the Scarlet Tanager.

The Summer Tanager is a common, breeding, summer resident throughout Alabama but is uncommon on the immediate coast. In the mountains where the Scarlet Tanager is present in summer, the two species are about equally common. Like the Scarlet, the Summer Tanager frequents hardwoods and prefers oaks.

NESTING. This tanager is a rather poor builder, but it contrives a shallow nest of weed stems, inner bark, grasses, and other plant fibers and lines it with fine grasses. Usually it builds in a hardwood five to thirty feet from the ground and far out from the trunk on a horizontal limb. The female lays two to four eggs which are pale greenish or pale bluish and marked variously with brownish and purplish colors.

FOOD. Most of the food of this tanager consists of bees, wasps, beetles, caterpillars, spiders, certain flying insects, and many other insects. It varies this diet with small wild fruits such as blackberries, huckleberries, blueberries, black gum, mulberries, and French mulberries.

DISTRIBUTION. The Summer Tanager breeds from southeastern California, central New Mexico, southern Iowa, central Ohio, West Virginia with the exception of the mountains, and Delaware south to central Mexico and southern Florida. It winters from central Mexico south to Peru, western Brazil, and British Guiana.

[520]

OCCURRENCE IN ALABAMA. (Normal: March 25 to November 7; Out-of-season: March 17.) *Tennessee Valley*: March 31 (1889, Leighton, F. W. McCormack) to October 9 (1960, Brownsboro, J. C. and Margaret Robinson). *Mountain Region*: April 3 (1954, Birmingham, Blanche Dean) to October 31 (1954, Gadsden, Edith Clark); most seen, 32, May 2, 1949 (Birmingham, T. A. Imhof). *Piedmont*: April 7 (1937, Auburn, H. G. Good) to October 3 (1958, Delta, Clay Co., T. A. Imhof and C. T. Hornady). *Upper Coastal Plain*: March 31 (1878, Coosada, N. C. Brown) to October 7 (1958, Livingston, Jenkins Jackson); most seen, 16, April 23, 1955 (Autauga Co., T. A. Imhof and E. G. Holt). *Lower Coastal Plain*: April 2 (1953, Andalusia, W. R. Middleton) to October 18 (1958, Camden, Lovett Williams). *Gulf Coast*: March 25 (1961, Dauphin Island, Ava Tabor and others) to November 7 (1959, Dauphin Island, Ala. Orn. Soc.); also March 17, 1960 (Dauphin Island, J. L. Dorn); most seen, 45, April 26, 1958 (Spring Count, Mobile Bay Area).

TIME OF BREEDING. Data on 34+ nestings: Building, May 4 to July 30; eggs, May 12 to July 12; young in nest, May 27 to June 21; dependent young out of nest, June to July 23.

FAMILY FRINGILLIDAE: GROSBEAKS, FINCHES, SPARROWS, AND BUNTINGS

Finches are distinguished by a strong, stout, conical bill, admirably adapted for cracking seeds. Most of the family is northern in distribution, and although fourteen of the forty species recorded in Alabama breed in the state, the other species and most of the individuals are here only in winter. As seed-eaters they are able to survive cold weather well, but when snow covers much of their food supply, ground-feeding finches invade the state in large numbers. This family is noted for its highly-developed song.

SUBFAMILY RICHMONDENINAE: CARDINALS AND ALLIES

These are more highly-colored finches in which reds and blues predominate and males are more brilliant than females. Birds in this subfamily often have larger bills, even better adapted for cracking seeds, for they are capable of feeding on seeds that other finches are unable to crack.

Cardinal

Richmondena cardinalis (Linnaeus)   [593]   (Plate 39, facing page 528)
OTHER NAME: Redbird

A solid *red body, crested head* with a *black face,* and a thick, bright red bill mark the *male* of this species. The *female* is grayish-brown, but with a *strong red tinge,* especially *on* the crest, *wings,* and *tail.* The female's bill is as bright as that of the male. Immature birds look like the female except that the bill is dark gray. The call is a short, sharp chink, and the song is a series of loud, clear whistles, sometimes slurred, ascending or descending the scale, followed by several rapid notes. Although the composition varies, the quality remains the same.

The Cardinal is a common to abundant permanent resident throughout Alabama. It nests here in hedgerows, shrubbery around houses, thickets in woods, and in a great variety of places as long as they provide a reasonable amount of cover within ten feet of the ground. Except for water areas, marshes, beaches, and the like, scarcely a square mile of Alabama is without Cardinals. In winter they often occur in loose flocks.

NESTING. The nest is generally below eight feet from the ground in dense shrubbery or a vine tangle. It is loosely built of small twigs, bark strips, weed stems, grasses, and leaves, and lined almost invariably with fine grass stems. The two to four eggs are whitish, greenish, or bluish, variously marked with brown, reddish-brown, or purple.

FOOD. This species feeds on weed seeds, other seeds, wild fruits, noxious insects, and grain, mostly waste grain. Items are wild grapes, dogwood berries, blackberries, raspberries, mulberries, hackberries, pokeberries, cherries, fruit of spicebush, sumac, cactus, and poison-ivy, corn, oats, wheat, sorghum, rice, beetles of many sorts (including boll weevils), locusts, caterpillars, scale insects, cicadas, and many other insects and seeds. At feeding stations sunflower, melon, and other seeds, peanuts, and starter scratch feed attract it.

DISTRIBUTION. The Cardinal is resident from southern California (introduced), northern Texas, South Dakota, northern Wisconsin, southern Ontario, New York, and Connecticut south to southern Mexico, British Honduras, and southern Florida.

ABUNDANCE IN ALABAMA (*most seen in a day*). Birmingham, 345, December 20, 1958 (Christmas Count); Piedmont, 56, January 2, 1954 (Christmas Count, Auburn); Gulf Coast, 180, November 1, 1958 (Fall Count, Mobile Bay Area) and 120, January 2, 1960 (Christmas Count, Dauphin Island).

TIME OF BREEDING. Data on over 100 nestings: Building, February 28 to May 14; eggs, March 11 to August 6; young in nest, April 27 to September 6; dependent young out of nest, May 4 to September 6.

BANDING. Normally Cardinals wander little, and at least 95 recaptures of banded birds in Alabama are within 3 miles of the place of banding. However, the following 3 Alabama recoveries show that some Cardinals do travel. *Banded*, Memphis, Tennessee, February 18, 1936; *recovered*, Russellville, November 25, 1936, distance in miles, 145; *banded*, Nashville, Tennessee, January 1, 1938; *recovered*, Buffalo, Chambers Co., April 1, 1939, distance in miles, 230; *banded* Wheeler Refuge, August 19, 1950; *recovered*, Berry, Fayette Co., February 11, 1951, distance in miles, 72.

Rose-breasted Grosbeak

Pheucticus ludovicianus (Linnaeus)   [595]   (Plate 39, facing page 528)

The male Rose-breasted Grosbeak is a handsome bird, patterned much like a Rufous-sided Towhee and about the same size, but with a short tail. This grosbeak is black on the head and upper parts and white on the rump and under parts and in the wings. On the breast and extending onto the under wing linings is a heart-shaped patch of beautiful rose-red. The *bill is thick* and *white* in both sexes. The female is streaked brown and white with white wing bars, *wide brown and white head stripes* and orange-yellow wing linings. Immature birds look much like the female but are buffier. Fall males also look like the female but show rosy-red on the breast and wing linings. The call is a sharp chink which somewhat resembles the call of the Cardinal, and the song is a rapid warble, somewhat like a robin's but sweeter. The Rose-breasted Grosbeak usually sings in Alabama in a low tone when on migration.

In Alabama this grosbeak is common on migration in most of the state and appears to be most numerous in the Mountain Region. It is not known to breed here. It occurs generally in upper and middle levels of hardwoods.

NESTING AND FOOD. The nest is a shallow cup of weed stems, small twigs, rootlets, and grass, rather poorly built. It is usually in the crotch of a low tree within fifteen feet of the ground, and it holds three to five greenish-blue eggs spotted with brown and purple. The male takes part in incubation and often sings softly while on the nest. This bird eats blossoms and buds of forest and orchard trees, wild fruits and weed seeds of many kinds, occasional garden peas, and a large number of injurious beetles, bugs, caterpillars, and moths. It is the only bird known to eat the Colorado potato beetle in large quantities.

DISTRIBUTION. The Rose-breasted Grosbeak breeds from northeastern British Columbia, central Manitoba, southern Quebec, and Nova Scotia south to Kansas, Missouri, central Ohio, and central New Jersey, and in mountains to northern Georgia. It winters from central Mexico, rarely southern Louisiana, south to Ecuador and Venezuela.

OCCURRENCE IN ALABAMA. (Normal: April 3 to May 23 and August 28 to November 1; Out-of-season: lingering to November 28, November 14, and November 29 to December 5.) *Tennessee Valley:* April 19 (1959, Huntsville, J. C. and Margaret Robinson) to May 8 (1948, Russellville, E. O. Willis) and September 22 (1960, Brownsboro, Madison Co., J. C. and Margaret Robinson) to November 1 (1949, Courtland, D. C. Hulse); also November 14, 1953 (Wheeler Dam, Gordon Hight). *Mountain Region:* April

15 (1956, Gadsden, Edith Clark) to May 18 (1955, Birmingham, Harriett Wright and Mims Williamson) and August 28 (1958, Gadsden, Edith Clark) to October 25 (1935, Birmingham, H. M. Stevenson); also a cripple, October 31 to November 28, 1936 (Birmingham, H. M. Stevenson) and a female, November 29 to December 5, 1957 (Gadsden, Edith Clark); most seen, 75, May 7, 1955 (DeSoto Park, Ala. Orn. Soc.). *Piedmont*: April 15 (1937, specimen, Auburn, H. G. Good) to May 23 (1953, Auburn, F. W. Fitch) and October 3 (1958, Lineville, T. A. Imhof and C. T. Hornady) to October 17 (1959, Waverly, J. L. Dusi). *Upper Coastal Plain*: April 17 (1918 and 1921, Prattville, L. S. Golsan) to May 13 (1939, Tuscaloosa, H. M. Stevenson)

and September 23 (1890, Greensboro, W. C. Avery) to October 23 (1954, Valley Creek State Park, Ala. Orn. Soc.); most seen, 9, October 11, 1956 (Marion, Lois McCollough). *Lower Coastal Plain*: April 28, 1952 (Andalusia, W. R. Middleton), several times in late April (Grove Hill, G. A. Carleton) and October 2 (1958, Camden, Lovett Williams) to October 22 (1958, Camden, Lovett Williams); most seen, 25, October 18, 1958 (Camden, Lovett Williams). *Gulf Coast*: April 3 (1960, Dauphin Island, J. L. Dorn) to May 13 (1960, Dauphin Island, J. L. Dorn) and September 12 (1955, Bon Secour, J. L. Dusi) to November 1 (1958, Lillian, B. L. Monroe, Jr. and F. M. Weston); most seen, 20, May 3, 1960 (Dauphin Island, J. L. Dorn).

[Black-headed Grosbeak]
Pheucticus melanocephalus (Swainson)   [596]   (Plate 39, facing page 528)

This western bird is much like the Rose-breasted Grosbeak, for it is about the same size and has dark upper parts with much white in the wings and a black head. But the thick *bill* is *dark*, and the *under parts*, including the sides of the neck, are *rich rusty-brown* which becomes paler on the belly. The *wing linings* are *yellow* instead of rosy-red. The *female* resembles the female Rose-breasted Grosbeak except that it is *rusty brown below* with *few* if any *streaks*, and the wing linings are lemon yellow. The call is a strong, sharp, single syllable, similar to that of the Rose-breasted Grosbeak.

The Black-headed Grosbeak is casual in fall, winter, and spring in the Coastal Plain of Alabama, and is not known to nest in the state. Like the Rose-breasted Grosbeak, it frequents the upper and middle levels of hardwoods.

NESTING AND FOOD. These habits differ little from those of the Rose-breasted Grosbeak.

DISTRIBUTION. The Black-headed Grosbeak breeds from British Columbia, southern Saskatchewan, and North Dakota south to central Mexico and east to Kansas and western Oklahoma. It winters throughout Mexico and in Louisiana, and casually farther east.

OCCURRENCE IN ALABAMA. (October 4, December 21, February 23, March 22, and May 4.) *Tennessee Valley*: No record. *Mountain Region*: No record. *Piedmont*: No record. *Upper Coastal Plain*: May 4, 1928 (Booth, Autauga Co., L. S.

Golsan, a singing male at close range, probably present since April 29) and October 4, 1959 (a male at close range, Montgomery, R. W. Skinner). *Lower Coastal Plain*: No record. *Gulf Coast*: December 21, 1957 (Dauphin

Island, Ava Tabor and Electa Levi); February 23, 1958 (Fowl River, Cora Evans and others) and March 22, 1958 (Dauphin Island, S. A. Gauthreaux and others).

Blue Grosbeak
Guiraca caerulea (Linnaeus)   [597]   (Plate 39, facing page 528)

The *male* Blue Grosbeak, about the size of a Cardinal, has a *thick, silvery bill* and is *dark purplish-blue* except for *two chestnut-brown wing bars,* and sometimes a little brown elsewhere on the body. The male on breeding territory often sits on an exposed perch and strikes a pose—very erect, crown feathers fluffed out, and tail held under the body. The female, immature, and fall birds are chestnut brown, darker on the back, wings, and tail, and they have darker bills than the male. In puzzling plumages, the species is perhaps best distinguished because it is an *even brown* color *without streaks,* has a *thick bill,* two *pale wing bars,* and a *dark tail.* The call is a sharp chink and the song, a rather short, pleasing warble, rises and falls in pitch and volume.

The Blue Grosbeak is a common summer resident in Alabama but is rare near the coast except on migration when it is common and at times abundant. It is most common in the center of the state, particularly in the Black Belt, and although formerly rare on our northern mountains, it now seems to occupy all of them, at least about farms. The species breeds in field borders, shrubby fields, roadsides, and other brushy areas in the vicinity of grain and legume fields, and sometimes also in openings in woods.

NESTING. The nest is usually in a shrub or sapling, often in blackberry bushes, within ten feet of the ground, but it may be on the ground or as high as thirty feet up a tree. This grosbeak makes a well-built cup of grasses and other plant fibers, often interweaves a cast-off snake skin or some paper, and lines it with hair, rootlets, and finer grass. The two to four eggs are pale blue.

FOOD. Crickets and grasshoppers are the most frequent food, but it also eats cotton-boll weevils, other beetles, caterpillars, moths, snails and spiders in quantity. The rest of its diet consists mainly of weed seeds and waste grain.

DISTRIBUTION. The Blue Grosbeak breeds from central California, southern Colorado, South Dakota, southern Illinois, northern Georgia, southeastern Pennsylvania, and southern New Jersey south to Costa Rica. It winters from northern Mexico and Cuba south to Panama.

[525]

OCCURRENCE IN ALABAMA. (Normal: April 6 to November 8; Out-of-season: November 29.) *Tennessee Valley*: April 18 (1952, Wheeler Refuge, D. C. Hulse) to September 24 (1959, Huntsville, J. C. and Margaret Robinson). *Mountain Region*: April 17 (1956, Gadsden, Edith Clark) to October 10 (1936, Easonville, St. Clair Co., H. M. Stevenson); most seen, 22, May 2, 1949 (Birmingham, T. A. Imhof). *Piedmont*: April 7 (1927, Auburn, H. G. Good and 1954, Auburn, F. W. Fitch) to September 10 (1958, Auburn, Lovett Williams). *Upper Coastal Plain*: April 7 (1956, Hayneville, T. A. Imhof) to October 16 (1958, Livingston, Jenkins Jackson); most seen, 20, May 17, 1952 (Hayneville, Ala. Orn. Soc.). *Lower Coastal Plain*: April 2 (1958, Camden, Lovett Williams) to November 1 (1957, Jackson, T. A. Imhof and W. U. Harris). *Gulf Coast*: April 6 (1960, Dauphin Island, J. L. Dorn) to May 16 (1960, Dauphin Island, J. L. Dorn) and July 31 (1959, Robertsdale, H. M. Stevenson) to November 8 (1959, Dauphin Island, T. A. Imhof); also November 29, 1957 (Fort Morgan, B. L. Monroe, Jr. and H. M. Stevenson); most seen, spring, 73, May 2, 1959 (Spring Count, Mobile Bay Area) and 50, April 15, 1961 (Dauphin Island, T. A. Imhof and others), fall, 76, October 6, 1956 (Fall Count, Mobile Bay Area).

TIME OF BREEDING. Data on 22 nestings: Eggs, May 10 to August 2; young in nest, May 26 to July 3; dependent young out of nest, June 21 to August 26.

Indigo Bunting

Passerina cyanea (Linnaeus) [598] (Plate 39, facing page 528)
OTHER NAMES: Indigo Bird, Swamp Bluebird

The *male* Indigo Bunting, about the size of a small sparrow, is *solid blue* in summer. From *fall* to early spring it is *unstreaked rusty-brown* but shows some blue in the wings and tail. Similar to the winter male are the *female* and the immature bird, *plain rusty-brown* with little or no blue in the wings or tail. These are the only finches in Alabama without any prominent streaks, wing bars, or other marks, although they have a few faint, blurry streaks on the belly. They are best learned by their association with the male. The call is a sharp, thin chip, and the song is a lively warble with two or three notes to a phrase and each phrase alternately higher, then lower, in pitch. Except for the distinctive phrasing, the song bears a close resemblance to the song of the American Goldfinch.

The Indigo Bunting is an abundant, breeding, summer resident everywhere in Alabama except on the Gulf Coast, where it is rare in summer, common to abundant on migration, and casual in winter. (Howell, 1924:254, states, "It does not breed in the southern counties, nor has it been seen there in migration." Evidently either the species or knowledge of it has increased substantially in south Alabama.) This bird frequents brushy areas, roadsides, woods borders, and openings in deciduous woods.

NESTING. This bunting builds a well-woven cup of grasses, weed stems, bark strips, and leaves and lines it with finer grass and hair. Usually it is in a crotch of a shrub or sapling about three or four feet from the ground in dense cover. The female lays two to four pale blue eggs.

FOOD. Seeds (especially those of weeds), berries, and other small fruits are its major foods. It also eats, especially in midsummer, such insects as caterpillars, grasshoppers, beetles, and bugs.

DISTRIBUTION. The Indigo Bunting breeds from southern Manitoba and southern Quebec south to southern Texas and northern Florida. It winters from central Mexico, Cuba, and the Bahamas south to Panama, and rarely north to Texas, the southern parts of the Gulf states, and Florida.

OCCURRENCE IN ALABAMA. (Normal: March 26 to November 11; Out-of-season: March 15, November 28, and December 22.) *Tennessee Valley*: April 15 (1948, Russellville, E. O. Willis) to October 26 (1956, Scottsboro, T. A. Imhof and M. W. Gaillard); most seen, spring, 650+, May 4, 1957 (Wheeler Refuge, Ala. Orn. Soc.), fall, 110, October 10, 1959 (Wheeler Refuge, T. A. Imhof). *Mountain Region*: April 5 (1937, Birmingham, H. M. Stevenson) to November 4 (1953, Fairfield, T. A. Imhof) and November 11, 1946 (Birmingham, T. A. Imhof); also March 15, 1959 (Cardiff, Barto Country); most seen, spring, 115, May 4, 1940 (Birmingham, H. M. Stevenson) and 80, April 20, 1957 (eastern Jefferson Co., Blanche Chapman), fall, 110, October 8, 1954 (Birmingham T. A. Imhof and F. B. Daniel). *Piedmont*: April 7 (1925, Auburn, J. M. Robertson and 1953, Auburn, H. G. Good) to October 3 (1958, Clay Co. and Randolph Co., T. A. Imhof and C. T. Hornady). *Upper Coastal Plain*: April 4 (1953, Tuscaloosa, Blanche Dean) to October 23 (1938, Tuscaloosa, H. M. Stevenson) and 1954, Valley Creek State Park, Ala. Orn. Soc.). *Lower Coastal Plain*: April 5 (1956, Abbeville, J. E. Keeler) to October 22 (1958, Camden, Lovett Williams). *Gulf Coast*: March 26 (1961, Dauphin Island, Ava Tabor and others) to May 25 (1957, Dauphin Island, T. A. Imhof) and July 31 (1959, Elberta, H. M. Stevenson) to November 8 (1959, 5 birds, Dauphin Island, T. A. Imhof); also November 28, 1958 (Summerdale, H. M. Stevenson) and December 22, 1945 (a male, Mobile, W. W. Frech), breeds rarely at Spring Hill (J. L. Dorn); most seen, spring, 130, April 21, 1956 (Spring Count, Mobile Bay Area), fall, 300, October 17, 1958 (Dauphin Island, T. A. Imhof, A. J. Murphy, and others) and 112, November 1, 1958 (Fall Count, Mobile Bay Area).

TIME OF BREEDING. Data on 30+ nestings: Building, May 5 to June 21; eggs, May 12 to August 12; young in nest, June 3 to August 28; dependent young out of nest, June 17 to August 24.

Painted Bunting

Passerina ciris (Linnaeus)   [601]   (Plate 39, facing page 528)

OTHER NAME: Nonpareil

The *highly-colored male* has a *purple head, red rump, eye ring*, and *under parts*, a green back, and darker green wings, and this striking plumage remains the same throughout the year. This species is about the size of the Indigo Bunting. The *female* Painted Bunting is *bright green* fading to *yellowish-green below*,

Richard A. Parks

and is the only really green finch in Alabama. The sharp call is a chip, similar to that of the Indigo Bunting, and the song, a bright, pleasing warble, resembles those of the Yellowthroat and Blue Grosbeak in phrasing, but is weaker, faster, and higher in pitch.

On the Gulf Coast of Alabama the Painted Bunting is an uncommon to fairly common spring transient, a rare and local summer resident, and a rare fall transient. It is known to breed only in suburban Mobile. In the remainder of the Coastal Plain, or slightly north of it, it is a rare spring transient. (See Map 92.) Although much more secretive than the Indigo Bunting, it inhabits the same type of woods borders and other bushy areas, although it usually prefers those close to streams and often in or near towns.

NESTING. The nest is very much like that of the Indigo Bunting except that the site is a little lower. The three to four eggs are whitish marked with reddish-brown or lavender.

FOOD. Most of this bird's food is seeds, especially those of foxtail grass, but it also eats many insects including caterpillars and cotton-boll weevils.

DISTRIBUTION. The Painted Bunting breeds from southern New Mexico, Kansas, southern Missouri, southwestern Tennessee, and southwestern Alabama south to northern Mexico, and southeastern North Carolina south to east-central Florida. It winters from central Mexico, southern Louisiana, central Florida, and the Bahamas south to Panama and Cuba.

OCCURRENCE IN ALABAMA. (Normal: March 26 to July 2; Out-of-season: October 15 to 17 and November 1.) *Tennessee Valley*: No record. *Mountain Region*: No record. *Piedmont*: April 19, 1958 (Auburn, D. W. Speake). *Upper Coastal Plain*: April 25, 1941 (3 birds, Autaugaville, L. S. Golsan). *Lower Coastal Plain*: April 13 (1958, Jackson, *fide* W. U. Harris) to May 23 (1954, Grove Hill, Julia Helms). *Gulf Coast*: March 26 (1960, Dauphin Island, Ava Tabor and Electa Levi) to July 2 (1958, Mobile, T. A. Imhof); also October 15 to 17, 1959, 2 males banded (Dauphin Island, T. A. Imhof, A. J. Murphy, and others) and November 1, 1958 (Dauphin Island, S. M. Russell, J. P. Gee, and Mary Lewis); most seen, 20, April 10, 1937 (Gulf Shores, H. G. Good).

TIME OF BREEDING. Data on 2 nestings, in suburban Mobile, state only that young were raised but no dates are included.

Dickcissel

Spiza americana (Gmelin)   [604]   (Plate 39, facing page 528)

The male Dickcissel is streaked brown above and has a dark gray head with a yellow stripe over the eye and another at the jaw angle. The center of the *throat* is *black*, the *breast* is *yellow*, and the *shoulder* has a *rusty-red patch*. The female has a brown head, no black on the throat and little if any yellow

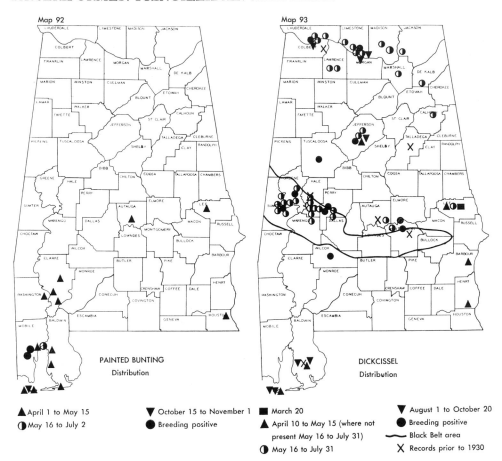

PAINTED BUNTING
Distribution

DICKCISSEL
Distribution

▲ April 1 to May 15
◐ May 16 to July 2

▼ October 15 to November 1
● Breeding positive

■ March 20
▲ April 10 to May 15 (where not
   present May 16 to July 31)
◐ May 16 to July 31

▼ August 1 to October 20
● Breeding positive
— Black Belt area
✗ Records prior to 1930

on the breast. In *winter, female* and *immature* birds look much like a female House Sparrow or a fall Bobolink, but the Dickcissel is more prominently streaked on the back than the House Sparrow, and *usually* shows some *yellow* on the *head* and *breast* and some *rust* in the *wing*. The song, suggestive of its name, is a series of thick, heavy notes, varying in the way they are combined. It is somewhat like that of the Short-billed Marsh Wren, but is heavier, thicker, and without the trill at the end.

This species, although often very local, is a common to abundant, breeding, summer resident in many parts of Alabama south through the Black Belt, and it is said to have wintered once at Auburn. South of the Black Belt it is a rare transient, recorded mostly on the immediate coast. (See Map 93.) It is very erratic in its summer distribution and often may appear or disappear from a locality without apparent cause, but changes in land use such as mowing, grazing, and crop rotation are probably responsible, at least in part. Certainly it does not occupy all of the available habitat in Alabama. It occurs mainly in fields planted to legumes, especially clover and alfalfa, but sometimes it also frequents weedy or grassy fields.

NESTING. The nest is usually on the ground in dense grass, often in a sedge tussock, but it may be in a small tree or shrub as high as fifteen feet from the ground. It is built of dry grass, weed stems, and rootlets lined with finer grass, finer rootlets, and hair. The three to five eggs are pale blue.

FOOD. This bird destroys great numbers of grasshoppers, locusts, and crickets, and it also consumes beetles, moths, caterpillars, snails, and spiders. Seeds, such as those of millet, oats, pigeon grass, other grasses, and weeds, form a large portion of its food.

DISTRIBUTION. The Dickcissel breeds from eastern Montana, southern Manitoba, southern Ontario, central New York, and Massachusetts south to Colorado, southern Texas, central Alabama, and South Carolina, but rarely east of the Appalachian Ridge. It winters from southern Mexico to Colombia and French Guiana, and rarely northward in the United States around feeding stations and farmyards.

OCCURRENCE IN ALABAMA. (Normal: April 10 to October 20; Out-of-season: March 10.) *Tennessee Valley*: April 10 (1938, Wheeler Refuge, Paul Bryan and 1941, Wheeler Refuge, T. Z. Atkeson, Jr. and J. H. Steenis) to October 5 (1940, Florence, H. M. Stevenson); most seen, 30, June 10, 1955 (Florence, T. A. Imhof and others). *Mountain Region*: April 19 (1950, Birmingham, T. A. Imhof) to October 8 (1954, 2 ceilometer casualty specimens in Auburn Wildlife and Auburn Univ. collections, Birmingham, T. A. Imhof and F. B. Daniel). *Piedmont*: April 17 (1953, Auburn, Blanche Dean and H. G. Good) to at least June (no dates available). *Upper Coastal Plain*: April 18 (1956, Marion, Lois McCollough) to at least July 17 (1876, Greensboro, W. C. Avery); most seen, 1000+, several dates in July 1958 (Montgomery, R. W. Skinner and J. E. Keeler). *Lower Coastal Plain*: May 7, 1954 (Eufaula, T. A. Imhof); May 25 to 27, 1958 (Camden, Lovett Williams) and rare spring transient, no dates (Columbia, T. Z. Atkeson, Sr.). *Gulf Coast*: April 25, 1959 (Dauphin Island, Lovett Williams); April 26, 1958 (Dauphin Island, Lovett Williams and D. W. Speake and Foley, H. M. Stevenson); May 3 and 4, 1961 (Dauphin Island, Owen Davies); undated specimen taken locally (Glennon collection, Point Clear Hotel); July 1953 (Robertsdale, J. L. Dorn); August 9, 1953 (Robertsdale, H. M. Stevenson); October 6, 1956 (3 birds, Dauphin Island, S. M. Russell and E. O. Willis); October 17, 1960 (netted and banded, Dauphin Island, J. C. and Margaret Robinson); October 19, 1957 (Dauphin Island, T. A. Imhof, Idalene Snead, and G. Melcher); and October 20, 1956 (Dauphin Island, S. A. Gauthreaux and others).

TIME OF BREEDING. Data on 17 nestings: Eggs, May 14 to July 17; young in nest, May 24 to August 18; dependent young out of nest, June 13 to August.

SUBFAMILY CARDUELINAE: PURPLE FINCHES, GOLDFINCHES, AND ALLIES

The characteristics of the family are quite strongly marked in the members of this subfamily. They are generally short-tailed, and the males are predominantly red or yellow, while the females are dull. Most of them breed in the far north and wander southward at irregular intervals when seed crops are low. Thus many of them occur irregularly in Alabama.

Evening Grosbeak

Hesperiphona vespertina (Cooper) [514] (Plate 40, facing page 536)

A chunky finch about the size of a Starling, the Evening Grosbeak can be identified in any plumage by its *big pale bill, short black tail,* and the large amount of *white in* the *black wings.* The male is mostly dull yellow shading to brownish-yellow and to brown on the head, but a prominent area above the eye and bill is bright yellow. The female is gray with some yellow, but immature birds show very little yellow. The short tail causes the bird to have a bounding flight typical of many finches. The call is similar to that of the House Sparrow but is much louder, more ringing, and more pleasing to the ear. The song is a series of short, uneven warbles which usually end in a shrill trill.

Since 1956 at least, this grosbeak has become rare and local in winter in the Mountain Region of Alabama, especially around Gadsden, from which it sometimes spreads in April to the Piedmont and Upper Coastal Plain. (See Map 94.) Although it has been noted once in summer at Gadsden, it is not known to nest in the state. In some years this very erratic bird remains all winter on its breeding grounds, but at other times it wanders far south and east during this period. In winter it frequents both deciduous and coniferous trees, but during the breeding season it prefers a spruce forest.

NESTING AND FOOD. The female lays three or four bluish-green eggs marked with olive, dark brown, and gray. The nest is a shallow saucer of twigs, grass, rootlets, and bark strips lined with hair and many fine rootlets and it is placed near the top of a conifer. The diet of this species consists of seeds, buds, and in summer a few insects. It especially likes fruits, either dried or frozen, and prefers the fruits of ash, maple, box-elder, sumac, and frozen apple seeds. Around feeding stations it readily feeds on salt and a variety of seeds, especially those of sunflowers which it eats in great quantity.

DISTRIBUTION. The Evening Grosbeak breeds from British Columbia and central Quebec south to our most northern states and in mountains to southern Mexico. It winters irregularly from Saskatchewan and northern New England south to Mexico, Kansas, the Ohio Valley, and Maryland, rarely but increasingly in recent years in the southern Appalachians to central Alabama and Georgia.

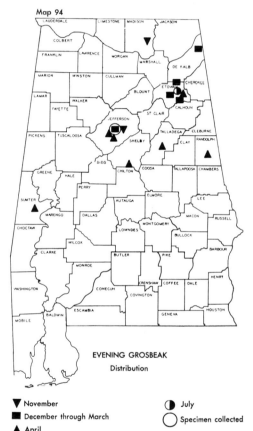

Map 94

EVENING GROSBEAK
Distribution

▼ November
■ December through March
▲ April

◑ July
◯ Specimen collected

OCCURRENCE IN ALABAMA. (Normal: November 21 to April 27; Out-of-season: July 11.) *Tennessee Valley*: No record. *Mountain Region*: Monte Sano, November 21, 1959 (14 birds, J. C. and Margaret Robinson); Hammondville, December 24, 1959 (2 birds, Naomi Banks); Gadsden and vicinity, December 7 (1959, Katherine Bates) to April 23 (1958, Katherine Bates and Edith Clark); also July 11, 1960 (a female or immature male, William Bates); 6 birds banded by Edith Clark, 1 set of tail feathers deposited in Univ. of Ala. collection, and several kodachrome slides taken; most seen, 50, February 21, 1958 (William and Katherine Bates); Birmingham, November 21, 1959 (Pat Riley) and February 24, 1959 (Elizabeth Eddy); Bessemer, February 13 to April 23, 1960 (up to 14 daily, Dorothy Davis, and 3 banded, T. A. Imhof); February 13 to April 27, 1960 (up to 20 daily, Clustie McTyeire) and specimen found dead now mounted in possession of T. A. Imhof, first week in April 1960 (G. H. McKinney, Jr.); Talladega, April 13, 1960 (6 birds, C. T. Hornady); and Montevallo, April 21, 1960 (10 birds, Carol C. Mahan). *Piedmont*: Wedowee, April 10, 1958 (a male, William Bates). *Upper Coastal Plain*: Livingston, April 10, 1958 (about 15 birds, Jenkins Jackson). *Lower Coastal Plain*: No record. *Gulf Coast*: No record.

Purple Finch
Carpodacus purpureus (Gmelin)   [517]   (Plate 40, facing page 536)

The Purple Finch is about the size of a large sparrow. Heavily streaked with dark brownish-gray on the back, wings, and tail, it is white on the belly and has two white wing bars and a stout bill. The fully adult *male* is *rosy-red* on the *head, breast, back,* and *rump,* and the *females* and *young males,* which lack the red color, are distinguished by their heavy stripes, in particular a prominent *wide white stripe over* the *eye* and a *dark jaw stripe.* This bird's call consists of two metallic ticking notes, and the song is a rather high-pitched liquid warble that is pleasing and melodious.

This finch, not known to nest in the state, is common in winter in most of Alabama, but it is often abundant in the Mountain Region and usually uncommon to fairly common on the Gulf Coast. It occurs in nearly all woodlands except the densest and those of nearly pure pine and is most frequent around openings, along the edges, and in the tops of budding or fruiting trees.

NESTING AND FOOD. The Purple Finch usually nests away from the trunk of a conifer at varying heights. It builds a neat cup with small twigs, grasses, rootlets, bark strips, and other plant fibers and lines it abundantly with hair. The four to six greenish-blue eggs are spotted with brown. The main foods are seeds and small fruits, particularly those of juniper, mountain-ash, dogwood, beech, hawthorn, crab apple, cherry, grape, mulberry, ash, elm, sycamore, tulip-poplar, ironwood, hemlock, and many weeds, especially ragweed and burdock. In spring it feeds on buds, preferring those of elm, apple, maple, cherry, and other fruit trees, and this pruning action is usually beneficial to the setting fruit. It frequently visits feeding stations where it eats seeds of sunflower, hemp, and millet.

DISTRIBUTION. The Purple Finch breeds from northern British Columbia, northern Ontario, central Quebec, and Newfoundland south to Lower California (in mountains), North Dakota, northern Ohio, Maryland (in mountains), northern New Jersey, and southern New York. It winters from southern British Columbia, southern Manitoba, and southern Quebec south to Lower California, southern Arizona, southeastern Texas, and central Florida.

OCCURRENCE IN ALABAMA. (October 25 to May 10.) *Tennessee Valley:* November 9 (1948, Wheeler Refuge, T. A. Imhof) to May 10 (1912, specimen, Leighton, A. H. Howell). *Mountain Region:* October 25 (1948, Birmingham, T. A. Imhof) to May 6 (1955, Birmingham, Harriett Wright); most seen, 248, December 20, 1958 and 186, December 31, 1949 (Christmas Counts, Birmingham). *Piedmont:* November 29 (1952, 20 birds, Roanoke, H. M. Stevenson) to May 6 (1952, 6 birds, Auburn, H. G. Good). *Upper Coastal Plain:* November 19 (1938, Tuscaloosa, H. M. Stevenson) to mid-April (1878, Coosada, N. C. Brown); most seen, 45, February 7, 1959 (Sumter Co., T. A. Imhof and others). *Lower Coastal Plain:* November 26 (1958, 9 birds, Camden, Lovett Williams) to April 12 (1958, Camden, Lovett Williams); most seen, 17, March 26, 1960 (Florala, H. M. Stevenson). *Gulf Coast:* December 21 (1957, Alabama Port, E. O. Willis) to March 20 (1912, 20 birds, Lower Tensaw River, A. H. Howell).

Map 95
PURPLE FINCH

Banding location of 30 birds recovered
in Alabama
○ May through August
△ September through April

Recovery location of 2 birds banded
in Alabama during winter
● May through August

BANDING. At least 15 Purple Finches banded at Birmingham have been recaptured in a later winter at the same place, and 1 was at least 5 years old. Two others banded there in winter were recovered in Maine and Nova Scotia. Thirty others banded in other states (see Map 95) have been re-captured in Alabama during the period November 30 to about April 20. Almost half of these recaptures were in the Mountain Region and Lower Coastal Plain, and the balance were fairly evenly distributed over the rest of the state.

[Common Redpoll]
Acanthis flammea (Linnaeus) [528] (Plate 40, facing page 536)

The Common Redpoll is a small finch, about the size of a goldfinch. It is streaked dark gray above and on the flanks and has a *black chin patch.* In *adults,* the front of the *crown* is *bright red,* and *males* also have a *rosy breast and rump,* but immature birds have no red at all, and the chin patch must serve to identify them. The call is metallic, rattling, and four-syllabled, and the song is a trill which begins with a twitter much like the call.

This redpoll is casual in winter in northern Alabama and is not known to breed here. It feeds on the ground in open areas near brush, or in shrubs and weeds, usually near woods borders. Occurrences of this bird in Alabama are associated with severe cold and snow.

[535]

PLATE 40

RED CROSSBILL
Adult Male
Page 540

EVENING GROSBEAK
Adult Male
Page 532

RED CROSSBILL
Adult Female
Page 540

EVENING GROSBEAK
Adult Female
Page 532

PINE SISKIN
Adult, Sexes Alike
Page 537

PURPLE FINCH
Adult Male
Page 533

AMERICAN GOLDFINCH
Adult Female, Summer
Page 538

PURPLE FINCH
Adult Female
Page 533

AMERICAN GOLDFINCH
Adult Male, Summer
Page 538

COMMON REDPOLL
Adult Male, Sexes Similar
Page 535

SLATE-COLORED JUNCO
Adult Female
Page 554

OREGON JUNCO
Adult Male, Sexes Similar
Page 556

SLATE-COLORED JUNCO
Adult Male
Page 554

[536]

Richard A. Parks

NESTING AND FOOD. The female lays two to six eggs marked with brown and black in a loose and bulky cup of plant fibers warmly lined with feathers, fur, or down. Usually the nest is low in a willow or birch. The main foods of this bird are the seeds of alder and willow, but it also feeds on many other seeds, especially those of weeds.

DISTRIBUTION. In the Western Hemisphere, the Common Redpoll breeds from northern Alaska, northern Mackenzie, Baffin Island, and Greenland south to northern British Columbia, northern Manitoba, southern Quebec, and Newfoundland. It winters from central Alaska, southwestern Mackenzie, southern Quebec, and Newfoundland south usually to our most northern states but irregularly to northern California, Kansas, the Ohio Valley, and Delaware, casually farther.

OCCURRENCE IN ALABAMA. (January 15 and 20 and February 13.) *Tennessee Valley*: January 15, 1938, 3 birds (Decatur, Paul Bryan) and January 20, 1893, 2 birds during a severe cold spell, temperature, -6°F. (Florence, F. W. McCormack). *Mountain Region*: No record. *Piedmont*: No record. *Upper Coastal Plain*: February 13, 1924, a male seen at 15 feet with siskins (Prattville, L. S. Golsan). *Lower Coastal Plain*: No record. *Gulf Coast*: No record.

Pine Siskin
Spinus pinus (Wilson)   [533]   (Plate 40, facing page 536)

Slightly smaller than the American Goldfinch, the Pine Siskin has a conical but *pointed bill* and is *heavily streaked above and below*. It can always be identified by the small flashes of *yellow in* the *wings* and on the base of the *tail*. The usual call is a long, buzzy note which rises in pitch and volume, and the song is much like that of the American Goldfinch but huskier and coarser.

The Pine Siskin is uncommon to abundant almost every winter in the Mountain Region of Alabama where it has been recorded every year since 1946. About every third or fourth winter the species occurs uncommonly to abundantly throughout most of the state, but it is rare on the coast and, strangely, unrecorded in the Tennessee Valley. Sometimes in pure flocks, but often with American Goldfinches, it ranges throughout all the more open woodlands in the state and often visits feeding stations or feeds on lawns. The Pine Siskin is not known here as a breeder.

NESTING AND FOOD. The female lays three to six bluish-green eggs marked with brown or black in a large, shallow cup of plant fibers lined thickly with plant down, fur, feathers, or hair. The nest is concealed in a dense clump of a conifer. The species subsists on buds, tender leaves, insects, and seeds in summer. At other seasons, it lives on a large variety of seeds, more prominently those of pine, hemlock, tamarack, spruce, white cedar, alder, birch, willow, larch, sweetgum, juniper, dandelion, ragweed, and sunflower. Sunflower seeds and starter scratch feed attract it at feeding stations.

DISTRIBUTION. The Pine Siskin breeds from southern Alaska, southern Mackenzie, southern Quebec, and Newfoundland south to Guatemala (in mountains), Kansas, Iowa, central Michigan, northern Pennsylvania, and Connecticut. It winters at lower elevations sometimes as far north as it breeds, south to Guatemala, southeastern Texas, the northern Gulf Coast, and Florida.

OCCURRENCE IN ALABAMA. (October 26 to May 12.) *Tennessee Valley*: No record. *Mountain Region*: October 26 (1916, Sand Mountain, Jackson Co., A. H. Howell) to May 12 (1954, Birmingham, T. A. Imhof); most seen, 100+, March 21 to April 1, 1923, last bird noted May 11 (Anniston, R. H. Dean) and 45, May 8, 1958 (Gadsden, Edith Clark). *Piedmont*: November 29 (1952, 10 birds, Roanoke, H. M. Stevenson) to April 28 (1953, Auburn, H. G. Good); most seen, 99, banded between February 26 and March 7, 1923 (Auburn, J. M. Robertson). *Upper Coastal Plain*: November 3 (1957, flock of 20, Blue Creek, Chilton Co., Harriett Wright) to April 28 (1939, Tuscaloosa, H. M. Stevenson). *Lower Coastal Plain*: November 23 (1916, 6 birds, Abbeville, A. H. Howell) to April 10 (1954, Grove Hill, G. A. Carleton). *Gulf Coast*: November 2, 1958 (2 birds, 1 now specimen in Dept. of Conservation collection, Dauphin Island, R. W. Skinner and Lovett Williams); November 8, 1959 (5 birds, Dauphin Island, T. A. Imhof and others); January 31, 1958 (Alabama Point and Fort Morgan, 1 each, T. A. Imhof and others) and March 19, 1949 (Elberta, H. M. Stevenson).

American Goldfinch

Spinus tristis (Linnaeus) [529] (Plate 40, facing page 536)
OTHER NAMES: Wild Canary, Thistle Bird

In spring, the *male* of this species is *bright canary yellow* with a *black,* jauntily-placed *crown* patch, *black wings and tail,* white wing bars, and a white rump. In immature, winter, and female plumages, the bright yellow is replaced by unstreaked olive-green or gray, and little if any black appears on the head. The flight call, usually given at the lowest point in its undulating flight, is a simple four-syllabled phrase, and another call is a canary-like note. The song is a sweet, lively warble similar to that of the Indigo Bunting, but not grouped into phrases of two or three notes.

As a breeder in Alabama, the American Goldfinch is common in summer in the Mountain Region and uncommon in the remainder of the state south at least to the Upper Coastal Plain. In winter this species is common on the Gulf Coast and abundant in the rest of the state, frequenting open woods and their edges, but not those of pure pine. It feeds in any woodland opening where composites grow. In spring, flocks, often of over a hundred, forage for seeds on lawns and about houses.

NESTING. This species is a very late nester, apparently because it lines the nest heavily with thistle down which is not available in quantity until the season is well advanced. The nest is an open, thick-walled cup of grass, bark strips, plant stems, and other plant materials bound together with cobwebs. Usually it is in a fork of a bush or brier within five feet of the ground, and it normally contains five very pale blue eggs. But, at least in Alabama, according to Summerour, and in Georgia, according to Burleigh, it often nests at the outer end of an upper limb of a loblolly or shortleaf pine (Burleigh, 1958: 630-631).

FOOD. The American Goldfinch feeds mostly on seeds, mainly those of birch, alder, sweetgum, buttonbush, various conifers, thistle, dandelion, lettuce, ragweed, sunflower, and wild clematis. In spring and early summer it feeds to some extent on buds and fresh leaves, and in summer consumes many insects such as plant lice, caterpillars, small grasshoppers, and beetles, many of which it feeds to the young. In fall it occasionally takes berries.

DISTRIBUTION. The American Goldfinch breeds from southern British Columbia, southern Quebec, and Nova Scotia south to northern Lower California, northeastern Texas, the central parts of the Gulf states, and South Carolina. It winters almost as far north as it breeds and south to central Mexico, the northern Gulf Coast, and southern Florida.

OCCURRENCE IN ALABAMA. (Throughout the year.) *Tennessee Valley*: Permanent resident; most seen, 200, February 25, 1955 (Marshall Co., T. A. Imhof and others). *Mountain Region*: Permanent resident; most seen, 495, December 26, 1954 and 400, December 26, 1959 (Christmas Counts, Birmingham). *Piedmont*: Permanent resident; most seen, 84, January 2, 1954 (Christmas Count, Auburn). *Upper Coastal Plain*: Permanent resident; uncommon June to November; most seen, 250+, March 18, 1950 (Montgomery, C. W. Summerour). *Lower Coastal Plain*: November 2 (1956, Columbia, H. M. Stevenson) to May 13 (1956, Choctaw Bluff, T. A. Imhof and M. W. Gaillard); also August 13, 1958 (Camden, Lovett Williams), August 18, 1943 (Abbeville, H. M. Stevenson); August 21, 1956 (Barbour Co., J. E. Keeler) and "rare in summer" (Columbia, the T. Z. Atkesons). *Gulf Coast*: October 19 (1957, Dauphin Island, Ala. Orn. Soc.) to May 4 (1932, Rosington, D. H. McIntosh); most seen, 350, February 8, 1957 (Gulf State Park, T. A. Imhof, H. C. Loesch, and M. W. Gaillard).

TIME OF BREEDING. Data on 7 nestings: Building, July 13 to August 22; eggs, July 13 and 27.

BANDING. At Birmingham, a May-banded goldfinch was recaptured at the same place in September of the same year, and a January-banded bird returned in December almost 2 years later.

[Red Crossbill]
Loxia curvirostra Linnaeus   [521]   (Plate 40, facing page 536)

The Red Crossbill is a real curiosity. About as large as a Purple Finch, it has a *big head, short neck, short tail,* and a peculiar bill, the *upper mandible being crossed over* the *lower one near* the *tip.* The wings and tail are dark brown, and the upper back is streaked. The *male is* brick *red,* very bright on the rump, the *female is yellowish-green* with a bright yellow rump, and the *immature* bird is gray, about as *heavily streaked* as the Pine Siskin. The usual flight call is a shrill double chip similar in quality to that of a baby chicken. The song is a variable warble preceded or followed by a thin trill which trill may also be used as a call.

In the Mountain Region of Alabama, the Red Crossbill is a highly irregular, sometimes uncommon and local visitor at any season but principally in winter and spring, and it has probably bred at least once. It has also been noted at least twice in winter in the Upper Coastal Plain. (See Map 96.) Almost invariably it occurs in small flocks in conifers where it usually feeds quietly near the ends of the branches.

NESTING. The usual nest is saddled on a conifer branch well out from the trunk in dense foliage about twenty feet from the ground. It is built of evergreen twigs, grasses, bark strips, and rootlets and lined with mosses, plant down, and often a few green hemlock or cedar twigs. The four or five eggs are pale bluish-green.

FOOD. The staple foods of this crossbill, for which the peculiar bill is marvelously adapted, are the seeds of conifers and other evergreens. These it extracts neatly. Failure of northern cone crops accounts for the erratic movements of the Red Crossbill—far south of the usual range. This bird sometimes eats many other seeds, buds, wild fruits, and insects such as caterpillars and plant lice. At feeding stations it is attracted by water, salt, and peanut butter.

DISTRIBUTION. In the Western Hemisphere, the Red Crossbill breeds from southern Alaska, southern Quebec, and Newfoundland south to Nicaragua (in mountains), southern Michigan, Tennessee (in mountains), North Carolina (in mountains), and southern New England, and irregularly farther south. It winters as far north as it breeds and irregularly south to southeastern Texas, southeastern Louisiana, northern Alabama, and northern Florida.

[540]

OCCURRENCE IN ALABAMA. (Any time of year but mostly December to March.) *Tennessee Valley*: No record. *Mountain Region*: Sand Mountain, west of Trenton, Ga., Jackson Co., last of January 1913 (flock of 8, E. W. Graves); Gadsden, March 21, 1953 (flock of 15, T. A. Imhof and many others); December 5, 1955 to July 19, 1956 (2 to 17 birds seen almost daily, often at feeders, Edith Clark) and August 23, 1957 to April 1958 (small flock almost daily, Edith Clark); Cullman, St. Bernard College, winter 1957-58 (*fide* David Brown). *Piedmont*: No record. *Upper Coastal Plain*: Autaugaville, about 1883 (a flock of 25 to 30, several shot for identification purposes, L. S. Golsan); Montgomery, 1 about January 1, 1950 and a flock of 8 to 15, January 11, 1950 (C. W. Summerour, Jr.). *Lower Coastal Plain*: No record. *Gulf Coast*: No record.

TIME OF BREEDING. Data on 1 possible nesting: Gadsden, a male and female, observed gathering tent caterpillar silk, carried it out over a valley to a roadless area on a mountain about 3 miles distant, February 7 and 8, 1956 (Edith Clark).

Map 96

RED CROSSBILL

Distribution

■ October through March   ● Breeding evidence
◑ April through September   ○ Specimen collected (not preserved)

SUBFAMILY EMBERIZINAE: SPARROWS AND BUNTINGS

These ground-feeding finches are duller in color than other finches, generally predominantly brown and usually with distinctive head markings of black, brown, or white. Except for the towhees the sexes are similar.

Rufous-sided Towhee

Pipilo erythrophthalmus (Linnaeus) [587] (Plate 39, facing page 528)

OTHER NAMES: Joree, Ground Robin, Chewink, Towhee

The male Rufous-sided Towhee has a *black head, breast,* and *upper parts,* a white belly with *rusty flanks,* and some *white* spots in the *wings* and *tail.* The female is similar but is dark brown where the male is black. The call, a whistle

[541]

of two syllables which suggest its names, Towhee and Joree, is usually shortened to one syllable by birds which breed in Alabama. The song, a simple whistle of three notes, the last of which is almost trilled, is similarly shortened by dropping the second note. Birds which breed near the coast have wheezier voices.

This bird is a permanent resident, common in summer and abundant in winter throughout Alabama except in a few places, mostly in the northwestern part of the state, where it is rare or absent in summer. It breeds in brushy and scrubby areas usually in dry and rather open woods of pine or oak. Most often it occurs on or near the ground, but when singing it often chooses a rather high perch.

NESTING. The early nest is on the ground or very close to it, and generally well concealed in the shelter of a shrub, grass clump, or other ground cover. Later in the season it is usually in a shrub or small tree about two to seven feet from the ground. The cup of dead leaves, twigs, rootlets, grass, bark strips, pine needles, and other plant fibers is lined with finer grasses and sometimes hair, and is usually protected by overhanging vegetation. This bird lays two to four whitish or pale pinkish-white eggs variously marked with chestnut-brown.

FOOD. This species feeds mainly on the ground where it scratches vigorously among fallen leaves and other litter for insects and weed seeds. The usual animal items in the diet are beetle larvae, ants, moths, caterpillars, grasshoppers, flies, and earthworms. It also eats many small wild fruits when in season.

DISTRIBUTION. The Rufous-sided Towhee breeds from southern British Columbia, southern Ontario, and southern Maine south to Guatemala, southern Louisiana, and southern Florida. It winters from southern British Columbia, Utah, Iowa, the southern Great Lakes area, and southern New England southward.

ABUNDANCE IN ALABAMA (*most seen in a day*). Birmingham, 300, December 26, 1955 and 275, December 26, 1959 (Christmas Counts); Auburn, 102, January 2, 1954 (Christmas Count); Gulf Coast, 137, April 13, 1956 (Spring Count, Mobile Bay Area), 107, November 1, 1958 (Fall Count, Mobile Bay Area), and 165, January 2, 1960 (Christmas Count, Dauphin Island).

TIME OF BREEDING. Data on over 85 nestings: Building, February 27 to May 15; eggs, April 6 to July 24; young in nest, April 17 to July 11; dependent young out of nest, April 9 to August 1.

BANDING. One towhee, banded at Nashville, Tenn. on October 11, 1938, was found at Partridge Crossroads, Jefferson Co., on January 26, 1940. Of 25 other towhees recaptured at the place of banding, 1 at least 5 years later, half were found in an opposite season and half in a later winter. This indicates that we have 2 populations, those that stay all year and those that come down and winter in the same place each year.

SUBSPECIES. The western *Pipilo erythrophthalmus montanus* Swarth, formerly known as the Spotted Towhee and easily recognized in the field, has been identified once in Alabama (Camden, December 8, 1958, Lovett Williams, specimen too badly shot to be preserved).

Savannah Sparrow

Passerculus sandwichensis (Gmelin)   [542]   (Plate 41, facing page 552)
OTHER NAMES: Grass Sparrow, Grass Bird, Grass Finch

The three other names given to the Savannah Sparrow are also applied to many other field-dwelling sparrows. This species is rather plain, grayish-brown, *finely streaked* with *dark above* and *below*, and it has a *yellowish eye stripe* and a slightly forked tail. It sometimes has a large central breast spot like the Song Sparrow, but the Savannah Sparrow does not have coarse streaks nor does it pump its tail in flight. Its flight is generally bounding, and its call is a thin, rather distinctive chip of one syllable. The song has the lisping, insect-like quality of that of the Grasshopper Sparrow although the phrasing is different. It consists of several short notes followed by two trills, the second lower in pitch than the first.

Throughout Alabama the Savannah Sparrow is abundant in winter, but it is not known to breed here. It occurs on almost any grass field in sparse or tall cover, so long as it can feed on the ground and woody plants are far apart. The bird generally feeds in short grass and roosts in bad weather in tall grass, which makes partially-mowed fields or weedy fields next to pastures especially attractive. Usually it flushes close at hand and bounds away, often at right angles, dropping back into the grass a short distance away.

NESTING AND FOOD. The nest is a shallow open cup of grasses and other plant materials lined with finer plant fibers, located on the ground in dense grass, usually in the shelter of a tussock. The four or five eggs are pale bluish-green heavily marked with reddish-brown and lavender. Most of the food of this bird consists of grass seeds, weed seeds, grass-dwelling insects, and a small amount of waste grain. Although its insect food comprises mainly beetles, eaten in summer, it consumes many cotton-boll weevils during its sojourn in Alabama.

DISTRIBUTION. The Savannah Sparrow breeds from northern Alaska, northern Mackenzie, and northern Labrador south locally to Guatemala, Missouri, Indiana, West Virginia, southeastern Pennsylvania, and southeastern New York. It winters from southern British Columbia, Colorado, Oklahoma,

[543]

the Ohio Valley, and southeastern New York south to El Salvador, Cuba, and the Bahamas.

OCCURRENCE IN ALABAMA. (September 15 to May 26.) *Tennessee Valley*: September 26 (1950, 5 birds, Wheeler Refuge, T. A. Imhof) to May 25 (1941, 3 birds, Florence, H. M. Stevenson); most seen, 68, December 31, 1955 (Wheeler Refuge, T. A. Imhof). *Mountain Region*: September 15 (1959, Birmingham, T. A. Imhof, Idalene Snead, and Emmy Brownlie) to May 26 (1956, 3 birds, Birmingham, Idalene Snead and Emmy Brownlie); most seen, fall, 200, October 27, 1959, winter, 250+, January 29, 1960, and spring, 220+, March 10, 1960 (Birmingham, T. A. Imhof). *Piedmont*: October 3 (1958, Lineville, T. A. Imhof and C. T. Hornady) to April 30 (1955, Auburn, H. G. Good and T. A. Imhof). *Upper Coastal Plain*: September 21 (1956, Marion, Lois McCollough) to May 14 (1958, Prattville, Lovett Williams); most seen, 300, March 15, 1958 (Barachias, T. A. Imhof and R. W. Skinner). *Lower Coastal Plain*: October 3 (1958, 50 birds, Camden, Lovett Williams) to April 24 (1960, Leroy, Washington Co., T. A. Imhof and others). *Gulf Coast*: October 7 (1956, Dauphin Island, Lovett Williams and others) to May 13 (1960, Theodore, J. L. Dorn); most seen, 210, December 28, 1959 (Mobile, J. L. Dorn).

BANDING. One bird, banded on August 10, 1932 at McMillan, Michigan, was found at Beatrice, Monroe Co., on January 24, 1933. Another, banded near Montgomery on April 11, 1953, was recaptured near Fort Fairfield, Aroostook Co., Maine in March 1957. At least 75 winter-banded birds have returned to the same field in Birmingham in a later winter. One bird was at least 4 years old.

Grasshopper Sparrow
Ammodramus savannarum (Gmelin)   [546]   (Plate 41, facing page 552)

The Grasshopper Sparrow has a streaked back, an *unstreaked buffy breast,* a *whitish crown stripe,* a collar of reddish-brown stripes on the hindneck, and a yellow spot on the bend of the wing. The young bird is finely streaked on the upper breast and lacks the buffy color, and it usually can be identified by anyone who knows the adult. This bird *appears* to be very *flat headed* because it has a deep bill and a low crown. The spines of the tail feathers protrude so that each feather has a sharp point, a characteristic of this and the next three species. The flight of these sharp-tails is generally low and direct, but this sparrow sometimes bounds like the Savannah Sparrow. The song is a long insect-like buzz or a series of see-sawing, squeaky notes.

This species as a breeder is common but local in summer in Alabama south to and including the Black Belt, but many of the state's apparently suitable places remain unoccupied at this season. In winter it is uncommon to common south of the Fall Line and rare to uncommon north of it. (See Map 97.) This bird habitually skulks in tall grass and is often difficult to flush. More extensive field work, especially winter banding, has resulted in a much better knowledge of its winter status.

NESTING. The nest is well hidden, usually in a slight depression in the ground or in a clump of grass. It is made of grasses, lined with rootlets and hair, and arched over so that the contents cannot be seen from above. The three to five whitish eggs are sparingly marked with reddish-brown.

FOOD. This sparrow probably eats more insects than any other sparrow in Alabama and it takes grasshoppers in quantity. The remainder of its food consists mainly of weevils, other beetles and their grubs, caterpillars, weed seeds, and a small amount of grain.

DISTRIBUTION. The Grasshopper Sparrow breeds from southeastern British Columbia, southern Manitoba, southwestern Quebec, and Maine south to Ecuador and the Greater Antilles. It winters from central California, Oklahoma, Tennessee, and North Carolina southward.

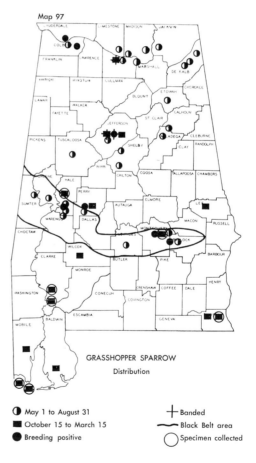

Map 97

GRASSHOPPER SPARROW
Distribution

◗ May 1 to August 31   ✛ Banded
■ October 15 to March 15   ━ Black Belt area
● Breeding positive   ◯ Specimen collected

OCCURRENCE IN ALABAMA. (Throughout the year.) *Tennessee Valley*: April 2 (1951, Wheeler Refuge, D. C. Hulse) to November 6 (1942, Wheeler Refuge, L. S. Givens); also December 23, 1942 (3 birds, Wheeler Refuge, J. H. Steenis) and December 23, 1950 (trapped and banded, Wheeler Refuge, D. C. Hulse); most seen, 23, July 12, 1936 (Florence, H. S. Peters and N. H. Giles). *Mountain Region*: Permanent resident; common mid-March to mid-October; most seen, 35, May 3, 1957 (Birmingham, Idalene Snead and others). *Piedmont*: March 20 (1924, Auburn, J. M. Robertson) to at least June (no dates available). *Upper Coastal Plain*: Permanent resident; common mid-March to mid-October; most seen, 35, May 5, 1956 (Marion, Lois McCollough). *Lower Coastal Plain*: November 6 (1958, Camden, Lovett Williams) to March 12 (1912, Dothan, A. H. Howell). *Gulf Coast*: October 19 (1957, Foley, H. M. Stevenson) to April 26 (1952, Foley, H. M. Stevenson).

TIME OF BREEDING. Data on 16 nestings: Eggs, May 11 to July 15; young in nest, May 20 to August 5; dependent young out of nest, June 20 to August 5.

BANDING. Four banded Grasshopper Sparrows have been recaptured on the same field in Birmingham as follows: A March-banded bird retaken in June and twice in January, a June-banded bird recaptured in October, a November bird returned in August, and a June bird came back in August of the next year.

Le Conte's Sparrow

Passerherbulus caudacutus (Latham)   [548]   (Plate 41, facing page 552)

This sparrow is *orange-buff* or yellowish-orange on the *head, breast,* and *flanks* and is *streaked* on the *sides* from neck to tail. Like the Grasshopper Sparrow, it has a *collar* of *reddish-brown stripes* on the hindneck and a *pale central* crown stripe bordered by two dark stripes. It has the same flight and the same secretive actions as the other sharp-tailed sparrows. The song is a thin grasshopper-like hiss, preceded by a short squeak and followed by a short chip.

Le Conte's Sparrow is rare to uncommon in winter and on migration in Alabama, but because of its secretive habits it is probably more common than the records thus far indicate. It frequents damp, weedy or grassy fields, especially those near water, and is not known to nest in Alabama, for it breeds in prairie marshes.

NESTING AND FOOD. The nest, on or near the ground in old, thick weedy or grassy growth, is a cup of grasses lined with hair, and the four eggs are pale green marked with brown. Little is known of the food of this bird except that it chiefly eats weed and grass seeds and in summer also feeds on some insects.

DISTRIBUTION. Le Conte's Sparrow breeds from southern Mackenzie and northern Ontario south to Montana, North Dakota, and northern Michigan. It winters from western Kansas, northern Alabama, and South Carolina south to southern Texas, the northern Gulf Coast, and southeastern Georgia.

OCCURRENCE IN ALABAMA. (September 23 to May 15.) *Tennessee Valley*: Wheeler Refuge (September 23, 1943, H. M. Stevenson); December 27, 1941 (J. H. Steenis); January 12, 1957 (Idalene Snead) and May 14 and 15, 1941 (Clarence Cottam). *Mountain Region*: October 24 (1955, Birmingham, 15 birds, T. A. Imhof and others) to April 20 (1957, T. A. Imhof, Idalene Snead, and Grace Snead); most seen in winter, 9, January 19, 1957 (T. A. Imhof, Idalene Snead, and Emmy Brownlie). *Piedmont*: No record. *Upper Coastal Plain*: Coosada, Elmore Co., 7 specimens taken between late February and late March 1878 (N. C. Brown) and December 31, 1955 (Marion, Lois McCollough). *Lower Coastal Plain*: February 11, 1954 (Clayton, Barbour Co., 1 trapped and banded, J. E. Keeler) and March 17, 1954, 1 seen (J. E. Keeler). *Gulf Coast*: December 28 (1955, Mobile, J. L. Dorn) to March 26 (1960, Dauphin Island, Ava Tabor and others); also April 22, 1961 (Dauphin Island, C. W. Summerour); most seen, 3, December 29, 1956 (Theodore, T. A. Imhof and D. C. Holliman) and January 31, 1958 (Fort Morgan, T. A. Imhof and others).

Henslow's Sparrow

Passerherbulus henslowii (Audubon) [547] (Plate 41, facing page 552)

Henslow's Sparrow has an *olive-green head, reddish-brown* in the back and *wings,* and *streaked breast* and *flanks.* The adult resembles the Grasshopper Sparrow, and very young birds are somewhat buffy and unstreaked below, so that their resemblance is even closer. The wings of Henslow's Sparrow, however, are usually reddish-brown. Observers familiar with the adults of both species have little difficulty identifying the young. The insect-like song is a very short, two-syllabled phrase, a poor effort but one that is far carrying.

North of the Fall Line in Alabama, this sparrow is rare in winter and on migration. In the Coastal Plain it is uncommon in winter but undoubtedly more numerous than recorded because it is difficult to flush and identify. It is not known to nest in Alabama. The species frequents weedy, rank growths like other sharp-tailed sparrows, but also occurs in open, wet, shrubby areas. On or near the coast, it usually lives in broomsedge or other grasses in boggy places in the pine flats.

NESTING AND FOOD. The nest, a loosely-built cup of grasses lined with hair, is on the ground usually well hidden in a clump of grass. The four or five eggs are grayish or greenish-white spotted with brown. The bird is known to eat grass seeds, weed seeds, blackberries, beetles and their grubs, bugs, grasshoppers, caterpillars, and spiders.

DISTRIBUTION. Henslow's Sparrow breeds from South Dakota, central Wisconsin, southern Ontario, and southern New Hampshire south to Kansas, Missouri, and North Carolina. It winters from northeastern Texas, central Alabama, and central South Carolina south to southeastern Texas, the northern Gulf Coast, and central Florida.

OCCURRENCE IN ALABAMA. (October 31 to May 4.) *Tennessee Valley:* December 17, 1951 (Wheeler Refuge, D. C. Hulse) and March 30, 1950 (trapped and banded, D. C. Hulse). *Mountain Region:* Birmingham (October 31, 1954, T. A. Imhof) to November 4 (1953, T. A. Imhof) and March 28 (1935, H. M. Stevenson) to May 4 (1953, T. A. Imhof). *Piedmont:* No record. *Upper Coastal Plain:* December 23 (1939, Tuscaloosa, H. M. Stevenson) to April 26 (1894, specimen in U. S. National Museum, Gallion, Hale Co., C. P. Rowley). *Lower Coastal Plain:* No record. *Gulf Coast:* November 30 (1947, Elberta, F. M. Weston) to March 30 (1912, specimen in U. S. National Museum, Bay Minette, E. G. Holt).

Sharp-tailed Sparrow

Ammospiza caudacuta (Gmelin) [549] (Plate 41, facing page 552)
OTHER NAME: Nelson's Sparrow

This sparrow is best identified by the wide *orange stripes which outline* a *triangular gray cheek patch*. Except for this mark, it resembles Le Conte's Sparrow, but it lacks the reddish collar and the pale central crown stripe. The song of the Sharp-tailed Sparrow is a wheezy trill with two introductory notes.

In Alabama this sparrow, which is not known to breed here, is common on the Gulf Coast in winter in salt marshes and their borders. It has been noted once inland on migration. Usually it flushes from the *Spartina* grass out in the marsh and gives the observer little opportunity to see it well. This bird is inquisitive, however, and a squeaking noise usually brings it out in the open for better inspection. The same device is often effective on other birds that are skulkers.

NESTING AND FOOD. The nest is a cup of grass usually concealed in a tussock or pile of drift in meadows of marsh grass a few inches above the mud. The four or five eggs are pale bluish to pale brownish marked with chestnut-brown. The species feeds on insects, small aquatic animals, and grass seeds. These include leafhoppers, bugs, flies (including midges), seeds of salt marsh grass, wild rice, and sand fleas, all in large quantity. In lesser amounts it eats caterpillars, weevils, army worms, small mollusks, and other grass seeds.

DISTRIBUTION. The Sharp-tailed Sparrow breeds locally in fresh marshes from northeastern British Columbia, southern Mackenzie, and the area around James Bay south to southern Alberta and South Dakota and in salt marshes along the Atlantic Coast from the Gulf of St. Lawrence south to North Carolina. It winters in salt marshes and their borders from Long Island to Texas.

OCCURRENCE IN ALABAMA. (September 21 to May 16.) *Tennessee Valley*: No record. *Mountain Region*: October 5, 1958 (1 banded, Cheaha, at elevation 2407 feet, T. A. Imhof and C. T. Hornady). *Piedmont*: No record. *Upper Coastal Plain*: No record. *Lower Coastal Plain*: No record. *Gulf Coast*: September 21 (1911, specimen in U. S. National Museum, Orange Beach, A. H. Howell) to May 16 (1911, specimen in U. S. National Museum, Bayou La Batre, A. H. Howell); most seen, fall, 37, October 6, 1956 and November 1, 1958 (Fall Counts, Mobile Bay Area), winter, 34, December 27, 1958 and January 2, 1960 (Christmas Counts, Dauphin Island).

Seaside Sparrow
Ammospiza maritima (Wilson)   [550]   (Plate 41, facing page 552)

This sparrow is *larger* and *darker than* the *other* grass-dwelling, *sharp-tailed sparrows*. The best field marks are the *yellow* line *above* the *eye*, the *white jaw line*, and the *white throat* area. The song, often given in the twilight hours, is similar to that of the Sharp-tailed Sparrow but is much huskier, thicker, and wheezier.

Confined solely to salt marshes, this species breeds on the Alabama coast and occurs there throughout the year. Although it often associates with the Sharp-tailed Sparrow, it usually frequents the wetter and muddier parts of the marsh. The Seaside Sparrow is absent from many apparently suitable marshes on the Gulf Coast in Alabama during the breeding season, but it often visits them at other times.

NESTING. The nest is a cup of grass like that of the Sharp-tailed Sparrow, but it is farther out in the marsh, sometimes even over water, and often lacks the tuft of grass for partial concealment. The clutch is three to five pale greenish or pale brownish eggs spotted with reddish-brown and dull purple.

FOOD. This sparrow subsists mainly on insects such as grasshoppers, crickets, caterpillars, flies, moths, wasps, weevils, and spiders and aquatic animals which include snails, mollusks, and small crabs, especially fiddlers. It also eats the seeds of salt grasses and weeds.

DISTRIBUTION. The Seaside Sparrow breeds in salt marshes from Massachusetts to southern Texas. It winters almost as far north as it breeds but commonly from Virginia to the mouth of the Rio Grande.

ABUNDANCE IN ALABAMA (*most seen in a day*). Spring, 49, April 13, 1957 (Spring Count, Mobile Bay Area), summer, 30, June 27, 1958 (Cedar Point to Coffee Island, T. A. Imhof and H. C. Loesch), fall, 43, November 1, 1958 and 37, October 6, 1956 (Fall Counts, Mobile Bay Area) and winter, 33, December 27, 1958 (Christmas Count, Dauphin Island).

TIME OF BREEDING. Data on 19 nestings: Building, April 11; eggs, April 22 to June 25; young in nest, June 27; dependent young out of nest, May 15 to June 27.

Vesper Sparrow
Pooecetes gramineus (Gmelin)   [540]   (Plate 41, facing page 552)

The Vesper Sparrow is a rather large sparrow with *white outer tail feathers*, streaked breast and flanks, *whitish eye ring*, and *reddish-brown shoulders*.

[549]

The song is quite similar to that of the Song Sparrow but it is more musical and begins with two instead of three clear whistles followed by a jumbled trill.

In the Coastal Plain of Alabama this species is common to abundant in winter and on migration. North of the Fall Line, it is common on migration and locally common to uncommon in winter. It is not known to breed in the state. It inhabits short-grass or even bare fields, especially recently-plowed or fallow fields or pastures.

NESTING AND FOOD. This sparrow fashions a cup of grasses, rootlets, weed stems, and bark strips, placing it either in or near a tussock of grass or in a depression just deep enough to make the rim of the nest level with the ground. The four eggs are grayish-white to bluish-white usually marked heavily with brown. In summer the bird lives primarily on such injurious insects as beetles, grasshoppers, and caterpillars. During the rest of the year, it subsists mainly on weed seeds with much smaller portions of grass seeds and waste grain.

DISTRIBUTION. The Vesper Sparrow breeds from northeastern British Columbia, southern Mackenzie, southern Quebec, and Nova Scotia south to central California, northern Arizona, Missouri, northeastern Tennessee, and North Carolina. It winters from central California, central Texas, the Ohio Valley, and Connecticut south to southern Mexico and central Florida.

OCCURRENCE IN ALABAMA. (Normal: October 13 to April 20; Out-of-season: May 7.) *Tennessee Valley*: November 1 (1890, Leighton, F. W. McCormack) to April 12 (1941, Florence, H. M. Stevenson); most seen, 30, December 31, 1954 (Wheeler Refuge, Robert Helle). *Mountain Region*: October 20 (1936, Birmingham, H. M. Stevenson) to April 20 (1940, Birmingham, H. M. Stevenson); most seen, 41, January 1, 1952 (Christmas Count, Birmingham). *Piedmont*: November 17 (1936, specimen, Auburn, H. G. Good) to April 11 (1950, trapped and banded, Wedowee, J. E. Keeler); also May 7, 1914 (specimen in U. S. National Museum, Auburn, J. L. Peters). *Upper Coastal Plain*: October 17 (1937, Booth, Autauga Co., L. S. Golsan) to April 13 (1957, Marion, Lois McCollough and 1958, Livingston, Jenkins Jackson); most seen, 60, March 19, 1958 (Marion, Lois McCollough). *Lower Coastal Plain*: October 13 (1958, Camden, Lovett Williams) to April 15 (1957, Jackson, W. U. Harris); most seen, 41, February 10, 1956 (Monroe Co., T. A. Imhof and W. F. Colin). *Gulf Coast*: November 8 (1959, Dauphin Island, T. A. Imhof) to April 13 (1957, Foley, Lovett Williams and H. M. Stevenson); most seen, 80, February 1, 1958 (Elberta to Bon Secour, T. A. Imhof and others).

Lark Sparrow

Chondestes grammacus (Say)   [552]   (Plate 42, facing page 560)

This large, handsome sparrow has wide *reddish-brown* and *white stripes* on the *head,* a *black central breast spot,* and a dark, fan-shaped *tail* with *white edges* much *like a towhee.* The under parts are unstreaked in adults and streaked on the breast in immature birds. The song is a series of trills, similar to that of a Song Sparrow, but usually introduced by two clear notes and characterized by churring sounds.

In Alabama the Lark Sparrow is rare to uncommon and local as a breeder in summer in the western parts of the Tennessee Valley and the Black Belt. It has wintered once in the Tennessee Valley. (See Map 98.) On migration it is uncommon in fall on the coast and rare elsewhere. It inhabits prairies and open farming areas such as poor pastures, corn fields, and their borders and hedgerows. It seems to require some bare earth in its breeding habitat.

NESTING. This bird usually conceals its nest in a slight depression on the ground in the shade of a weed or cornstalk but sometimes it selects a low bush. The nest is built of dry grass, weed stems, and rootlets and lined with finer strands of the same materials. The female lays three to six whitish eggs marked with dark brown and black.

FOOD. Most of the food of this sparrow consists of weed seeds, grass seeds, grain, and grasshoppers.

DISTRIBUTION. The Lark Sparrow breeds from southern British Columbia, southern Manitoba, southern Ontario, and western New York south to northern Mexico, southern Louisiana, and central Alabama, and east to the western parts of North Carolina, Virginia, and Pennsylvania. It winters from central California, central Texas, and central Florida, occasionally farther north, south to El Salvador and southern Florida.

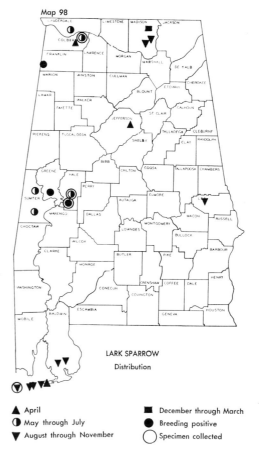

Map 98

LARK SPARROW
Distribution

▲ April   ■ December through March
◐ May through July   ● Breeding positive
▼ August through November   ◯ Specimen collected

OCCURRENCE IN ALABAMA. (Normal: April 7 to November 1; Out-of-season: Through February 7.) *Tennessee Valley:* April 25 (1914, Leighton, A. H. Howell) to July 14 (1947, Red Bay, Franklin

[552]

Richard A. Parks

Co., H. M. Stevenson); also October 4, 1958 to February 7, 1959 (Huntsville, J. C. and Margaret Robinson); most seen, 7, July 1 and 2, 1940 (Florence, H. M. Stevenson). *Mountain Region*: April 7, 1935 (East Lake, Birmingham, H. M. Stevenson). *Piedmont*: August 22, 1956 (Auburn, J. E. Keeler). *Upper Coastal Plain*: April 10 (1958, Livingston, Jenkins Jackson) to September 11 (1890, Greensboro, W. C. Avery); most seen, 12, July 13, 1957 (Epes, Boligee, and Forkland, T. A. Imhof and others). *Lower Coastal Plain*: No record. *Gulf Coast*: August 22 (1958, Dauphin Island, Ava Tabor) to November 1 (1958, Foley, B. L. Monroe, Jr. and F. M. Weston); also April 23, 1960 (Fort Morgan, F. M. Weston and Ernest Stevenson) and November 25, 1960 (Dauphin Island, H. A. J. and Cora Evans).

TIME OF BREEDING. Data on 5 nestings: Dependent young, May 27 to September 11; young out of nest by July.

Bachman's Sparrow

Aimophila aestivalis (Lichtenstein)   [575]   (Plate 42, facing page 560)
OTHER NAME: Pine-woods Sparrow

This sparrow is *streaked reddish-brown above* and *unstreaked buffy below,* and has a rather large bill and flat head. It resembles the Grasshopper Sparrow, but Bachman's Sparrow has a longer tail and lacks the whitish crown stripe. With its reddish upper parts it also resembles the Field Sparrow but the bill is dark, and the eye ring is absent. Bachman's Sparrow is difficult to flush and this is a good clue to its identity as is its habit of skulking along the ground in dry woods. The song, reputed to be one of the finest in the bird world, has much of the quality of the Field Sparrow but is sweeter and richer. It consists of a clear whistle and a trill followed by another similar whistle and a slow trill, each in a different pitch.

In Alabama this sparrow is a common permanent resident in suitable habitat almost everywhere, but in the Tennessee Valley it is uncommon and local and has been noted only in summer. In Alabama it breeds in dry piney and scrub-oak woods, particularly the drier ridge tops with few shrubs. It forages on the ground often near stumps or fallen logs. In summer this bird is easily located by its song, but in winter it is silent and difficult to find. Probably few of the birds breeding in Alabama migrate.

NESTING. The nest, which has a dome-shaped top, is made of dry grasses and weed stems and lined with fine grass tops. Generally it is in woods on the ground in clumps of grass, palmetto, or vine tangles. The usual clutch is four pure white eggs.

FOOD. In Alabama most of the food of this sparrow consists of insects and their allies. It takes beetles (including weevils), bugs, grasshoppers,

[553]

crickets, millipedes, snails, and spiders. Its vegetable diet includes the seeds of grasses, sedges, wood sorrel, and Indian strawberry.

DISTRIBUTION. Bachman's Sparrow breeds from southeastern Missouri, northeastern Illinois, southwestern Pennsylvania, and Maryland south to central Texas, the northern Gulf Coast, and central Florida. It winters from northeastern Texas, northern Alabama, and central North Carolina south to southeastern Texas and southern Florida.

OCCURRENCE IN ALABAMA. (Throughout the year.) *Tennessee Valley*: March 7 (1959, Huntsville, Margaret Robinson) to at least June 30 (1943, Wheeler Refuge, H. M. Stevenson). *Mountain Region*: Permanent resident; most seen, spring, 14, March 28, 1950 (Fairfield, T. A. Imhof); summer, 8, June 4, 1952 (Fairfield, T. A. Imhof); winter, 7, December 26, 1960 (Birmingham, J. B. Sullivan). *Piedmont*: Permanent resident. *Upper Coastal Plain*: Permanent resident; most seen, summer, 14, June 22, 1957 (Fitzpatrick and vicinity, Bullock Co., T. A. Imhof and R. W. Skinner); winter, 8, December 31, 1955 (Marion, Lois McCollough). *Lower Coastal Plain*: Permanent resident. *Gulf Coast*: Permanent resident.

TIME OF BREEDING. Data on 21+ nestings: Eggs, May 8 to July 3; young in nest, May 9 to July 26; dependent young out of nest, May 19 to early August.

Slate-colored Junco

Junco hyemalis (Linnaeus)   [567]   (Plate 40, facing page 536)

OTHER NAMES: Junco, Blue Snowbird, White-tailed Sparrow

This bird is *slate gray* except for a *well-defined white belly* and *white outer tail feathers. Female* and *immature* birds have much of the slate *gray replaced* by *brown*, particularly on the back and flanks, but they are still easily recognized as juncos. The call is a smacking note or a high-pitched twitter of three or more notes. The song is a rapid trill, a bit more musical than that of the Chipping Sparrow, and occasionally varied in pitch and time.

This species is abundant in winter in Alabama except on the Gulf Coast where it is irregular and uncommon. Although it has been recorded in summer in Alabama, no evidence of nesting has been noted. It occurs on the ground in woods or their borders usually in flocks of from ten to a hundred birds. It is frequent around houses, where it visits feeding stations and big lawns and gardens.

NESTING AND FOOD. The nest is a deep cup of grasses, moss, and bark lined with hair, fur, and feathers. It is usually on the ground under a fallen tree, in its upturned roots, under an overhanging bank, in rocks, or in dense vegetation. The four to five pale greenish eggs are spotted with reddish-brown. During most of the year this junco eats the seeds of a great many weeds and

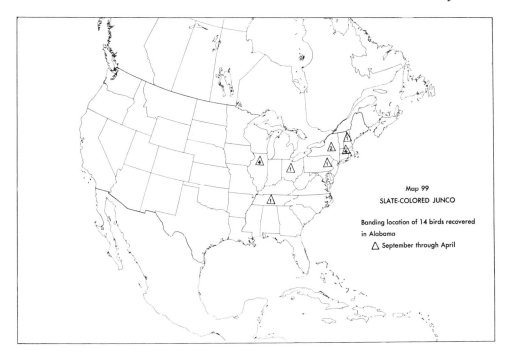

Map 99
SLATE-COLORED JUNCO

Banding location of 14 birds recovered
in Alabama
△ September through April

grasses, including broomsedge, ragweed, and crabgrass. In summer it also eats many insects, especially caterpillars.

DISTRIBUTION. The Slate-colored Junco breeds from northwestern Alaska, northern Quebec, and Newfoundland south to British Columbia, southern Manitoba, southern Wisconsin, in mountains to northern Georgia, southeastern New York, southern New England, and Nova Scotia. It winters from southeastern Alaska, southern British Columbia, southern Manitoba, western Ontario, southern Quebec, and Newfoundland south to northwestern Mexico, southern Texas, the northern Gulf Coast, and northern Florida.

OCCURRENCE IN ALABAMA. (Normal: October 7 to April 21; Out-of-season: May through August.) *Tennessee Valley*: October 21 (1893, Leighton, F. W. McCormack) to April 18 (1948, Russellville, E. O. Willis); also a pair through May 4, 1959 (Huntsville, Margaret Robinson). *Mountain Region*: October 7 (1956, Gadsden, Edith Clark) to April 21 (1934, Birmingham, H. M. Stevenson); also an injured bird to May 17, 1959 (Birmingham, Harriett Wright); most seen, 814, December 28, 1957 (Christmas Count, Birmingham). *Piedmont*: Late October (Auburn, *fide* H. G. Good) to April 15 (1914, Dadeville, W. B. Fulton); also 4 birds, May through August 1957 (Goodwater, Clay Co., *fide* Blanche Dean); most seen, 87, January 2, 1954 (Christmas Count, Auburn). *Upper Coastal Plain*: October 23 (1954, Valley Creek State Park, Ala. Orn. Soc.) to April 12 (1960, Livingston, Jenkins Jackson). *Lower Coastal Plain*: October 20 (1956, Coffee County Lake, L. C. Crawford and T. A. Imhof) to April 16 (1912, Myrtlewood, E. G. Holt); most seen, 150, February 10, 1956 (Monroe Co., T. A. Imhof and W. F. Colin). *Gulf Coast*: November 7 (1959, Dauphin Island, Ala. Orn. Soc.) to March 17 (1960, Spring Hill, J. L. Dorn); also October 19, 1957 (Foley, H. M. Stevenson); most seen, 50, February 4, 1933 (Fairhope, Homer Flagg).

BANDING. At least 8 Alabama-banded juncos have been retrapped at the same place in a later winter. For place of banding of 14 others recaptured in Alabama, mostly in the northern half of the state, see Map 99.

[Oregon Junco]
Junco oreganus (Townsend)   [567]   (Plate 40, facing page 536)

This junco closely resembles the Slate-colored Junco of the east with which it often hybridizes or intergrades. Like the female and immature Slate-colored Juncos, the Oregon Junco is brown on the back and sides. A *hood*, which may be almost black (subspecies *oreganus*) or bluish (subspecies *mearnsi*), is *sharply separated from the sides*, which may be *rusty-brown, pinkish-brown, or yellowish-brown*.

This species is accidental in winter in the Mountain Region of Alabama, but it probably occurs more frequently than noted, for it is easily overlooked among the female and immature Slate-colored Juncos with which it usually associates.

NESTING AND FOOD. Except as modified by its more western distribution, the nest and food of this junco differ little from its eastern relative.

DISTRIBUTION. The Oregon Junco breeds from southeastern Alaska and southwestern Saskatchewan south to Lower California and northeastern Wyoming. It winters almost as far north as it breeds but at lower elevations and south to northern Mexico, central Texas, and rarely east to the Atlantic Coast.

OCCURRENCE IN ALABAMA. *Mountain Region only*: March 2 to 17, 1956, a male of the race *mearnsi* (Ensley Highlands, Birmingham, T. A. Imhof).

[Tree Sparrow]
Spizella arborea (Wilson)   [559]   (Plate 42, facing page 560)

Closely resembling the Field Sparrow, the Tree Sparrow has a light gray head and breast, two *reddish-brown* areas on the *sides of* the *breast,* a prominent *spot in* the *center of* the *breast,* a dark upper mandible, and a yellow lower one. Winter flocks seem to keep up a twittering, but this is the result of the clear two-noted whistle of the individual birds. The sweet, variable, and canary-like song usually consists of several clear notes followed by a rapid warble.

This northern sparrow is accidental in winter in northern Alabama, but it probably occurs more often than noted, for it is overlooked among the similar Field and Chipping Sparrows with which it often is found. The Tree Sparrow, very poorly named, usually frequents weedy fields and open brushy or shrubby areas.

NESTING AND FOOD. This sparrow builds a bulky nest of vegetable fibers warmly lined with hair and feathers. It always chooses thick cover but the nest may be on the ground or in low trees. The three to five pale greenish-blue eggs are marked with reddish-brown. Its staple foods are grass seeds and weed seeds.

DISTRIBUTION. The Tree Sparrow breeds from northern Alaska, northern Mackenzie, and northern Quebec south to northern British Columbia and central Quebec. It winters from southern British Columbia, central Ontario, southwestern Quebec, and Nova Scotia south to northeastern California, central New Mexico, central Texas, Arkansas, Tennessee, and North Carolina, casually farther south.

OCCURRENCE IN ALABAMA. *Mountain Region only*: February to March 16, 1953, 1 studied frequently on a feeding shelf from a distance of 2 feet (Gadsden, Naomi Banks and Edith Clark).

Chipping Sparrow
Spizella passerina (Bechstein)   [560]   (Plate 42, facing page 560)

The Chipping Sparrow is small with *clear gray under parts*, a *reddish-brown cap*, a *white line over* the *eye*, and a *black line through it*. Summer adults have a black bill. *Immature birds* have much duller head markings and a brown cheek patch, and very young birds have finely streaked breasts, but they can always be distinguished by their *gray rumps*. The song is a steady trill or a rapid series of rather monotonous and unmusical chips, and the call is a single chip of the same quality.

In summer as a breeder in Alabama this species is abundant in the Mountain Region, locally common elsewhere south to the Black Belt, and rare south to the Gulf Coast. In winter it is abundant south of the Fall Line and locally common north of it, while on migration it is common throughout. In the breeding season this sparrow frequents evergreens near short grass, especially lawns. In winter it occurs in moderate-sized short-grass areas such as lawns, small pastures, golf courses, and the borders of cultivated fields.

NESTING. Usually the nest is in a tall shrub or low in an evergreen, but it may be in various other places. Grasses and rootlets form the outside of the cup while the thick lining is of horsehair or some substitute. The female lays three or four bluish-green eggs marked around the larger end with dark brown spots.

FOOD. In summer this sparrow feeds almost entirely on such insects as caterpillars, grasshoppers, beetles (including weevils), ants, wasps, bugs, plant lice, and scale insects. In the cold months weed seeds, especially those of crabgrass, are the staple, and it occasionally takes a little grain and some berries.

DISTRIBUTION. The Chipping Sparrow breeds from Alaska, northern Manitoba, southern Quebec, and Newfoundland south to northern Nicaragua, the northern Gulf Coast, and northern Florida. It winters from central California, central Oklahoma, southwestern Tennessee, Virginia, and Maryland, rarely farther north, south to Nicaragua and southern Florida.

OCCURRENCE IN ALABAMA.

(Throughout the year.) *Tennessee Valley*: Permanent resident; most seen, summer, 40, June 13, 1953 (Marshall Co., T. A. Imhof). *Mountain Region*: Permanent resident; most seen, summer, 105, June 7, 1957 (Fort Payne to Flat Rock to Section, T. A. Imhof), migration, 125, March 11, 1950 (Fairfield, T. A. Imhof), winter, 188, December 31, 1949 (Christmas Count, Birmingham). *Piedmont*: Permanent resident; most seen, 120+, October 3, 1958 (Clay Co. and Randolph Co., T. A. Imhof and C. T. Hornady). *Upper Coastal Plain*: Permanent resident; most seen, 300+, February 1, 1958 (Sardis, Dallas Co., T. A. Imhof and others). *Lower Coastal Plain*: Permanent resident; common, October 20 (1956, Coffee County Lake, T. A. Imhof and L. C. Crawford) to April 28 (1952, Andalusia, W. R. Middleton); most seen, 355, February 26, 1955 (Covington Co. and Geneva Co., T. A. Imhof) and 212, February 25, 1955 (Evergreen to Andalusia, T. A. Imhof). *Gulf Coast*: October 11 (1958, Dauphin Island, T. A. Imhof and others) to May 1 (1954 and 1955, southern Baldwin Co., H. M. Stevenson); also June 3, 1940 (streaked young, Lillian, H. M. Stevenson) and August 31, 1948 (4 birds, Robertsdale, H. M. Stevenson and T. A. Imhof); most seen, 114, December 28, 1959 (Mobile, J. L. Dorn).

TIME OF BREEDING. Data on 22 nestings: Building, April 14 to June 21; eggs, April 2 to June 28; young in nest, April 27 to July 20; dependent young out of nest, May 8 to June 23.

BANDING. At least 25 Chipping Sparrows banded in Alabama have been recaptured at the same place in a later winter. Recoveries on 1 Alabama-banded bird and 4 Alabama-recovered birds are listed below: *Banded*, Auburn, April 2, 1923; *recovered*, Newcomb, Tennessee, May 1926; *banded*, Orlando, Florida, March 24, 1939; *recovered*, Marion, December 25, 1939; *banded*, Cobourg, Ontario, August 22, 1939; *recovered*, Eufaula, January 25, 1940; *banded*, Collegedale, Tennessee, October 24, 1949; *recovered*, Bessemer, January 13, 1950; *banded*, Goshen, Virginia, May 7, 1947; *recovered*, Sylacauga, March 30, 1949.

[Clay-colored Sparrow]
Spizella pallida (Swainson)   [561]   (Plate 42, facing page 560)

This sparrow with its clear whitish under parts and white line over the eye closely resembles the Chipping Sparrow of the same size, but the adult Clay-colored Sparrow may be identified by the *pale stripe through its brownish crown, black-bordered brown cheeks,* and *buffy rump.* Immature Clay-colored Sparrows are often difficult to separate from Chipping Sparrows of the same age, which also have dark cheeks, but Clay-colored Sparrows are distinguished by *buffy rumps in any plumage.* The thin-noted chip resembles that of others of the *Spizella* genus, but the song is an insect-like buzz.

In Alabama this species is a casual fall transient on the Gulf Coast and is not known to breed here. It frequents openings in woods, woodland borders, and open shrubby areas.

NESTING AND FOOD. The bulky grass nest is in thick grass on the ground or less than six feet high in a shrub or sapling. A clutch usually consists of four bluish-green eggs spotted with black or brown. This species feeds on weed seeds, waste grain, and insects.

DISTRIBUTION. The Clay-colored Sparrow breeds from northern British Columbia and western Ontario south to Colorado and Iowa, rarely to northern Texas, and possibly also in Illinois and Indiana. It winters in Mexico and southern Texas and wanders casually eastward on migration to most of the southeastern states.

OCCURRENCE IN ALABAMA. *Gulf Coast only*: Dauphin Island, September 16, 1960, after Hurricane Ethel (3 birds, J. L. Dorn); November 6, 1959 (an adult, T. A. Imhof) and November 8, 1959 (4 birds, Idalene Snead and many others).

Field Sparrow
Spizella pusilla (Wilson)   [563]   (Plate 42, facing page 560)
OTHER NAME: Grass Sparrow

The Field Sparrow is readily identified by its *pink bill, clear,* light grayish *under parts,* and a *white eye ring* which gives it a blank expression. The *crown* and a streak on each side of the breast are *reddish-brown.* The call is a thin, high-pitched note, and the song is a sweet and plaintive whistle of many syllables, ascending the scale.

[559]

PLATE 42

BACHMAN'S SPARROW
Adult, Sexes Alike
Page 553

WHITE-THROATED SPARROW
Adult, Sexes Alike
Page 565

WHITE-THROATED SPARROW
Immature
Page 565

TREE SPARROW
Adult, Sexes Alike
Page 556

WHITE-CROWNED SPARROW
Adult, Sexes Alike
Page 563

WHITE-CROWNED SPARROW
Immature
Page 563

FIELD SPARROW
Adult, Sexes Alike
Page 559

CHIPPING SPARROW
Adult, Sexes Similar
Page 557

HARRIS' SPARROW
Adult, Spring, Sexes Alike
Page 562

HARRIS' SPARROW
Immature
Page 562

CLAY-COLORED SPARROW
Immature
Page 559

LARK SPARROW
Adult, Sexes Alike
Page 550

CLAY-COLORED SPARROW
Adult, Sexes Alike
Page 559

[560]

Richard A. Parks

NEST OF FIELD SPARROW. This compact nest was found at the base of dog fennel.

In Alabama this sparrow is common as a breeder in summer south at least to the Lower Coastal Plain and is possibly rare on the Gulf Coast. In winter it is abundant and widespread throughout the state. Usually it occurs in brushy fields, old overgrown pastures, woods borders, and the like, and it is the most common sparrow of broomsedge fields.

NESTING. The nest is a well-built structure of grasses, weed stems, and rootlets lined with finer grasses and hair. Usually on the ground in a tuft of grass, it also is often low in thick bushes. The female lays three to five pale greenish-white or bluish-white eggs marked with reddish-brown.

FOOD. The diet of this bird consists of insects and seeds in almost equal amounts; the insects are consumed mainly in summer and seeds primarily in winter. Animal items include beetles of many kinds, grasshoppers, caterpillars, leafhoppers, sawflies, bugs, ants, flies, wasps, and also spiders. The seeds chiefly include those of broomsedge, pigeongrass, crabgrass, and some grain, mainly oats from stubble fields. It also consumes a few berries.

DISTRIBUTION. The Field Sparrow breeds from northwestern Montana, central Minnesota, and southern Quebec south to eastern Texas, the southern parts of the Gulf states, and rarely northern Florida. It winters from Kansas, central Ohio, southern Pennsylvania, and southern Massachusetts south to northern Mexico and southern Florida.

OCCURRENCE IN ALABAMA. (Throughout the year.) *Tennessee Valley*: Permanent resident; most seen, 249, December 23, 1943 (Christmas Count, Decatur). *Mountain Region*: Permanent resident; most seen, 733, December 26, 1959 (Christmas Count, Birmingham) and 400, December 24, 1915 (Anniston, R. H. Dean). *Piedmont*: Permanent resident. *Upper Coastal Plain*: Permanent resident; most seen, 171, December 25, 1937 (Christmas Count, Tuscaloosa). *Lower Coastal Plain*: Permanent resident. *Gulf Coast*: August 28 (1946, Foley, T. A. Imhof) to May 1 (1954, Gulf Shores, T. A. Imhof); most seen, 83, December 27, 1940 (Foley, H. M. Stevenson) and 81, December 28, 1956 (Christmas Count, Mobile).

TIME OF BREEDING. Data on 39 nestings: Building, April 8 to May 7; eggs, April 22 to August 23; young in nest, May 9 to August; dependent young out of nest, May 16 to August.

BANDING. At least 40 Alabama-banded Field Sparrows have been recaptured in a later winter at the place of banding. One August-banded bird was recaptured at the place of banding at Birmingham in January.

[Harris' Sparrow]
Zonotrichia querula (Nuttall)　[553]　(Plate 42, facing page 560)

This large, handsome sparrow is about the size of a towhee and is gray-brown streaked with darker brown. Its *crown, front of face,* and *throat* are *black,* the *bill* is *pink,* and the rest of the head is clear gray. The *immature* bird lacks the black area but has a *necklace* of *dark streaks.* The *pink bill* and *unmarked sides of head—buffy,* instead of gray—are distinctive marks. The call is a sharp chink and the song, although often containing chucking notes, is much like that of the White-crowned Sparrow. It consists of one or two clear whistled notes in a minor key and a third note in a different pitch.

This species has been recorded only once in Alabama—at Birmingham in spring. In winter the species frequents brushy and weedy areas near woods borders, hedgerows, brush piles, or along stream bottoms.

NESTING AND FOOD. The nest of vegetable fibers lined with grass is on the ground at the base of a shrub or small tree, often in a wet, mossy spot. The three to five eggs are pale greenish-white, heavily spotted with brown. This sparrow subsists mainly on the seeds of weeds and grasses including those of ragweed, sunflower, wild fruits, June grass, Johnson grass, pigeon-grass, crabgrass, and also some waste corn, wheat, and oats. Animal food consists of insects, spiders, and snails with a rather high proportion of leafhoppers.

DISTRIBUTION. Harris' Sparrow breeds from northern Mackenzie and southern Keewatin south to northeastern Saskatchewan and northern Manitoba. It winters from southern British Columbia and central Iowa south to southern California, southern Texas, Louisiana, and western Tennessee, casually farther east.

OCCURRENCE IN ALABAMA. *Mountain Region only*: April 7, 1953, an immature bird in a flock of White-crowned Sparrows at close range (Midfield, Birmingham, A. M. Imhof and T. A. Imhof).

White-crowned Sparrow
Zonotrichia leucophrys (Forster)   [554]   (Plate 42, facing page 560)

Slightly larger than its close relative, the White-throated Sparrow, the White-crowned Sparrow has *prominent black* and *white stripes* set at a *jaunty angle on its head*. The back is brown, streaked with dark brown, and the rump, under parts, and the rest of the head are pearly gray. The *immature* bird has *dark brown* and *light brown head stripes,* and in any plumage the species has a *pink bill*. The call is a sharp, almost Cardinal-like chink. The song is a plaintive whistle consisting of a long, loud note, usually the first or second, followed by several husky notes which are lower in pitch and volume.

In Alabama in winter the White-crowned Sparrow is common in the Tennessee Valley and uncommon and local in the rest of the state. It is unknown here as a breeder. (See Map 100.) Howell (1924:237) lists only two records for this conspicuous sparrow, and therefore it seems obvious that the species has increased considerably in the last forty-five years. Since this bird seems to require open weedy or grassy areas for feeding and thick shrubs for cover, it occurs most often in roadside thickets, hedgerows, woodland borders, and streamside thickets close to fields. In Alabama, flocks of about twenty occur in these places and apparently return each winter unless changes in land use alter the habitat.

NESTING AND FOOD. The bulky nest, on the ground or close to it in thick shrubs, is made of twigs, grass, rootlets, and bark strips and heavily lined with finer materials, including hair. The clutch consists of three to five greenish-blue eggs marked with brown. Most of this sparrow's food is vegetable, chiefly weed and grass seeds, but occasionally it varies its diet with buds, blossoms, wild fruit, and waste grain. It takes such insects as caterpillars, beetles, ants, wasps, bugs, and scale insects.

PASSERIFORMES: FRINGILLIDAE: WHITE-CROWNED SPARROW

DISTRIBUTION. The White-crowned Sparrow breeds from northern Alaska, northern Mackenzie, northern Quebec, and Newfoundland south to central California, northern New Mexico, central Manitoba, and southeastern Quebec. It winters from southern British Columbia, Wyoming, Kansas, Kentucky, and western North Carolina south to central Mexico, coastal Alabama, and northwestern Florida.

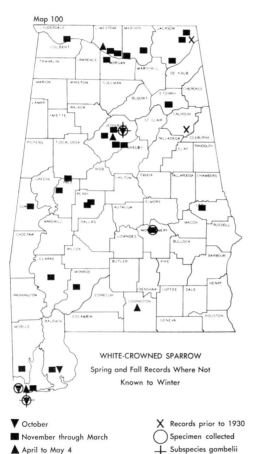

Map 100

WHITE-CROWNED SPARROW
Spring and Fall Records Where Not
Known to Winter

▼ October   X Records prior to 1930
■ November through March   ◯ Specimen collected
▲ April to May 4   + Subspecies gambelii

OCCURRENCE IN ALABAMA.
(October 7 to May 14.) *Tennessee Valley*: October 26 (1956, Scottsboro, T. A. Imhof and M. W. Gaillard and 1958, Huntsville, J. C. and Margaret Robinson) to May 14 (1960,

Marysville, Madison Co., J. C. and Margaret Robinson); most seen, 50, January 2, 1954 (Christmas Count, Decatur). *Mountain Region*: October 17 (1956, Birmingham, T. A. Imhof, F. B. Daniel, and Emmy Brownlie) to April 26 (1917, Sand Mountain near Carpenter, Jackson Co., E. W. Graves); most seen, 47, December 26, 1953 (Christmas Count, Birmingham). *Piedmont*: January 2 (1954, Auburn, J. L. Dusi) to April 13 (1924, Auburn, J. M. Robertson). *Upper Coastal Plain*: October 27 (1956, Marion, Lois Mc-Collough) to April 28 (1953, trapped and banded, Montgomery, O. L. Austin, Jr.); most seen, 42, December 27, 1957 (Christmas Count, Marion). *Lower Coastal Plain*: Most of January 1954 (Grove Hill, G. A. Carleton); February 10, 1956 (Wainwright, Monroe Co., T. A. Imhof and W. F. Colin); and April 2, 1953 and April 27, 1952 (Andalusia, W. R. Middleton). *Gulf Coast*: October 7 (1956, specimen in the Florida State Univ. collection, Dauphin Island, R. T. Lynn and others) to April 13 (1957, Theodore, Mr. and Mrs. R. T. Lynn and M. W. Gaillard).

SUBSPECIES. *Zonotrichia leucophrys gambelii* (Nuttall) of the west, which can be identified at close range by the fact that the white stripe starts from the eye instead of from the bill, has been recorded twice in fall in Alabama, November 3, 1956, specimen in Univ. of Ala. collection taken during banding operations (Birmingham, T. A. Imhof, Idalene Snead, and Lois McCollough) and November 7, 1959, specimen in Florida State Univ. collection (Dauphin Island, T. A. Imhof, H. M. Stevenson, and others). See Map 100.

BANDING. A bird banded at Deerfield, Mass., May 17, 1950 was found at Mooresville, Limestone Co., February 7, 1951. At least 1 Alabama-banded bird has returned to the place of banding the next winter.

[564]

[Golden-crowned Sparrow]
Zonotrichia atricapilla (Gmelin)   [557]

This species looks much like a White-crowned Sparrow, but the adult Golden-crowned Sparrow is more olive-colored on the upper parts and is easily distinguished by the *black-bordered yellowish crown* and lack of white eye stripe. Because the crown stripes are duller in immature birds of both species, the immatures are more difficult to separate, but the young Golden-crowned Sparrow can be distinguished by the fact that it *does not have* the *pale eye stripe* of the other species, and thus can always be identified.

In Alabama this species is accidental in fall on the Gulf Coast. Like the White-crowned Sparrow, the Golden-crowned frequents hedgerows and field borders.

NESTING AND FOOD. These habits are essentially the same as those of the White-crowned Sparrow.

DISTRIBUTION. The Golden-crowned Sparrow breeds from western Alaska and southern Yukon south to northern Washington and southwestern Alberta. It winters from British Columbia south to Lower California and Sonora and east to Utah and New Mexico, casually, mostly in fall, to the Atlantic and Gulf coasts.

OCCURRENCE IN ALABAMA. *Gulf Coast only*: November 9, 1957, an adult observed at very close range (Little Dauphin Island, Ava Tabor and others).

White-throated Sparrow
Zonotrichia albicollis (Gmelin)   [558]   (Plate 42, facing page 560)
OTHER NAME: Whitethroat

This sparrow has *black* and *white stripes* on the *crown* similar to those of the White-crowned Sparrow, although they are not set at a jaunty angle. The *white throat* outlined in black stands out against the unmarked gray of the under parts to distinguish the White-throated Sparrow in any plumage. The immature bird has dark brown and light brown head stripes and some streaking below, but is easily recognized. This species is more reddish brown than others of its genus. The call is a high, thin note and the song is a pleasing refrain of eleven syllables, the second of which is longest, loudest, and highest in pitch.

[565]

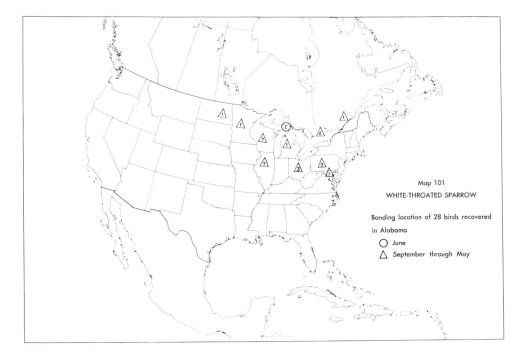

Map 101

WHITE-THROATED SPARROW

Banding location of 28 birds recovered
in Alabama

○ June
△ September through May

This species is abundant in winter throughout Alabama and it has summered here several times although it is not known to breed. Frequenting thickets in or near woods and feeding on the ground near cover, it is especially common in shrubbery around houses, and it is probably the best winter customer at most feeding stations in Alabama. It is decidedly more active at dusk than most sparrows.

NESTING AND FOOD. The nest, on the ground or slightly above it in a thick conifer, is a bulky cup of bark strips, coarse grass, rootlets, and moss, lined with finer grass and hair. The four to five pale greenish eggs are marked with brown. This sparrow feeds on weed and grass seeds, especially those of ragweed and bindweed, and also on plant buds. Fruits such as those of blueberry, wild cherry, mountain-ash, greenbrier, strawberry, spicebush, sarsaparilla, elder, blackberry, dogwood, and cranberry are also prominent in its diet. It also takes such insect food as beetles (including boll weevils), ants, and wasps. Much of its food is obtained by scratching on the ground among old leaves like a towhee.

DISTRIBUTION. The White-throated Sparrow breeds from southern Yukon, central Quebec, and Newfoundland south to central British Columbia, southern Saskatchewan, central Wisconsin, northern Ohio, southeastern New York, and central New England. It winters from northern California, eastern Kansas, the Ohio Valley, central New York, and central New England south to southern Texas, the northern Gulf Coast, and northern Florida.

OCCURRENCE IN ALABAMA. (Normal: October 2 to May 21; Out-of-season: September 20 and 24 and several times through the summer.) *Tennessee Valley*: October 7 (1951, Wheeler Refuge, D. C. Hulse) to May 21 (Wheeler Refuge, *fide* T. Z. Atkeson, Jr.). *Mountain Region*: October 2 (1948, Talladega, C. T. Hornady) to May 21 (1940, Birmingham, H. M. Stevenson); also September 20 and 24, 1958 (Birmingham, Idalene Snead); July 2, 1931, a singing bird (Jasper, H. M. Stevenson) and 1 bird, apparently the same individual, throughout the summers of 1958, 1959, 1960, and 1961 (Mountain Brook, Birmingham, Emmy Lou Grimley); most seen, 778, December 26, 1959 (Christmas Count, Birmingham). *Piedmont*: October 3 (1948, Auburn, H. G. Good) to May 10 (1953, 12 birds, Auburn, H. G. Good); most seen, 204, January 2, 1954 (Christmas Count, Auburn). *Upper Coastal Plain*: October 9 (1953, specimen in Univ. of Ala. collection, Tuscaloosa,

Ottilie Chermock) to May 14 (1939, Tuscaloosa, H. M. Stevenson); also a pair, June 19 to July 4, 1921 (Pine Creek, Autauga Co., L. S. Golsan); most seen, 419, December 25, 1937 (Christmas Count, Tuscaloosa). *Lower Coastal Plain*: October 13 (1958, 5 birds, Camden, Lovett Williams) to May 13 (1954, trapped and banded, Clayton, Barbour Co., J. E. Keeler); most seen, 350, February 10, 1956 (Monroe Co., T. A. Imhof and W. F. Colin). *Gulf Coast*: October 11 (1958, Dauphin Island, Lovett Williams and R. W. Skinner) to May 20 (1957, Spring Hill, M. W. Gaillard); most seen, 878, December 28, 1959 (Mobile, J. L. Dorn).

BANDING. At least 65 Alabama-banded "Whitethroats" have returned to the place of banding in a later winter; 3 of them were at least 5 years old and 3 of them at least 4 years old. For place of banding of 28 others recovered in a fairly even distribution throughout Alabama, see Map 101.

Fox Sparrow

Passerella iliaca (Merrem)   [585]   (Plate 41, facing page 552)

This big sparrow has the *same gray* and *red colors* as a *fox*. It is gray above and whitish below, *heavily streaked* with reddish-brown, and has a *reddish-brown* rump and *tail*. Although the Hermit Thrush is about the same size and has the same reddish-brown tail, these two species are otherwise very different. The loud, clear, and sweet song of the Fox Sparrow consists of various combinations of short whistles slurred into other notes so that it rises and then falls in pitch.

In Alabama the Fox Sparrow, which is not known to breed here, is common but somewhat local in winter south to the Black Belt. In the Lower Coastal Plain it is rare to uncommon and local, but in severe, snowy winters it becomes more common throughout the state, and small numbers reach the Gulf Coast. It frequents the same general areas in this state as does the White-throated Sparrow, but the Fox Sparrow usually chooses more open places. After a snowfall it often appears in places from which it is normally absent.

Richard A Parks

NESTING AND FOOD. The nest, on or near the ground in thick evergreens, is made of plant fibers lined with fine grass, fur, or feathers. The female lays four or five pale greenish eggs heavily marked with reddish-brown. Weed seeds, especially those of ragweed and smartweed, and small wild fruits are the major food items, and it eats less grass seeds and waste grain than other sparrows. It also consumes such animal food as ground beetles and millipedes. To obtain its food it scratches vigorously on the ground among dead leaves. At feeding stations it eats suet and cracked corn.

DISTRIBUTION. The Fox Sparrow breeds from northwestern Alaska, northern Mackenzie, northern Manitoba, and northern Quebec south to southern California, Colorado, central Ontario, southern Quebec, and Newfoundland. It winters from British Columbia, Kansas, southern Wisconsin, southern Ontario, and New Brunswick south to Lower California, southern Texas, and central Florida.

Map 102

LINCOLN'S SPARROW
Distribution

▼ October 14 to November 30
■ December to March 15
▲ March 16 to May 25

◯ Specimen collected
✝ Banded

OCCURRENCE IN ALABAMA. (October 24 to April 7.) *Tennessee Valley*: October 24 (1959, 2 birds, Huntsville, J. C. and Margaret Robinson) to April 7 (1951, Wheeler Refuge, D. C. Hulse). *Mountain Region*: October 31 (1952, Gadsden, Edith Clark) to April 6 (1954, Gadsden, Edith Clark); most seen, 41, December 20, 1958 (Christmas Count, Birmingham). *Piedmont*: November 28 (1953, Roanoke, H. M. Stevenson and 1957, Auburn, Lovett Williams) to March 25 (1959, Auburn, Lovett Williams). *Upper Coastal Plain*: November 1 (1957, Livingston, Jenkins Jackson) to March 22 (1958, Marion, Lois McCollough); most seen, about 200, mid-December 1953 to early February 1954 (Tuscaloosa, R. L. Chermock). *Lower Coastal Plain*: December 1 (1958, Camden, Lovett Williams) to March 29 (1957, Jackson, W. U. Harris); most seen, 7, December 9, 1958 (Camden, Lovett Williams). *Gulf Coast*: January 21 to 27, 1940, 15 to 20 birds (Spring Hill, J. L. Dorn); January 22, 1958, netted and banded (Hurricane, D. D. Stamm); and January 28 to March 7, 1960, up to 5 birds (Spring Hill, J. L. Dorn).

[569]

Lincoln's Sparrow

Melospiza lincolnii (Audubon)   [583]   (Plate 41, facing page 552)

Closely resembling its near relatives, the Swamp and Song Sparrows, Lincoln's Sparrow can be distinguished by its *broad creamy-buff breast band* with *fine, sharp streaks*. It has fine, sharp streaks on the rusty crown stripes, a narrow, pale eye ring, gray or slightly greenish sides to the head, and an occasional bird has a small central breast spot. Many sparrows, especially the immature Swamp Sparrow, partially fit the description of Lincoln's Sparrow, but they usually have blurry or coarse streaks, are extensively buffy below, or possibly lack buffiness altogether. The observer must spot *both* of the *italicized field marks* exactly in order to identify Lincoln's Sparrow with certainty. The song of this species is a hurried trill, sweet and gurgling, with some buzzier notes, and suggestive of songs of the House Wren and Purple Finch.

In Alabama this shy sparrow has thus far proved to be rare in winter in the western part of the Black Belt and on the Gulf Coast. On migration it is uncommon in the Tennessee Valley (spring only), the Upper Coastal Plain, and the Gulf Coast, rare around Birmingham, and unknown elsewhere. It is not known to breed in the state. (See Map 102.) The species is a skulker which frequents streamside thickets and other wet, shrubby areas where it usually remains on the ground out of sight, but a squeaking noise usually brings it into full view.

NESTING AND FOOD. The female lays three to five pale greenish eggs, heavily marked with brown, in a nest of grass and sedges well hidden on the ground in swampy places. Like the Song Sparrow, this species subsists on weed and grass seeds in great variety, supplemented, mostly in summer, with insects, but Lincoln's Sparrow appears to eat more ants and fewer grasshoppers. One Alabama specimen was full of black weed seeds.

DISTRIBUTION. Lincoln's Sparrow breeds from northwestern Alaska, northern Quebec, and Newfoundland south to southern California, northern New Mexico, northern Minnesota, central Michigan, New York, and Nova Scotia. It winters from northern California, northern New Mexico, Oklahoma, Missouri, and northern Georgia south to El Salvador and central Florida.

OCCURRENCE IN ALABAMA. (Normal: October 14 to May 11; Out-of-season: May 25.) *Tennessee Valley*: May 2 (1959, trapped and banded, Huntsville, Margaret Robinson) to May 11 (1941, Florence, H. M. Stevenson); also May 25, 1941

(Florence, H. M. Stevenson); most seen, 3, May 10, 1941 (Florence, H. M. Stevenson). *Mountain Region*: Birmingham (April 11, 1937, H. M. Stevenson); May 4, 1940 (H. M. Stevenson); and November 3, 1956 (3 birds netted, 1 now specimen in Univ. of Ala. collection, T. A. Imhof, Idalene Snead, and Lois McCollough). *Piedmont*: No record. *Upper Coastal Plain*: October 17 (1958, Livingston, Jenkins Jackson) to May 1 (1937, Tuscaloosa, H. M. Stevenson); most seen, 10, March 9, 1957 (Marion, Lois McCollough). *Lower Coastal Plain*: No record. *Gulf Coast*: October 14 (1960, 2 birds netted, banded, and photographed in color, Dauphin Island, T. A. Imhof, Ethel Floyd, and many others) to April 13 (1957, Gulf Shores, B. L. Monroe, Jr., F. M. Weston, and L. E. Goodnight).

Swamp Sparrow
Melospiza georgiana (Latham)   [584]   (Plate 41, facing page 552)

The Swamp Sparrow has *reddish-brown upper parts* and *crown,* a *white throat,* and unstreaked grayish under parts which become paler on the belly. In fall it is buffier, and in immature plumages it is streaked on the breast. As an immature it resembles Lincoln's Sparrow, but the Swamp Sparrow has darker and redder upper parts, more extensively buffy under parts, and blurry, instead of fine and sharp, streaks on the breast and crown. Its song is a slow trill, louder and more musical than that of the Chipping Sparrow, and often with two notes in a different pitch trilled at the same time. The call is a sharp chink, suggestive of that of the White-throated Sparrow and also quite similar to the call of the Eastern Phoebe.

This species is abundant in winter throughout Alabama, but it is not known to breed here. It is most numerous in fresh marshes and pond borders but generally occurs wherever shrubs, grasses, and weeds grow in or near water. These places are often dry in summer, but when flooded by winter rains, they adequately fit the requirements of this sparrow. On migration birds often frequent woods borders or other grassy or weedy places far from water.

NESTING AND FOOD. The female lays four or five pale greenish or bluish eggs marked with brown in a nest of grasses and leaves on or near the ground in dense marsh vegetation. Most of this bird's diet consists of the seeds of bindweed, millet, ragweed, other weeds, sedges, and other grasses. Grasshoppers, caterpillars, weevils, other beetles, bugs, ants, and flies are the main insect items.

DISTRIBUTION. The Swamp Sparrow breeds from central Mackenzie, northern Manitoba, central Quebec, and Newfoundland south to northeastern British Columbia, Nebraska, northern Illinois, West Virginia, and coastal Maryland. It winters from Nebraska, southern Wisconsin, central New York, and Massachusetts south to central Mexico and southern Florida.

[571]

OCCURRENCE IN ALABAMA. (Normal: September 29 to May 11; Out-of-season: September 14.) *Tennessee Valley*: October 14 (1941, Wheeler Refuge, J. H. Steenis) to May 11 (1941, Florence, H. M. Stevenson). *Mountain Region*: September 29 (1958, Fairfield, T. A. Imhof) to May 11 (1955, Birmingham, J. B. Sullivan); most seen, 181, December 26, 1959 (Christmas Count, Birmingham). *Piedmont*: October 29 (1958, Auburn, Lovett Williams) to May 4 (1955, Auburn, H. G. Good). *Upper Coastal Plain*: October 6 (1956, Livingston, Jenkins Jackson) to May 6 (1939, Tuscaloosa, H. M. Stevenson); also September 14, 1958 (Marion, Lois McCollough). *Lower Coastal Plain*: October 14 (1958, 6 birds, Camden, Lovett Williams) to May 1 (1952, Andalusia, W. R. Middleton). *Gulf Coast*: October 6 (1956, by 4 parties, Fall Count, Mobile Bay Area) to April 26 (1958, Cedar Point, T. A. Imhof and Baldwin Co., H. M. Stevenson); most seen, migration, 320, October 19, 1957 (Fall Count, Mobile Bay Area), winter, 122, January 2, 1960 (Christmas Count, Dauphin Island).

BANDING. At least 8 Swamp Sparrows banded in Alabama have returned to the same place in a later winter.

Song Sparrow

Melospiza melodia (Wilson)   [581]   (Plate 41, facing page 552)

This medium-sized, plain sparrow has dark grayish-brown streaks on lighter grayish-brown and is lighter-colored below where the *coarse streaks* converge to form a *prominent central breast spot*. The Song Sparrow can generally be distinguished from other streaked sparrows because its breast streaks are so conspicuous. A good clue to its identity is a jerky flight movement caused by the pumping of the rather long tail. The call is a low, rather nasal chip, distinctive in quality; and the song starts off with three or four similar notes and ends in a variable jumble of sounds that is almost a trill.

In winter this species is abundant throughout the state, and since 1954 or possibly earlier it has occurred in summer in at least three towns in DeKalb County in northeastern Alabama where one instance of its breeding is known. Since it is an adaptable species which breeds abundantly in disturbance habitats, it will probably follow the pattern of the Eastern Phoebe, Horned Lark, Robin, Loggerhead Shrike, Brown-headed Cowbird, and others that have recently extended their breeding ranges in this state. The Song Sparrow occupies sunlit, brushy, weedy, or shrubby places near water, although on migration and in winter it often frequents thickets far from water.

NESTING. The nest is a well-built structure of grass, weed stems, and leaves lined with finer grass and hair. It is well hidden on the ground or, usually later in the season, a few feet up in the dense cover of a conifer, thick shrub, or in matted grass or weeds. The four or five greenish eggs are usually marked heavily with various shades of brown.

[572]

FOOD. Most of the food of this sparrow consists of the seeds of grasses, bindweed, ragweed, various grains, sunflower, clover, dandelion, chickweed, dock, amaranth, spurge, and many another weed. Insect food mainly includes weevils and other beetles, but also ants, wasps, bugs, caterpillars, and grasshoppers.

DISTRIBUTION. The Song Sparrow breeds from southern Alaska, including the Aleutian Islands, southern Mackenzie, central Quebec, and Newfoundland south to central Mexico, northern Arkansas, northeastern Alabama, northern Georgia, northwestern South Carolina, and coastal Virginia. It winters from the Aleutian Islands, British Columbia, Montana, southern Wisconsin, southern Ontario, and Nova Scotia south to central Mexico and southern Florida.

OCCURRENCE IN ALABAMA. (Throughout the year, common, September 22 to May 10.) *Tennessee Valley*: October 9 (1913, Long Island, E. W. Graves) to May 4 (1947, Wheeler Refuge, J. L. Dusi and others); also May 15, 1941 (Wheeler Refuge, J. H. Steenis) and June 5, year unknown (Wheeler Refuge, T. Z. Atkeson, Jr.); most seen, 209, December 31, 1954 (Christmas Count, Wheeler Refuge). *Mountain Region*: September 22 (1949, Birmingham, T. A. Imhof) to May 10 (1931, Jasper, H. M. Stevenson); summers in DeKalb Co.; most seen, 278, December 22, 1956 (Christmas Count, Birmingham). *Piedmont*: October 29 (1958, Auburn, Lovett Williams) to April 30 (1959, Auburn, Lovett Williams). *Upper Coastal Plain*: September 29 (1958, Marion, Lois McCollough) to April 18 (1956, Marion, Lois McCollough). *Lower Coastal Plain*: October 11 (1949, Andalusia, W. R. Middleton) to April 17 (1958, Jackson, W. U. Harris). *Gulf Coast*: October 12 (1957, Dauphin Island, S. A. Gauthreaux) to April 21 (1956, Alabama Port, T. A. Imhof and others); most seen, 100, December 28, 1956 (Christmas Count, Mobile).

TIME OF BREEDING. Data on 1 nesting: Young in nest, June 4, 1954 (Valley Head, T. A. Imhof, H. M. Stevenson, and many others).

BANDING. Two Song Sparrows, banded at Branchport, N. Y., have been found in Alabama, 1 at Keener, Etowah Co., January 2, 1932, and the other at Wetumpka, November 28, 1932. At least 7 others banded in Alabama have been recaptured at the same place in a later winter.

Lapland Longspur
Calcarius lapponicus (Linnaeus)   [536]   (Plate 43, facing page 568)

Open-country birds that often associate with Horned Larks, longspurs have the conical bill of sparrows, but in addition have *long, pointed wings* and a hind claw about as long as the hind toe. In *winter* the Lapland Longspur is a rather plain, streaked brown bird with *two white wing bars*, a little white in the *outer tail feathers, streaked flanks*, and a few *dark* but indistinct *markings* on the *head*. As *spring* advances, the *male* acquires a *black crown, face, throat*, and sides and a *reddish-brown collar*. The *female* is *whiter* on the *belly* and more *prominently streaked* than other female longspurs. This longspur may be distinguished from a lark by its shorter tail and more bounding flight. The flight call is a dry, rattling, distinctive ticking of four notes, the last of which is prolonged, and the song is a pleasing, gurgling refrain a good deal like that of the Bobolink.

The Lapland Longspur, which is not known to nest in Alabama, is common to abundant in winter in the Tennessee Valley, the northern parts of the Mountain Region, and in the Black Belt. Elsewhere it is irregular and usually occurs only when regions to the north are covered with snow. (See Map 103.) Like the Horned Lark, it frequents such open places as airports, barren fields, pastures, and beaches.

NESTING AND FOOD. The nest, made of grass and moss and lined with feathers, fur, or hair, is on the ground, sheltered by grass or a small shrub, and the three to six pale greenish-gray eggs it holds are heavily marked with brown and purple. The usual diet of this species includes many different grass seeds.

DISTRIBUTION. The Lapland Longspur breeds in the Eastern and Western hemispheres, in North America from northwestern Alaska to central Greenland south to the limit of trees (Aleutian Islands, central Alaska, northern Mackenzie, northern Manitoba, and northern Quebec). It winters from British Columbia, central Minnesota, and southern Quebec south to northeastern California, northeastern Texas, central Alabama, and South Carolina, rarely farther south.

OCCURRENCE IN ALABAMA. (November 14 to March 27.) *Tennessee Valley*: December 26 (1949, Wheeler Refuge, T. A. Imhof) to March 27 (1960, Courtland, J. C. and Margaret Robinson); most seen, 3000+, March 20, 1960 (Courtland, J. C. and Margaret Robinson). *Mountain Region*: November 14 (1957, Gadsden, Edith Clark) to February 23 (1957, Gadsden, Edith Clark); most seen, 25, December 26, 1959 (Birmingham, Frederick T. Carney) and 22, including 2 specimens in Univ. of Ala. collection, January 21, 1956 (Gadsden, T. A. Imhof and others). *Piedmont*: No record. *Upper Coastal Plain*: December 1 (1956, 60 birds, Marion, Lois McCollough) to February 26 (1959, Montgomery, R. W. Skinner); most seen, 210, December 13, 1958 (Montgomery, T. A. Imhof and R. W. Skinner), 80, January 26, 1957 (Marion, Lois McCollough and Harriett Wright), 2 specimens in Dept. of Conservation collection, December 12, 1958 (Montgomery, R. W. Skinner and J. E. Keeler). *Lower Coastal Plain*: No record. *Gulf Coast*: No record.

Smith's Longspur
Calcarius pictus (Swainson)   [537]   (Plate 43, facing page 568)

In winter, Smith's Longspur has dark brown streaks on buff with white outer tail feathers. It is best separated from other longspurs by its lightly-streaked, *buffy-brown under parts*. Besides the usual longspur characteristics—the long pointed wing, long hind claw, short tail, and conical bill—it can be recognized as a longspur by its flight, its actions, and the open-country habitat it frequents. This species has one prominent wing bar, more noticeable in the male. In *spring* the *male* becomes richer buff on the under parts and acquires a black crown and a *triangular black ear patch* with a *white center*. The dry, rattling flight call differs from that of the Lapland Longspur in lacking the final prolonged note. The song is quite similar to the flight call, but longer.

Smith's Longspur is rare or casual in winter in short-grass areas in Alabama, and it is not known to breed here. It often occurs in this state immediately after a snowstorm to the north. This longspur usually forms flocks of its own, but in Alabama, at the edge of its range, the few individuals which do occur generally flock with Lapland Longspurs.

NESTING AND FOOD. The clutch consists of four to six clay-colored eggs marked with purplish-brown. The nest, on the tundra in a cluster of moss or sedges or in a self-dug hole, is made of grass and lined with plant down and feathers. Little is known of the food of this species, but it probably feeds on grass seed supplemented in summer by grass-dwelling insects and berries. The Alabama specimen contained many grass seeds.

DISTRIBUTION. Smith's Longspur breeds from northern Alaska and northern Mackenzie south to northern Manitoba and northern Ontario. It winters from Kansas and Iowa south to central Texas and Louisiana, and east somewhat irregularly to Ohio, western Tennessee, and central Alabama.

OCCURRENCE IN ALABAMA. (December 5, 13, and 27 and January 17.) *Tennessee Valley:* No record. *Mountain Region:* December 5, 1955 (2 birds in a flock of Lapland Longspurs, Birmingham, T. A. Imhof, Idalene Snead, and Emmy Brownlie) and January 17, 1956 (1 lone female, now specimen in Univ. of Ala. collection, Birmingham, T. A. Imhof and Idalene Snead). *Piedmont:* No record. *Upper Coastal Plain:* December 13, 1958 (2 with Lapland Longspurs, No. 4 prison farm, Montgomery, T. A. Imhof and R. W. Skinner) and December 27, 1957 (1 with Lapland Longspurs, Lakeland Farm, Marion, T. A. Imhof and D. C. Holliman). *Lower Coastal Plain:* No record. *Gulf Coast:* No record.

[Snow Bunting]
Plectrophenax nivalis (Linnaeus) [534] (Plate 43, facing page 568)

The Snow Bunting looks like a *longspur with much white* in its plumage. In fall and winter, it is streaked reddish-brown above with patches of the same color on the head, cheeks, and breast. The head, belly, *wing patches*, and rump are largely *white*. As spring advances, the bill changes from pale to black

[575]

and the head and under parts lose the reddish-brown and become pure white, but the female usually retains some reddish-brown, especially on the back. The calls, which sound much like that of a melodious longspur, are a sweet whistle, a purring note, and a rough, sharp buzz.

This species is accidental in winter in Alabama in the same type of open country as that frequented by larks and longspurs. (See Map 103.) Elsewhere it occurs on beaches and on balds in the southern Appalachian Mountains.

NESTING AND FOOD. The deep and thick-walled nest of moss, dry grass, and earth is profusely lined with feathers and fur and well hidden in rocks or low foliage. The four to six whitish eggs are spotted with reddish-brown. This bird feeds on the seeds of many grasses and of such weeds as pigweed and ragweed, and it also eats locust eggs.

Map 103

LONGSPURS AND SNOW BUNTING

Distribution

Lapland Longspur (November 14 to March 27)

Smith's Longspur

Snow Bunting

Specimen collected

DISTRIBUTION. The Snow Bunting breeds in the Western Hemisphere from northern Alaska and northern Greenland (at latitude 83°, farther north than any other land bird) south to central Alaska, central Mackenzie, and northern Quebec. It winters from southern Alaska, southern Manitoba, and southern Quebec south to Oregon, Kansas, Indiana, Pennsylvania, in mountains to Tennessee, coastal North Carolina, and rarely farther south in cold winters.

OCCURRENCE IN ALABAMA. *Mountain Region only*: January 24, 1940 (during a severe freeze, 1 bird, Municipal Airport, Birmingham, H. M. Stevenson).

BIBLIOGRAPHY

ADAMS, WILLIAM H., JR. 1958. Some nesting records from Cleburne County, Alabama. Ala. Birdlife, 6:17.

ALLEN, ROBERT P. 1942. The Roseate Spoonbill. Nat. Aud. Soc. Res. Rept. No. 2. Pp. 142.

AMERICAN ORNITHOLOGISTS' UNION COMMITTEE. 1957. Check-list of North American birds. 5th ed. Baltimore. Pp. xiii, 691.

ARANT, FRANK S. 1939. The status of game birds and mammals in Alabama. Ala. Coop. Wildlife Research Unit. Auburn. Pp. 38.

ARFWEDSON, C. D. 1834. The United States and Canada in 1832, 1833, and 1834. 2 vols. London.

ATKESON, THOMAS Z., JR. 1954. Wintering Blue and Snow Geese in northern Alabama. Wilson Bull., 66:63-64.

———. 1955. Ground Dove records from the Tennessee Valley. Ala. Birdlife, 3:5-6.

———. 1955. White Pelican records from Wheeler Reservoir. Ala. Birdlife, 3:4-5.

———. 1956. Anhinga records from northern Alabama. Ala. Birdlife, 4:22-23.

———. 1956. Pied-billed Grebe nesting records from the Tennessee Valley. Ala. Birdlife, 4:6.

———. 1957. Ibis records from the Tennessee Valley. Ala. Birdlife, 5:9-10.

———. 1957. A White-fronted Goose record for Alabama. Ala. Birdlife, 5:24-25.

———. 1958. Goldeneye, Old Squaw, and Greater Scaup records from Wheeler Reservoir. Ala. Birdlife, 6 (Nos. 3, 4):15-16.

———. 1958. Whistling Swan records from Wheeler Refuge. Ala. Birdlife, 6:11-12.

———. 1958. White-winged Scoter records from Wheeler Reservoir. Ala. Birdlife, 6 (Nos. 3, 4):14.

———. 1959. Godwit and Curlew records from Wheeler Refuge. Ala. Birdlife, 7:10-11.

———. 1959. Plover records from the Mid-Tennessee Valley. Ala. Birdlife, 7:19.

———, Edith Clark, Julian L. Dusi, M. Wilson Gaillard, Dan C. Holliman, Thomas A. Imhof, James E. Keeler, James C. Robinson, Margaret L. Robinson, and Harriett H. Wright. 1959-61. Regional wingbeats. Ala. Birdlife, 7:20-23; 8:9-12, 15-17, 26-27; 9:7-10, 17-20.

——— and David C. Hulse. 1954. Northern Alabama notes on the Caspian Tern (*Hydroprogne caspia*). Ala. Birdlife, 2:35.

AVERY, W. C. 1884. Bird migration. Amer. Field, 21:545.

———. 1886. Domestication of the Wild Turkey. Amer. Field, 26:343.

———. 1886. Migration of the Coot. Orn. and Ool., 11:107.

———. 1887. Wiles of the Peregrine Falcon. Orn. and Ool., 12:74-75.

———. 1888. King Rail in Louisiana [misprint for Alabama]. Orn. and Ool., 13:80.

———. 1889. *Chondestes grammacus*. Amer. Field, 32:200.

———. 1889. Notes. Amer. Field, 32:223.

———. 1889. Observations on the Grasshopper Sparrow in Hale County, Alabama. Orn. and Ool., 14:122.

———. 1890. Number of eggs in a set of the Cardinal. Orn. and Ool., 15:185.

———. 1890. Swainson's Warbler in Hale County, Alabama. Orn. and Ool., 15:157.

———. 1890. The Woodcock. Amer. Field, 33:584.

———. 1890-91. Birds observed in Alabama. Amer. Field, 34:584, 607-08; 35:8, 32, 55.

———. 1893. [Natural history]. Amer. Field, 40:7.

———. 1893. [Rapidity of flight of the Duck Hawk]. Orn. and Ool., 18:144.

AUDUBON, JOHN JAMES. 1831-39. Ornithological biography, or an account of the habits of the birds of the United States of

BIBLIOGRAPHY

America, with descriptions of the American birds and delineations of American scenery and manners. 5 vols. Edinburgh.

BAERG, W. J. 1951. Birds of Arkansas. Univ. Ark. Agric. Exp. Sta. Bull. No. 258 (rev.). Pp. 188.

BAKER, MAURICE F. 1960. Bald Eagle at Gulf Shores. Ala. Birdlife, 8:14.

BAMBERG, JOHN. 1935. Nocturnal migration in stormy weather—a symposium by members. Migrant, 6:77-78.

———.1937. Notes from Wheeler Dam. Migrant, 8:40.

BARKALOW, FREDERICK S., JR. 1939. Records of the Sooty Tern and Swallow-tailed Kite in Alabama. Wilson Bull., 51: 121.

———. 1940. Black Vulture and red fox in unusual association. Wilson Bull., 52:278-79.

———. 1949. A game inventory of Alabama. Ala. Dept. of Conservation, Montgomery. Pp. x, 140.

BASKETT, JAMES NEWTON. 1899. Bird notes—south. Wilson Bull., 6 (No. 3):36-37.

BAUM, GEORGE. 1922. Notes from South Alabama. Wilson Bull., 34:234-35.

BENDIRE, CHARLES E. 1888. Notes on the nest and eggs of *Peucaea aestivalis bachmani* Aud., Bachman's Sparrow. Auk, 5:351-56.

———. 1892. Life histories of North American birds, with special reference to their breeding habits and eggs. U. S. Nat. Mus. Spec. Bull. Pp. 446.

———. 1896. Life histories of North American birds from the Parrots to the Crakles, with special reference to their breeding habits and eggs. U. S. Nat. Mus. Spec. Bull. Pp. 518.

BENT, ARTHUR CLEVELAND. 1919-58. Life histories of North American birds. U. S. Nat. Mus. Bull. 20 vols.

BESHEARS, W. WALTER, JR. 1955. Alabama waterfowl habitat investigation. Ala. Dept. of Conservation, Montgomery. Pp. iv, 194.

BRANNON, PETER A. 1918. The Starling in Montgomery, Alabama. Auk, 35:224.

———. 1920. Another occurrence of a Starling near Montgomery, Alabama. Auk, 37:298.

———. 1921. Blue Jay feeding on pecans. Auk, 38:603-04.

———. 1921. Notes on Alabama birds. Auk, 38:463-64.

———. 1922. Pelicans in the interior of Alabama. Auk, 39:411.

BRIMLEY, C. S. 1890. Correspondence. Orn. and Ool., 15:128.

BROWN, NATHAN CLIFFORD. 1878-79. A list of birds observed at Coosada, central Alabama. Bull. Nutt. Orn. Club, 3:168-74; 4:7-13.

BROWNLIE, EMMIE and Idalene Snead. 1956. Breeding-bird census, Birmingham, Ala. Aud. Field Notes, 10:427.

——— and Idalene Snead. 1956. Winter bird-population study, Birmingham, Ala. Aud. Field Notes, 10:298.

——— and Idalene Snead. 1957. Winter bird-population study, Birmingham, Ala. Aud. Field Notes, 11:302.

BRYAN, PAUL. 1945. Use of Wood Duck nesting boxes in Wheeler Wildlife Refuge, Alabama. Journ. Tenn. Acad. Science, 20:35-40.

———. (Comp.) 1946. Christmas bird count at Wheeler Refuge, Ala., 1945. Aud. Mag., 48 (Supp.):45.

BURLEIGH, THOMAS D. 1938. Second record of Brewer's Blackbird in Alabama. Auk, 55:545.

———. 1941. Barn Swallow breeding in southern Alabama. Auk, 58:261-62.

———. 1944. The bird life of the Gulf Coast region of Mississippi. Occ. Paper Mus. Zool., La. State Univ. No. 20:329-490. (1945. Miss. Game and Fish Comm. Reprint.)

———. 1958. Georgia birds. Norman: Univ. Okla. Press. Pp. xxix, 746.

BURNS, FRANK L. 1911. A monograph of the Broad-winged Hawk (*Buteo platypterus*). Wilson Bull., 18:143-320.

CAHN, A. R. and Paul Bryan. 1938. Shoveler breeding in northern Alabama. Auk, 55: 271-72.

CALHOUN, JOHN B. and J. C. Dickinson. 1942. Migratory movements of Chimney Swifts *Chaetura pelagica* (Linnaeus) trapped at Charlottesville, Virginia. Bird-banding, 13:57-69.

CARLETON, GEORGE A. 1954. Notes on Clarke County migrants. Ala. Birdlife, 2:37.

CHAMBLISS, SUE and L. A. Wells. 1960. Concentration of Chimney Swifts. Ala. Birdlife, 8:22.

CHAPMAN, BLANCHE H. 1960. Evening Grosbeaks. Ala. Birdlife, 8:20.

———. 1960. Observations and reports. Ala. Birdlife, 8:21.

———. 1961. Unusual records and specimens. Ala. Birdlife, 9:12.

———, Ruth Schumacher, Blanche E. Dean, and Kathleen Landes. 1953. Black-bellied Plovers. Ala. Birdlife, 1:23.

CHAPMAN, FRANK M. 1892. A preliminary study of the Grackles of the *subgenus Quiscalus*. Amer. Mus. Nat. Hist. Bull., 4:1-20.

CHRISTIE, EDWARD H. 1914. Christmas bird count, Coden, Ala., 1913. Bird-Lore, 16:41.

CLARK, EDITH. 1958. Evening Grosbeak in Alabama. Ala. Birdlife, 6 (Nos. 3, 4):12-13.

———, Thomas A. Imhof, Amelia R. Laskey, James C. Robinson, Margaret L. Robinson, J. Bolling Sullivan III, and Harriett H. Wright. 1960-61. Banders' corner. Ala. Birdlife, 8:18-19, 28; 9:10-11.

CLAWSON, STERLING G. 1958. A Wild Turkey population on an area treated with heptachlor and dieldrin. Ala. Birdlife, 6 (Nos. 3, 4):4-8.

CLEMMONS, REV. WILLIAM B. (Comp.) 1940-41. Christmas bird counts [2] at Marion Junction, Ala. 1939-40. Bird-Lore, 42:107; Aud. Mag., 43:119.

———. (Comp.) 1942-43. Christmas bird counts [3] at Geneva, Ala., 1941-1942. Aud. Mag. Supp., 44:45; 45:38; 46:40.

———. (Comp.) 1945. Christmas bird counts at Prattville, Ala., 1944. Aud. Mag., 47 (Supp.):41.

COFFEY, BEN B., JR. 1936. A preliminary list of the birds of Mississippi. Mimeo. Distributed by the author. Pp. 18.

———. 1943. Post-juvenal migration of Herons. Bird-banding, 14:34-39.

COOKE, W. W. 1904. Distribution and migration of North American Warblers. U.S.D.A. Biol. Survey Bull., 18:142.

———. 1904-06. The migration of Warblers. Bird-Lore, 6:91; 7:32; 8:26.

———. 1908. The migration of Flycatchers. Bird-Lore, 10:168.

———. 1910-11. The migration of North American Sparrows. Bird-Lore, 12:12, 139; 13:198-99.

———. 1913. Distribution and migration of North American Herons and their allies. U.S.D.A. Biol. Survey Bull., 45:70.

———. 1914. Distribution and migration of North American Rails and their allies. U.S.D.A. Biol. Survey Bull., 128:50.

———. 1914. The migration of North American Sparrows. Bird-Lore, 16:19-23, 176, 439, 441.

———. 1915. Bird migration. U.S.D.A. Biol. Survey Bull., 185. Pp. 48.

———. 1915. The migration of North American birds. Bird-Lore, 17:199-203, 443-45.

CUNNINGHAM, H. B. and others. 1954. Christmas bird count, Auburn, Alabama. Ala. Birdlife, 2:16.

DEAN, BLANCHE E. 1955. Christmas census, December 27, 1954, Goodwater, Ala. Ala. Birdlife, 3:7.

———. 1957. Shrike. Ala. Birdlife, 5:16.

———. 1958. *Coturnix* Quail observation. Ala. Birdlife, 6:17-18.

———. 1959. Wild Turkeys. Ala. Birdlife, 7:18.

DEAN, ROBERT H. 1916-25. Christmas bird counts [7] at Anniston, Ala. 1915 to 1924. Bird-Lore, 18:32; 19:29; 22:40; 24:36; 25:40; 26:45; 27:54-55.

———. 1923. Pine Siskin in Alabama in the winter of 1922-23. Bird-Lore, 25:394-95.

DENTON, J. FRED. 1953. The summer birds of Lookout Mountain, Georgia-Alabama. Oriole, 18:25-31.

DORN, REV. JOSEPH LAMBERT, S. J. 1955-61. Christmas bird counts [6] at Mobile, Ala., 1954 to 1960. Aud. Field Notes, 9:160; 10:153-54; 11:157-58; 13:177-78; 14:192; 15:201.

DUSI, JULIAN L. 1953. A Phoebe's nest at Auburn. Ala. Birdlife, 1:11.

———. 1955. A bird list from DeSoto State Park. Ala. Birdlife, 3:10.

———. 1955. Some records of banded White-throated Sparrows. Ala. Birdlife, 3:2-4.

———. 1956. An annotated list of birds seen at the nature camp at DeSoto State Park, June 1 to 9, 1956. Ala. Birdlife, 4:2-5.

———. 1956. Baird's Sandpiper at Gulf Shores. Ala. Birdlife, 4:28.

———. 1957. Barn Owl food habits. Ala. Birdlife, 5:7-8.

BIBLIOGRAPHY

————. 1958. Dispersion of Little Blue Herons from a pond in Macon County, Alabama. Ala. Birdlife, 6 (Nos. 3, 4): 9-11.

————. 1959. Fall migration mortality, Waverly, Alabama. Ala. Birdlife, 7:17.

————. 1959. Status of the Buff-breasted Sandpiper in Alabama. Ala. Birdlife, 7:12.

———— and Rosemary T. Dusi. 1955. An annotated list of birds observed on the Gulf Coast. Ala. Birdlife, 3:27-33.

———— and Rosemary T. Dusi. 1959. Some observations of early fall migration on the Gulf Coast of Alabama, 1959. Ala. Birdlife, 7:4-7.

EDWARDS, HELEN M. 1929-33. Christmas bird counts [5] at Fairhope, Ala., 1928 to 1932. Bird-Lore, 31:57; 32:58; 33:54; 34: 56; 35:38.

————. 1931. Another early hour's bird list. Wilson Bull., 43:223.

————. 1932. A Cardinal's odd way of catching ants. Wilson Bull., 44:235.

FISHER, G. CLYDE. 1908. A Golden Eagle taken in Alabama. Wilson Bull., 15:55.

FLAGG, HOMER. 1934. Christmas bird count at Fairhope, Ala., 1933. Bird-Lore, 36:43.

FRECH, WILLIAM W. 1944-46. Christmas bird counts [3] at Mobile, Ala., 1943-1945. Aud. Mag., 46 (Supp.):40; 47 (Supp.):41; 48 (Supp.):44.

GANIER, ALBERT F. 1933. A distributional list of the birds of Tennessee. Tennessee Ornithological Society, Nashville. Pp. 65.

————. 1945. A Duck Hawk eyrie on the Tennessee River. Migrant, 16:14.

————. 1945. Gulls on the Tennessee River. Migrant, 16:13-14.

———— and S. A. Weakley. 1936. Nesting of the Cliff Swallow in Tennessee. Migrant, 7:29-30.

GATCHELL, LILLIAN and Blanche E. Dean. 1953. Fall observations, 1953. Ala. Birdlife, 1:24.

GOLSAN, LEWIS S. 1922. A large gathering of Kingbirds. Auk, 39:417.

————. 1922. White-throated Sparrow summering in Autauga County, Alabama. Auk, 39:263.

————. 1923. Wintering of the Yellow Palm Warbler at Prattville, Alabama. Auk, 40: 133.

————. 1930. Records. Oologist, 47:22.

————. 1939. Three records from Autauga County, Alabama. Auk, 56:482.

———— and Ernest G. Holt. 1914. Birds of Autauga and Montgomery Counties, Alabama. Auk, 31:212-35.

———— and Ernest G. Holt. 1917. Further notes on Alabama birds. Auk, 34:456-57.

GOOD, HENRY G. 1925. A report from Alabama for the spring of 1925. Wilson Bull., 37:103.

———— and T. R. Adkins. 1927. Notes on the wintering habits of the White-throated Sparrow (Zonotrichia albicollis). Wilson Bull., 39:75-78.

GOSSE, PHILIP HENRY. 1859. Letters from Alabama (U. S.) chiefly relating to natural history. London. Pp. xii, 306.

GRAVES, EDWARD W. 1910, 1912. Christmas bird counts [2] at Long Island, Ala., 1909 and 1911. Bird-Lore, 12:30; 14:33.

GREEN, WYMAN R. 1940. Banding of Chimney Swifts (Chaetura pelagica) in the region of Chattanooga, Tennessee. Bird-banding, 11:37-57.

GRISCOM, LUDLOW and J. T. Nichols. 1920. A revision of the Seaside Sparrows. Abstr. Proc. New York Linnaeau Soc., 32: 18-30.

HARPER, ROLAND M. 1928. Economic botany of Alabama. Monograph 9, Geological Survey of Alabama, University. Pp. 357.

————. 1943. Forests of Alabama. Monograph 10, Geological Survey of Alabama, University. Pp. 230.

HASBROUCK, EDWIN M. 1891. The Carolina Paroquet (Conurus carolinensis). Auk, 8:369-79.

————. 1891. The present status of the Ivory-billed Woodpecker (Campephilus principalis). Auk, 8:174-86.

————. 1893. The geographical distribution of the genus Megascops in North America. Auk, 10:250-64.

HELMS, WILLIAM. 1953. Florida Gallinule's nest near Auburn. Ala. Birdlife, 1:23.

HELTON, JOHN, Jr. 1935. Alabama 1935 nesting dates. Oologist, 52:104-05.

HERBEL, M. H. 1922. A one-legged Cardinal. Bird-Lore, 24:97.

HICKEY, JOSEPH J. 1943. A guide to bird

watching. New York: Oxford Univ. Press. Pp. 262.

———. 1953. A guide to bird watching. Garden City, N. Y.: Garden City Books. Pp. xiv, 264.

HODGSON, ADAM. 1824. Letters from North America, written during a tour in the United States and Canada. 2 vols. London.

HOLLIMAN, DANIEL CLARK. 1959. Christmas bird count at Tanglewood, Ala. Aud. Field Notes, 13:178.

———. 1960. Recent record for Hudsonian Curlew in Alabama. Ala. Birdlife, 8:19.

HOLT, ERNEST G. 1913. Notes on the Loggerhead Shrike at Barachias, Montgomery County, Ala. Auk, 30:276-77.

———. 1918. Birds and mulberries. Auk, 35:359-60.

———. 1919. Red-bellied Nuthatch (*Sitta canadensis*) in Alabama. Auk, 36:584.

———. 1920. Bachman's Warbler breeding in Alabama. Auk, 37:103-04.

———. 1921. Annotated list of the Avery bird collection. Museum Paper No. 4, Geological Survey of Alabama, University. Pp. 142.

———. 1923. Christmas bird count at Barachias, Ala., 1922. Bird-Lore, 25:40.

———. 1924. Golden Eagle (*Aquila chrysaetos*) in Alabama. Auk, 41:601-02.

———. 1924. *Phalaropus fulicarius*: A new bird for Alabama. Auk, 41:601.

———. 1924. Redpoll (*Acanthis linaria*) in Alabama. Auk, 41:482.

———. 1924. Redstart (*Setophaga ruticilla*) breeding in Alabama. Auk, 41:162-63.

———. 1925. Early shooting and some late breeding records for Alabama. Auk, 42:147-48.

———. 1926. Nature-wasters and the sentimentalist. Auk, 43:409-10.

HOWELL, ARTHUR H. 1913. Descriptions of two new birds from Alabama. Proc. Washington Biol. Soc., 26:199-202.

———. 1921. A biological survey of Alabama. North American Fauna No. 45, U.S.D.A. Biol. Survey Bull. Pp. 88.

———. 1924. Birds of Alabama. Dept. of Game and Fisheries of Alabama. Montgomery. Pp. 384. 1928. 2nd ed. Dept. of Game and Fisheries of Alabama. Montgomery. Pp. 384.

HULSE, DAVID C. and Thomas Z. Atkeson. 1953. Notes on breeding waterfowl of the Tennessee Valley in Northern Alabama. Ala. Birdlife, 1:16-17.

——— and Thomas Z. Atkeson. 1953. Avocets in Alabama. Wilson Bull., 65:48.

IMHOF, THOMAS A. (Comp.) 1948-61. Christmas bird counts [12] at Birmingham, Ala., 1947 to 1960, except 1950 and 1951. Aud. Field Notes, 2:86; 3:107; 4:123-24; 7:127; 8:146-47; 9:159; 10:152-53; 11:156; 12:165-66; 13:176-77; 14:191; 15:200.

———. 1948, 1954. Breeding-bird censuses [2] at Birmingham, Ala., 1948, 1954. Aud. Field Notes, 2:238; 8:367-68.

———. 1949. Winter bird-population study, Fairfield, Ala., 1948-1949. Aud. Field Notes, 3:187-88.

———. 1949-54. Breeding-bird censuses [3] at Fairfield, Ala., 1949, 1950, 1954. Aud. Field Notes, 3:267; 4:300-01; 8:368.

———. 1950. Christmas bird count at Fairfield, Ala., 1949. Aud. Field Notes, 4:124-25.

———. (Comp.) 1950-56. Christmas bird counts [5] at Decatur, Ala., 1949, 1952-55. Aud. Field Notes, 4:124; 7:127-28; 8:147; 9:159-60; 10:153.

———. 1953. Effect of weather on spring bird migration in Northern Alabama. Wilson Bull., 65:184-95.

———. 1953. Our present knowledge of Alabama's breeding birds. Ala. Birdlife, 1:2-9.

———. 1954. Bird mortality at Birmingham ceilometer. Ala. Birdlife, 2:38-39.

———. 1954. When do the birds occur at Birmingham? Ala. Birdlife, 2:25-33.

———. 1956. Present status of the Alabama bird list. Ala. Birdlife, 4:24-26.

———. (Comp.) 1957-61. Christmas bird counts [5] at Dauphin Island, Ala., 1956-1960. Aud. Field Notes, 11:156-59; 12:166; 13:177; 14:191-92; 15:200-01.

———. 1958. Recent additions to the avifauna of Alabama. Auk, 75:354-57.

———. 1960. The Barn Swallow breeding in DeKalb County. Ala. Birdlife, 8:20.

———. 1960. The Song Sparrow breeding in DeKalb County. Ala. Birdlife, 8:17.

———. 1960. Winter bird-population study, Birmingham, Ala. Aud. Field Notes, 14:354-55.

———, J. L. Dorn, S. J., and Julian L. Dusi. 1960. Christmas bird counts, Alabama, 1959. Ala. Birdlife, 8:3-6.

BIBLIOGRAPHY

——, J. L. Dorn, S. J., and Julian L. Dusi. 1961. Christmas bird counts, Alabama, 1960. Ala. Birdlife, 9:2-6.

—— and Morton H. Perry. 1947. Breeding-bird census at Birmingham, Ala., 1947. Aud. Field Notes, 1:214.

JACKSON, JENKINS. 1960. MS. Birds of Sumter County, Alabama. Pp. 7.

——. 1960. Krider's Red-tailed Hawk. Ala. Birdlife, 8:8.

——. 1960. Nesting of the Baltimore Oriole at Livingston. Ala. Birdlife, 8-17.

——. 1960. Pass the berry. Ala. Birdlife, 8:8.

JOHNSON, EULALIA. 1953. Scarlet Tanagers. Ala. Birdlife, 1:24.

——. 1958. Summer record of Junco. Ala. Birdlife, 6:18.

JONES, LESLIE. 1911. The Robin and Cedar Waxwing. Oologist, 28:77.

JORDAN, C. L. 1892. Hawks as garden protectors. Amer. Field, 37:674.

KALMBACH, E. R. and Ira N. Gabrielson. 1921. Economic value of the Starling in the United States. U.S.D.A. Dept. Bull. 868. Pp. 66.

KEELER, JAMES E. 1952. The Mourning Dove study. Ala. Dept. of Conservation, Montgomery. Pp. iv, 73.

——. 1956. Alabama waterfowl band recoveries, 1929-1956. Special Report No. 1, Federal Aid in Wildlife Restoration. Ala. Dept. of Conservation, Montgomery. (Unpaged.)

——. 1956. White Ibis—a new bird breeding in Alabama. Ala. Birdlife, 4:16-19.

——. 1957. Cattle Egret, a new bird for Alabama. Ala. Birdlife, 5:26.

——. 1959. Spring meeting bird count, Mt. Cheaha, April 24, 25, and 26, 1959. Ala. Birdlife, 7:2-3.

KEMP, DAVID W. 1944. Christmas bird count at Weaver, Ala., 1943. Aud. Mag., 46 (Supp.):40.

KIRKPATRICK, J. M. 1906. A move to protect Alabama game. Amer. Field, 65: 384.

KORTRIGHT, FRANCIS H. 1942. The Ducks, Geese, and Swans of North America. American Wildlife Inst., Washington. Pp. vii, 476. Rep., 1953.

LACK, DAVID. 1960. The influence of weather on Passerine migration. A review. Auk, 77:171-209.

LANMAN, CHARLES. 1856. Adventures in the wilds of the United States and British American provinces. 2 vols. Philadelphia.

LASKEY, AMELIA R. 1955. Tennessee Bluebird recovered in Alabama. Ala. Birdlife, 3:6.

LAUDEN, MAY S. 1954. The territorial range of the Alabama Towhee. Ala. Birdlife, 2:3-15.

LINCOLN, FREDERICK C. 1944. Chimney Swifts' winter home discovered. Auk, 61: 604-09.

——. 1950. Migration of birds. U. S. Fish and Wildlife Service, Circular 16. Pp. 102.

——. 1951. A set of twelve eggs of the Woodcock, *Philohela minor*. Auk, 65:376.

LOWERY, GEORGE H., JR. 1949. The season, Central Southern Region. Aud. Field Notes, 3:19-21, 172-74, 211-13, 240-43.

——. 1955. Louisiana birds. Baton Rouge: La. State Univ. Press. Pp. xxix, 556. 1960. 2nd ed. Pp. xxiv, 567.

—— and Robert J. Newman. 1950-54. The season, Central Southern Region. Aud. Field Notes, 4:19-21, 205-07, 245-47, 279-81; 5:22-24, 208-10, 259-61, 292-95; 6:20-23, 199-201, 249-52, 285-86; 7:20-23, 217-20, 276-79, 312-13; 8:23-25, 256-58.

—— and Robert J. Newman. 1954. The birds of the Gulf of Mexico, in The Gulf of Mexico, its origin, waters, and marine life. U. S. Fish and Wildlife Service Bull. 89:519-40.

MAGNESS, EDGAR. 1898. Shearwater inland. Osprey, 3:45.

MARTIN, ALEXANDER C., Herbert S. Zim, and Arnold L. Nelson. 1951. American wildlife and plants. New York: McGraw-Hill. Pp. ix, 500.

MARTIN, LEO M. and Thomas Z. Atkeson, Jr. 1954. Swimming by Wild Turkey poults. Wilson Bull., 66:271.

MASON, C. RUSSELL. 1938. A Warbler wave of interest. Auk, 55:282-83.

McATEE, W. L. 1923. Local names of migratory game birds. U.S.D.A. Misc. Circular No. 13. Pp. 96.

——. 1947. Attracting birds. U. S. Fish and Wildlife Service, Conservation Bulletin No. 1. Pp. 13.

————, Thomas D. Burleigh, George H. Lowery, Jr., and Herbert L. Stoddard. 1944. Eastward migration through the Gulf states. Wilson Bull., 56:152-60.

McCOLLOUGH, ALICE LOIS. (Comp.) 1956-58. Christmas bird counts [3] at Marion, Ala., 1955 to 1957. Aud. Field Notes, 10:153; 11:157; 12:166-67.

————. 1957. A comparison of waterbirds at U. S. fish hatchery and Lakeland Farm near Marion, Alabama. Ala. Birdlife, 5:19-23.

McCORMACK, F. W. 1888. Orioles as foster parents. Oologist, 5:131.

————. 1891-92. Notes on Colbert County (Ala.) birds. Leighton, (Ala.) News, 2 (Nos. 3-25): Feb. 1, 1891—Jan. 2, 1892. (Unpaged.)

————. 1943. Nesting of the Prairie Horned Lark in northwestern Alabama. Auk, 60:105.

————. 1943. Nesting of the Southern Robin in northwestern Alabama. Auk, 60:282.

McELHONE, HELEN KIMBERLY. (Comp.) 1924. Christmas bird count, Fairhope, Ala., 1923. Bird-Lore, 26:45.

McMILLAN, NEIL T. 1938. Birds and the wind. Bird-Lore, 40:397-406.

MOORE, GEORGE C. and Allen M. Pearson. 1941. The Mourning Dove in Alabama. Ala. Coop. Wildlife Research Unit. Auburn. Pp. 38.

NATIONAL AUDUBON SOCIETY. 1953. Your book of nature activities. Audubon Nature Program. Nelson Doubleday, Inc.

NEWMAN, ROBERT J. 1954-59. The season, Central Southern Region. Aud. Field Notes, 8:316-19, 349-50; 9:31-34, 262-65, 335-38, 382-85; 10:29-32, 256-60, 338-41, 387-90; 11:30-34, 270-74, 350-57, 409-13; 12:36-39, 284-87, 358-62, 417-21; 13:37-41.

————, Thomas A. Imhof, Douglas A. James, Frances Crews James, and Stuart L. Warter. 1959-61. The season, Central Southern Region. Aud. Field Notes, 13:298-302, 376-80, 434-37; 14:41-47, 314-18, 392-97, 454-56; 15:46-51, 334-37, 416-19, 473-75.

NORRIS, J. P. 1890. A series of eggs of the Tufted Titmouse. Orn. and Ool., 15:147-48.

————. 1891. A series of eggs of the Mary-land Yellow-throat. Orn. and Ool., 16:150-52.

NUTTALL, THOMAS. 1832-34. Manual of the ornithology of the United States and Canada. 2 vols. The land birds, Cambridge, Mass., 1832; The water birds, Boston, 1834.

OBERHOLSER, HARRY C. 1908. A list of the principal birds to be found in Alabama. First Bien. Rept., Dept. of Game and Fish of Ala., 1908:104-10.

————. 1911. A revision of the forms of the Hairy Woodpecker (Dryobates villosus [Linnaeus]). Proc. U. S. Nat. Mus., 40:595-621.

————. 1912. A revision of the subspecies of the Green Heron (Butorides virescens [Linnaeus]). Proc. U. S. Nat. Mus., 42:529-77.

————. 1913. A revision of the forms of the Great Blue Heron (Ardea herodias Linnaeus). Proc. U. S. Nat. Mus., 43:531-59.

————. 1914. A monograph of the genus Chordeiles Swainson, type of a new family of Goatsuckers. U. S. Nat. Mus. Bull. 86:123.

————. 1917. Critical notes on the eastern subspecies of Sitta carolinensis Latham. Auk, 34:181-87.

————. 1918. The Common Ravens of North America. Ohio Journ. Sci., 18 (No. 6):213-25.

————. 1918. The migration of North American birds. Second Series. II. The Scarlet and Louisiana Tanagers. Bird-Lore, 20 (No. 1):16-19. III. The Summer and Hepatic Tanagers, Martins, and Barn Swallows. Op. cit. (No. 2):145-53. IV. The Waxwings and Phainopepla. Op. cit. (No. 3):219-22. VI. Horned Larks. Op. cit. (No. 5):345-49.

————. 1920. Ibid. XIII. European Starling and Bobolink. Bird-Lore, 22:213.

————. 1921. Ibid. XVII. Rusty Blackbird and Brewer Blackbird. Bird-Lore, 23:297.

————. 1922. Ibid. XX. Baltimore Oriole. Bird-Lore, 24:339.

ODUM, EUGENE P. 1958. Lipid deposition in nocturnal migrant birds. Proc. 12th Int. Ornith. Cong., Helsinki, Finland, pp. 563-76.

PALMER, WILLIAM. 1898. Our small eastern Shrikes. Auk, 15:244-58.

PARK, F. T. 1893. Acanthis linaria in Alabama. Auk, 10:205.

BIBLIOGRAPHY

"A PARTICIPANT." 1894. Dove shooting in Alabama. Amer. Field, 41:558-59.

PEARSON, ALLEN M. and George C. Moore. 1939. Nesting habits of the Mourning Dove in Alabama. Trans. 4th North Am. Wildlife Conf., pp. 468-73.

PEARSON, T. GILBERT. 1936. Birds of America. Garden City, N. Y. Pp. xliv, 832.

————, Clement Samuel Brimley, and Herbert Hutchinson Brimley. Revised, David L. Wray and Harry T. Davis. 1959. Birds of North Carolina. N. C. Dept. of Ag., State Museum Division, Raleigh. Pp. xxviii, 434.

PERRY, MORTON H. 1951. Christmas bird count, Birmingham, Ala., 1951. Aud. Field Notes, 5:124.

PETERS, HAROLD S. 1937. Chimney Swift banding in Alabama during the fall of 1936. Bird-banding, 8:16-24.

————. 1937. Christmas bird count, Auburn, Ala., 1936. Bird-Lore, 39:56-57.

PETERSON, ROGER TORY. 1947. A field guide to the birds. Rev. ed. Boston. Pp. xxiv, 290.

————. 1961. A field guide to western birds. Rev. ed. Boston. Pp. 366.

PETTINGILL, OLIN SEWALL, JR. 1951. A guide to bird finding east of the Mississippi. New York: Oxford University Press. Pp. xxi, 659.

————. 1956. A laboratory and field manual of ornithology. 3rd ed., rev. Minneapolis. Pp. viii, 379.

POUGH, RICHARD H. 1953. Audubon guides. All the birds of eastern and central North America: Small land birds, pp. xlii, 312; Water, game, and large land birds, pp. xxviii, 352. New York: Doubleday & Co.

PRATHER, MILLARD F. (Comp.) 1942-52. Christmas bird counts [4] at Birmingham, Ala., 1941-51. Aud. Mag., Supp., 44:45; 45:37 and Aud. Field Notes, 1:84; 6:119.

———— and Morton H. Perry. (Comps.) 1940-46. Christmas bird counts [5] at Birmingham, Ala., 1939 to 1945. Bird-Lore, 42:106; Aud. Mag., 43:118; 46 (Supp.): 39; 47 (Supp.):41; 48 (Supp.):44.

RAGSDALE, G. H. 1889. On the hiatus existing between the breeding ranges of the Loggerhead and White-rumped Shrikes. Auk, 6:225.

REICHERT, ROBERT J. and Elsa Reichert.
1951. Know your binoculars. Mirakel Repair Co.: Mount Vernon, N. Y. Reprinted from Aud. Mag. 53: Jan.-Feb. and Mar.-Apr. issues. Pp. 12.

RHOADS, S. N. 1895. Contributions to the zoology of Tennessee, No. 2, Birds. Proc. Acad. Nat. Sci., Philadelphia, 1895:481.

RICE, JULIAN M. (Comp.) 1954-55. Christmas bird counts [2] at Montgomery, Ala., 1953, 1955. Aud. Field Notes, 8:147; 9: 160.

RIDGEWAY, A. M. 1883. Notes on the birds of Alabama. Forest and Stream, 20:323 (May 24).

RIDGWAY, ROBERT. 1880. Note on *Peucaea illinoensis*. Bull. Nutt. Orn. Club, 5:52.

————. 1901-19. The birds of North and Middle America. Parts I-VIII. U. S. Nat. Mus. Bull. 50.

1931. A Robin Family. Ala. Game and Fish News (Montgomery), 3:(2)14.

ROBINSON, J. M. 1923. Alabama bird banding station, Alabama Polytechnic Institute. Wilson Bull., 35:111-12.

ROBINSON, JAMES C. and Margaret L. Robinson. 1960. Hawk migration—Huntsville (Brownsboro). Ala. Birdlife, 8:28.

———— and Margaret L. Robinson. 1960. Observations and reports. Ala. Birdlife, 8:21.

ROBINSON, MARGARET L. 1959. Recent record for Lincoln's Sparrow in Alabama. Ala. Birdlife, 7:13-14.

————. 1960. Prothonotary Warbler parasitized by Cowbird. Ala. Birdlife, 8:8.

ROGERS, GERALD. 1945. Arkansas Kingbird in Alabama. Auk, 62:147.

ROSENE, WALTER, JR. 1954. Nesting of the Carolina Wren. Ala. Birdlife, 2:23-25.

————. (Comp.) 1939. Christmas bird count at Dadeville, Ala., 1938. Bird-Lore, 41:36.

RUFF, FREDERICK J. 1940. Brewer's Blackbird in Alabama. Auk, 57:575.

SAUNDERS, ARETAS A. 1908. Some birds of central Alabama. Auk, 25:413-24.

————. 1951. A guide to bird songs. Garden City, N. Y. Pp. 307.

SAXE-WEIMAR, BERNARD, DUKE OF. 1828. Travels through North America, during the years 1825 and 1826. 2 vols. Philadelphia.

SKINNER, ROBERT W. 1958. The Mississippi Kite in Alabama. Ala. Birdlife, 6:13-14.

———. 1958. Birds and snakes. Ala. Birdlife, 6:19-20.

———. 1958. Cattle Egret records. Ala. Birdlife, 6:19.

———. 1959. Krider's Hawk in the Black Belt of Alabama. Ala. Birdlife, 7:8-9.

———. 1960. Taxonomic problems of the Red-tailed Hawk and notes on other related species. Ala. Birdlife, 8:24-25.

SMITH, ROBERT H. and Albert H. Trowbridge. 1941. Mallard Duck returns to destroyed nest. Auk, 58:92.

SNEAD, IDALENE FULLER. 1958. Resident bird-populations of an abandoned airfield in Birmingham, Alabama. Unpublished Master's thesis, Birmingham-Southern College. Pp. 48.

———. 1959. Fall A. O. S. meeting. Ala. Birdlife, 7:18.

——— and others. 1958. Winter bird-population study, Birmingham, Ala. Aud. Field Notes, 12:313-14.

SPEAKE, DAN WEBSTER. 1954. The waterfowl of Lee County, Alabama. Unpublished Master's thesis, Alabama Polytechnic Institute [Auburn University]. Pp. 42.

———. 1958. Spring meeting bird count. Ala. Birdlife, 6:15-16.

SPRUNT, ALEXANDER, JR. 1954. Florida bird life. New York: Coward-McCann, Inc. Pp. xlii, 527.

——— and Edward Burnham Chamberlain. 1949. South Carolina bird life. Columbia: Univ. S. C. Press. Pp. xiv, 585.

STEENIS, JOHN H. (Comp.) 1941-45. Christmas bird counts [5] at Wheeler National Wildlife Refuge, Decatur, Ala., 1940-1944. Aud. Mag., 43:119-20; 44 (Supp.): 45-46; 45 (Supp.):37; 46 (Supp.):40; 47 (Supp.):42.

STEVENSON, HENRY M. 1932. A Bell's Vireo for Alabama. Oologist, 49:107-08.

———. (Comp.) 1935-37. Christmas bird counts [3] at Birmingham, Ala., 1934-36. Bird-Lore, 37:60; 38:69-70; 39:57.

———. 1937-41. Christmas bird counts [4] at Tuscaloosa, Ala., 1937-1940. Bird-Lore, 40:54; 41:36-37; 42:107; Aud. Mag., 43: 119.

———. (Comp.) 1940-48. Christmas bird counts [3] at Foley, Ala., 1939-1947. Bird-

Lore, 42:106-07; Aud. Mag., 43:118-19; Aud. Field Notes, 2:86.

———. 1943. Christmas bird count at Decatur, Ala., 1942. Aud. Mag., 45 (Sec. II): 37.

———. 1943. Christmas bird count at Florence, Ala., 1942. Aud. Mag., 45 (Sec. II):37-38.

———. 1943. Recent records of the Duck Hawk and Ruffed Grouse in Alabama. Migrant, 14:61.

———. 1943. A record of the Snow Bunting in Alabama. Migrant, 14:20.

———. 1944. European Widgeon in Alabama. Auk, 61:650.

———. 1944. Southeastern limits of the Spotted Sandpiper's breeding range. Auk, 61:247-51.

———. 1944. A summer bird count from Lookout Mountain. Oriole, 9:16-17.

———. 1950. Distribution of certain birds in the southeastern United States. Am. Midl. Nat., 43:605-26.

———. 1950. A Western Meadowlark, *Sturnella neglecta,* in Alabama. Auk, 67: 396.

———. 1953. Additional comments on Alabama's breeding birds. Ala. Birdlife, 1:22.

———. 1953. A spring day on the Alabama coast. Ala. Birdlife, 1:18-21.

———. 1954. Vermilion Flycatcher added to Alabama list. Ala. Birdlife, 2:36.

———. 1960. Breeding-bird census, Hurricane, Alabama. Aud. Field Notes, 14:498.

——— and Arthur Stupka. 1948. The altitudinal limits of certain birds in the mountains of the southeastern states. Migrant, 19:33-60.

STEWART, PAUL A. 1952. Dispersal, breeding behavior, and longevity of banded Barn Owls in North America. Auk, 69: 227-45.

STEWART, ROBERT E. and Chandler S. Robbins. 1958. Birds of Maryland and the District of Columbia. North American Fauna No. 62. U. S. Dept. of Int. Pp. vi, 401.

STUART, JAMES. 1833. Three years in North America. 2 vols. Edinburgh.

SUMMEROUR, CHARLES WILLIAM, JR. 1953. A Woodcock nest near Auburn. Ala. Birdlife, 1:10.

SWINDELL, MAXIE. 1959. Broad-winged Hawks caught in crosswinds. Ala. Birdlife, 7:24.

BIBLIOGRAPHY

TIPTON, SAMUEL R. (Comp.) 1945-46. Christmas bird counts [2] at Tuscaloosa, Ala. Aud. Mag., 47 (Supp.):41-42; 48 (Supp.):44.

TORDOFF, HARRISON B. and Robert M. Mengel. 1956. Studies of birds killed in nocturnal migration. Univ. Kans. Pub. Mus. Nat. Hist., 10:1-44.

VAN TYNE, JOSSELYN. 1956. What constitute scientific data for the study of bird distribution? Wilson Bull., 68:63-67.

———— and Andrew J. Berger. 1959. Fundamentals of Ornithology. New York: John Wiley and Sons. Pp. ix, 624.

"W. A. C." 1906. Alabama must have a better game law. Amer. Field, 65:408-09.

WALLACE, GEORGE J. 1955. An introduction to Ornithology. New York: The Macmillan Co. Pp. 443.

WARREN, J. E. 1896. Quail shooting opens in Alabama. Amer. Field, 46:459.

WEAKLEY, S. A. 1936. Great Blue Herons nesting at Muscle Shoals. Migrant, 7:71.

————. 1936. Additional Cliff Swallow colonies. Migrant, 7:73.

————. 1945. White Pelicans and Cliff Swallows on the Tennessee River. Migrant, 16:33.

WEST, MRS. E. M. (Adele). 1957. Blackburnian Warbler near Birmingham. Ala. Birdlife, 5:15.

WESTON, FRANCIS M. 1929-48. The season, Pensacola (Fla.) region. Bird-Lore, 32:14, 140, 208, 269, 284, 360, 434; 33: 15, 130, 197, 221-23, 268, 334, 408-09; 34: 14, 130, 140, 209, 274, 332, 341, 399-400; 35:104, 159, 213, 274, 323-24, 330; 36:16, 183, 244; 40:288; 41:121, 256; 42:384-85. Aud. Mag., 45 (Nov.-Dec. Supp.):7; Aud. Field Notes, 1:129; 2:9-11, 138, 203-04.

————. 1953. Red Phalarope (Phalaropus fulicarius) wintering near Pensacola, Florida. Auk, 70:491-92.

WHEELER, HARRY E. 1931. The status, breeding range, and habits of Marian's Marsh Wren. Wilson Bull., 43:247-67.

WHEELER, ROBERT J., JR. 1948. The Wild Turkey in Alabama. Ala. Dept. of Conservation, Montgomery. Pp. 92.

WILLIAMS, LOVETT E., JR. 1958. A breeding bird study in Wilcox County, Alabama. Ala. Birdlife, 6:4-10.

————. 1958. Breeding record for Dickcissel. Ala. Birdlife, 6:20.

————. 1959. Ash-throated Flycatcher in Alabama. Auk, 76:528.

WILLINGHAM, ROBERT S., JR. 1943. Breeding-bird census, LaFayette, Alabama. Aud. Mag., 45 (Sept.-Oct. Supp.):20.

WISE, C. 1889. Notes from an Alabama collector. Oologist, 6:14-15.

————. 1889. The Robin wintering in the South. Oologist, 6:129.

————. 1889. The Turkey Buzzard. Oologist, 6:13.

WORLEY, BETTY D. 1954. Christmas bird count, Scottsboro, Alabama. Ala. Birdlife, 2:16.

WRIGHT, HARRIETT H. 1958. Oriole observations. Ala. Birdlife, 6:18.

INDEX

INDEX

INDEX